D1539559

ORGANIC ANALYSIS

Volume III

ORGANIC ANALYSIS

VOLUME **III**

INTERSCIENCE PUBLISHERS, INC., NEW YORK

INTERSCIENCE PUBLISHERS LTD. LONDON

Copyright © 1956 by
INTERSCIENCE PUBLISHERS, INC.

Library of Congress Catalog
Card Number 53-7163

INTERSCIENCE PUBLISHERS, INC.
250 Fifth Avenue, New York 1, N. Y.

For Great Britain and Northern Ireland:
INTERSCIENCE PUBLISHERS LTD.
88/90 Chancery Lane, London, W. C. 2

PRINTED IN THE UNITED STATES OF AMERICA BY MACK PRINTING CO., EASTON, PA.

PREFACE

Organic Analysis is designed to present an up-to-date picture of techniques for direct analyses of organic systems, particularly for functional groups. In Volume III the pattern of the two previous volumes is continued with chapters on determinations of important functional groups and modern techniques used in organic analysis. Emphasis is placed on the more general methods. However, information also is included on "specific" determinations of widely used compounds, particularly where the methods show promise of broader applicability. For example, thermometric procedures described for determining acetic acid and acetic anhydride also should be useful in analyses for other acids and anhydrides. Numerous methods for analysis of synthetic organic coating resins might well form the basis for similar determinations of other materials. Procedural details are given for all recommended methods.

Volume II contained a cumulative index for the first two volumes. The index of Volume III includes a complete listing of all major subjects in the previous volumes plus those materials in Volumes I and II which are pertinent to the subject matter of the present volume.

The editors wish again to thank the members of the Advisory Board and other friends for helpful suggestions in the planning of this series.

THE EDITORS

October 1956

23216

CONTENTS

CONTRIBUTORS

VERNON H. DIBELER, *National Bureau of Standards, Washington, D. C.*

C. W. HAMMOND, *E. I. du Pont de Nemours & Co., Inc., Kinston, North Carolina*

E. F. HILLENBRAND, JR., *Carbide and Carbon Chemicals Co., South Charleston, West Virginia*

J. L. JUNGNICKEL, *Shell Development Co., Emeryville, California*

R. H. KINSEY, *E. I. du Pont de Nemours & Co., Inc., Victoria, Texas*

JOHN MITCHELL, JR., *E. I. du Pont de Nemours & Co., Inc., Wilmington, Delaware*

BARBARA A. MONTAGUE, *E. I. du Pont de Nemours & Co., Inc., Wilmington, Delaware*

C. A. PENTZ, *Carbide and Carbon Chemicals Co., South Charleston, West Virginia*

A. POLGÁR, *Shell Development Co., Emeryville, California*

O. D. SHREVE, *E. I. du Pont de Nemours & Co., Inc., Philadelphia, Pennsylvania*

Determination of
ORGANIC ACIDS

JOHN MITCHELL, JR., BARBARA A. MONTAGUE, AND R. H. KINSEY

E. I. du Pont de Nemours & Co., Inc.

I. INTRODUCTION

Arrhenius's classical theory defined an acid as a compound which ionized in water to form hydrogen ions. The neutralization process required the formation of a salt and water. This concept does not account for the neutralization reaction in a nonaqueous system. Of the several definitions now being considered those of Brønsted and G. N. Lewis more logically fulfill the broader requirements. The Lewis theory defines acids as electron acceptors, and, consequently, acids need not contain hydrogen. The Brønsted theory defines acids as proton donors. On this basis the Brønsted or H-acids would appear to form a subclass of the broader Lewis or L-acid system. Further details of current acid-base theory are available in the literature and will also appear in a later volume of this series in a chapter discussing nonaqueous systems.

Essentially all of the literature on acid-base titrimetry deals with H-acids for which adequate systems are available for detecting the end points. This chapter will be limited to this class with emphasis on the most important group, the carboxylic acids. These compounds contain the common function $-C(=O)OH$. They are weaker than the mineral acids and are not completely ionized in aqueous solution. An equilibrium exists between the ionized form, $[RCOO]H$, and the undissociated form, $RC(=O)OH$. The dissociation or ionization constant of acetic acid, for example, is 1.75×10^{-5}. Compared with hydrochloric acid, $0.1\ N$ acetic acid is only about $1/100$ as much dissociated and is correspondingly weaker.

In addition to a thorough discussion of carboxylic acids the current chapter describes some of the methods for determining other types of organic H-acids. These include typical analyses for the sulfonic acids, which are comparable in strength to the mineral acids, and analyses for phenols and related compounds. Emphasis is placed on the more general techniques for the determination of organic acids. However, numerous examples of methods for special types of acids and in some cases for specific acids are also described where they represent important classes or compounds and illustrate a useful variation in technique. In volume II of this series, Steyermark described micro methods for determining carboxyl groups. In this chapter emphasis is placed on macro and semimicro methods.

Neutralization by an alkali hydroxide is most commonly employed for determinations of organic acids. Where applicable, this technique provides the basis for rapid and reliable analyses. Through proper choice of system the individual can determine total acidity or differentiate among acids of varying strengths. Numerous other techniques have been employed for determining organic acids. Some are based on stoichiometric or at least reproducible reactions; others, on molecular or group vibrational characteristics. Many separation schemes have been used with considerable success for classifying and determining acids. The following sections describe the most important techniques used in analyses for organic acids with emphasis on neutralization. Reference is made to over two hundred reliable publications which can be consulted for further details of analysis. Although every effort was made to include all publications describing general methods of analysis or specific methods for important acids singly or in groups, doubtless some have been omitted. Several unpublished items from the authors' laboratory are also noted, together with recommendations based on several years experience with the many techniques.

II. NEUTRALIZATION

The most widely applicable procedures for the determination of organic acids are based on direct neutralization, as illustrated by the general reaction for carboxylic acids:

$$RCOOH + MOH \longrightarrow RCOOM + H_2O \qquad (1)$$

where M represents an alkali metal, usually sodium or potassium. There is no single general method employing this reaction which can be used in analyses for all types of organic acids. The particular means for detecting the end point and the solvent system depend on the nature of the acids to be titrated.

1. Methods for Detecting the End Point

A. VISUAL TITRATION

Early studies on direct titration methods stressed the use of aqueous systems and visual titration using an indicator, such as phenolphthalein, to ascertain the neutralization point. Although this method is the simplest available, it is not always reliable for determining the acid function quantitatively. In aqueous solution the end point, or equivalence point, is dependent upon the equilibria among the various ions in solution. Since most organic acids are not completely ionized, the ionization constant, K_a, must be considered before the true end point can be ascertained. With carboxylic and weaker acids the neutralization reaction produces the salt of the weak acid and a strong base. Consequently, the equilibrium solution will be slightly alkaline, having a pH of greater than 7. Usually phenolphthalein is a satisfactory indicator for detecting the end point since most carboxylic and stronger acids ($K_a \geq$ about 1×10^{-8}) have been neutralized at a pH of about 8.4, where this indicator changes color. Table I shows the ionization constants of some representative organic acids. With the exception of phenol, hydroquinone, and the acidic hydroxyl of salicylic acid all of these acids will have been neutralized at the phenolphthalein end point. (K of phenolphthalein = 2×10^{-10}; see Table II).

TABLE I

Ionization Constants of Typical Organic Acids

Acid	Formula	K_a	
Formic...............	HCOOH		1.77×10^{-4}
Acetic................	CH_3COOH		1.75×10^{-5}
Chloroacetic...........	$ClCH_2COOH$		1.40×10^{-3}
Benzoic...............	C_6H_5COOH		6.30×10^{-5}
Oxalic...............	$(COOH)_2$	$K_1 =$	6.5×10^{-2}
		$K_2 =$	6.1×10^{-5}
Phenol...............	C_6H_5OH		1.3×10^{-10}
Hydroquinone........	HOC_6H_4OH		1.1×10^{-10}
o-Phthalic............	$C_6H_4(COOH)_2$	$K_1 =$	1.3×10^{-3}
		$K_2 =$	3.9×10^{-6}
Salicylic.............	HOC_6H_5COOH	$K_1 =$	1.06×10^{-3}
		$K_2 =$	3.6×10^{-4}

Acid-base indicators are weak organic acids or bases that reproducibly undergo a change in color at a given pH. The action of an acid indicator can be represented by the scheme (121):

$$\underset{\text{Acidic form}}{\text{HIn}} \quad \rightleftharpoons \quad \underset{\text{Basic form}}{\text{H}^+ + \text{In}^-}$$

The ionization constant, K_{In}, determines the pH at which an indicator will undergo its color change. A list of some common indicators with pH ranges and colors of the acidic and basic forms are given in Table II.

The choice of indicator for a titration is dictated by the strength of the acid to be determined, i.e., one where the color change will include the pH of the equivalence point of the acid. Usually the most convenient and reliable method for determining the proper indicator for a given system is by reference to potentiometric titration. With indicator present during this process the color change can be established unequivocally in relation to the equivalence point. Spectrophotometric methods also aid in de-

TABLE II

Some Acid-Base Indicators

Indicator	pH interval	Color	
		Acidic	Basic
Thymol blue[a]	1.2–2.8	Red	Yellow
Methyl orange	3.1–4.4	Red	Yellow
Bromphenol blue	3.0–4.6	Yellow	Blue
Bromcresol green	3.8–5.4	Yellow	Blue
Methyl red	4.4–6.2	Red	Yellow
Chlorphenol red	4.8–6.4	Yellow	Red
Bromthymol blue	6.0–7.6	Yellow	Blue
Neutral red	6.8–8.0	Red	Yellow
Cresol red	7.2–8.8	Yellow	Red
Thymol blue[a]	8.0–9.6	Yellow	Blue
Phenolphthalein	8.3–10.0	Colorless	Red
Thymolphthalein	9.4–10.6	Colorless	Blue

[a] Thymol blue undergoes a color change in both the acid and the alkaline regions.

termining relative strengths of organic acids. Bhattacharya and Ghose (15) described the use of sensitized Schiff reagent for this purpose. Schiff reagent is normally employed for the colorimetric estimation of aldehydes (see Volume I of this series, p. 284). Ammonium salts of acids weaker than sulfurous acid remove sulfur dioxide from Schiff reagent by the displacement reaction:

$$2RCOONH_4 + SO_2 + H_2O \rightleftharpoons (NH_4)_2SO_3 + 2RCOOH \qquad (2)$$

The intensity of the color developed is a measure of strength of these acids

TABLE III

Relative Strengths of Carboxylic Acids Based on Schiff Reagent Test (15)

Acid	Ionization constant, K	Absorbance, A	Relative strength
Oxalic	$K_1 = 6.5 \times 10^{-2}$	0.005	100
Citric	$K_1 = 8.7 \times 10^{-4}$	0.019	26.3
D-Tartaric	$K_1 = 5.9 \times 10^{-4}$	0.027	18.5
Formic	1.77×10^{-4}	0.029	17.5
Lactic	1.39×10^{-4}	0.037	13.5
Succinic	$K_1 = 6.4 \times 10^{-5}$	0.085	5.88
Acetic	1.75×10^{-5}	0.298	1.68
n-Butyric	1.51×10^{-5}	0.323	1.55
Propionic	1.34×10^{-5}	0.337	1.48

relative to sulfurous acid. The weaker the acid the greater the displacement of sulfur dioxide as indicated in Table III.

The use of mixed indicators is often desirable for obtaining a sharp end point in the regions where single indicators exhibit a broad range or where color of the single indicator may be obscured. Sandin and co-workers (193) utilized this principle to improve the sensitivity of thymolphthalein in alcoholic solutions by adding 5 drops of 0.5% thymolphthalein and 3 drops of 0.02% methyl orange to solutions of fatty acids. The end point was determined by the first appearance of a green color instead of the usual pale blue. Burshtein (*32*) mixed fluorescein with methyl red to provide an internal indicator for deeply colored solutions. The red ions masked the green fluorescence until enough base had been added to produce the yellow form of the methyl red, at which time the fluorescence could be observed in the dark colored solution. Kolthoff and Stenger (121) described numerous mixed indicator solutions for use in acid-base titrimetry.

It should be pointed out that in alcoholic solutions many indicators show slightly different color changes than those observed in an aqueous medium. This is due to the increased solubility of the undissociated part of the indicator. Hildebrand and co-workers (17) investigated the action of a number of common indicators in ethanol. By referring to their indicator table and a set of standard potentiometric curves, which were obtained by titrating a series of common acids whose K_a values varied from 10^{-2} to 10^{-12}, it is possible to select a suitable indicator for a variety of acids of differing strengths. Kolthoff (118) reviewed recent developments in the field including the role of indicators in the newer concepts of acid-base titrimetry. A number of new acid-base indicators for aqueous and non-aqueous titrations were included in his discussion.

In aqueous systems the pH at the equivalence point sometimes may be estimated. It is possible to calculate the hydrogen ion concentration if the ionization constant of the acid is known and the concentration of the acid salt in the solution is established. Willard and Furman (239) derived the following equation for calculating the hydroxyl ion concentration, $[OH^-]$, at the equivalence point in the neutralization of a weak acid ($K_a = 10^{-3}$ to 10^{-8}) with a strong base:

$$[OH^-] = \sqrt{(K_w/K_a)\,c}$$

where K_w = the ionization constant of water = 10^{-14}; K_a = the ionization constant of the acid; c = the concentration of the salt of a weak acid.

Unless the equivalence point is known, the system under study should be analyzed by potentiometric or other absolute electrical method. Once this point is established an indicator often can be chosen whose color change coincides with the stoichiometric end point of the neutralization reaction and is, therefore, suitable for quantitative visual titrations.

The internal indicator is not always applicable, especially for determining the end point in highly colored solutions, for very weak acids, or for mixtures of acids of varying strengths. The measurement of a physical property of the system, such as potential, conductance, or absorption, that will change in value at the equivalence point is often employed in such instances.

B. POTENTIOMETRIC TITRATION

Today the ready availability of commercial pH meters in conjunction with stable indicator and reference electrodes has encouraged the development and use of potentiometric methods. This expansion has been

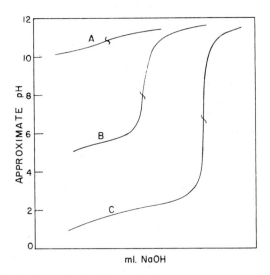

Fig. 1. Typical potentiometric titration curves in an aqueous system: A = weak acid, e. g., phenol; B = carboxylic acid; C = strong acid, e. g., sulfonic acid.

exceptionally fruitful in the field of acidimetry. There are a number of electrode combinations which will measure the pH of a solution accurately. Of these the glass electrode and saturated calomel reference electrode are the most convenient and most widely applicable. Very often, in acid-base titrations an indication of the end point is sufficient, and many simplified electrode systems have been described which accomplish this purpose without measuring the absolute pH of the system. A detailed discussion of electrodes, however, is beyond the scope of this chapter. For further information the reader might study the periodic reviews of potentiometric titrations by Furman (72) which provide broad coverage of recent developments in this field. The application of potentiometric titrations will be discussed further in the section reviewing nonaqueous systems.

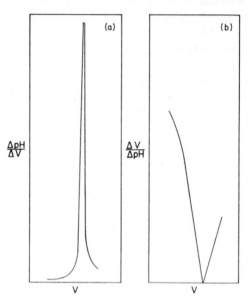

Fig. 2. Potentiometric data: (a) plotted for ΔpH/ΔV as a function of volume of titrant; (b) plotted for ΔV/ΔpH as a function of volume of titrant.

A plot of the data obtained by potentiometric titration provides a convenient means for determining the equivalence point. Figure 1 shows the shapes of the curves obtained by plotting the volume of titrant vs. pH from the titration of acids of various strengths with a strong base, e. g., sodium hydroxide, in an aqueous system. The equivalence point is represented where the slope of the curve is a maximum. With acids having ionization constants, K_a, of $> 10^{-7}$ this inflection point is quite sharp and the midpoint can be determined without question. For weaker acids, however, the slope of pH $= f(V)$ at the equivalence point is small and difficult to determine directly. In such cases the end point often can be estimated with more certainty by plotting ΔpH/ΔV as a function of V or

$\Delta V/\Delta \mathrm{pH}$ against V, as shown in Figure 2. Gran (77) recommended the latter approach. As indicated in Figure 2b, the curves consist of two straight lines which intersect each other and the V-axis at the equivalence point.

Titration of mixtures of strong and weak acids with alkali hydroxide will give curves showing more than one inflection. Quantitative results can be obtained only when the ionization constants differ by several orders of magnitude. According to Kolthoff and Stenger (121), if the acids are present in equal concentrations, results accurate to 0.5% can be obtained only if the ratio, $K_1:K_2 = 10^5$ or greater. If the concentration of the weaker acid is about 100 times that of the stronger acid, $K_1:K_2$ must be at least 10^6. This is illustrated later in Figures 5 and 6, which show, respectively, the titration curves of (a) approximately equivalent amounts of hydrochloric acid and acetic acid ($K_a = \sim 10^{-5}$) in water and in methanol and (b) hydrochloric plus acetic acid in a ratio of about 1:100 in the same solvents.

C. CONDUCTIMETRIC TITRATION

There are some occasions when the measurement of conductance of a solution is more advantageous than potentiometric titration. When titrating strong acids with base, the conductance decreases sharply prior to the end point and then increases after neutralization of the acid is completed. The end point is represented as the intersection of the two lines in a plot of conductance vs. titer (see Fig. 3). In dealing with weak acids the curves obtained by plotting the conductance against the volume of standard alkali added are usually curved or show a gradual increase in conductance over that part of the slope preceding the end point, followed by a straight and steeper slope with continued addition of base. The difficulty in extrapolating or interpreting the first part of this curve from weak acids might lead to an inaccurate determination of the end point.

Maron and co-workers (134) made an extended study of conductimetric analysis in the determination of fatty and rosin acids, soaps, and acid–soap mixtures in a medium consisting of equal volumes of doubly distilled water and isopropyl alcohol. Results from the conductimetric method compared favorably with potentiometric titration. Table IV presents a comparison of Maron's results by conductimetric and potentiometric methods for the direct titration of fatty and rosin acids with 0.1 N sodium hydroxide and also of sodium oleate with 0.1 N hydrochloric acid.

In the determination of rosin acid in rosin soap, and soap solutions of

TABLE IV

Conductimetric and Potentiometric Titrations of Fatty
and Rosin Acids

Substance	Acid found, meq./g. sample	
	Cond.	Potent.
Lauric acid..........	(4)[a] 4.963 ± 0.22%	(3) 4.952 ± 0.14%
Palmitic acid........	(4) 3.923 ± 0.23%	(3) 3.899 ± 0.15%
Resin 731[b]..........	(10) 2.787 ± 0.21%	(2) 2.791 ± 0.04%
Sodium oleate.......	(4) 3.496 ± 0.06%	(3) 3.502 ± 0.29%

[a] Figures in parentheses represent number of individual determinations.
[b] Product of Hercules Powder Co.

rosin, the potentiometric method was unsuitable, whereas the conductometric method was accurate to ±0.5% relative.   Standard conductivity

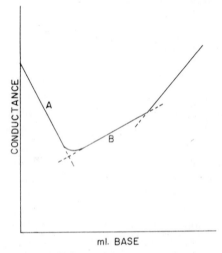

Fig. 3. Conductimetric titration of a mixture of
strong acid (A) and a weak acid (B).

bridge and dip-type platinized, platinum electrodes were used, and in this
instance very straight lines were obtained on both sides of the end point.

This technique also can be used for differential titrations of mixtures of
strong and weak acids (see Fig. 3).   The conductance first decreases until
the strong acid has been neutralized, and then gradually increases during
titration of the weak acid.   After neutralization of the weak acid, the final
portion of the curve has a steeper slope from addition of excess alkali.

D. HIGH-FREQUENCY TITRATION

Applications of high-frequency measurements are comparable to conductimetry. Since no electrodes are required, this technique is particularly useful for samples containing corrosive materials and also permits the use of small vessels. However, each system must be studied individually since changes either in ionic or in dipole properties materially affect the slope of the current–volume curve. For example, Jensen and Parrack (104) were required to use a benzene solution of sodium methylate in order to obtain a sharp end point in the titration of benzoic acid in acetone. When the usual sodium methylate in methanol reagent was used, the increase in methanol molecules caused a change in the polarity of the solution as well as an increase in the degree of ionization of the sodium benzoate. This combined effect completely masked the end point. Anderson and co-workers (6) described the titration of acetic acid with ammonium hydroxide to demonstrate the stability of their high-frequency apparatus for titrating a weak acid with a weak base.

Ishidate and Masui (97) determined the following compounds by high-frequency titration: the sodium salts of oxalic, benzoic, salicylic, and citric acids, lead acetate, calcium lactate, calcium gluconate, acid potassium carbonate, and potassium sodium tartrate. Most determinations were made in a mixture of methanol and benzene. If necessary, acetic acid and ethylene glycol were used as solvents and perchloric acid or sodium acetate in acetic acid as the titrants. Sodium salts titrated directly with perchloric acid showed an accuracy of 0.2 to 0.3%; potassium salts were back-titrated with an accuracy of about 0.4%, and calcium and lead salts with an accuracy of 0.4 to 0.7%.

E. PHOTOMETRIC TITRATION

The use of a photometric titrimeter for determining the equivalence point was described by Nichols and Kindt (163) based on titration to a predetermined galvanometer setting, obtained by balancing the photometer circuit against a buffer solution. The method offered a means for rapid analyses of some routine samples. In acid-base titrations it was possible to detect indicator color changes which were normally difficult to find visually. Because of this increased sensitivity, the precision of the titration was 0.05% relative.

Goddu and Hume (75) used a photometric titration to determine weak acids and bases which differed in light absorption characteristics in the ionized and unionized forms. Satisfactory end points were obtained only if the product of ionization constant and concentration was equal to or greater than 10^{-12} at concentrations of 10^{-5} M and above. The titration of various substituted phenols was used to demonstrate the capabilities and limitations of the method for the determination of weak acids individually, in mixtures and in the presence of strong acids.

F. THERMOMETRIC TITRATION

Another property used to measure the neutralization of an acid is the change in temperature which results from the neutralization reaction. This thermometric approach was described by McClure, Roder, and Kinsey (139) for the determination of 0.5 to 6% acid in acetic anhydride by titration with concentrated triethylamine. A standard curve was prepared for ΔT in °C. vs. per cent acetic acid by measuring the temperature rise when 1.2 ± 0.1 ml. portions of reagent grade triethylamine were added to a small dewar flask containing 20 ml. quantities of acetic anhydride of known acetic acid content. Temperatures were estimated to 0.01°C. by means of a thermometer with a range of 20 to 50°C. graduated in 0.1°C. Samples containing unknown concentrations of acetic acid were run in the same way, recording the maximum temperature rise after mixing. Actual percentage composition was taken from the standard curve.

Other mixtures also can be analyzed by this technique. Since the procedure is empirical, however, each system must be calibrated and, consequently, no general method is feasible.

2. Solvent Systems

The choice of system in which acidity can be measured quantitatively is dictated by two considerations: first, the solubility of the sample and, second, the relative strength of the acid. In general, an aqueous system where applicable is most convenient and reliable because it is less encumbered by errors arising from handling, atmospheric contamination, and the like. However, sample solubility and strength of the acid often preclude the use of an aqueous system.

A. AQUEOUS SOLVENTS

Subject to the limitations to be discussed, water and homogeneous water–organic compound mixtures should be used in preference to other solvents. Aqueous systems are the simplest and most versatile, since nearly all methods for detecting the neutralization point can be used.

As mentioned in Section II. 1A, acids having ionization constants, K_a, of 10^{-8} or greater can be determined quantitatively. Thus, the method is applicable to the lower fatty acids and many aliphatic dibasic, hydroxy, and other soluble acids.

However, in this, like all methods of functional group analysis, the nature of other constituents in the sample to be analyzed must be considered to be sure that no significant interferences will be encountered. Formates, acetates, glycolates, and other easily hydrolyzed esters will interfere because of the ease with which they saponify. Many formates, for example, titrate as free acids in an aqueous system. Usually the presence of easily hydrolyzed esters is evidenced by a fading end point during titration. Acid anhydrides and acyl halides also hydrolyze to the free acids during titration with aqueous alkali. Active aldehydes interfere because of the ease with which they condense under the influence of aqueous caustic reagents. The extent of reaction of these classes of compounds varies considerably. In some cases reaction is complete or consistently reproducible and, consequently, suitable corrections can be applied to the apparent acidity found by titration. This, of course, requires that the concentration of the interfering constituents be known through an independent analysis. Often the reaction of these types of compounds is variable. Occasionally, the interference can be minimized by titration at reduced temperature; the hydrolysis of methyl acetate is relatively slow at 0°C. In general, however, use of an inert nonaqueous system is recommended if the presence of lower esters, anhydrides, acyl halides, or aldehydes is known or suspected. Further information will be given in the following section on nonaqueous solvents.

Weak acids ($K_a = <10^{-8}$) interfere by consuming caustic and producing an indefinite end point. These include the phenols and carbonic acid. Phenols can be titrated in basic nonaqueous media (see Section II. 2 D). Carbonic acid interferes in all methods. Absorption of carbon dioxide by water is considerably less than that in many organic compounds. For aqueous systems dissolved carbon dioxide usually can be removed by boiling or sparging the water prior to use. Most organic systems require that the titration flask be protected from contact with the atmosphere and other sources of carbon dioxide.

Peroxides may interfere with all methods. Peracids titrate quantitatively. Other classes of peroxides will cause bleaching of indicators used in visual titrations. Addition of more indicator suffices for samples containing small amounts of peroxides. Otherwise potentiometric or other electrical method for detecting the end point is required.

Some early work by Baggesgaard-Rasmussen (9) involved titration of a variety of organic acids in aqueous–alcoholic media of varying ratios. He concluded that titration in alcoholic solution offers no advantages other than being a much better solvent than water. (Choice of nonaqueous solvent is dictated by other considerations also, as indicated in the following section.) Phenolphthalein was applicable in nearly all cases to the alcoholic system. His study included investigation of the special relations of the medium, i. e., the range of the reaction scale in aqueous alcohol and the transition range of the indicators in the medium.

In addition to alcohols other water miscible organic liquids are often useful as solvents in aqueous systems. These include pyridine, dioxane, glycol, and glycol-ethers. It should be borne in mind that all mixtures containing more than a few per cent water behave similarly to water systems.

The simplest procedure for visual and other titration methods is based on delivery of standardized aqueous caustic solution from a calibrated buret. The volume of base required to neutralize the sample is equivalent to the amount of acid in the sample. In macro work, using 50 or 100 ml. burets, the volume delivered can be estimated to about 0.02 ml. Actual limit of detection is a function of the reliability with which the buret can be read, size of sample (should require no more than one buret filling), total volume of solution which can be titrated conveniently, and precision of the method for detection of the end point. The visual titration can be expected to give a precision and accuracy of 1 to 2 parts per thousand under optimum conditions.

Macro Procedure. Visual Titration. The sample, containing from 5 to 45 meq. of acid, is weighed accurately into a 250 ml. volumetric or other suitable flask. If the sample is water soluble, 25 to 50 ml. of preneutralized distilled water, containing indicator, is added. (The solvent containing phenolphthalein or other indicator —see Table II—is conveniently neutralized with 0.01 N sodium hydroxide.) The solution is titrated to the end point with standardized 0.5 N sodium hydroxide. The milliequivalents of alkali consumed equals the milliequivalents of acid in the sample.

If the sample is not water soluble, methanol, pyridine, dioxane, or other water-miscible solvent can be used. Samples containing less than 5 meq. of acid should be titrated with lower normality sodium hydroxide, e. g., 0.1 or 0.01 N. In cases in which water is undesirable because of solubility problems or presence of some interfering compounds, the sample should be dissolved in dry methanol or other suitable organic solvent and titrated with standardized sodium methoxide in methanol. Reagent of satisfactory purity usually can be prepared by dissolving the proper weight of powdered sodium methoxide, which is available commercially, in dry methanol. The mixture should be allowed to stand overnight to permit settling of the insoluble carbonate. Then the clear supernatant liquid can be decanted into a clean reservoir.

Precision and accuracy can be improved considerably by use of large samples and addition of standard caustic solution on a weight basis.

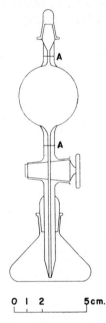

Fig. 4. Weighing pipet.

Neutral equivalents showing a precision of 1 part in 10,000 have been obtained in the authors' laboratory using a combined gravimetric-volumetric titration for the analysis of nearly pure acids. The following procedure is used:

About 55 meq. of the acid is accurately weighed into an erlenmyer flask and 50 ml. of deionized distilled water added, plus neutral alcohol if necessary, to effect solution. Approximately 50 ml. of standardized 1 M aqueous sodium hydroxide is weighed into the flask. The weighing pipet shown in Figure 4 is used for this purpose. Points A–A are index marks to permit reproducible delivery. The analysis is completed by titration with 0.1 N aqueous sodium hydroxide delivered from a calibrated 100 ml. buret.   Thymol blue is used as indicator and precise color matching is made by comparison with a color standard of thymol blue in an equal volume of solvent.

This variation in technique provides a means for using relatively large samples.   Since most of the standard caustic is weighed, temperature variations are relatively unimportant and final titration can be made with dilute base contained in a standard buret.   The following are typical results from duplicate analyses of C. P. phthalic acid samples, expressed as neutral equivalents: (a) 83.2174, 83.2109;   (b) 83.0721, 83.0726;   (c) 83.1463, 83.1399.

Where feasible, a homogeneous system is to be preferred for titrations, since this eliminates problems associated with distribution between two phases.   In some special cases, however, two-phase systems have been used.   Hillig (90) for example, described a method for determining fatty acids in butter by titration of an ether solution of the sample with aqueous caustic.   He found that a slight excess of sodium hydroxide was necessary to assure complete reaction of the fatty acids.

B. NONAQUEOUS NEUTRAL SOLVENTS

The step from mixed systems containing aqueous-organic phases to nonaqueous homogeneous systems represented an important trend in acidimetry.   Initially the use of nonaqueous solutions served as a means for maintaining a single phase throughout the titration of such water-insoluble materials as petroleum products, fats, and waxes.   Two approaches were used: (a) the sample was dissolved in a water-miscible solvent such as methanol or ethanol and titrated with sodium hydroxide in water, and (b) a water-immiscible solvent such as chloroform or benzene was used together with alkali alkoxide in alcohol.   Bishop, Kittredge, and Hildebrand (17) recommended the use of ethanol as solvent for higher fatty acids.   They reported that end points were often sharper in alcohol solution, due partly to the fact that alcoholysis of salts of weak acids tends to be less than corresponding hydrolysis in aqueous solutions.   Usually the positions of indicator color changes in ethanol are close to those in water.   The colors of some indicators with corresponding e. m. f. readings in volts are reported in Table V along with results obtained by titrating palmitic acid in palmitin using 0.157 N sodium ethoxide in ethanol with thymolphthalein as indicator (17).

Following the recommendations of Bishop et al. (17), Sandin and coworkers (193) determined the neutral equivalents of higher fatty acids in

TABLE V

Color Changes of Indicators in Ethanol

Indicator	Concn., g./l.	E.m.f. of color changes
Bromphenol blue	1	Yellow, 0.34 green, 0.47 blue
Methyl orange..............	1	Pink, 0.20 orange, 0.23 yellow
Methyl violet..............	1	Violet, 0.95 colorless
Methyl red................	Satd.	Red, 0.54 orange, 0.62 yellow
Phenolphthalein............	10	Colorless, 0.68 red
Thymol blue..............	1	Red, 0.30 golden
Thymolphthalein...........	10	Colorless, 0.82 blue

Palmitic Acid in Palmitin

Solvent	Palmitic acid	
	Added, g.	Found, g.
Abs. ethanol...................	0.467	0.467
	0.493	0.490
95% ethanol..................	0.513	0.512
	0.436	0.439

absolute ethanol at 65°C. using 0.05 N sodium ethoxide in ethanol as the standard reagent. A sample size was chosen to contain 0.5 meq. acid. Purified stearic acid proved to be a satisfactory primary acid standard for their work. They increased the sharpness of the end point with a mixed indicator of thymolphthalein and methyl orange. Titrations were performed in Nessler tubes where the color change from yellow to green was readily detected. Some of their results are shown in Table VI (193).

TABLE VI

Analytical Data for Fatty Acids in Ethanol System

Acid	Neutral equivalent		
	Calcd.	Found	Semimicro method[a]
Palmitic................	256.3	256.5	255
		256.8	256
Lauric..................	200.2	200.2	200
		200.0	201
			199
Myristic................	228.2	227.7	229
		228.0	227
			227

[a] These results were obtained by titrating not more than 50 mg. of fatty acid with 0.017 N sodium ethoxide.

Alcoholic media minimize interference from a few classes of compounds which react in the aqueous system. These include easily hydrolyzed esters and aldehydes. In the authors' laboratory use of dry methanol as solvent and standardized sodium methoxide in methanol as titrant has permitted direct titrations for formic acid in methyl formate and for free acids in the presence of aldehydes. In all cases end points using phenolphthalein indicator have been sharp, stable, and reproducible. Reported data on analyses for acids in a variety of aldehydes indicate precision and accuracy comparable to results in the absence of these carbonyl compounds. For example, $0.28 \pm 0.00\%$ formic acid was found on titration of 5 to 10 g. samples of formaldehyde and $10.83 \pm 0.02\%$ acid, in a sample of benzaldehyde (150). The preparation of sodium methoxide is mentioned in Section II.2A. The use of a water-immiscible solvent is illustrated in the report of Folin and Flanders (64), who in 1912 observed that water-insoluble carboxylic acids, including palmitic, oleic, and stearic acids, could be titrated to sharp phenolphthalein end points using solvents like chloroform, carbon tetrachloride, benzene, and toluene with sodium ethoxide in ethanol as the titrating agent. To improve the solubility of some acids they suggested that the sample be dissolved first in 10 ml. of ethanol and then diluted to 100 ml. with chloroform or one of the hydrocarbon solvents mentioned above.

Lykken and co-workers (130) contributed a great deal of information on nonaqueous solvents in their search for a suitable method of determining acidity in such water-insoluble mixtures as petroleum lubricants, detergents, fats, waxes, greases, asphalt resins, polymers, and distillate bottoms. This work included a comprehensive investigation of the important variables which affect the potentiometric determination of the end point in such liquids as isopropyl alcohol, chloroform, carbon tetrachloride, petroleum ether, cyclohexanol, methyl ethyl ketone, dioxane, benzyl alcohol, and mixtures of these solvents. In considering the solvent action, equilibrium rate of the electrodes, electrical conductivity, inherent acidity of the solvent, chemical stability of the solvent, and the nature of inflection point, Lykken et al. (130) found that an equal volume mixture of purified dry benzene and isopropyl alcohol containing 1% water provided the most suitable medium for the determination of free acids, using a glass–calomel electrode system.

The reproducibility and accuracy of a determination was found to be dependent on the establishment of an equilibrium after addition of each increment of reagent. This was usually achieved by allowing a constant equilibration period of 1 minute between addition of 0.10 ml. increments of 0.1 N alcoholic potassium hydroxide. Lykken et al. also found that the presence of metallic salts produced a serious interference which necessitated their removal before titration.

The benzene–isopropanol potentiometric procedure has been accepted by the A. S. T. M. as method D 664-52 (4). It was used as standard in cooperative studies between petroleum companies on single-phase and two-phase systems for use in determining acidities of oils (60a). The results indicated that single-phase titration is more reliable. For routine use, the following visual titration method was recommended.

Visual Procedure for Petroleum Products (4). The following reagents are required: (a) *Solvent* prepared in 1 liter quantities from 500 ml. benzene, 5 ml. water, and 495 ml. dry isopropanol; (b) *α-naphtholbenzein indicator solution*, 10 g. per liter of dry isopropanol. The indicator can be purchased from Allied Chemical and Dye Corporation, National Aniline Division, 40 Rector Street, New York 6, New York; (c) *0.1 N potassium hydroxide*. 6 g. solid KOH is added to 1 liter dry isopropanol (<0.9% H_2O) and the solution boiled gently 10 to 15 minutes. To remove carbonate about 2 g. $Ba(OH)_2$ is added and the solution boiled gently for an additional 5 to 10 minutes. (Deal and Wyld (50) reported that barium hydroxide treatment is unnecessary since potassium carbonate is nearly insoluble in the alcohol.) The mixture is cooled and allowed to stand several hours before filtration of the supernatant liquid through a fine filter. The reagent is standardized with potassium acid phthalate to the phenolphthalein end point. The coefficient of cubical expansion of organic liquids usually is significantly higher than that of water. Consequently, more care must be exercised in observation of temperature of the titrant at the time of use and suitable corrections made to the normality which may have been obtained at another temperature. Reference tables of normality vs. temperature are easily prepared.

The proper weight of sample (see table below) is added to a 250 ml. erlenmeyer flask followed by 100 ml. of solvent and 3 ml. of α-naphtholbenzein indicator. The solution is titrated immediately below 30°C. with 0.1 N potassium hydroxide in dry isopropanol to the visual end point, as indicated by a color change from yellow-orange to green-brown.

Expected acid No.	Wt. sample (g.)
0.0 to 3.0	20.0 ± 2.0
3.0 to 25.0	2.0 ± 0.2
25.0 to 250.0	0.2 ± 0.02

The use of alcoholic media provides a reliable means for determining strong acids, such as hydrochloric in the presence of carboxylic acids. This is illustrated in Figure 5, which shows a comparison of the potentiometric titration curves for approximately equivalent amounts of hydro-

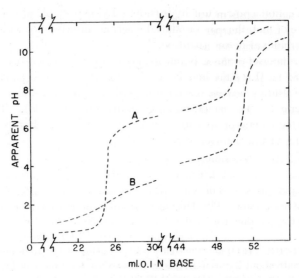

Fig. 5. Potentiometric titration of approximately equimolar mixture of hydrochloric and acetic acids: A = titration in methanol system; B = titration in water system.

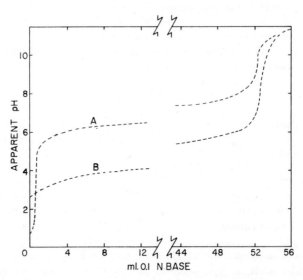

Fig. 6. Potentiometric titration of mixture of hydrochloric and acetic acids in molar ratio of about 1:100: A = titration in methanol system; B = titration in water system.

chloric and acetic acids in water and in methanol. The end point for the strong acid is much sharper in the alcoholic system. On the other hand, the equivalence point for acetic acid, and therefore for total acidity, is more clearly defined in the aqueous system. The differences become much more marked as the ratio of weak to strong acid is increased. Figure 6 shows the titration curves for hydrochloric and acetic acids in a molar ratio of about 1:100. In the aqueous system only total acidity can be measured. In methanol, however, clear inflections are observed for hydrochloric acid and also for acetic acid.

The standard potentiometric method D 664-52 of the A. S. T. M. (4) resolves constituents into groups of weak acids and strong acids provided the dissociation constants of the strong acids are at least 10^3 times those of the next weaker group. The method is applicable to acids whose dissociation constants in water are $>10^{-9}$.

Potentiometric Titration Procedure for Petroleum Products (4). The sample is dissolved in 125 ml. of solvent (500 ml. benzene + 5 ml. water + 495 ml. dry isopropanol) and titrated with 0.1 N KOH in dry isopropanol (prepared by same method as for visual titration). The course of the titration is followed with a glass–calomel electrode pair and a pH meter, adding 0.05 ml. increments in the vicinity of the inflection points. Some residues may require chloroform in place of benzene in the solvent to effect complete solution.

Ames and Licata (5) extended the studies of Lykken and co-workers to the determination of acid numbers in vegetable and marine oils, finding a favorable comparison between the potentiometric and visual titrations. For visual titrations the sample was dissolved in neutral isopropanol and titrated directly with standard potassium hydroxide in dry isopropanol to the phenolphthalein end point (1% in dry isopropanol). The obvious advantage of this visual method was the rapidity of the titration compared to the potentiometric procedure. A precision ±0.025 meq./g. was reported for the visual method as compared to ±0.043 for the potentiometric method.

According to Fritz (68), weak acids or the acidic moiety of a salt can be titrated visually with lithium or sodium methoxide in benzene–methanol using suitable indicators such as thymol blue in methanol or p-nitrobenzeneazoresorcinol in benzene. In such cases the sample is dissolved in a minimum amount of organic base such as dimethyl formamide, pyridine, n-butylamine, or ethylenediamine and diluted with a nonpolar solvent such as benzene. Nitrogen blanketing is suggested to exclude interference from carbon dioxide.

Fritz and Lisicki (70) described the titration of carboxylic acids, acid chlorides, and anhydrides in benzene–methanol or butylamine using sodium methoxide in benzene–methanol and thymol blue indicator.

A line operated Beckman pH meter equipped with glass and antimony electrodes was used for potentiometric titrations. The authors (70) reported that the glass–antimony electrode combination is satisfactory in basic solvents but is not suitable for benzene or benzene–methanol systems. For the latter, antimony and calomel electrodes were found satisfactory; lithium chloride was added to the solution to decrease the resistance.

Radell and Donahue (177) applied the method of Fritz and Lisicki (70) to the determination of fatty acids containing substituted bromine, amino, epoxy, dihydroxy, α-sulfonic acid, and ammonium α-sulfonate groups. Their work indicated that lactone, lactam, and epoxy functional groups do not interfere in the determination of the neutral equivalent.

The monomethyl ether of ethylene glycol was used by Ruehle (187) as a medium for the potentiometric titration of the acidity of materials soluble in this solvent. Acetone, anisole, or 1,4-dioxane were used to enhance the solvent powers of butyl alcohol without interfering with the functioning of a quinhydrone electrode in this solvent. Using a calomel–quinhydrone electrode system he obtained sharp end points with trichloroacetic, benzoic, and acetic acids in ethylene glycol monomethyl ether, anisole–n-butyl alcohol, and 1,4-dioxane–n-butyl alcohol. The addition of 20% LiCl to the solvent sharpened the end point.

Acid end groups have been determined in polymers such as polyamides and polyethylene terephthalate by titration with standard alkali. The end group data were used in the calculation of number average molecular weight of the polymer. Waltz and Taylor (234) and Schaefgen and Flory (194) determined acid end groups in polyamides by dissolving the polymer in hot benzyl alcohol (175°C.) and titrating the hot solutions with potassium hydroxide in the same solvent using phenolphthalein as the indicator. Benzyl alcohol was found to degrade slowly on heating at 175°C. with attendant development of acidic by products. It was necessary, therefore to heat and titrate solvent blanks along with samples. Schnell (197) described the titration of carboxyl end groups in polyaminocaproic acid using boiling α-phenylethanol solvent. The sample–solvent solution was then diluted with n-propanol–water azeotrope and indicator added consisting of phenolphthalein–thymol blue in ethanol. The solution was placed in a photometric colorimeter, stirred with nitrogen, and titrated with 0.01 N NaOH. Pohl (175) titrated carboxyl end groups in polyethylene terphthalate by dissolving the polymer in benzyl alcohol at 203°C., quickly quenching the solution with chloroform, and titrating with sodium hydroxide to the phenol red end point. The polymer degraded slightly while dissolving in the hot alcohol forming additional carboxyl groups. A small correction was applied to compensate for this degradation.

End group methods such as those described here are sufficiently sensitive to detect as little as 0.002 meq. acid per gram of polymer. The precision of the method was calculated from five duplicate determinations giving a sigma of 0.001 meq./g. at the 0.073 meq./g. acid level (148).

In addition to alcohol and alcohol mixtures, numerous other neutral solvents have been studied extensively. Of these acetone, acetonitrile, and methyl ethyl ketone have been most useful. Fritz and Lisicki (70) found that carboxylic acids could be determined in the presence of most phenols using acetone or acetonitrile as solvent and p-hydroxyazobenzene as indicator. In a few cases it was possible to add azoviolet when the p-hydroxyazobenzene end point had been reached (colorless to yellow), permitting titration of the phenolic constituent to the blue-green azoviolet end point. Differentiation between substituted phenols of significantly differing strengths was feasible by potentiometric titration. Harlowe, Noble, and Wyld (86b) found that methyl ethyl ketone with tetrabutylammonium hydroxide in isopropanol as titrant was a suitable system for determinations of phenol and other weak acids.

Siggia and Floramo (208) introduced a novel method for the direct determination of free maleic and phthalic acids in their anhydrides. The sample was dissolved in acetone and the free acid titrated potentiometrically, using an ordinary glass–calomel electrode pair, with an acetone solution of a tertiary amine such as tri-n-propylamine or N-ethylpiperidine. The anhydrides did not react with the tertiary amine. Methyl ethyl ketone was used alternatively as a solvent. Only acids having dissociation constants of 10^{-3} or greater (in water) could be titrated by this method. Other acids found too weak to be titrated were acetic ($K = \sim 10^{-5}$), benzoic ($\sim 6 \times 10^{-5}$), succinic ($\sim 7 \times 10^{-5}$), and camphoric ($K_1 = \sim 3 \times 10^{-5}$). It was observed that only the first acid group of maleic and phthalic acids was titrated; the second carboxyl group was too weak to give a potentiometric break. Analysis of mixtures of acid and anhydride of known composition gave an accuracy of 0.2% absolute over the range 0.1 to 100% anhydride. Safranski and Segal (190) extended the work of Siggia and Floramo to determine equimolar quantities of strong acids ($K = >10^{-3}$) such as dichloroacetic in the presence of weaker acids ($K = <10^{-3}$) such as acetic and glycolic acids.

McClure, Roder, and Kinsey (139) found that acids as weak as benzoic could be titrated in an acetic anhydride system with a benzene solution of triethylamine. Two techniques were employed to measure the end point of the reaction between free acid and tertiary amine. The first method depended on the color change of methyl red dissolved in acetonitrile while the second, as mentioned in Section II. 1 F, measured the temperature rise when the amine was added to the sample.

Visual Procedure for Carboxylic Acids in the Presence of Anhydrides (139). A solution is prepared for color comparison by adding 5 drops of the indicator solution to 100 ml. benzene in a 250 ml. erlenmeyer flask. (This solution is prepared by drying acetonitrile over anhydrous magnesium sulfate for an hour and saturating the dry solvent with methyl red indicator. The mixture is filtered and stored in a closed bottle to prevent contamination.) The flask is stoppered. A sample of anhydride containing 5 to 60 meq. of acid is weighed into another 250 ml. erlenmeyer flask. 5 drops of methyl red indicator solution is added to each 100 ml. of sample and the solution titrated immediately with 2 M triethylamine in benzene until the solution color matches that of the indicator in benzene. The color is stable in benzene but it will change rapidly in acetic anhydride after the end point has been reached. The 2 M triethylamine in benzene is prepared by drying the contents of a 500 g. bottle of C. P. triethylamine with potassium hydroxide pellets overnight. The solution is carefully decanted into a 1 liter flask followed by careful addition of 25 ml. of acetic anhydride. (This will usually provide a sufficient excess of anhydride.) The mixture is refluxed for 30 minutes and allowed to cool. 125 ml. of 10 M sodium hydroxide is added with constant stirring. (The small temperature rise which accompanies this reaction is an indication that an excess of anhydride was used.) The solution is stirred for 10 minutes. The solution is poured into a separatory funnel and 500 ml. benzene is added. The funnel is thoroughly shaken and the water layer is drawn off and discarded. The benzene is washed with another 125 ml. of sodium hydroxide. The benzene solution of the amine is transferred to a distilling flask fitted with a simple condenser set for distillation. At least 200 ml. is distilled and discarded (temperature >81°C.). The receiver and condenser are replaced with dry apparatus and the distillation is continued until 100 ml. remains in the pot. The receiver is protected with an Ascarite-Drierite tube at all times. The distillate is diluted with an equal volume of dry benzene (<0.05% water). The triethylamine solution is standardized by titrating potentiometrically with 0.5 N standard aqueous hydrochloric acid to a pH of 4 to 6. The reagent is stored in a dry glass-stoppered bottle or in an automatic buret protected with an Ascarite-Drierite tube.

This method was found applicable to the determination of acids with dissociation constants as small as benzoic acid ($K = 6 \times 10^{-5}$). It was used to determine acetic, propionic, and benzoic acids in acetic anhydride as well as acetic acid in acetic anhydride-hydrocarbon samples. A precision of 0.07% absolute over the range 0.5 to 3.5% acid was reported for the visual method and 0.09% absolute for the thermometric method over the range 0.8 to 5.5% acid.

C. ACIDIC SOLVENTS

The glacial acetic acid system has found many applications in analysis for the amine function. Although not directly applicable to the titration of carboxylic acids, the acetic acid system serves as a reliable means for determining some strong acids in the presence of carboxylic acids, for direct titrations of amino acids, and for analyses of metal salts of weak organic acids.

Markunas and Riddick (133) undertook a systematic study of the application of the glacial acetic acid system to the determination of the salts of carboxylic acids. Hall and Werner (85) had previously demonstrated the basic character of these salts in acetic acid and showed that perchloric acid was the most useful titrant. Markunas and Riddick found that this medium was suitable for the determination of a number of amino acids, tertiary amines, and basic nitrogen compounds as well as many of the alkali metal salts of the lower monobasic acids. Those carboxylic acid salts showing a sharp break in the potentiometric titration curve were subsequently analyzed by using a 1% solution of crystal violet in acetic acid as the indicator. The limitation of this method was the near insolubility of some alkali metal salts in glacial acetic acid. Details of the glacial acetic acid system using perchloric acid are given in the chapter, "Determination of Amines and Amides," in this volume.

It is not possible to titrate amino acids quantitatively in aqueous solution because of the buffering action rendered by amine group. Nadeau and Branchen (159) demonstrated the usefulness of the nonaqueous technique by determining a number of representative amino acids in glacial acetic acid using perchloric acid as the titrant and crystal violet as the indicator.

Palit (170) studied the properties of mixtures of glycol-type solvents with hydrocarbons. He concluded that equal volumes of ethylene or propylene glycol and isopropyl alcohol might be regarded as a universal solvent for alkali metal salts of any monobasic organic acid. Utilizing this solvent mixture, Palit quantitatively titrated a number of alkali metal salts with a standard solution of perchloric acid in the same solvent. Calomel-glass electrodes were used in the potentiometric titration. By weighing the glycolic caustic reagent to eliminate drainage errors he reported that the method was capable of an accuracy of ±0.02%.

The sensitivity of nonaqueous titrations of weak bases and salts of weak acids can be effectively increased by addition of an organic solvent of low dielectric constant. This observation was made by Pifer et al (174), who were able to use titrants as dilute as 0.001 N and still obtain sharp inflections by potentiometric titration. The organic solvent also had the advantage of aiding in solubilizing the sample. These titrations cannot be performed in an aqueous system. The authors used small glass and calomel electrodes mounted at right angles by inserting the calomel electrode through a hole bored in the side of a small beaker. A mechanical stirrer was employed. They reported that best results were obtained with chloroform. When other solvents such as benzene, toluene, or xylene were used, fluctuations were sometimes observed, caused by the capacity of the operator's body, which could not be fully overcome by grounding the instrument.

The authors (174) found that a weak base such as sodium acetate gave the sharpest inflection if dissolved in a small amount (5 ml.) of an acidic solvent such as glacial acetic acid to increase its relative basicity followed by dilution with a neutral solvent such as p-dioxane. Comparative titrations substituting absolute ethanol for dioxane produced weaker end points. Use of water in place of the acetic acid greatly reduced the sharpness of the end points. It was also observed that stronger inflections resulted when dioxane instead of ethanol or acetic acid was used as solvent for the titrating agent, perchloric acid. Pifer et al. also pointed out that salts of organic bases and acids which are normally not soluble in organic solvents could be titrated after dissolving them in a few milliliters of water and diluting the solution with an excess of p-dioxane. The basicity could then be determined by titration with 0.1 N perchloric acid in dioxane using an ethanolic solution of methyl red as indicator.

Although titration of salts or organic bases could not be performed accurately with 0.01 N or weaker solutions of perchloric acid, such titrations were made possible by dissolving the salt in a minimum of acetic acid followed by dilution with a large excess of an aprotic solvent such as benzene and using crystal violet indicator.

Sideri and Osol (207) described a simplified technique for removing impurities from dioxane used to prepare standard reagents such as perchloric acid solutions. Certain impurities produce a coloration with perchloric acid, thus interfering with visual indicator end point determinations. Their purification procedure consisted of adding asbestos, such as Powminco brand, in the proportion of approximately 20 grams per liter of dioxane, shaking the mixture occasionally during an hour or so, and filtering the solution through a plug or pad of asbestos.

Wolff (243) stated that the relative acidity constants of acid-base couples vary from one solvent to another according to the value of the dielectric constant and the acidic or basic property of the solvent. With decreasing dielectric constant of the solvent the relative strength of uncharged acids such as HF, HNO_2, and RCOOH would remain constant, that of positively

TABLE VII

Neutral and Acidic Solvent Systems for Use in Analyses
of Organic Acids

Solvent system	Type of sample	Method	Page ref.
Aqueous	Water sol. acids having $K = {>}10^{-8}$	Visual, potentio-metric	2,8,12
Ethanol	Higher fatty acids	Visual	16
Hydrocarbon + ethanol	Higher fatty acids	Visual	18
Benzene–isopropanol (1% H_2O)	Petroleum lubricants, detergents, fats, waxes, greases, asphalt resins, polymers, distillate bottoms	Potentiometric, visual	19,21
Isopropanol	Vegetable and marine oils	Visual	21
Glycol–isopropanol	Alkali metal salts of monobasic org. acids	Potentiometric	25
Chloroform or dioxane + acetic acid (min.)	Salts of org. acids	Potentiometric, visual	26
Benzene + min. of DMF or pyridine	Weak acids	Visual	21
Benzene–methanol	Carboxylic acids, acid chlorides, anhydrides	Visual, potentiometric	22
Benzene–methanol	Fatty acids containing substituted bromine, amino, epoxy, dihydroxy, α-sulfonic acid, ammonium-α-sulfonate groups	Visual, potentiometric	22
Butanol + acetone, anisole, Cellosolve, or 1,4-dioxane	Trichloroacetic, benzoic, acetic acids	Potentiometric	22
Acetone	Acids in anhydrides, $K = {>}10^{-3}$	Potentiometric	23
Acetone	Mixts. strong acids, $K = {>}10^{-3}$; in presence of weak acids $K = {<}10^{-2}$	Potentiometric	23
Acetic anhydride	Acids in anhydrides, $K = {>}10^{-6}$	Visual, thermo-metric	23
Acetic acid	Salts of carboxylic acids, amino acids, basic nitrogen compds.	Visual	25

charged acids ($NH_4{}^+$), salts of amines, and hydrated cations increases, and that of negatively charged acids (acid salts of polybasic acids, etc.) would decrease. If a solvent has acidic or basic properties, acids or bases stronger than the solvent itself cannot exist in solution, i. e., the range of strengths of the acids is limited compared with that in an inert solvent.

A list of acids and acid-containing materials is presented in Table VII along with neutral or acidic solvent systems in which they can be titrated. In general potentiometric methods can be used for all systems.

D. BASIC SOLVENTS

Dimethyl formamide (DMF) is one of the most important all-around solvents for use in nonaqueous titrations of acids because it is an excellent solvent for most organic compounds and provides a system in which varying strengths can be determined. Samples containing strong mineral acids, carboxylic acids, and very weak acids can be analyzed and all three acidic components resolved in DMF. This solvent is basic enough to increase the acidity of many very weak acids, enabling their potentiometric inflection to be measured. On the other hand, DMF is not as basic as ethylenediamine, which supresses the activity of strong and carboxylic acids and merges their potentiometric inflection into a single break.

Fritz and Keen (69) described a method for the visual titration of phenols in dimethyl formamide. They reported that most phenols with negative substituents are sufficiently acidic to permit titration in DMF using azo-violet indicator. Phenol and alkyl-substituted phenols are weaker acids and are determined with better accuracy when in a more basic solvent such as ethylenediamine. (See p. 32.)

These authors (69) used potassium methoxide in benzene–methanol as the titrating agent. They recommended using only enough methanol to provide a homogeneous, clear solution because the acidic nature of the alcohol results in poor end points. Sodium methoxide also could be used but required more methanol (1 volume alcohol to 6 of benzene) than the potassium methoxide (1 volume alcohol to 10 to 12 of benzene) and did not give as sharp end points as the potassium titrant. Benzoic acid was used as a primary standard for the titrating agent. Du Pont technical grade DMF was found to be sufficiently pure for use as a solvent: due to its highly toxic nature DMF was dispensed and handled in a well-ventilated hood. Of several indicators studied azoviolet (p-nitrobenzenazoresorcinol) in benzene solution was the most reliable for detecting the visual end point in DMF. The titration assembly consisted of a 10 ml. buret, a 50 to 100 ml. titration vessel (covered to prevent absorption of CO_2 from the air), and a magnetic stirring motor with a glass enclosed stirring bar. Fritz and Keen used this procedure for determinations of the more acidic phenols which have a negative group in the ortho or para position. These substituted groups include —CHO, —COR, —COOR, —CONH$_2$, and —NO$_2$.

Ortho-halogen substituted phenols were titrated quantitatively by this procedure. They noted that a carboxyl group has no activating influence and may even decrease the acidity of the phenol as for example in salicylic acid. In general precision and accuracy were about 0.3%.

Kirrmann and Daune-Dubois (116) used DMF as solvent in determining constituents of a mixture of carboxylic acids. They employed platinum and calomel electrodes to follow the potentiometric titrations and used aqueous potassium hydroxide as the titrating agent. With this system they were able to differentiate: (a) phthalic anhydride (first acid function), (b) succinic acid (first H) or monomethylphthalate, and (c) succinic acid

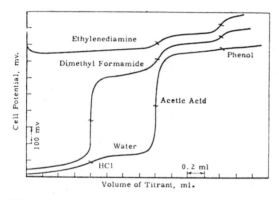

Fig. 7. Curves for an acid mixture titrated with 0.1 N
potassium hydroxide in three solvents (50).

(second H) or oleic acid or phthalic anhydride (second acid function). The authors claimed that an effective separation between two acid functions is possible if the difference between the neutralization potentials is of the order of 200 mv. They found that succinic acid (first H) and monomethyl phthalate, which have similar dissociation constants, were titrated simultaneously. Only one inflection was observed for succinic acid (second H), oleic acid, and phthalic anhydride (second acid function). The precision was reported in general to be 1 to 5%.

An extensive study was made by Deal and Wyld (50) on the titration of mineral acids, carboxylic acids, and phenols in DMF using a convenient electrode pair consisting of an ordinary glass and a sleeve-type calomel electrode. Isopropanol solutions of both potassium hydroxide and of tetrabutylammonium hydroxide (TBAOH) were used successfully as titrating agents although the quaternary amine being a stronger base gave slightly sharper potentiometric breaks. TBAOH was also preferred in some cases, e. g., p-phthalic acid, where undesirable precipitation occurred during titration with potassium hydroxide reagent resulting in a rough, uncertain titration curve. The authors (50) reported that strong mineral acids, carboxylic acids, and phenols could be differentiated successfully by titration in DMF. (Figure 7 shows a comparison of titrations in DMF, water, and ethylenediamine (50).)

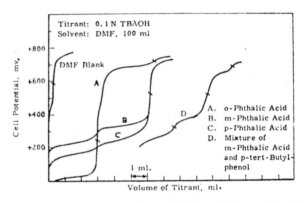

Fig. 8. Phthalic acid isomers titrated in dimethyl formamide (50).

One of the advantages of using DMF is the wide range of cell potentials obtainable in this solvent, approximately 900 mv. In contrast, ethylenediamine tends to compress this range so that an entire titration covers only about 200 mv. Consequently, where applicable the inflections obtained in DMF are more definite than in ethylenediamine. DMF, however, appears to be somewhat unstable in the presence of excess base and therefore may be less desirable than ethylenediamine under some circumstances.

Some interesting titration curves, shown in Figure 8, were obtained with the three isomers of phthalic acid in DMF (50). Two inflections were obtained for each isomer. o-Phthalic acid gave a very strong initial inflection and a very weak break for the second carboxyl group. The reverse was observed for m- and p-phthalic acids. A mixture of m-phthalic acid and p-$tert$-butylphenol exhibited three distinct inflections representing ionization constants in water of ca. 10^{-3}, 10^{-6}, and 10^{-10}, respectively.

Since the presence of water in the titration cell has been shown to be detrimental to the determination of very weak acidity, the use of nearly dry solvent improves the sharpness of the inflections. Since DMF is

TABLE VIII

Potentiometric Titration of Acidic Compounds in DMF

Compound	Formula	Number of Inflections	Ref.
1,2-Dihydroxybenzene (catechol)	$C_6H_4(OH)_2$	2	50,69
1,4-Dihydroxybenzene (hydroquinone)	$C_6H_4(OH)_2$	2	50
2,2'-Dihydroxydiphenylmethane	$CH_2(C_6H_5OH)_2$	1	50
4,4'-Dihydroxydiphenyldimethylmethane	$(CH_3)_2C(C_6H_5OH)_2$	2	50
2,6-Di-*tert*-butyl-4-methylphenol	$(C_4H_9)_2(CH_3)C_6H_2OH$	1	50
2,2'-Methylenebis(4-methyl-6-*tert*-butylphenol)	$CH_2[(C_4H_9)(CH_3)C_6H_2OH]_2$	1	69
4-Hydroxybenzaldehyde	$CHOC_6H_4OH$	1	69
2-Hydroxyacetophenone	$CH_3COC_6H_4OH$	1	69
2,4-Dihydroxyacetophenone	$CH_3COC_6H_3(OH)_2$	1	69
4-Hydroxypropiophenone	$CH_3CH_2COC_6H_4OH$	1	69
Methyl salicylate	$CH_3COOC_6H_4OH$	1	69
Vanillalacetone	$(CH_3COCH{=}CH)(CH_3O)C_6H_3OH$	1	69
Vanillin	$(CHO)(CH_3O)C_6H_3OH$	1	69
Salicylamide	$CONH_2C_6H_4OH$	1	69
Trichlorophenol	$Cl_3C_6H_2OH$	1	69
2-Aceto-1-naphthol	$CH_3COC_{10}H_6OH$	1	69
8-Hydroxyquinoline	C_9H_6NOH	1	69
{Acetic acid Phenol Hydrochloric acid	CH_3COOH C_6H_5OH HCl	3	50
Oleic acid	$C_{17}H_{33}COOH$	1	116
Oxalic acid	$(COOH)_2$	2	148
Succinic acid	$HOOC(CH_2)_2COOH$	2	116
{Oleic acid Succinic acid		2	116
Monomethylphthalate	$CH_3COOC_6H_4COOH$	1	116
{Oleic acid Monomethylphthalate		2	
o-Phthalic acid	$C_6H_4(COOH)_2$	2	50
m-Phthalic acid	$C_6H_4(COOH)_2$		
p-Phthalic acid	$C_6H_4(COOH)_2$		116
{*m*-Phthalic acid *p*-*tert*-Butylphenol	$C_6H_4(COOH)_2$ $C_4H_9C_6H_4OH$		
Phthalic anhydride	$C_6H_4(CO)_2O$		

Table continued

TABLE VIII (*continued*)

Compound	Formula	Number of inflec- tions	Ref.
⎧ Oleic acid		2	116
⎩ Phthalic anhydride			
p-Toluenesulfonic acid	$CH_3C_6H_4SO_3H$	1	148
o-Phosphorous acid	H_3PO_3	2	50
o-Phosphoric acid	H_3PO_4	2	50
⎧ *p*-Toluenesulfonic acid		3	148
⎩ *o*-Phthalic acid			

somewhat hygroscopic, it should be stored with protection from the air. Although the presence of water in the titration cell was shown to be serious (if $>1\%$), absorption of water from the air did not appear to be sufficiently rapid to cause difficulty when titrations were carried out in an open beaker. Deal and Wyld (50) obtained promising results with the Precision-Dow Recordomatic Titrator. The rapidity with which titrations could be made eliminated any difficulty from decomposition of DMF. Transfer of the titrant directly from the storage container to the cell solution was an additional advantage of this type of instrument, preventing any contamination of the titrant which might arise through the use of a conventional buret. Procedural details for use of the DMF and ethylenediamine systems are given on page 40.

Table VIII lists some of the acidic compounds which have been titrated in the DMF system together with the number of inflections observed from potentiometric titration.

From an examination of Table VIII it is apparent that the nature and location of other groups on dihydroxybenzenes affect the relative strengths of the acidic hydroxyl groups. Thus, catechol gives two inflections by potentiometric titration, one from each of the hydroxyl groups. 2,2′-'hydroxydiphenylmethane, on the other hand, gives a single inflection suent to the two hydroxyl groups.

titralliot, and Hall (156) were among the first workers to develop a ethylen hod for titrating phenols and other acids too weak to be ethoxide, ous medium. Their procedure employed a basic solvent, is increased inciple 4), and an even more basic titrant, sodium amino- This principle on the theory that the relative acidity of an acid following equatio dium through its reaction with that solvent. Brønsted theory and is illustrated in the enol:

$$C_6H_5OH + H_2NC_2H_4NH_2 \rightleftharpoons C_6H_5O^- + H_2NC_2H_4NH_3^+ \qquad (3a)$$

$\quad$ Acid $\qquad\qquad$ Base $\qquad\qquad\qquad$ Base $\qquad\qquad$ Acid

$$NaOC_2H_4NH_2 \rightleftharpoons Na^+ + {}^-OC_2H_4NH_2 \qquad (3b)$$

$\qquad\qquad\qquad\qquad\qquad$ Acid $\qquad\qquad$ Base

$$H_2NC_2H_4NH_3^+ + {}^-OC_2H_4NH_2 \rightleftharpoons H_2NC_2H_4NH_2 + HOC_2H_4NH_2 \qquad (3c)$$

$\quad$ Acid $\qquad\qquad\qquad$ Base

If the equilibrium of equation (3a) is to be shifted appreciably to the right, the solvent must be more basic than the conjugate base of the acid $(C_6H_5O^-)$. Thus, in a basic solvent, weak acids such as phenol show a much greater acid strength than in water or alcohols. This principle was applied earlier by Hall and Conant (84) and Hall (83) to the analogous case of the titration of very weak bases such as amines using glacial acetic acid as the solvent and perchloric acid as titrant.

In the EDA system, Moss et al. (156) found that carboxylic acids, such as benzoic, behave like a strong mineral acid in water giving sharp, steep potentiometric inflections and that weaker acids, such as phenol, exhibit behavior characteristic of a carboxylic acid titrated in water. They obtained quantitative separation of mixtures of benzoic acid and phenol, and observed two separate breaks when titrating the difunctional compounds salicylic acid and resorcinol. (Figure 7 illustrates the inflections for phenol and stronger acids.) Amino acids, such as glycine and ϵ-aminocaproic acid, were found to behave as typical substituted carboxylic acids with no interference contributed by the amine group whose ionization was suppressed by the strongly basic ethylene diamine.

Moss et al. (156) found that potentiometric titration gave the most satisfactory end points of the various methods considered including conductometric and visual indicator techniques. Their titration flask, buret, and electrode assembly were designed to exclude atmospheric moisture and carbon dioxide (see Figure 9, which shows a reduced scale assembly for micro titrations). The latter reacts very readily with EDA to form the carbonate or carbamate and results in high blank values. Both antimony and hydrogen indicator electrodes were used but the former was recommended due to convenience in handling. The reference electrode consisted of an antimony rod mounted in the buret below the stopcock. The reference electrode immersed in the titrant was connected electrically through the buret tip with the solution being titrated. This afforded the advantage of a continual flushing of the reference electrode to prevent diffusion. Renewal of the liquid junction occurred at the end of the buret tip, serving as a salt bridge, with addition of each new increment of titrant. The authors used a Leeds & Northrup Cherry amplifier (Catalog No. 7673), portable potentiometer (Catalog No. 7655), and galvanometer (Catalog No. 2420-C). Although the resistance of this system was relatively low, an amplifier was used to increase the sensitivity of the measuring system. Amplification was found to be especially desirable with the hydrogen–calomel electrode combination used for much of the development work, although it later proved to be less convenient than the antimony electrode pair. A pH meter equipped with a hydrogen or antimony electrode was suitable for e. m. f. measurements, although the authors preferred a potentiometer graduated in millivolts. They discovered that the glass electrode was unstable in the system, whether filled with the usual aqueous solutions or with a buffer in EDA. It registered a sharp change in potential at the end point but drifted back immediately in the direction of its original potential. Later investigators, however, modified the method to permit use of the more common electrode combinations.

As their titrating agent Moss and co-workers used ca. 0.2 N sodium aminoethoxide prepared by dissolving ca. 2.5 g. of sodium, which was washed successively in ethanol and triply distilled ethanolamine, in 100 ml. of ethanolamine with cooling, and diluting to 500 ml. with EDA. The solution was standardized against benzoic acid. Dry EDA was prepared from the commercial 70% aqueous grade (Carbide and Carbon) by treatment with sodium hydroxide and, finally, distillation over sodium. These authors felt that best results were obtained with anhydrous EDA because the sharpness of the end points tended to deteriorate progressively as the concentration of water increased. They claimed that removal of even the last 1% of moisture was advantageous for this system.

Katz and Glenn (108) applied the procedure of Moss et al. (156) to the determination of the phenolic content of coal hydrogenation products. Their article describes improvements made in apparatus and technique and reports some of the data obtained from the application of the procedure to the determination of: (a) pure phenols, both unhindered and hindered, (b) carboxylic acids, (c) mixtures of (a) and (b), and (d) coal hydrogenation products, both before and after acid and alkali extraction. The auxiliary electrical equipment as described by Moss et al. was modified by Katz and Glenn (108) to allow automatic recording of the e. m. f. changes during titration. A Brown Electronik strip-chart recorder with a Beckman model H pH meter serving as a millivoltmeter and intermediate amplifier was connected in such a way that graphs of either the differential or the direct titration curve could be obtained directly. These authors found that, in this case, platinum electrodes could be used during continuous and automatic addition of titrant from a standard hypodermic syringe, and continuous recording of the e. m. f.   They claimed that an accuracy of 1% can be obtained easily by their method.

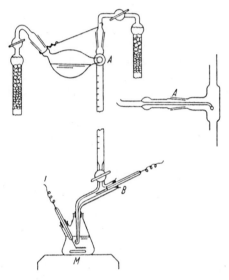

Fig. 9. Microtitration apparatus for use in ethylenediamine system (25): A = buret connection to reagent supply; B = reference electrode; I = indicator electrode; M = magnetic stirrer.

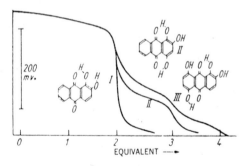

Fig. 10. Titration curves for polyoxyanthraquinones in ethylenediamine (25): I = alizarin; II = purpurin; III = quinalizarin.

Brockmann and Meyer (25) reduced the procedure of Moss et al. to a micro scale for the analysis of 2 to 10 mg. samples, employing the apparatus shown in Figure 9.   They reported single inflections for the titration of alizarin, two breaks for purpurin, and three inflections for quinalizarin (see Fig. 10).

Gran and Althin (78) reported that a modified calomel electrode could be used successfully in EDA systems. The new electrode, shown in Figure 11, was made of Pyrex brand glass with the capillary tube (2.0 to 2.5 mm. bore) sealed through the bottom of the wide upper portion. The lower end of the capillary tube was drawn out. The upper tube contained mercury covered with a paste of mercury and mercurous chloride and was

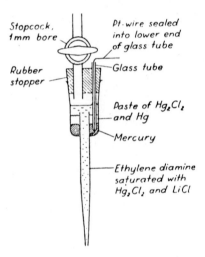

Fig. 11. Schematic drawing of "calomel electrode" for use in ethylenediamine (78).

closed with a two hole rubber stopper through which a 1 mm. bore glass stopcock was fitted. The other hole was fitted with a piece of glass tubing and a sealed-in platinum wire dipping into the lower layer of mercury. The electrode vessel was filled with a saturated solution of mercurous chloride and lithium chloride in ethylenediamine by applying gentle suction to the stopcock tube. When the vessel was filled, the stopcock was closed and the electrode allowed to stand for a day to equilibrate. When in use the platinum wire was connected to a potentiometer and the drawn out capillary tube dipped into the solution to be titrated. An ignited bright platinum electrode served as the indicator electrode for the system. Gran and Althin (78) titrated a lignin derivative and phenol with sodium methoxide in ethylenediamine and benzoic acid and methyl p-hydroxybenzoate with sodium aminoethoxide in the same solvent.

Deal and Wyld (50) were able to determine very weak acids by titration with hydroxides in EDA using a glass–calomelelectrode system. The titration agents used were potassium hydroxide and tetrabutylammonium hydroxide (TBAOH), both in isopropanol. The advantage in the hydroxide titrants lay in the ease of preparation and greater stability than that of sodium alkoxide reagents; the latter tend to react with moisture and are converted to hydroxides. They found that the glass electrode was insensitive in EDA solutions when titrants containing sodium were used, possibly because it responded to sodium ions as well as to hydrogen ions in strongly alkaline solution. The use of potassium hydroxide or quaternary ammonium hydroxides as the titrant enabled the glass electrode to function satisfactorily as an indicating electrode, resulting in cell potentials which were very reproducible. The sleeve-type calomel electrode was satisfactory as a reference. The fiber-tip calomel electrode was found to be unsuited for nonaqueous titrations because the precipitation of potassium salts on the small fiber destroyed the liquid junction. The quaternary amine hydroxide, TBAOH, was substitued for potassium hydroxide for certain titrations where a precipitate, formed with the latter, resulted in a rough, uncertain titration curve. TBAOH being a stronger base than KOH gave sharper inflections for the weak acids.

Deal and Wyld (50) made a study of the effect of the relative concentrations of carboxylic acid and phenol mixtures and of mineral acids and phenol mixtures. They found that at a 15 to 1 molar ratio of hydrochloric acid to phenol, good distinction is still obtained between the two acids; benzoic and acetic acid inflections begin to blend with the phenol inflection at a 6 to 1 ratio.

The amine carbonate or carbamate formed by exposure of ethylenediamine to carbon dioxide in the atmosphere titrates as a strong acid and accounts for most of the blank correction found in this solvent. Titrations in EDA must be carried out rapidly, preferably under a blanket of nitrogen, and the solvent must be protected from the air during storage. The authors (50) reported that up to 5% water in EDA will not seriously affect the sharpness of the potentiometric breaks for weak acids such as phenol. As much as 10% benzene or isopropanol can be tolerated whereas 5% methanol seriously obscures the inflection.

Deal and Wyld found that EDA did not appear to have a deleterious affect upon the glass and calomel electrodes, although the saturated potassium chloride solution was replaced daily in the calomel electrode. Moss

TABLE IX

Potentiometric Titration of Acidic Compounds in EDA

Compounds	Formula	Number of inflections	Ref.
Phenol	C_6H_5OH	1	25,78,108, 156
1,2-Dihydroxybenzene (catechol)	$C_6H_4(OH)_2$	2	25,50,108
1,3-Dihydroxybenzene (resorcinol)	$C_6H_4(OH)_2$	2	108,156
1,4-Dihydroxybenzene (hydroquinone)	$C_6H_4(OH)_2$	1	50,108
3,4-Xylenol	$(CH_3)_2C_6H_3OH$	1	108
2,2'-Dihydroxydiphenyldimethylmethane	$CH_2(C_6H_5OH)_2$	1	50
2-Isopropylphenol	$C_3H_7C_6H_4OH$	1	108
2,3,5-Trimethylphenol	$(CH_3)_3C_6H_2OH$	1	108
2,6-Di-*tert*-amyl-4-*tert*-butylphenol	$(C_5H_{11})_2(C_4H_9)C_6H_2OH$	1	108
2,6-Di-*tert*-butyl-*p*-cresol	$(C_4H_9)_2(CH_3)C_6H_2OH$	1	108
2,6-Di-*tert*-butyl-4-cyclohexylphenol	$(C_4H_9)_2(C_6H_{11})C_6H_2OH$	1	108
2,4,6-Tri[(dimethylamino)methyl]phenol	$[(CH_3)_2NCH_2]_3C_6H_2OH$	1	108
Quinizarin		1	25
Alizarin		1	25
Purpurin		2	25
Quinalizarin		3	25
Salicylic acid	HOC_6H_4COOH	2	25,108,156
Methyl-4-hydroxy benzoate	$HOC_6H_4COOCH_3$	1	78,156
3-Hydroxybenzoic acid	HOC_6H_4COOH	2	108
Acetic acid	CH_3COOH	1	50
Acetic acid / Phenol		2	50
Hydrochloric acid	HCl	1	50

Table continued

TABLE IX (*continued*)
Potentiometric Titration of Acidic Compounds in EDA

Compounds	Formula	Number of inflections	Ref.
{Hydrochloric acid / Phenol		2	50
Glycine	H_2NCH_2COOH	1	156
ϵ-Aminocaproic acid	$H_2NC_5H_{10}COOH$	1	156
Benzoic acid	C_6H_5COOH	1	25,50,78, 108,156
{Benzoic acid / Phenol		2	25,50,156
o-Phthalic acid	$C_6H_4(COOH)_2$	1	148
Anthranilic acid	$H_2NC_6H_4COOH$	1	156
p-Aminobenzoic acid	$H_2NC_6H_4COOH$	1	156
p-Toluenesulfonic acid	$CH_3C_6H_4SO_3H$	1	148
{p-Toluenesulfonic acid / o-Phthalic acid / Phenol		2	148
Dibutyl phosphite	$(C_4H_9)_2HPO_3$	1	50
Phosphorous acid	H_3PO_3	1	50
Boric acid	H_3PO_3	3	156

and co-workers (156) found the glass electrode to be unstable for titrations with sodium aminoethoxide in anhydrous ethylenediamine. This insensitivity to changes in acidity was verified by Deal and Wyld (50), who also found that substitution of alcoholic KOH and commercial 95 to 100% EDA resulted in restored sensitivity and stable readings for the glass-calomel electrode assembly.

Harlow, Noble, and Wyld (86a) further improved the technique of Deal and Wyld by the use of platinum electrodes in place of the glass-calomel pair. Anodically polarized platinum wire served as the indicating electrode and platinum wire, inserted into the standardized titrant delivery tube, was satisfactory as reference electrode. The new electrode system led to a significantly increased potential range, resulting in sharper inflections for very weak acids.

Table IX lists compounds which can be titrated for acidity in ethylenediamine.

Although catechol gave two inflections, as indicated in Table IX, the first was not stoichiometric. The second inflection, however, was satisfactory for calculating total acidity. Hydroquinone, on the other hand, gave only one break equivalent to a single acidic hydroxyl group. The behavior of quinizarin and related compounds is interesting. Quinazarin gave a single sharp inflection equivalent to the total acidity (25). As shown in Figure 10, alizarin also gave a single break, while purpurin gave two, the first of which was equivalent to two of the phenolic hydroxyl groups. Although quinalizarin showed three inflections, only the first two were satisfactory for use in quantitative analyses. Phosphorous acid gave a single break equivalent to two hydrogens.

The following procedure (50) is recommended for titrations in ethylene-diamine. The apparatus is also suitable for titrations in the DMF system (50).

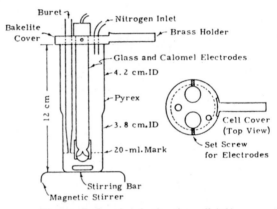

Fig. 12. Reduced scale titration cell (50).

Apparatus. The titration cell shown in Figure 12 is that used by Deal and Wyld (50). The apparatus consists of a meter, glass electrode (such as Beckman general purpose, No. 4990–80), calomel reference electrode (such as Beckman sleeve-type, No. 4970–71) and stand prepared, maintained, and tested as described by Lykken et al. (130), and the American Society for Testing Materials (4). The cell potential may be read on any electronic voltmeter or potentiometer which meets the ASTM requirements (4), that is, any instrument which has a grid current of less than 5×10^{-12} ampere and which covers a range of $+800$ to -800 mv.

An alternate assembly (86a) consists of an anodically polarized platinum wire indicating electrode which is placed in a titration flask similar to that shown in Figure 12 and a platinum wire reference electrode inserted into the titrant delivery tube in a manner like that shown in Figure 9. The indicating electrode must be anodically polarized before each titration in order to obtain reproducible data. After prolonged use the electrode tends to lose sensitivity and should be rejuvenated by allowing it to stand in hot hydrochloric acid $(1 + 1)$ for 3 to 4 hours. This electrode system has proved to be unstable initially and should be allowed to stand in the EDA for 2 to 3 minutes before starting the titration.

The Precision Dual AC Titrometer is well suited but not essential for nonaqueous titrations because it has a range of $+1650$ to -1650 mv. and a meter of high sensitivity, 250 mv. full scale. A 5 ml. microburet graduated in 0.02 ml. increments and protected by a small Ascarite absorber tube at the top is satisfactory. A glass-covered 4 × 18 mm. magnetic stirring bar and a special titration beaker fitted with a Bakelite cover are illustrated in Figure 12.

Reagents. Ethylenediamine (Eastman Kodak Co. 95 to 100%) or dimethyl formamide (E. I. du Pont de Nemours & Co.) are dispensed from the original container so that the solvents are protected from atmospheric carbon dioxide and water by an absorber tube containing Ascarite and indicating Drierite. Potassium hydroxide solution, 0.1 and 0.2 N in dry isopropanol is prepared as described by Lykken and co-workers (130). The use of barium hydroxide to precipitate carbonate is not necessary because potassium carbonate is essentially insoluble in the alcohol. Tetrabutylammonium hydroxide solution, 0.1 N alcoholic, is prepared by dilution of 1.0 M aqueous hydroxide (Southwestern Analytical Chemicals, Austin, Texas) with dry isopropanol.

Procedure. The sample, containing 0.2 to 0.4 meq. of acid, is weighed into the titration beaker. While allowing a slow stream of carbon dioxide-free nitrogen to flow into the beaker, the solvent is added rapidly up to the 20 ml. mark. Clean dry electrodes are placed in position and the magnetic stirrer started and adjusted to give vigorous agitation but without spattering. The solution is titrated with 0.02 to 0.05 ml. increments of standardized reagent (KOH or TBAOH). The potential is allowed to become constant, i. e., a meter change of less than 2 mv. in 30 seconds, between each addition and buret volume and meter readings are taken. The titration is continued stepwise until the potential approaches that of the completed blank titration and remains relatively constant or begins to drop steadily. Data from the titration, ml. titrant vs. mv., are plotted and the center of the inflection point estimated.

The calculation of acidity depends on the nature of the curves obtained and information desired. Usually, a mixture of strong and weak acids will give two or more inflections. However, small concentrations of weak or strong acids in the presence of large concentrations of a strong or weak acid, respectively, may be obscured by the major component. Often this condition can be found by comparison of the titration curve of the unknown with curves of representative strong and weak acids.

Where desirable, this same general procedure can be used for titrations of larger quantities of acids. Both the titration cell and buret are scaled up in this case.

For a limited number of cases, Fritz and Keen (69) devised a visual titration procedure which employed ethylenediamine as solvent and o-nitroaniline as indicator. o-Nitroaniline was found to be rapidly reversible and potentiometric titration in ethylenediamine showed that its color change coincided approximately with the steepest portion of the curve. By the visual procedure phloroglucinol was titrated as a dibasic acid but resorcinol and catechol gave no definite end point. Several phenols could not be titrated using the visual indicator due to the deep color formed during titration; o- and p-aminophenol and pyrogallol exhibited such behavior. During the titration of p-hydroxybenzoic acid a heavy precipitate formed causing a fading end point and inaccurate results. Where applicable the visual titration procedure showed a precision and accuracy of about 0.6%.

Several other amines, among them butylamine and pyridine, also have been used as solvents in the titration of weak acids. Harlow, Noble, and Wyld (86b), for example, found that pyridine was satisfactory in analyses for weak acids using 0.2 N tetrabutylammonium hydroxide in isopropanol as titrating agent. Nearly anhydrous reagent was prepared by passing a saturated solution of tetrabutylammonium iodide in isopropanol through an ion exchange column containing Amberlite IRA-400 resin. The resin had been previously converted to the hydroxide form by washing with aqueous potassium hydroxide followed by rinsing with isopropanol to remove the water.

Cundiff and Markunas (45a) also found that pyridine was useful as solvent with tetrabutylammonium hydroxide in benzene-methanol (10 + 1) as titrant. These investigators prepared 0.1 N reagent by dissolving the iodide in methanol and shaking the solution with an excess of silver oxide at room temperature. The filtered iodide-free solution was diluted with dry benzene. Both potentiometric and visual titrations were described. For the former the electrodes were glass and calomel modified by replacement of saturated aqueous potassium chloride in the outer jacket with saturated methanolic potassium chloride. Visual titrations employed thymol blue in iso-propanol or azo violet in benzene as indicators.

E. SUMMARY AND RECOMMENDATIONS FOR METHODS BASED ON NEUTRALIZATION

The authors have found in general that only a limited number of solvents—water, methanol, dimethyl formamide (DMF), and ethylenediamine (EDA)—are necessary for the determination of a wide spectrum of acids ranging from strong mineral or sulfonic acids to phenols. This, of course, does not take into consideration possible solubility problems which might require the use of other solvents. Where applicable water is recommended since it represents the simplest system and permits accurate titrations using visual and instrumental end point detection methods.

The influence of each of these solvents on titrations for acids of varying strengths is illustrated in Figure 13. The curves are plots of observed values during titrations of approximately equivalent amounts of p-toluene-sulfonic acid (comparable in strength to the mineral acids), o-phthalic acid ($K_1 = \sim10^{-3}$, $K_2 = \sim10^{-6}$), and phenol ($K = \sim10^{-10}$). In the water system, aqueous sodium hydroxide was used as titrant while, in methanol and DMF, sodium methoxide in methanol–benzene was employed. In the EDA system, titrations were made with sodium aminoethoxide.

In water, two strong breaks and one very weak break were observed. The first break apparently represented toluenesulfonic acid merged with the first carboxyl group of phthalic acid. The second inflection was equivalent to the second carboxyl group of phthalic acid, and the third very weak

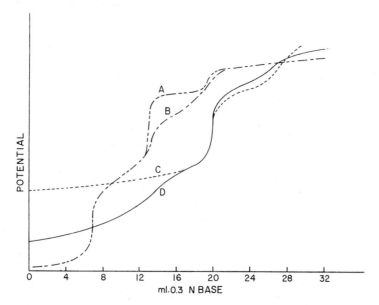

Fig. 13. Curves for p-toluenesulfonic acid–o-phthalic acid–phenol mixture in four solvents: A = dimethyl formamide system; B = methanol system; C = ethylene-diamine system; D = water system.

break, the phenol. The behavior in methanol was similar to that in DMF, namely, three separate breaks corresponding to toluenesulfonic acid, the first and second carboxyl groups of phthalic acid, respectively, while no significant break was observed for phenol. (However, samples containing three or less acid components, one of which was phenol, were resolved in DMF. Deal and Wyld obtained satisfactory resolution of a mixture of hydrochloric acid, acetic acid, and phenol as shown in Figure 7.) Titration in the EDA system produced two breaks; the first was equivalent to toluenesulfonic acid plus both carboxyl groups of phthalic acid and the second inflection corresponded to phenol.

Table X outlines the separations readily obtained and suitable for essentially quantitative differentiation on titration of mixtures of acids in each of the four systems discussed.

TABLE X

Resolution of Mixtures of Acids in Four Solvent Systems

No.	Mixture	Solvent[a]			
		H_2O	CH_3OH	DMF	EDA
1	HX, RSO₃H	X	X	X	Total only
	RCOOH	X	X	X	
	/COOH[b]		X	X	
2	RCH (with ⟍ COOH)	Total only			Total only
	⟍COOH		X	X	
3	HX, RSO₃H	{ X	X	X	Total only
	COOH		X	X	
	/RCH⟍				
	⟍COOH	X	X	X	
4	HX, RSO₃H	X	X	X	{ X
	RCOOH	X	X	X	
	C₆H₅OH			X	
5	/COOH		X	X	{
	RCH	{ X			{ X
	⟍COOH		X	X	{
	C₆H₅OH			X	X
6	HX, RSO₃H	{ X	X	X	{
	COOH		X	X	
	/RCH⟍				} X
	⟍COOH	X	X	X	
	C₆H₅OH				X

[a] X = titratable.
[b] Dibasic acid, where $K_1 = \sim 10^{-2}$ to 10^{-3} and $K_2 = \sim 10^{-5}$ to 10^{-6}.

Strong acids ($K = \sim 10^{-2}$) are differentiated from carboxylic acids ($K = \sim 10^{-5}$) in water, methanol, and DMF, but not in ethylenediamine. As little as 1 part strong acid to 100 parts carboxylic acid is differentiated in methanol and in DMF. Both acid functions of a polycarboxylic acid such as phthalic are separated in the methanol and DMF but only the total acidity can be determined in water and EDA. The resolution of strong

ERRATA

ORGANIC ANALYSIS, VOLUME II

PAGE	LINE	CHANGE
81	4 of text	"Section II.4" to "Section IV.4"
261	Figure 3, dimensions	"250 mm.," "250 mm.," and "190 mm." to "25.0 mm.," "25.0 mm.," and "19.0 mm."
296	Equation (20) should read:	$$\theta S = \frac{2R^{1/2}(\beta - 1)}{\beta[\beta^2(K + 1) + \beta K + 1]^{1/2}} \qquad (20)$$
	2 below equation (20)	"1.74 θ" to "1.93 θ"
	3 " " "	"2" to "2.25" and "2.24" to "2.54"
	5 " " "	"2.6 θ" to "2.52 θ"

and polycarboxylic acids is complete in methanol and in DMF but only partial differentiation is possible in water and in ethylenediamine. The last group including strong acids, polycarboxylic acids, and phenol represents four acidic functions of differing strengths. The best resolution is obtained in DMF although the inflection (and hence accuracy of determination) for phenol is sharper in the ethylenediamine system.

The particular advantages of the DMF and EDA systems is in their ability to permit resolution between carboxylic acids and phenols and among phenols of slightly differing strengths. Examples are given in Section II.2.D.

III. OXIDATION METHODS

1. Methods Based on Evolution of Carbon Dioxide

The decomposition of the carboxylic group into carbon dioxide and water is commonly referred to as decarboxylation. Although all organic acids will undergo such oxidation in the presence of heat and soda-lime, there are a few classes of acids that are readily oxidized by less drastic methods. α-Aminohydroxy acids and keto acids, polycarboxylic acids containing adjacent carboxyl groups, formic acid, and many aromatic acids fall into the latter classification. In general quantitative analytical applications are limited to these types of compounds.

Analytical methods for carboxyl groups by oxidation usually are based on determination of one of the oxidation products, or on measurement of excess oxidizing agent. Long (129), using acid potassium permanganate (1 N $KMnO_4$ in 5% H_2SO_4) as the oxidizing agent, determined the purity of several α-keto acids by measuring the volume of carbon dioxide evolved. In the case of glyoxylic acid, however, formic acid was a product of the oxidation which slowly decomposed under these conditions to give high results.

Formic acid is an intermediate product in the oxidation of many complex organic acids; therefore, the only reliable procedure employing permanganate is one in which the conditions are established to oxidize all of the organic acids completely to carbon dioxide and water. This is accomplished by using first acid and then alkaline permanganate followed by the addition of sulfuric acid. At this point excess standard oxalate is added, and the excess is determined by back-titration with permanganate.

Permanganate oxidation has been used widely for determining formic acid (73,82). Occasionally, direct titration can be used, the permanganate serving as its own indicator. A more accurate and precise method, however, is based on oxidation by permanganate in alkaline solution (73). The solution is then acidified, oxalic acid added, and the excess determined by titration with standard permanganate. Oxidation by mercuric oxide (168) or mercuric acetate (180) is probably more selective for formic acid. Reid and Weihe (180) used mercuric acetate, which they found to be better than the oxide, to oxidize formic acid, determining the evolved carbon dioxide titrimetrically. Another fairly specific method for formic acid is based on oxidation by bromine (67):

$$HCOOH + Br_2 \longrightarrow 2HBr + CO_2 \tag{4}$$

In this procedure, particularly suited for micro analyses, bromine water is added dropwise to the aqueous sample solution until a slight excess is present. Carbon dioxide formed is determined titrimetrically. Frehden and Fürst (67) reported that as little as 2.5 micrograms of formic acid could be detected.

Under controlled conditions, permanganate oxidation can be used for the preferential determination of propionic acid in mixtures which also contain formic and acetic acids. McNair (141) described a lengthy procedure in which the propionic acid was oxidized to oxalic acid by alkaline permanganate. The oxalic acid was converted to calcium oxalate, which was recovered by filtration and determined by titration with standard potassium permanganate.

In place of the lengthy permanganate oxidation methods, Willard and Young (240) proposed the use of ceric sulfate as oxidizing agent for the determination of certain organic acids. They found that formic, acetic, succinic, fumaric, and maleic acids were not decomposed appreciably by hot ceric sulfate after one hour in 30% sulfuric acid. On the other hand, tartaric, malonic, malic, glycolic, and citric acids were oxidized quantitatively yielding carbon dioxide, formic acid, and water. One major difficulty with this method is that in some cases the accuracy of the determination is dependent on narrow concentration limits. The method is applicable, only to specific cases since the oxidation equivalent of each acid to ceric sulfate is different. Although evolved carbon dioxide can be measured, it is usually more convenient to determine excess ceric sulfate by back-titration with standard ferrous sulfate to an electrometric end point. A similar reagent, hexanitratoammonium cerate, also has been used in nitric acid solution to estimate oxalic acid (191).

An excellent report on organic microanalysis by cerimetry was prepared by Takahashi and co-workers (220). Amino acids are quite stable to oxidation by ceric sulfate. However, amino acids can be determined after their conversion to hydroxy acids by the action of nitrous acid. Unfortunately oxidation is not complete although it is reproducible. These workers (220) also described an indirect coulometric method for determining oxalic acid. Excess ceric sulfate was used to oxidize the oxalic acid at 80 to 100°C. After reaction was complete, excess ceric ions were determined coulometrically by generation of ferrous ions. Actually, oxalic acid will decarboxylate readily. Clark (42) obtained quantitative yields of carbon dioxide from oxalic acid in glycerol at temperatures above 150°C. Below this temperature two competing reactions appeared to take place: relatively fast decarboxylation and a slower reaction probably esterification.

Brissaud (24), in a comparison of methods for the determination of carboxyl in oxycellulose, found that measurement of carbon dioxide evolved by heating the sample in acid solution was the most accurate. The other methods that he investigated included back-titration of excess base, absorption of methylene blue, and double decomposition with lead or barium acetate.

Uronic acids were determined by treatment in 19% hydrochloric acid for 1.5 to 2 hours at 145°C. (140). The carbon dioxide evolved was absorbed in alkali and then back-titrated with standard hydrochloric acid. Quantitative results were reported for galacturonic acid, citrus pectin, and pectic and alginic acids.

A method for decarboxylation of aromatic acids by heating with quinoline in the presence of copper was described by Shepard, Winslow, and Johnson (204). A thorough study was made by Hubacher (93) of inorganic catalysts for decarboxylation of aromatic acids by quinoline. He showed that basic cupric carbonate was the most efficient general catalyst. Where this proved ineffective, silver carbonate often was satisfactory. Hubacher (93) reported essentially quantitative results on a variety of aromatic acids, using samples containing from 2 to 20 millimoles of acid. The carbon dioxide was determined gasometrically. Compounds studied included benzoic acid and a variety of substituted benzoic acids. Of fifteen acids analyzed only two, 2,4-dichlorobenzoic and coumarilic, required the use of silver catalyst.

Roberts and Ambler (183) described a method for the quantitative determination of aconitic acid by decarboxylation in boiling potassium acetate–acetic acid solution. To increase the accuracy toward analyses for carbon dioxide, Roberts (182) devised the simple absorption-titration cell shown in Figure 14. The absorption cell was filled to a volume of 110 ml.

with standard caustic solution.   Sufficient alkali was added to leave about a 50% excess over the expected amount of carbon dioxide to be absorbed. During an analysis the gas stream containing the carbon dioxide was passed through the bubbler into the alkaline scrubber solution.   After reaction was complete, the bubbler was removed and washed with water.   Then a long

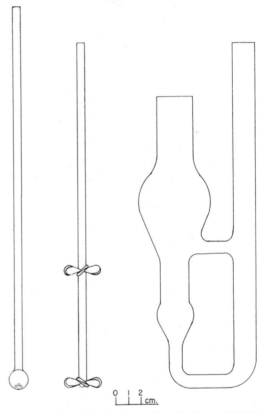

Fig. 14. Carbon dioxide absorption-titration cell (182).

tipped buret was inserted in the right side of the cell and the stirrer was placed on the left side.   Excess caustic was determined by titration with standard hydrochloric acid to the phenolphthalein end point.   Pyridine and acetone have been used as absorbants for carbon dioxide in micro and semimicro methods (19).   The quantity of carbon dioxide was determined by titration with sodium methylate to the thymol blue end point.

One of the most important oxidation techniques is that based on the nearly specific determination of α-amino acids. In an acid system these acids are oxidized by triketohydrindene hydrate (ninhydrin) to an aldehyde, carbon dioxide, and ammonia:

$$\text{RCHCOOH} + \underset{\text{NH}_2}{|} \quad \overset{\text{CO}}{\underset{\text{C(OH)}_2}{\bigcirc}} \longrightarrow$$

$$\overset{\text{CO}}{\underset{\text{CHOH}}{\bigcirc}} + \text{RCHO} + \text{CO}_2 + \text{NH}_3 \qquad (5)$$

The ammonia produced reacts with the reduced ninhydrin (hydrindantin) and the unreduced form at a pH above 3 to form the blue condensation product, diketohydrindylidendiketohydrindamine:

$$\overset{\text{CO}}{\underset{\text{CHOH}}{\bigcirc}} + \text{NH}_3 + \overset{\text{CO}}{\underset{\text{C(OH)}_2}{\bigcirc}} \rightleftharpoons$$

$$\overset{\text{O} \quad \text{O}}{\underset{\text{CH—N=C}}{\bigcirc}} + 3\text{H}_2\text{O} \qquad (6)$$

Van Slyke and co-workers (227,228) studied the ninhydrin reaction extensively, and after considering the various products concluded that measurement of the evolved carbon dioxide offered the most reliable means for determining α-amino acids. They found that in general molecular structures of the type $\text{RCH(NH}_2)\text{COOH}$ and $\text{RCH(NHCH}_2\text{R}')\text{COOH}$ yield carbon dioxide quantitatively by reaction with ninhydrin under proper conditions. If the amino group was in the β- or γ-position, the reactivity of the carboxyl groups was usually negligible. Aspartic acid, however, which contains carboxyl groups in both the α- and β-positions, evolved two moles of carbon dioxide. Keto acids interfered because of their tendency to decompose in boiling water with the loss of CO_2; however, if the aqueous sample solution was boiled prior to the addition of ninhydrin, no interference was observed. Two methods were proposed for measuring the evolved carbon dioxide, a manometric procedure (229) and a titrimetric method (231).

Titration was simpler and yielded results of the same order of precision for micro analyses as the manometric procedure (231).   The reported data indicated an accuracy of better than 1% with an average deviation of 0.3%.   The entire reaction was conveniently carried out in a small flask

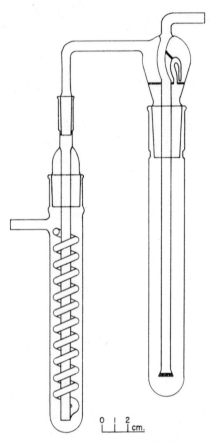

Fig. 15. Apparatus for determining α-amino acids by ninhydrin procedure.

which contained the ninhydrin, citrate buffer, and sample.   This was connected through a U-tube to a second flask, containing a standard barium hydroxide solution.   An outlet in the U-tube allowed for the partial evacuation of the system by a water aspirator.   The two flasks were immersed in boiling water for a period long enough to ensure complete reaction. The carbon dioxide evolved by the action of ninhydrin distilled from the reaction flask into the flask containing excess barium hydroxide. This was accomplished by lifting the receiver flask from the boiling water and immersing it in cold water. Carbon dioxide absorption was completed by shaking the barium hydroxide solution. The system was returned to atmospheric pressure with carbon dioxide free air before removing the receiver flask for titration of the excess base with standard hydrochloric acid. Van Slyke's method (229,231) was used for the determination of the purity of isolated free amino acids in protein digests.

A convenient and simple modification of the Van Slyke method has been used successfully in the authors' laboratory.

Procedure for α-Amino Acids. A sample, containing not more than 0.7 meq. of amino acid, is weighed into the aeration tube (Fig. 15). The volume is adjusted to 5–10 ml. by addition of distilled water, if necessary, and 200 mg. of dry buffer added. (The buffer is prepared by mixing intimately 2.06 g. trisodium citrate with 19.15 g. citric acid monohydrate.) Any dissolved carbon dioxide or carbonate is removed by slow aeration with purified nitrogen through the warmed solution for about 15 minutes. At the end of this time the aeration tube is chilled in ice water. The jacket of the scrubber is lowered and 10 ml. of 0.2 N barium hydroxide is quickly added plus 5 ml. of carbon dioxide-free distilled water. The apparatus is closed immediately, then both flasks are heated for 30 minutes, the aeration flask at 90–95°C. and the scrubber at 60–65°. During this period a slow flow of nitrogen is maintained. At the end of the heating period, the scrubber is cooled and its contents transferred quantitatively to a flask for titration with 0.05 N hydrochloric acid to the phenolphthalein end point. A blank is run identical in all details except no ninhydrin is added. The carbon dioxide evolved is equivalent mole for mole to the amount of α-amino acid in the sample.

2. Iodimetric Methods

Iodimetric methods based on oxidation by iodide–iodate are most useful for determining small amounts of strong acids in solution (120). For these compounds the sample is treated with iodide–iodate reagent and the iodine formed is determined by titration with thiosulfate.

Application of this technique to weaker acids, such as the carboxylic acids, requires modification of the direct method. The rate of reaction:

$$6RCOOH + KIO_3 + 5KI \longrightarrow 3I_2 + 3H_2O + 6RCOOK \qquad (7)$$

is relatively slow. By use of excess thiosulfate, which removes iodine as it is formed, the reaction velocity is increased considerably. Ultimately, the excess thiosulfate remaining after reaction is complete may be determined by titration with standard iodine solution. This approach was used for estimating the acid value of lac (107), and for determinations of fatty acids (189), glycolic, some dibasic acids (212), and amino acids (188). Kamath and Mainkar (107) compared the iodimetric method with acidimetric titration for determining the acid value of lac. They concluded that, for this particular application, the iodimetric method was more reliable because of interference by hydrolysis in the acidimetric titration. Their method, which follows, was written for analysis of lac but should be applicable with slight modifications to other carboxyl group determinations.

Procedure (107). The weighed sample (ca. 0.4 g. of lac) is dissolved in 20 ml. of 95% ethanol in an iodine flask. 10 ml. of 1 M potassium iodide, 10 ml. of 0.1 M potassium iodate, 10 ml. of 0.1 M sodium thiosulfate, and 10 ml. of distilled water are added. The mixture is shaken until a clear solution is obtained and then 20 ml. of 0.1 N iodine solution is added. Finally, excess iodine is determined by titration with standard 0.1 N sodium thiosulfate using starch as indicator.

Singh and Singh (212) used the iodimetric method with a catalyst for determinations of oxalic, tartaric, citric, malic, and glycolic acids. The sample was dissolved, a small volume of solution containing barium, zinc, or magnesium ions was added, followed by excess potassium iodide and potassium iodate solutions. The liberated iodine was determined by potentiometric titration with standard sodium thiosulfate, using platinum and calomel electrodes.

Oxidation by periodate followed by iodimetric titration has been used in special cases of acids having other active functional groups. For example, tartaric acid (7,63) and gluconic acid (63) which contain hydroxyl groups on adjacent carbon atoms, may be determined in this way. Details of the periodate method for glycols and related compounds were given by Mehlenbacher in Volume I, page 41, of this series. β-Hydroxyamino acids also are subject to oxidative cleavage by the action of periodate:

$$RCH(OH)CH(NH_2)COOH + HIO_4 \longrightarrow RCHO + CHOCOOH + NH_3 + HIO_3 \quad (8)$$

Methods of analysis have been based on calculation of periodate consumed and on separation and determination of aldehyde or ammonia. In a procedure for estimating threonine, Nicolet and Shinn (164) recovered acetaldehyde, which was determined by the bisulfite method. Van Slyke and co-workers (230) used a more general approach. The ammonia formed was removed from the system by aspiration, absorbed in boric acid, and titrated with standard hydrochloric acid. Wiseblatt and McConnell (242) utilized micro diffusion for isolation of ammonia, which ultimately was determined by titration. The periodate method is applicable to analyses for β-hydroxyamino acids, such as threonine, serine, and hydroxyly-sine, in the presence of other types of amino acids. The periodate pro-cedure, of course, is generally applicable to compounds having active func-tional groups on adjacent carbon atoms. Therefore, all compounds having amino groups vicinal to other amine groups or to hydroxyl groups will react to form ammonia.

IV. DISPLACEMENT METHODS

Displacement methods find limited applications for special systems. Foremost among these is the analysis of cellulose and derivatives. The determination of carboxyl groups in cellulose and oxycellulose by direct neutralization was shown to be unreliable by several investigators (88,161). The anomalous results were due in part to the immobility of the anion group of the acid. To eliminate this difficulty Neale and Stringfellow (161) added excess sodium chloride to the suspended solution of cellulose. In effect, this allowed an exchange or displacement of the hydrogen ions from the carboxyl group by the sodium ions. The amount of hydrochloric acid produced was considered to be equivalent to the carboxyl content. In practice it was found that a drifting end point, probably due to the hydroly-sis of lactone groups, could be eliminated by addition of excess alkali and back titration with standard hydrochloric acid.

Heymann and Rabinov (88) verified this technique using potassium chlo-ride. Both investigations indicated that the neutralization of the acid pro-duced by the addition of excess calcium acetate, a method used by Yackel and Kenyon (245), was unreliable.

More recently Meesook and Purves (142) found that the buffering action of excess acetate produced high results compared to the method of Sookne and Harris (216), who used an aqueous solution of silver o-nitrophenolate as the displacing reagent in the determination of carboxyl in starch:

$$RCOOH + AgOC_6H_4NO_2 \longrightarrow RCOOAg + HOC_6H_4NO_2 \qquad (9)$$

Since the carboxyl is determined indirectly by the titration of the excess silver this method also has its disadvantages. A long reaction period, 24–72 hours, is required and the presence of aldehydes or strong light will reduce part of the unused reagent causing high results.

Brissaud (24) compared four methods for determining organic acidity in cellulose: (a) decomposition by heat in the presence of acid, followed by determination of the carbon dioxide evolved, (b) addition of excess alkali and back-titration with standard acid, (c) double decomposition with lead or barium acetate, and (d) absorption of methylene blue. He concluded that for the materials he studied method (a) was the most accurate; it was unaffected by the ash of the cellulose, or by mineral or stable organic acids, such as oxalic. For oxycellulose, in particular, results by methods (b) and (d) compared favorably with those by method (a).

Elizer (57) in his study of commercial starches compared the silver method to a similar technique using copper acetate. He found the latter method gave values that were slightly higher whenever the starch was highly oxidized. The standing period in this instance was only 18 hours and the excess copper was determined iodimetrically.

In contrast, the solubility of their copper salts was utilized to determine amino acids by the same method. Schroeder and co-workers (198) reviewed the earlier work of Pope and Stevens (176), who reported that in most cases two moles of an amino acid react stoichiometrically with one cupric ion to form a blue-colored copper salt. Schroeder, Kay, and Mills (198) modified the procedure to improve the precision of the method. Fourteen of nineteen naturally occurring amino acids were determined with an accuracy of 1% in quantities of 0.05 to 0.20 millimole. The amino acid was added to a suspension of copper phosphate. After five minutes the excess copper was removed by centrifuging and the quantity of copper in the supernatant liquid determined by iodimetric titration using the dead-stop end point method. When the amino acid formed an insoluble copper salt, a known amount of glycine was added to form the soluble double salt. Then the amount of glycine was subtracted from the total copper in solution to yield that due to the normally insoluble amino acid.

Another method that was developed by Fuchs (71) and later improved by Hunter and Edwards (94) is based upon the formation of hydrogen sulfide by the displacement reaction of potassium hydrosulfide with organic acids. The reaction was carried out in a solution of potassium hydrosulfide saturated with hydrogen sulfide:

$$RCOOH + KSH \xrightarrow{\text{H}_2\text{S}} RCOOK + H_2S \tag{10}$$

The amount of dry air displaced by the hydrogen sulfide formed was measured in an eudiometer. The advantage of this reaction over the direct neutralization procedure lies in the fact that most lactones, alcohols, or phenols do not interfere. Fuchs noted a few exceptions to this rule; halogenated phenols with two hydroxyl groups, p-nitro substituted phenols, and a few carbonyl containing phenols reacted to form hydrogen sulfide. Very weak organic acids, such as stearic acid, did not react. The modified apparatus of Hunter and Edwards (94) eliminated many of the more common sources of error usually encountered in a eudiometric measurement. However, one source of error, inherent in the method, results from the partition of the potassium cation between the hydrosulfide anion and the anion of the organic acid. Hence, in the weak monobasic acids studied the results were observed to be consistently low by about 2.5%.

V. AQUAMETRIC METHOD

A method which is nearly specific for the carboxyl function in aliphatic acids is based on esterification:

$$RCOOH + CH_3OH \xrightarrow{\text{BF}_3} RCOOCH_3 + H_2O \qquad (11)$$

The water formed is determined by titration with Karl Fischer reagent (149,151). This nonacidimetric procedure is particularly useful for determining carboxylic acids in the presence of inorganic acids (except sulfuric), sulfonic acids, and easily hydrolyzed esters. Typical results are given in Table XI.

TABLE XI
Analytical Data for Carboxylic Acids

	Acid found, wt. %	
Acid	Alkali titration	Esterification-Karl Fischer reagent titration[a]
Formic.	97.3	97.2
DL-Methylethylacetic.	95.2	95.1
Adipic.	99.2	99.0
Lauric.	98.6	98.9
Oleic.	99.5	99.2
Cyclohexylacetic.	99.4	99.3
Phenylacetic.	99.9	100.0
Glycolic.	99.9	99.6
Dichloroacetic.	99.0	98.8
2,4-Dichlorophenoxyacetic.	99.0	99.0

[a] Each value average of two to ten determinations. Standard deviation = 0.3%.

Procedure. The sample, containing up to 8 meq. of carboxylic acid, is weighed into a 250 ml. glass-stoppered volumetric flask. Then 20 ml. of esterification reagent (methanol containing about 100 g. of boron trifluoride per liter of solution) is added and the solution is heated for 1 hour at $60 \pm 1°C$. At the end of this time, the flask is allowed to cool to room temperature, 5 ml. of dry pyridine added, and the mixture titrated with Karl Fischer reagent. The net increase in millimoles of water found between sample and blank, after correction for free water originally present in the sample, is equal to the milliequivalents of free carboxyl in the sample.

In special cases a modification of the standard procedure can be used to determine aliphatic acids in the presence of aromatic acids. Acetic acid may be determined in the presence of benzoic and salicylic acids by using an esterification catalyst containing only 25 g. of boron trifluoride per liter of methanol and allowing the mixture to stand one hour at room temperature before titration with Karl Fischer reagent.

VI. GRAVIMETRIC METHODS

Quantitative gravimetric methods are limited to special cases in which the acid is usually precipitated as a salt. Swann (218) obtained some selectivity in the use of different metal ions for precipitating dibasic acids used in the alkyd resins field. Phthalic acid was precipitated as the lead salt from glacial acetic acid solution, while sebacic acid was separated as the zinc salt, fumaric as the cadmium or mercury salt, and adipic plus succinic as the silver salts.

Variations in the gravimetric technique can be used to advantage in some cases. For example, Goepfert (76) described a micro method for succinic acid. A measured amount of 0.02 M silver nitrate was added to the neutral sample solution. After precipitation was complete, the silver succinate was removed by filtration, and excess silver in solution was determined by titration with 0.02 M potassium bromide, using dichlorofluorescein as indicator. In another example formic acid was determined by reaction with mercuric chloride and the resulting insoluble mercurous chloride was recovered and determined gravimetrically (2). Dichloroacetic acid was estimated in the presence of monochloroacetic acid through its conversion by sodium hydroxide to oxalate. The oxalate was precipitated with calcium acetate and determined by titration with permanganate (47).

In some cases total fatty acid content of soaps and related products has been estimated from the amount of insoluble salt formed after treatment with calcium ions. This approach is not very reliable. Other methods depending on extraction of the acids are time consuming and, therefore, not suited for control analyses. Webster and Robertson (236) devised a rapid procedure in which calcium salts are precipitated using a measured volume of standard calcium chloride reagent. After filtration to remove the insoluble calcium salts, the excess calcium ions in solution are determined by titration with versene to the murexide (ammonium purpurate) end point as represented by a color change from red to purple. Results from thirteen analyses of a single sample showed a standard deviation of 0.21% in the 82–83% total acid range.

VII. POLAROGRAPHY

The carboxyl function as such is not reducible at the dropping mercury electrode, although most acids do give waves from discharged hydrogen ions. Consequently no general methods specific for carboxylic acids are available based on this important technique. However, numerous examples of quantitative analyses have been reported for specific acids containing groupings which can be reduced.

The technique of polarography was discussed by Elving in Volume II of this series. Examples were given of direct determinations of pyruvic acid, maleic, and fumaric acids, and of several other acids after preliminary reactions to form active compounds. Included among these were tartaric acid as the antimony complex, and citric acid after conversion to penta-bromoacetone.

Kolthoff and Lingane (119) in their outstanding text on polarography discussed principles and applications to inorganic and organic substances. These authors reviewed the literature on determinations of organic acids and noted that the diffusion current for a given capillary could be expressed as $i_d/C = a + b \log K$, where i_d = diffusion current, C = concentration of the organic acid, K = dissociation constant of the acid, and a and b = constants associated with the supporting electrolyte.

Kolthoff and Lingane (119) summarized data on the single hydrogen ion waves given by simple aliphatic, polybasic, and aromatic acids in 0.1 N lithium chloride, 0.1 N lithium sulfate, and 0.05 N tetramethylammonium bromide. Polyhydroxymonocarboxylic acids in 0.1 N tetraethylammonium chloride show only the hydrogen wave at from -1.65 to -1.75 v. vs. S. C. E. (138). Similar observations were made for crotonic acid (74,162,167), styrylacetic (167), itaconic, and levulinic acids (162). α-Unsaturated acids are reduced rapidly at the dropping mercury electrode. Schwaer (199,200) observed that acetylenedicarboxylic, maleic, fumaric, citraconic, mesaconic, aconic, sorbic, and cinnamic acids gave clearly defined waves. Ono and Hyashi (167) observed two waves, $E_{0.5} = -1.49$ to -1.56 and -1.86 to -2.03 vs. S. C. E., for cinnamic acid using 0.1 N tetramethyl ammonium bromide, lithium chloride, strontium chloride, or calcium chloride as supporting electrolyte. The first wave was attributed to reduction of H^+ and the second, to reduction of the carbon-

carbon double bond. Pyruvic acid, an α-keto acid, also was reduced. Nonconjugated unsaturated acids, such as itaconic and crotonic, levulinic acid (an α-keto acid), and citric acid (a hydroxy acid) were not reduced. After prior thermal treatment, however, two of these acids could be determined. At 180°C. levulinic acid is dehydrated to give angelic lactone, while citric acid loses water and carbon dioxide giving citraconic and mesaconic acids. Several investigators have studied the polarography of maleic and fumaric acids (199; see also Volume II of the series, p. 233). Procedures have been devised for 0–2.5% maleic acid in the presence of succinic (210), fumaric in the presence of maleic, itaconic, citraconic, cis- and trans-aconitic acids (202), and aspartic acid after conversion by dimethyl sulfate to a mixture of maleic and fumaric acids (235). The ultimate determination is made with 0.05 N hydrochloric acid as electrolyte where unsaturated acids are reduced at -0.5 to -1.1 v. vs. mercury pool. cis- and trans-Aconitic acids can be determined individually as the calcium salts in the presence of ammonium chloride (203).

Miscellaneous applications include determination of tartaric acid as the titanium complex (35), histidine in the presence of arginine and lysine (184,238), ascorbic acid (115), and the folic acid group (131). Caglioti and Sartoni (35) found that titanium tetrachloride formed a 1:1 complex with tartaric acid while titanium hydroxide formed at 2:3 complex with disodium tartrate. Kirk (115) found that 2% phosphoric acid was the best medium for determining ascorbic acid using a polarographic wave at -1.77 v. vs. S. C. E. Use of a phosphate buffer at pH 7, acetate or phthalate–acid buffers at pH 2.2, or 5% sulfuric acid were unsatisfactory for ascorbic acid analysis. Mader and Frediani (131) determined folic acid at pH 9–9.5 using 1% tetramethyl ammonium hydroxide and 0.2 M ammonium chloride buffer. A precision of about 2% was reported through use of cadmium as an internal standard. Several investigators have reported on the reduction of nitro groups in organic acids (119,126,143).

VIII. COULOMETRY

The technique of coulometry was discussed by W. D. Cooke in Volume II of this series. Where applicable coulometric methods offer convenient means for continuous analyses. Little work has been done on determinations of organic acids employing electrolytically generated base as titrant. Epstein and co-workers (59), however, discussed titrations of hydrochloric acid with hydroxyl ions generated electrolytically from potassium bromide using a divided cell connected by a salt bridge. The technique was particularly useful for determining small amounts of acid continuously.

Carson and Ko (36) described a constant current–time system in a divided cell method for micro determinations of carboxylic acids in the presence of mineral acids. Titrations were made in an aqueous isopropanol system using potassium hydroxide in methanol. The apparatus included a pH meter and the cell which consisted of: (a) the cathode compartment containing platinum wire cathode, stirrer, silver–silver chloride reference electrode, and a micro glass electrode and (b) the anode compartment, provided with a smooth platinum wire anode immersed in dilute potassium chloride solution, connected to the cathode compartment by a saturated potassium chloride salt bridge.

Procedure (36). A 400 microliter sample containing mineral and carboxylic acids, is placed in the cathode compartment and diluted to about 5 ml. with 70% isopropanol. 1 drop of 0.1 M lithium chloride is added and the initial pH of the solution is determined. Titration of the mineral acid is made by electrolyzing the solution at 10–15 ma., until a pH change of 1.5 units is observed. Then the current is reduced to 3 ma. and titration continued. For samples containing 0.3 g. or more of acetic acid equivalent per liter the electrolysis was performed at 10 second intervals. (Solution is electrolyzed for 10 seconds and then the current is turned off until a stable pH reading is obtained.) For more dilute solutions the interval is 5 seconds. The titration is continued until two breaks in the pH–time curve are obtained, corresponding to the end points of the mineral and organic acid, respectively.

Calculation. The time of the end points is calculated from the relation:

$$\text{E. P.} = E + \frac{A - B}{2A - (B + C)} \times d$$

where A = maximum pH change within one time increment, B = pH change in increment immediately preceding A, C = pH change in increment immediately following A, D = time increment in seconds, E = total time corresponding to start of A increment, and E. P. = total time in seconds of end point (from start of titration at 3 ma.).

The total milliequivalents of organic acid is calculated as follows:

$$\text{Meq. RCOOH} = (T_0 \times \text{ma.})/96{,}500$$

where T_0 = time for titration of organic acid, i.e., difference between two end points.

Carson and Ko (36) reported a precision of about 2% in analyses for about 0.2 g./liter of acetic acid in the presence of 3 to 7.5 g./liter of nitric acid. Satisfactory results also were obtained with propionic, butyric, valeric, oxalic, and adipic acids. The two dibasic acids gave two inflections in the pH–time curve. Weak acids, such as carbonic and silicic, seriously interfered with the titrations.

Lingane (127) recommended a silver–silver bromide anode rather than silver–silver chloride for use in automatic coulometric titrations of strong or weak acids. He pointed out that the former was preferred because of the smaller amount of Ag^+ ions in solution. This condition was desirable since the reduction of silver ions at the platinum electrode would cause the current efficiency in the reaction, $2H^+ + 2e = H_2$, to be less than 100%. Lingane (127) employed a cell fitted with platinum cathode and silver–silver bromide anode. A glass electrode was used to indicate the increase in pH resulting from reduction of hydrogen ions at the cathode. An automatic titrator unit was employed which monitored the titration, interrupting the generator current when the equivalence point was reached. The calomel reference electrode was connected through a salt bridge of saturated potassium chloride in 3% agar gel. The electrolyte was 0.04 M potassium bromide and 0.25 M sodium sulfate.

DeFord and co-workers (51) recommended external generation of base as a preferred method over internal generation for the following reasons: (a) the generator electrodes are not in contact with the sample solution thus eliminating possible undesirable side reactions, (b) optimum conditions for generation of reagent can be achieved, (c) the technique should permit the use of amperometric indication methods, (d) the need for divided cell compartments is eliminated, and (c) the generator cell can be used to prepare standard solutions for other titration methods.

DeFord et al. (51) used 0.1 M sodium sulfate as electrolyte adjusted to pH 7.0 ± 0.5. For analyses of samples containing 1–2 meq. of hydrochloric acid or potassium acid phthalate the flow of generator electrolyte through the cell was adjusted to a flow of about 0.1 ml./second. Time was noted between start of titration and the end point as given by an acid-base indicator; bromcresol green–methyl red was used for the mineral acid and phenolphthalein, for the acid phthalate. Times of about 8 minutes were required for titrations having a precision and accuracy of about 0.3%.

Specific applications of coulometry include methods of analysis for unsaturated fatty acids and salicylic acid. Cuta and Kucera (46) employed chlorine addition for determining unsaturated acids having a single double bond. Chlorine was generated from dilute hydrochloric acid in aqueous acetic acid. Acids with more than one double bond could not be determined quantitatively by this method. Bromine and iodine also were generated and tried as reagents but were unsatisfactory. A micro method was used for measuring salicylic acid (112). The acid was brominated in the system: 0.3 N HCl, 0.1 N CuSO$_4$, 0.1 N KBr. Excess bromine, liberated after quantitative bromination of salicylic acid, was determined by titration with cuprous ions generated electrolytically.

IX. COLORIMETRIC METHODS: ULTRAVIOLET—VISUAL ABSORPTION

The carboxyl group is a weak chromophore and as such does not absorb in the near ultraviolet or visual regions of the spectrum. Colorimetric methods, therefore, are usually based on analysis of suitable absorbing derivatives. Organic acids and other compounds having conjugated unsaturation, however, exhibit strong absorption in the near ultraviolet. Consequently, these acids can be determined by direct measurement provided no other compounds are present in the sample which absorb in the same wave length region. Approximate absorption maxima of several aromatic and other unsaturated acids are given in Table XII.

TABLE XII

Ultraviolet Absorption Maxima of Some Aromatic Acids
and Other Unsaturated Acids

Acid	Solvent	Absorption maxima, mμ	Ref.
α-Eleostearic	Cyclohexane	271.5	165
β-Eleostearic	"	269.0	165
Ascorbic (Vitamin A)	"	325	165
Benzoic	Methanol, isooctane	229,273,281	225
p-Ethyl benzoic	Water	213	a
p-Isopropylbenzoic	Ethanol	235	a
p-tert-Butylbenzoic	"	235	a
o-Phthalic	"	225–230,275–283	225
m-Phthalic (isophthalic)	"	278,289	
2-Methylbenzoic (o-toluic)	"	228,277	a
3-Methylbenzoic (m-toluic)	"	230,277	a
4-Methylbenzoic (p-toluic)	"	235	a
o-Hydroxybenzoic (salicylic)	"	227,308	a
o-Aminobenzoic (anthranilic)	Propanol	227,248,334	a
m-Aminobenzoic	"	317	a
Benzenesulfinic acid	Ethanol	218,245	53
p-Toluenesulfinic	"	223,242	53
p-Toluenesulfonic	"	257,263,268	a
Pyridine-2-carboxylic acid (picolinic)	"	218,264	225
Pyridine-3-carboxylic (nicotinic)	"	216,263	225
Pyridine-4-carboxylic (isonicotinic)	"	212,272	225
Pyridine-2,3-dicarboxylic (quinolinic)	"	263	225
3-Carboxypyridine 1-oxide	Water	220,260	98
4-Carboxypyridine 1-oxide	Water	216,280	98

a Unpublished results from the authors' laboratory.

α-Keto acids, $RC(=O)C(=O)OH$, show absorption at about 200 and 250 mμ due to conjugated unsaturation between the $>C=O$ groups. Unsaturated acids of the type, $RCH=CHC(=O)OH$, give maxima at about 215 and 320 mμ, while those having three conjugated chromophores of the type, $RCH=CHCH=CHC(=O)OH$, absorb at about 260 mμ; HOC$(=O)CH=CHC(=O)OH$ absorbs at 210 mμ.

Often extraction or other separation technique can be used to remove compounds which otherwise will interfere with direct spectroscopic analysis. This approach was used in analyses for phthalic acid in the presence of its anhydride (1). The latter was separated by extraction with chloroform and the acid was determined through measurement at 276 mμ.

Some nonconjugated unsaturated acids can be isomerized in the presence of alkali to give conjugated unsaturation. Alkaline isomerization can involve a shift of a single double bond from the β,γ-position to the α,β-position:

$$RCH=CHCH_2\overset{\overset{\displaystyle O}{\|}}{C}OH \rightleftharpoons RCH_2CH=CH\overset{\overset{\displaystyle O}{\|}}{C}OH$$

or a rearrangement of a nonconjugated polyethylenic acid to give conjugated ethylenic groups.

$$RCH=CHCH_2CH_2CH=CH(CH_2)xCOOH \rightleftharpoons$$
$$RCH_2CH=CHCH=CH(CH_2)xCOOH$$

Several workers in the oils and fats field have used this approach for determining naturally occurring fatty acids. Brice and co-workers (22) investigated methods proposed by previous workers and pointed out certain factors which must be controlled to obtain reliable results in analyses for linoleic, linolenic, and arachidonic acids. Moretti and Cheftel (155) refined the method further to simplify addition of reagents and protect the system from interfering oxidation reactions. Additional information on analyses for unsaturated acids are given in the chapter, "Determination of Olefinic Unsaturation," in this volume.

Procedure for Polyethylenic Fatty Acids (155). To prepare the alkaline reagent a quantity of glycerol is heated for 10 minutes at 190°C. in an oil bath. The temperature is lowered to 150° and sufficient potassium hydroxide pellets is added to give a concentration of 11 g. KOH per 100 g. glycerol (allowance is made for purity of the KOH). The final concentration is determined accurately by titration.

In carrying out an analysis, 11.0 g. of KOH in glycerol reagent is weighed or accurately pipetted (Moretti and Cheftel pipet the reagent at 180°C. where its viscosity is sufficiently low to permit reproducible delivery) into a tube containing 100 mg. of sample. The mixture is heated at 180° under nitrogen. After 10 minutes the tube is removed and shaken vigorously for 3 to 4 seconds and then replaced in the bath. This is repeated 3 times at 30 second intervals and then the tube is left at 180° for a total elapsed time for 45 minutes. At the end of this time the tube is cooled and 30 ml. of dry methanol added. The solution is transferred quantitatively to a 100 ml. volumetric flask and diluted to volume with additional methanol. Absorbance of the solution is measured at each of several wave lengths and individual acids calculated by solving a set of simultaneous equations.

Absorption maxima of isomerization products of acids studied were:

Acid	mμ
Linoleic	233
Linolenic	233, 268
Arachidonic	233, 268, 315
Pentenoic in C_{20}	233, 268, 315, 346
Hexenoic in C_{20}	233, 268, 315, 346, 374

This alkaline isomerization procedure requires rather drastic conditions and is subject to interference from esters, unsaturated aldehydes, and olefins having two or more unsaturated groupings.

One of the potential general colorimetric procedures is based on conversion of fatty acids (and esters) to the red-colored ferric hydroxamates, as outlined by Steyermark in Volume II of this series. Hill (89) developed the method for estimates of dibutyl sebacate and fatty acids and esters in palm oil, cottonseed oil, and sperm oil.

Procedure for Fatty Acids (89). From 0.05 to 1 mg. of acid is dissolved in 10 ml. of dry ether. Then 3 ml. of thionyl chloride is added and the mixture evaporated nearly to dryness. A few drops of dry methanol are added, the solution is heated briefly, and excess reagents finally removed by means of a current of dry air passed through the warm container. The residue is dissolved in 20 ml. of dry ether and the determination completed as for esters, described by Hall and Shaefer in Volume II, page 55, of this series.

Keto acids can be determined by measurement of the intensity of the red color of alkaline solutions of their 2,4-dinitrophenylhydrazine derivatives. This method was used by Long in analyses for α-keto acids (129) and by Koepsell and Sharpe for pyruvic and α-ketoglutaric acids (117). A suitable procedure is summarized in Volume I, page 284, of this series.

Rates of reaction of acids with diphenyldiazomethane may be used to estimate some carboxylic acids in the presence of others. Roberts and Regan (185) followed this reaction spectrophotometrically in determining chloroacetic acid in acetic acid, by measuring absorbance of benzene solutions at 525 mμ and in analyses of acetic–benzoic, m- and p-methoxybenzoic, and p-nitrobenzoic–p-aminobenzoic acid mixtures.

A direct method for oxalic acid is based on measurement of the intensity of the pink-colored compound formed after reaction with indole (12). The sample in 1 N sulfuric acid solution is mixed with indole in concentrated sulfuric acid and heated for 45 minutes at 80–90°C. Absorbance of the cooled solution is measured at 525 mμ. This procedure has been used successfully for determining 0.05 to 1 mg./ml. of oxalic acid in the presence of acetic, propionic, tartaric, citric, benzoic, and uric acids.

Grant (79) determined 0.25 and 15 micrograms of formic acid by first reducing the acid to formaldehyde with magnesium ribbon and then determining the aldehyde by the chromotropic acid method (see Volume I of this series, p. 287). Although yield was only about 30%, the precision of the method appeared to be within 5%.

Amino Acids.   The reaction of amino acids with ninhydrin (see Section III.1) can be used as a colorimetric method of analysis. Schlenker (196) found that at a pH of 11.0, with the removal of ammonia by aeration, reaction (6) (p. 49) was completely reversible. The amino nitrogen was collected as ammonia and determined colorimetrically with Nessler's reagent. Although cystine and aspartic acid reacted quantitatively at a pH of 1 to produce two and one moles of ammonia, respectively, Schlenker's work indicated that the majority of the amino acids studied did not react in the predicted manner under the same set of conditions. Variations in the concentration of ninhydrin, the pH of the solution, and the time of reaction effected the liberation of ammonia in many instances. Several other workers extended these studies before arriving at a generally applicable colorimetric method. As shown in equation (6), the blue-colored diketohydrindylidendiketohydrindamine, is formed in slightly acid solution. Yemm and Cocking (246) found that conditions must be controlled carefully to obtain reproducible results. These workers modified a method of Moore and Stein (153) for determining the blue compound.

Procedure (246).   The following special reagents are required: (a) 0.2 M, pH 5 citrate buffer is prepared by dissolving 21.008 g. citric acid monohydrate in 200 ml. of distilled water plus 200 ml. of 1 N NaOH and diluting to 500 ml. with water; (b) potassium cyanide reagent is made by diluting 5 ml. 0.01 M KCN to 250 ml. with methyl Cellosolve (this reagent is stable for at least 1 month); (c) ninhydrin reagent is prepared by dissolving 5.0 g. of ninhydrin in 100 ml. of methyl Cellosolve solution (this reagent is stable for at least 6 months); (d) mixed reagent is made from 50 ml. reagent (c) plus 250 ml. reagent (b) (this solution is red in color initially but soon becomes yellow; it should be stored overnight before use and is stable for at least 1 week).

To make an analysis 0.5 ml. of citrate buffer is added to 1 ml. of sample containing 0.05 to 5.6 micrograms of amino nitrogen. Either 1.2 ml. of reagent (d) or 0.2 ml. reagent (c) plus 1.0 ml. reagent (b) is added. The mixture is heated for 15 minutes at 100°C., cooled under tap water and made up to a convenient volume with ethanol–water (6 + 4). The resulting solution is transferred to a 1 cm. glass cell where its absorbance is measured at 570 mμ. (Proline and hydroxyproline are measured at 440 mμ.)

The procedure was found applicable to a variety of amino acids. The following gave from 99 to 100% yield:

Alanine	Glutamic acid	Isoleucine
Arginine	Glutamine	Methionine
Aspartic acid	Glycine	Serine
Cysteic acid	Histidine	Threonine
Cystine	Leucine	Valine

From 45 to 90% yield was given by asparagine, phenylalanine, tryptophan, and tyrosine. Ammonia, which interfered by reacting to the extent of about 30%, probably could be removed by aeration of an alkaline solution of the sample prior to analysis for amino acid.

Traces of certain cations have a marked effect on the color and the rate of color formation of the ninhydrin-amino acid reaction product (113). As little as 0.1 ml. of 0.01 M solutions of Al^{+3}, Hg^{+2}, Fe^{+2}, Fe^{+3}, Mn^{+2}, Sn^{+2}, Ag^+, and Cu^{+2} prevented the formation of the usual colored reaction product of alanine with ninhydrin. Ca^{+2}, Ba^{+2}, and Cd^{+2} at one microgram levels caused red colors showing absorption maxima at 510 and 410 mμ (Ca, Cd) and 530 and 410 mμ (Ba). Meyer and Riklis (144) eliminated the interference of cations by use of versene as complexing agent. Their method called for addition of 0.3% versene to the pH 5 citrate buffer used in the colorimetric analysis.

Other methods for estimating amino acids include: (a) formation of their cupric complexes by use of a cation exchange resin containing cupric ions followed by colorimetric analysis of iodine liberated on treatment of the solubilized copper with iodine (10), and (b) conversion of amino acids on paper chromatograms to chloramine derivatives (by reaction with chlorine), which are estimated from intensities of the blue colors produced by reaction with o-tolidine on benzene (181). Winter (241) studied numerous methods for determining glycine and concluded that measurement of the green color produced by reaction with o-phthalaldehyde was the most useful.

X. INFRARED ABSORPTION

A considerable amount of qualitative information has been obtained on characteristic infrared absorptions of carboxylic acids. A knowledge of the location of expected frequencies, together with background in general quantitative infrared spectroscopy, provides the basis for use of this increasingly important technique in organic functional group analysis. This is apparent in the discussions by Coggeshall of spectroscopic methods used in the petroleum industry in Volume I of this series, by Shreve of methods used in the analysis of synthetic coating resins in this volume, and by O'Connor of problems in fat and oil chemistry (166). A convenient reference table of infrared absorption bands is given by Mehlenbacher in Volume I, page 52, of this series.

Carboxylic acids are strongly associated, usually existing as dimers, with marked hydrogen bonding between the hydroxyl and carbonyl groups. The dimeric form may persist even in some dilute solutions and also at the boiling point of the acid. For this reason absorptions due to carboxyl vibrations associated with the carboxyl group are shifted from those of aldehydes, ketones, and esters. Absorptions due to the hydroxyl group stretching vibrations also are displaced from those of other hydroxyl-containing compounds. Harris and Hobbs (87) made a quantitative study of the monomer-dimer equilibria of acetic, chloroacetic, and benzoic acids using absorption intensity measurements of the —OH stretching frequencies. Carbon tetrachloride was used as solvent.

Among the most useful bands for identifying the carboxyl function are those occurring in the 3.70–4.00 μ (2700–2500 cm.$^{-1}$) region. Actually these are due to —OH stretching vibrations and, therefore, are not specific for carboxylic acids. However, few other types of compounds absorb in this region so that these bands provide strong evidence for dimeric carboxylic acids (11). Positive identification requires additional observations at

TABLE XIII

Principal Absorption Bands for the Carboxyl Group

Type	Absorption region	
	Microns	Cm.$^{-1}$
C=O stretching..............................	5.71– 6.01	1750–1665
C—O stretching and/or in-plane OH deformation.....	6.94– 7.17	1440–1395
	7.56– 8.26	1322–1210
O H stretching....................................	3.70– 4.00	2700–2500
O H deformation, out-of-plane....................	10.63–11.11	940– 900

other wavelengths. The most useful are noted in Table XIII, which shows principal absorptions of the carboxyl group in acids examined in the liquid or solid state (11,62,81).

Although observations of absorptions in the regions noted in Table XIII serve to identify the carboxyl function, more specific information is needed for quantitative analysis. This is apparent from the absorptions of particular acids as illustrated in Table XIV.

TABLE XIV

Absorption of Carboxylic Acids (62,81)

Acid	State	Absorption bands				
Acetic	Liquid	$3.76\ \mu$	5.84	7.75	7.08	10.73
		2660 cm.$^{-1}$	1712	1292	1413	933
Propionic	Liquid	$3.73\ \mu$	5.83	8.07	7.05	10.75
		2680 cm.$^{-1}$	1715	1240	1419	930
Adipic	Solid	$3.82\ \mu$	5.88	7.80	7.00	10.75
		2620 cm.$^{-1}$	1700	1282	1428	930
Benzoic	Solid	$3.88\ \mu$	5.94	7.76	7.05	10.70
		2580 cm.$^{-1}$	1685	1290	1420	935

An examination of the data of Table XIV shows that the exact location of absorption bands for each frequency noted depends on the acid. Also the intensity of absorption varies from compound to compound. Minor variations may be a function of chain length. However, other groups in the molecule which are located near the carboxyl function exert a strong influence. Aromatic acids, for example, show C=O absorption from 5.88–5.95 μ (1700–1680 cm.$^{-1}$) while acids with α,β-unsaturation absorb between 5.85 and 5.88 μ (1710–1700 cm.$^{-1}$) (11). Quantitative analyses are most readily made on systems containing known acids. Then absolute calibrations can be made through analyses of known mixtures.

For both qualitative and quantitative analyses care must be exercised in choice of system. As indicated, the absorption regions discussed above are based on observations of acids in the dimeric state. In dioxane and in very dilute solutions of inert liquids the acids may exist completely as monomers or more likely as mixtures of monomers and dimers. Flett (62) found that the C=O absorption of propionic acid in dioxane solution occurred at about 5.75 μ (1735 cm.$^{-1}$) compared to 5.83 μ (1715 cm.$^{-1}$) for the liquid acid alone. Grove and Willis (80) reported an average value of 5.68 μ (1760 cm.$^{-1}$) for C=O absorption of monomeric acids. Freeman (66) found a OH stretching vibration at about 2.83 μ (3540 cm.$^{-1}$) for monomeric acids at 10^{-2} to 10^{-6} molar concentration in carbon tetrachloride. He used absorbance at the wave length to determine the concentration of acid monomer in solution. Hadzi and Sheppard (81) observed a considerable change in position and in intensity of carboxyl group absorptions between the concentrated acids and equimolar mixtures of the acids with water. In the latter hydrogen bonding also occurred between the acid and water molecules. This was most marked for bands at about 7.05 μ (1420 cm.$^{-1}$), 7.95 μ (1260 cm.$^{-1}$), and 10.70 μ (935 cm.$^{-1}$). This last band had almost disappeared in the water system lending strong support to the assignment of this band to out-of-plane OH deformation vibrations. Shreve et al. (206) also obtained direct evidence in support of this assignment for the 10.7 μ (935 cm.$^{-1}$) band where this band was observed in long-chain fatty acids but was not present in esters of the same acids. A doublet in the 7.8 and 8.0 μ (1280 and 1250 cm.$^{-1}$) regions, associated with C—O vibrations, appeared to be a general characteristic of long-chain fatty acids. Jones, McKay, and Sinclair (105) in studies of C_{12}–C_{21} fatty acids in the liquid and solid states observed a regular series of evenly spaced absorptions in the 7.4–8.5 μ (1350–1180 cm.$^{-1}$) region. These bands were assumed to arise from interactions among the rocking and/or twisting vibrations of the methylene groups. The number and character of the bands probably could be used to estimate chain length of the higher fatty acids.

Von Sydow (232) observed significant differences in the infrared spectra of different crystalline forms of higher fatty acids. Purified n-pentadecanoic, palmitic, and stearic acids were examined as Nujol mulls and as melts in the 5 to 13 μ (2000 to 770 cm.$^{-1}$) region. Calibrations were made with a polystyrene spectrum to assure accuracy in measurements to ±0.01 μ. Maximum absorption values were recorded for the C=O stretching, CH_2 deformation, and OH out-of-plane deformation regions for the A′-, B′-, and C′-forms and melt of the C_{15} acid, the A- and C-forms and melt of C_{16}, and B- and C-forms of the C_{18} acid.

The B-form of stearic acid showed a well-defined doublet at 5.845 and 5.910 μ. Major frequency shifts among the different crystalline forms were observed in the 10.6–11.3 μ (940–890 cm.$^{-1}$) range. Measurements in this region together with those at 7.7–8.5 μ (1300–1180 cm.$^{-1}$) were considered to be best suited for identification purposes. The latter are a band progression series, due to CH_2 group vibrations the position and intensity of which are functions of chain length and crystal form. Sinclair and co-workers (211) and Bellamy (11) also reported on the large change in the OH absorption between the unstable crystalline B-form and stable crystalline C-form of stearic acid.   Sinclair et al. (211) noted that the absorption maximum for the OH out-of-plane deformation in the 11 micron (900 cm.$^{-1}$) region was essentially constant among the C-forms of C_{14}, C_{16}, C_{18}, and C_{20} acids and the B'-forms of the C_{17}, C_{19}, and C_{21} acids.

Shreve *et al.* (205) described an infrared method for determining *trans*-octadecenoic acids in the presence of *cis*-isomers. Analyses were based on measurements of the sample in carbon disulfide solution at 10.36 μ. This band probably was due to vibrations of the trans configuration of the $R_1CH\!\!=\!\!CHR_2$ structure.   Absorbance, plotted as a function of concentration in g./liter, obeyed Beer's law.

Sinclair and co-workers (211) used infrared analysis to determine the degree of unsaturation in mixtures of *cis*-unsaturated long chain fatty acids.   The intensity of a band at 3.01 μ (3020 cm.$^{-1}$), presumably due to stretching vibrations of C$=$C—H carbon-hydrogen bonds, increased with the number of *cis*-double bonds, while relative intensity of a methylene peak at 2920 cm.$^{-1}$ decreased.   A nearly linear plot was obtained of A_{2920} ($A_{2920} - A_{3020}$) versus number of double bonds for oleic, linoleic, linolenic, and arachidonic acids.   Cooled, solid films of binary mixtures of oleic and linoleic acids exhibited significant progressive changes with composition in the 13.3–14.7 μ (750–680 cm.$^{-1}$) region, associated with out-of-plane bending vibrations of the C$=$C—H carbon-hydrogen bonds.   After suitable calibrations these absorptions would appear adequate for quantitative analysis of binary mixtures of unsaturated acids (211).

Determination of the concentration of carboxyl groups in oxidized cellulose has been made by infrared analysis.   Forziati and co-workers (65) utilized the intensity of the C$=$O stretching vibration at 5.8 μ for this purpose. Analyses were made of mineral oil slurries of 1:1 mixtures of finely divided polystyrene and the cellulose.   Absorption of the polystyrene at 6.2 μ was used as internal reference band obviating the need for accurate control of cell thickness.   The method was used to detect as little as 0.1 millimole of carboxyl per gram of cellulose.

Sulfonic acids also show absorption in the 3.70–4.00 μ (2700–2500 cm.$^{-1}$) region (11) and sulfinic acids, in the range 3.59–4.28 μ (2790–2340 cm.$^{-1}$) (53) due to stretching vibrations of bonded OH groups.   Sulfonic acids show strong bands at about 8.35 and 7.46 μ (1200 and 1340 cm.$^{-1}$) probably due to hydroxyl deformation bands (43).   In addition to strong absorption in the 3.59–4.28 μ region, solid sulfonic acids show strong bands at 9.08–10.10 μ (1090–990 cm.$^{-1}$) and 11.50–12.35 μ (870–810 cm.$^{-1}$) due to S$=$O and S—O stretching vibrations, respectively (53).   In dilute solutions of sulfinic acids a new band appears in the 2.70–2.78 μ region (3700–3600 cm.$^{-1}$), probably due to OH stretching of the monomeric acid.

Group absorptions occur at slightly longer wave lengths by Raman spectroscopy. Thus the C=O stretching vibrations of dimeric acids occur at about 6.06 μ (1650 cm.$^{-1}$) in the Raman compared to about 5.82 μ (1720 cm.$^{-1}$) in the infrared (49). For acetic acid the C—O stretching or OH deformation band at 7.75 μ (1290 cm.$^{-1}$) in the infrared is found at 7.88 μ (1270 cm.$^{-1}$) in the Raman (81).

XI. MASS SPECTROMETRY

In a general study of the analysis of oxygenated compounds by mass spectrometry Kelley (114) demonstrated application to mixtures of C_1–C_4 monobasic acids. A mixture calculated on a dry basis of 86.1% formic acid, 2.5% acetic, 5.8% propionic, and 5.6% n-butyric analyzed 85.2, 2.0, 6.4, and 6.3%, respectively. A curious anomaly was observed in this system. Normally the 46 m/e peak (parent mass) would be used for calculating formic acid. In this case, however, better agreement was obtained by using the 29 peak. Details of mass spectrometry are given by Dibeler in this volume of the series.

XII. MICROSCOPY. X-RAY DIFFRACTOMETRY

Numerous publications have appeared on the use of the microscope and x-ray diffractometer for identifications of organic acids. Usually these are based on measurements of derivatives, such as the p-bromoanilides (28,29,152). Crystalline acids often can be examined directly (147,213).

Semiquantitative and quantitative analyses by these techniques are limited to known systems. Where applicable, however, they are rapid and particularly useful for analyses of binary and occasionally ternary mixtures of homologs. The specific examples described briefly below illustrate how microscopy and x-ray diffractometry can be applied.

Mixtures of acetic and propionic acids can be determined individually by determinations of certain of the primary crystallographic constants. The optic axial angle, measured with the aid of a petrographical microscope, varies regularly with change in composition (28,152). This was demonstrated by measurements at five different wave lengths of light suitably isolated by means of filters inserted in a mercury arc light source. The microscope was best suited for analyses in the range 20 to 60% of the propionic acid derivative using either optical axial angle values at several different wavelengths or the wave length of uniaxiality.

Determination of the intensity of the principal d spacing, as determined by x-ray diffractometry, also serves as a method of analysis of the acet–propion–p-bromoanilide system. Values were obtained from measurements of the powdered derivatives, using an x-ray diffraction tube with a copper target (152). An estimate of composition in the range 0 to 30% of the propionic acid derivative can be made by determination of the intensity ratio of the 4.06 to the 3.63 A. peak. Above 30% a small regular change in d spacing is observed.

In special cases comparison of the crystal habit of a system to be analyzed with knowns serves as a method of quantitative analysis. This technique has been demonstrated in analyses for small amounts of succinic in adipic acid (147). Under controlled conditions pure adipic acid crystallizes from the melt in sharply defined radial plates. In the presence of as little as 0.1% succinic acid there is a distinct feathering around the edges of the plates. This change in habit continues regularly up to about 1% succinic acid, permitting estimates of succinic acid in intervals of 0.1% in the range 0–1% succinic in adipic acid.

Melting point relationships often serve to provide semiquantitative analyses of binary acid mixtures. This approach is illustrated by the work of Houston and Van Sandt (92), who determined the melting points of pairs of dibasic acids containing from six to twelve carbon atoms.

XIII. CHROMATOGRAPHY

Chromatography provides one of the most reliable means for separating mixtures of acids. Subsequent analyses of the fractionated components then can be made to determine the individual acids. Partition chromatography is the basis of most of the reported separations, using column or paper techniques. Packed column methods may be based on partition between two liquid phases or between liquid and gas phase. Other methods depending on adsorption chromatography have been used to a limited extent. Ion exchange procedures have been used widely for separation of amino acids and to a limited extent for other acids. The general fundamentals of chromatography have been covered adequately in several books and papers.

1. Liquid–Liquid Partition Chromatography

The chromatogram was long recognized as being analogous to distillation and extraction. Martin and Synge (135) were among the first to work out the theory of chromatography in conjunction with a proposal based on two liquid phases. They demonstrated that the concepts developed for distillation could be applied to chromatography.

In essentially all liquid–liquid column separations of organic acids an aqueous system is used as the stationary liquid phase. Elsden (58), for example, refined a qualitative scheme reported by Smith (214) for separating several of the lower fatty acids quantitatively. The method depended on

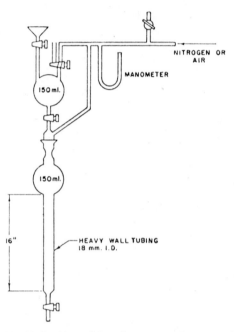

Fig. 16. Liquid–liquid partition chromatography apparatus (48).

use of wet silica gel impregnated with bromcresol green in the column, transfer of the sample in chroroform solution to the column, and displacement with chloroform–butanol. Displaced fractions were determined by titration with standard base. This technique was limited primarily due to the fact that separations of some acids were not clean and the position of zones in the column appeared to be a function of concentration. Synge (219) attributed this to the fact that the partition isotherm is deformed by the partition between associated molecules of the acids in the organic phase and dissociated molecules in the aqueous phase. He pointed out that the ratio of ionized to unionized acid could be kept constant by maintaining the pH constant. This could be done conveniently through the use of a buffer. Moyle, Baldwin, and Scarisbrick (157) made significant improvements in the method which permitted the separation and determination of most naturally occurring steam-volatile fatty acids (acetic to caprylic). Silica gel free of iron was used as solid phase and aqueous phosphate buffers were employed. Fixed concentrations of butanol in chloroform were used as solvent for the sample and for developing the chromatogram.

Several other investigators further refined the method through use of silicic acid (178) and Celite (30). Marvel and Rands (136) made a particularly important contribution based on a technique employing systematic increase in the polarity of the developing solvent. This was accomplished by adding increasing concentrations of butanol in chloroform. In this way mixtures of two to seven water soluble acids could be separated. Their general method called for use of an 18 mm. inner diameter by 480 mm. column packed with 20 g. of 100-mesh reagent grade silicic acid containing 12 g. of water. A convenient apparatus is shown in Figure 16 (48). From 10 to 80 mg. of sample was dissolved in 1 to 2 ml. of chloroform, which was transferred to the top of the column. Successive 100 ml. portions of water-saturated developing liquid were then passed through the column by application of slight pressure. The developing liquid was increased in polarity in the following order: chloroform, 5% butanol in chloroform, 10%, 15%, 20%, 25%, 30%, 40%, 50%, 70%, 100% butanol. Successive 10 ml. fractions were collected and titrated for acidity with 0.02 N caustic. From the results a graph was plotted of milliequivalents of acid per unit fraction vs. volume of effluent which in effect showed the efficiency of separation and the peak effluent volume of each acid. Through use of a fixed system, i. e., constancy of column dimensions, solvents, and rate of change of polarity of the eluant, the peak effluent volume served as a method of identification of the acid.

Marvel and Rands (136) reported peak effluent volumes of many acids based on separations of several known mixtures. The following illustrate typical compositions arranged in order of elution:

(a) Butyric, propionic, acetic, formic.
(b) Adipic, glutaric, succinic, malonic, oxalic.
(c) Benzoic, phthalic, trimesic, gallic, citric.

Some combinations were not separated completely by the standard procedure, including chloroacetic and trichloroacetic acids, itaconic and citraconic, sebacic and suberic acids. However, modifications could be made in the procedure to improve these separations.

TABLE XV.   Liquid–Liquid Partition Chromatography of Organic Acids

Acids	Solids	Phases for separation		Ref.
		Stationary	Displacing	
C_1–C_4 monobasic	Celite 545	Water	Benzene, 10 and 25% butanol in chloroform	173
C_1–C_4 "	Silicic acid	Water	0–10% butanol in chloroform	136
C_1–C_6 "	Celite	Aq. phosphate buffer	0, 1, 5, 20% butanol in chloroform	30
C_1–C_{10} "	Silicic acid	Aq. glycine, pH 2, 8.4, 10	1, 10, 25% isobutanol in chloroform	45
C_2–C_5 "	Silica gel	Water, bromcresol green	1, 5% butanol in chloroform	58
C_2–C_8 "	Silica gel	Aq. phosphate buffer	1, 10, 30% butanol in chloroform	157
C_4–C_8 "	Celite 545	Aq. sulfuric acid	Benzene	173
C_5–C_{10} "	Silicic acid	Methanol	2,2,4-Trimethylpentane	178
C_{16}–C_{24} "	Kieselguhr	Paraffin	50% aq. acetone	209
Palmitic and stearic	Carbon		95% ethanol	37
C_2–C_{10} dibasic	Silicic acid	Water	0–100% butanol in chloroform	136
C_{11}–C_{16} dibasic	Silicic acid	Aq. glycine, pH 8.5, 9	1, 3, 5, 10, 25% isobutanol in chloroform	45
Aliphatic	Silicic acid	Aq. sulfuric acid	35% butanol in chloroform	247
Aliphatic	Silicic acid	Aq. sulfuric acid	9–50% butanol in chloroform	31
Aromatic	Silicic acid	Water	0–10% butanol in chloroform	136
Aromatic	Silicic acid	Water–methanol–sulfuric acid	Ligroin	14
Hydroxy acids	Silicic acid	Water	0–100% butanol in chloroform	136
Amino acids	Silica gel	Water, methyl orange	1% butanol in chloroform	135

Other systems have proved advantageous for separating certain acid mixtures. For example, Peterson and Johnson (173) devised a benzene–aqueous sulfuric acid system for separating formic, acetic, propionic, n-butyric, caproic, caprylic, and capric acids, while Ramsey and Patterson (178) used methanol–isooctane for mixtures of C_5–C_{10} acids. Typical systems reported for separations of a variety or organic acids are shown in Table XV.

A significant improvement was described by Donaldson and co-workers (54) for separations involving changes in composition of the displacing phase. A liquid feed system was used which automatically increased solvent polarity during the separation process. This provision for a gradual change in solvent composition led to easier control of the operation and minimized the appearance of false peaks. These workers demonstrated its applicability to acid mixtures using butanol–chloroform solutions as displacing liquids.

2. Gas-Liquid Partition Chromatography

Probably the most significant advance in partition chromatography was proposed by James and Martin in 1951 (101). This involved the gas–liquid partition chromatogram. The new technique, where applicable, offers several advantages over liquid–liquid partition chromatography for separations of homologs and isomers. Since the ratio of vapor pressures of two homologs is usually greater than the ratio of partition coefficients between two liquid phases, cleaner separations are now feasible. Also by proper choice of stationary liquid phase one can often use adsorption effects to advantage. The method is based on use of an inert solid phase containing an inert relatively nonvolatile liquid phase. An inert gas, such as nitrogen or helium, is used as carrier. Usually the individual components of a mixture are eluted from the column in order of decreasing vapor pressures where they are determined usually by continuous analysis. Only a few milligrams of sample is required.

The technique is applicable to analyses of a wide variety of materials provided they are stable and have a significant vapor pressure at the temperature and pressure employed in the apparatus. For acids a number of detectors can be used for analysis of the eluant, including photometric or potentiometric titrators, thermal conductivity cells with platinum elements or thermisters (3), and vapor density equipment. A convenient design of a gas chromatography unit, built by S. Dal Nogare of the authors' laboratory, is shown in Figure 17. The column is enclosed in a vapor jacket which provides constant temperature during the separation. A second vapor jacket is used to house the thermal conductivity cells. The apparatus shown is used for liquid samples which are introduced by means of a micrometer hypodermic syringe through a serum bottle stopper inserted in the apparatus. The unit is designed for differential measurement of thermal conductivity between the effluent and the carrier gas. This signal is amplified and recorded continuously as indicated. The vapor jacket is

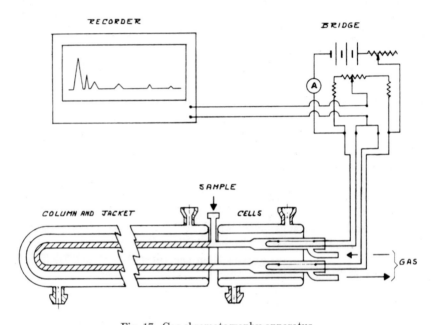

Fig. 17. Gas chromatography apparatus.

particularly convenient for use between room temperature and about 150°C. Electric heaters also can be used but these usually are not as easily controlled as the vapor system.

Included among the important discussions of gas or vapor phase chromatography are those given in: *Analyst*, December, 1952; *Analytical Chemistry*, February, 1955 (171); *Chemical and Process Engineering*, March, 1955 (99); and *British Medical Bulletin*, No. 3, 1955 (103).

James and Martin (100,102) separated a variety of fatty acids using apparatus equipped with a continuous photometric titrator. Their columns measured 4 mm. internal diameter by 4 or 11 feet in length enclosed in a vapor jacket to maintain constant temperature. The titration cell, containing water or other suitable absorber with phenol red indicator was connected at the effluent end of the tube and was provided with a lamp and photoelectric cell. The cell in turn was connected to an amplifier which controlled a recording buret. The unit was designed to maintain constant pH. As acid was absorbed the indicator color changed and standard alkali was delivered automatically from the buret until the acid was neutralized. A ball pen attached to the plunger of the buret recorded its movement on a chart moving at a known speed.

To carry out an analysis the sample is introduced at the entrance to the column. Nitrogen or other inert gas is supplied to the column at constant pressure. The choice of stationary phase is quite important (122). It must be nonvolatile, stable at the temperature used for the analysis, and inert toward the components in the sample. This is illustrated in James and Martin's investigations (100) in which they compared separation of C_3, C_4, and C_5 acids on columns containing DC 550 silicone as immobile phase with that on another containing DC 550 silicone with 10% stearic acid. Only the latter gave clear-cut separations. The poor separation in the former was reported to be due to dimerization of the fatty acids in the silicone which affected the partial pressures of the acids. This led to a concentration effect whereby the more dilute portions of the zone moved more rapidly than those of higher concentration. Stearic acid present in large excess on the column, however, competed with the volatile acids in forming the association complex and so reduced the partial pressure of the acids, rendering distribution between the two phases nearly independent of concentration.

James and Martin (100) reported results from the separation of eight acids from acetic to valeric. These data were obtained from a 4 mm. by 11 ft. column packed with Celite. DC 550 silicone containing 10% stearic acid was used as immobile liquid phase. Temperature was 137°C., rate of nitrogen flow was 18.2 ml. per minute, and nitrogen pressure was 74 cm. of mercury. The data show that a complete separation was obtained in 100 minutes even though some isomers such as isovaleric acid and N-methylbutyric acid boil only 0.3°C. apart. Under fixed conditions the separations are reproducible. Consequently, the time scale serves as a convenient means of qualitative analysis and the area under the differential of the experimental curve is equivalent to the amount of acid present. Less than 10 mg. of sample was used for this analysis. James and Martin (100) showed that the maximum loading of a 4 mm. column is about 1 mg. of each of the lower acids. Loading can be increased through use of larger diameter columns. The minimum amount of acid detectable in the equipment employed by James and Martin (100) using 0.038 N base, was 0.3 microgram, equivalent to 0.02 mg. of acetic acid. The lower limit is fixed only by the method of analysis used.

James and Martin (100,102) also successfully separated in a 4 ft. column a mixture of 14 acids ranging from acetic to hendecanoic. The temperature used, 137°, was too high for good resolution of the lower acids and, consequently, the complete analysis required two steps. Van de Kamer and co-workers (226) found that, by employing increasing temperature from

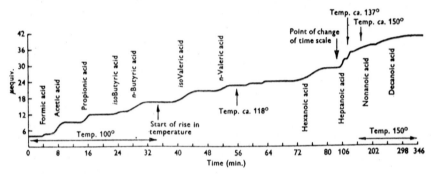

Fig. 18. Separation of mixture of acids by gas chromatography (226).

100° to 150°C., good separation of mixtures of C_1 through C_{10} acids could be realized in a single step. Column dimensions and packing were the same as those employed by James and Martin (100). An ether solution of the sample, containing from 1–5 microequivalents each of an eleven component mixture, was added into a small well at the entrance to the column. Nitrogen was introduced at a pressure of 550 mm. and a flow rate of 50 cc./min. After evaporation of the ether with the aid of a micro burner, the temperature of the tube was adjusted to 100°C. by circulating glycerol delivered from a thermostatically controlled reservoir. As separation progressed the eluted acids were titrated in the photometric analyzer. This temperature was maintained until the acids through C_4 were separated, after which the temperature was raised gradually to 150°. The temperature–time scale, together with a plot of the results, is shown in Figure 18. Recoveries varied from 97 to 108%.

3. Paper Chromatography

Widespread application of paper chromatography dates from 1944 when Consden, Gordon, and Martin published on qualitative separations of aminoacids (44). Since that time numerous new applications have been found. Several books have been published on the theory and applicability of this and other techniques of chromatography (18, 23, 125); Asselineau (8) has reviewed the paper chromatography of fatty acids and derivatives.

Since the technique requires only microgram quantities of sample, it has been used to an increasing extent by biochemists and others for analyses of acid mixtures. Foremost among the reported applications are separations of amino acids by one-dimensional paper chromatography. In this variation a narrow strip of filter paper is usually suspended over a support and the solution containing several micrograms of the sample is spotted near the end of the paper. The individual acids are separated by an ascending or descending procedure. After separation the acids can be located by a suitable color-forming reagent. For amino acids, ninhydrin is most often used. For other acids, indicators such as bromcresol green, methyl red, bromthymol blue, bromcresol purple, or bromphenol blue may be used to isolate the spots. Another approach involves the use of colored derivatives rather than the free acids for the separation step or the formation of derivatives after separation.

After R_f values have been established from known acids, the location of the spot serves to identify each component. Often semiquantitative estimates of the amount of acid can be made from the size or color intensity of the spot. Quantitative data can be obtained by separating the spots, if necessary, and titrating them or examining them by instrumental means. Wagner and co-workers (233), for example, measured the light absorption of the copper–ferrocyanide complexes of the separated saturated and unsaturated C_{12} to C_{22} acids. Isherwood and Cruickshank (95) and Cavallini and co-workers (38) separated the 2,4-dinitrophenylhydrazones of keto acids and determined them colorimetrically. De Jonge (52), on the other hand, prepared the corresponding anilides of acids ultimately determining them by ultraviolet absorption.

Resolution of complex mixtures often can be improved by two-dimensional paper chromatography. In this case a rectangular sheet of filter paper is employed. Partial separations are first made in one direction. Then the paper is rotated 90° and separations are completed using another solvent system. Two-dimensional methods were used by Cheftel and co-workers (40,41) for separating nonvolatile water-soluble acids. These included dibasic and other polyfunctional acids and involved the use of an alkaline followed by an acid solvent. The spots finally were located by spraying the paper with bromcresol green indicator solution. Woodward and Rabideau (244) used two-dimensional chromatography for separating

TABLE XVI. Paper Chromatography for Separations of Organic Acids

Acids	Solvent system	Ref.
C_1–C_{10} monobasic as anilides	Cyclohexane; methanol–ethanol–isopropanol–water	52
C_1–C_{20} monobasic as hydroxamates	Pentanol–acetic acid–water	221
C_1–C_{10} monobasic as hydroxamates	Benzene–formic acid–water	221
C_2–C_6 monobasic	n-Butanol–ethylamine–water	33
C_2–C_6 monobasic	n-Butanol–ammonia–water	55
C_{10}–C_{18} monobasic	Hydrocarbon (b. p. 190–220°C.)–acetic acid–water	110
C_{12}–C_{22} monobasic (saturated, unsaturated)	Hydrocarbon (b. p. 190–220°C.)–acetic acid–water	111,233
C_{16}–C_{21} monobasic (saturated, unsaturated)	Paraffin–benzene–methanol	237
C_2–C_{10} dibasic	Ethanol– or 2-ethoxyethanol–ammonia–water	40,41
C_2–C_{12} dicarboxylic	n-Propanol– or isopropanol–ammonia carbonate buffer; tetrahydro-furane–ammonia–water	106
Aliphatic (monobasic, dibasic, mixed functional group)	n-Propanol–ammonia–water	96
Mixed acids	Acetone–water; ethyl acetate–acetic acid–water	179
Keto acids as 2,4-dinitrophenylhydrazones	n-Butanol–ethanol–water	38,39

Acids	Solvent system	Ref.
Keto acids as 2,4-dinitrophenylhydrazones	tert-Amyl alcohol–n-propanol–ammonia–water; tert-amyl alcohol–ethanol–water	95
Keto acids as 2,4-dinitrophenylhydrazones	n-Butanol–water–sodium carbonate	201
Polyfunctional acids containing relatively high amts. of lactic acid	Isopropanol–tert-butanol–benzyl alcohol–formic acid–water	16
Polybasic acids	Mesityl oxide–formic acid–water	10
Alkoxy acids	n-Butanol–ammonia–water; Isooctane–acetone–ethanol–ammonia–water	160
Amino acids, aliphatic acids	Phenol–water–formic acid; isopropanol–tert-butanol–benzyl alcohol–formic acid–water	221,244
Amino acids	Phenol; isobutanol–ammonia–water	186
Aromatic acids	n-Butanol–ethanol or benzene–ammonium carbonate buffer	61
Hydroxybenzoic acid	Benzene–acetic acid–water; chloroform–acetic acid–water	20
Hydroxybenzoic acid	n-Butanol–pyridine–sodium chloride–ammonia–water	128
Aminohydroxybenzoic acid	Chloroform–acetic acid–water; benzene–acetic acid–water; isopropanol– or n-butanol–pyridine–sodium chloride–ammonia–water	21
Amino acids	Ethanol–n-butanol–water–piperidine; n-propanol–methyl ethyl ketone–water–dicyclohexylamine	86
Amino acids	Ethanol–n-butanol–water–diethylamine or ethanol–n-butanol–water–propionic acid; n-butanol–acetic–water–dicyclohexylamine	86

amino acids, aliphatic carboxylic acids, and sugars and Hardy, Holland, and Naylor for separating amino acids (86).

Reichl and Löffler (179) described an "inverse retention" method for the determination of organic acids by paper chromatography. Mixtures of aconitic, malic, citric, and gallic acids were separated using ethyl acetate–acetic acid–water as solvent. Then the acids were allowed to migrate through a diphenyl streak into a portion of the paper treated with lead acetate, using acetone–water. Sample sizes varied between 10 and 150 micrograms. As little as 0.03% of each of the acids mentioned above was detected. The method probably is applicable to all acids whose lead salts are insoluble in aqueous acetone.

An interesting variation in technique was employed by Ultee and Hartel (224) to determine carboxyl groups in filter paper. A chromatogram was developed through use of aqueous solutions of lead (II) acetate or nitrate. Strong bonds were formed between the lead and carboxyl groups of the paper which were ultimately spotted through reaction with hydrogen sulfide.

Bray and co-workers (20) found that solvents containing formic or acetic acid minimized tailing during separations of hydrobenzoic acids.

Radiometric methods also have been employed for determination of high molecular weight fatty acids. Kaufmann and Budwig (109) converted the acids to radioactive salts, which were determined by their iodine values. Typical pairs separated were oleic and linoleic acids, oleic and stearic, and elaidic and linoleic.

Typical systems used for separating organic acids are summarized in Table XVI.

The type or treatment of paper used has some effect on separations, primarily leading to differences in R_f value. Micheel and Albers (145) have made a number of investigations of acylated papers, included butyrocellulose, benzoylcellulose, and phthaloylcellulose. All of these showed higher R_f values for separations of hydrophobic substances than acetylcellulose paper. It is interesting to note that only one of the carboxyl groups of phthalic acid is esterified on the phthaloyl paper. Smith and Spriesterbach (215) used papers coated with alginic acid in separations of a variety of polyfunctional organic acids. The papers were prepared by dipping them into 1% aqueous ammonium alginate solution and precipitating alginic acid on the paper by treatment with 1 N hydrochloric acid. Since the papers were acidic, the common acid-base indicators could not be used. Acids such as citric, tartaric, and malic were detected with ammoniacal silver nitrate. Other mono- and dibasic acids were located by spraying the paper with an aromatic amine, sodium nitrite solution, and a phenol or aromatic amine. Acids were thus located through formation of colored azo dyes.

Ionophoresis was used to advantage in paper chromatographic separations of C_2–C_{16} fatty acids. Perila (172) used 10×50 cm. paper strips immersed in $0.2 N$ sodium hydroxide in glycerin. The mixture of acids in ethanol solution were spotted on the paper laid horizontally between electrode vessels enclosed in a chamber at 90°C. Marked differences in mobilities of the different acids were observed at a voltage of 20 v./cm. The separated acids were located by spraying the paper with copper acetate solution and rhodamine B and observing the dried paper in ultraviolet light. Acid mixtures up to C_9 were separated using aqueous sodium hydroxide buffered with boric acid at pH 9 (172).

4. Ion Exchange

With wider availability of analytical grade ion exchange resins, increasing uses are being found for concentration and separation of acids. Both anion and cation exchange resins find application. The anion exchangers are insoluble resins containing basic groups usually the amine function, RNR_2' where $R' = H$ or alkyl group. Those containing the primary, secondary, or tertiary amine function are usually weakly basic in nature. Those with quaternary ammonium groups, RNR_3^+, are strongly basic. Cation exchangers usually contain the sulfonic acid group, RSO_3H, or the carboxyl function, $RCOOH$.

The weakly basic anion exchange resins serve primarily as a means for separating strong from weak acids. The former are retained quite strongly on the column. The strong anion exchangers retain the weaker acids, including amino acids, which subsequently can be eluted by displacement with a stronger acid.

The strong cation exchange resins serve as a convenient means for separating organic acids. They are adsorbed to varying degrees and can be eluted by water. According to Samuelson (192) absorption of organic acids on sulfonated phenol-formaldehyde type resins is due to absorption forces of the van der Waals type arising from the resin skeleton and not due to the presence of sulfonic acid groups. Thus, separations of organic acids by use of strong cation exchangers are dependent on the type of resin and also on particle size. Erler (60) demonstrated the latter on studies of the lower monobasic and dibasic acids. The carboxylic acid type exchange resins are useful for separating aminoacids. Typical anion and cation exchange resins available from commercial sources are shown in Table XVII. General discussions of ion exchange resins are given in several books (124,125,146,158,192).

Block (158) and Cohn (146) reviewed applications of ion exchangers for

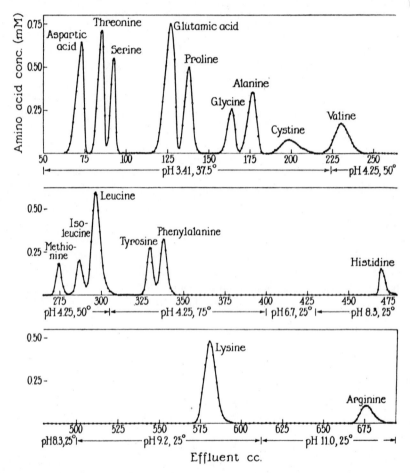

Fig. 19. Separation of mixture of amino acids by ion exchange chromatography (154.)

separations of amino acids. One of the most extensive separations was reported by Moore and Stein (154), who studied the sorption and elution of amino acids on the sodium form of a sulfonated polystyrene resin. Results on the separation of seventeen amino acids from a synthetic mixture simulating the composition of a protein hydrolyzate are shown in Figure 19. As indicated in the figure these clear-cut separations were achieved by eluting with sodium buffers of continually increasing pH and by varying the temperature. Thus, eight of the seventeen acids were eluted at 37.5°C. with a buffer at a pH of 3.41. A similar technique was used by Dustin and co-workers (56).

TABLE XVII

Typical Ion Exchange Resins

Name	Type	Manufacturer
	Anion Exchangers	
Amberlite 1R-4B	Weakly basic	Rohm & Haas, Philadelphia, Pa.
De-Acidite	" "	Permutit Co., New York, N. Y.
Dowex 3	" "	Dow Chemical Co., Midland, Mich.
Lewatit M	" "	Farbenfabriken Bayer, Leverkusen, Germany
Lewatit MI	Moderately basic	Farben. Bayer
Amberlite 1RA-400	Strongly basic	Rohm & Haas
Dowex 2	Strongly basic	Dow Chemical
Permutit S,D-735	Strongly basic	Permutit
	Cation Exchangers	
Amberlite 1R-100	Sulfonated phenolic resin	Rohm & Haas
Lewatit KS	" " "	Farben. Bayer
Wofatit K	" " "	I. G. Farben., Wolfen, Germany
Zero-Rex	" " "	Permutit
Amberlite 1R-120	Sulfonated hydrocarbon	Rohm & Haas
Dowex 50	" "	Dow Chemical
Permutit Q	" "	Permutit
Amberlite 1RC-50	Carboxylic	Rohm & Haas
Lewatit C	"	Farben. Bayer
Permutit H-70	"	Permutit

Stark and co-workers (217) separated amino acids from oxalic, citric, and succinic acids by passage through a cation exchange resin. The dibasic acids were then absorbed on a strongly basic anion exchange resin and eluted by displacement with aqueous sulfuric or hydrochloric acid.

Tolliday and co-workers (222) studied absorption of miscellaneous salts of organic acids on cation exchange resins. Both static and percolation methods were investigated. The latter was preferred since the released organic acid could be washed away from the resin quickly.   This minimized pH changes prevalent in the static method.

With a sulfonated phenol-formaldehyde type resin Samuelson (192) found that the absorption of aliphatic monobasic acids increased with increasing chain length.   The following sequence was observed for a mixture of acids: formic < lactic < acetic < succinic < propionic < butyric. Kunin and Myers (123) studied adsorption of several organic acids on the hydroxyl form of an anion exchanger.   The order of adsorption was benzoic < oxalic < formic < acetic = citric < salicylic.

Bryant and Overell (27) used a strong base anion exchange resin to isolate carboxylic acids from plant tissue extracts.   Included were citric, isocitric, malic, succinic, and fumaric acids.   These were separated by paper chromatography using mesityl oxide–formic acid–water as solvent system.   Busch and co-workers (34) used aqueous formic acid in increasing concentration to elute acids of the citric acid cycle adsorbed on an anion exchange column.   The acids were eluted in the following order: glutamic and aspartic; lactic; succinic, malic; a mixture of pyruvic, malonic, citric, and isocitric; fumaric; α-ketoglutaric; cis-aconitic.   Pyruvic acid was separated from the mixture as the 2,4-dinitrophenylhydrazone and the remaining acids were separated by liquid–liquid partition chromatography on silica gel columns.

Berntsson and Samuelson (13) studied the sorption and elution of glycolic, oxalic, pyruvic, gluconic, maleic, and p-toluenesulfonic acids using the acetate form of a strongly basic resin and the free base form of a weakly basic resin.   With the exception of gluconic all acids were sorbed quantitatively by both resins.   Glycolic, oxalic, gluconic, and maleic acids were eluted completely from both types of resin by displacement with sulfuric acid or ammonium carbonate solution.   From the strongly basic resin pyruvic acid was displaced with acidic eluants while aqueous hydrochloric acid was most effective for eluting p-toluenesulfonic acid from the resin.

XIV. EXTRACTION. DISTRIBUTION METHODS

A knowledge of distribution coefficients of acids between two immiscible liquid phases often can be used to advantage in separations and ultimate analysis.   Pagel and McLafferty (169) found that tributyl phosphate was one of the most effective agents for extracting organic acids from aqueous solution.   Tributyl phosphate was more efficient than ethyl ether, isopropyl ether, benzene, toluene, or chloroform.   These investigators found a definite relationship between distribution coefficient and structure of the acid. With monobasic and dibasic acids the extraction increased with length of the carbon chain. Hydroxyl groups attached to the acid molecule depressed extraction by the phosphate while chlorine and phenyl groups increased extraction per unit volume.

Marvel and Richards (137) determined distribution coefficients of a variety of polybasic acids between water and organic solvents. Extracting solvents studied are noted below in order of increasing effectiveness:

Skellysolve B	Diethyl ether
	Methyl isobutyl ketone
Carbon tetrachloride	Ethyl acetate
Benzene	Methyl propyl ketone
Chloroform	Methyl ethyl ketone
Diisopropyl ketone	Cyclohexanone
Butyl acetate	n-Butanol

Polybasic acids studied are listed in order of relative affinity for the aqueous phase:

Oxalic	Fumaric
Citric	Pimelic
Malonic	Suberic ·
β-Carboxyadipic	β-Phenyladipic
Succinic	Azelaic
Glutaric	Sebacic
Adipic	

Weisiger, in Volume II of this series, page 277, reported partition ratios of several of the higher acids and reviewed a countercurrent distribution method for separating saturated and unsaturated fatty acids in the C_{12}–C_{18} range.

Malm, Nadeau, and Genung (132) published an extensive review of partition methods for analyzing binary and ternary mixtures of the lower fatty acids. Partition coefficients of acetic, propionic, and butyric acids were determined between water and several organic solvents. Of those studied n-butyl acetate and n-propyl acetate gave the greatest spread in numerical values. A method was presented for analysis of the three acids based on extraction by two different volumes of butyl acetate. A set of simultaneous equations was solved to determine the concentration of the individual acids in admixture.

Tsai and Fu made further studies of the extraction technique for the determination of the lower acids (223). Rather than employing extractions of separate samples or successive extractions of the aqueous phase by the organic solvent, Tsai and Fu recommended extraction of an aqueous solution of the sample with isopropyl ether followed by extraction of the organic layer with dilute sulfuric acid. The aqueous layers were titrated for total acidity. After correction for a blank, extraction constants and coefficients were used to calculate the amounts of the individual acids. Results accurate to 1% absolute were reported for various mixtures of formic, acetic propionic, and butyric acids.

Phase solubility analysis has proved particularly useful for small quantities of amino acids. Mader, in Volume II of this series, page 253, described applications to a variety of materials.

Fractional solvent crystallization has been used to advantage for separating saturated from unsaturated higher fatty acids (26).

XV. DISTILLATION

Direct distillation methods can be used to separate acids for other compounds and to isolate individual acids. Usually, however, distillation is too time consuming and not always reliable as a method of analysis. Advantage often can be taken of azeotropes of acids and hydrocarbons as a means for separating and determining individual acids in mixtures containing other acids. Aromatic hydrocarbons are particularly useful for separating the lower fatty acids, as indicated in Table XVIII.

TABLE XVIII

Monobasic Acid—Aromatic Hydrocarbon Binaries

Acid		Hydrocarbon		Binary		
Name	B. p.[a]	Name	B. p.[a]	B. p.[a]	Wt. % acid	Ref.
Formic	100.8	Benzene	80.5	71.1	31	91
Acetic	118.1	Benzene		80	2	91
Propionic	141.1	Toluene	110.8	109–110	2	b, 195
Isobutyric	154.5	Toluene		110	0.6	b, 195
n-Butyric	163.5	Toluene		110	0.2	b, 195
Isobutyric		Xylene	139.9	134	8	b
n-Butyric		Xylene		136.5	5	b
n-Valeric		Xylene		139	3.5	b
Caproic	207	p-Cymene	177	171.5	3	b
Heptanoic	221	p-Cymene		176	0.5	b

[a] Boiling point at 760 mm.
b Unpublished data from the authors' laboratory.

References

1. Agarwal, M. M., and F. Spagnolo, *Anal. Chem.*, *25*, 1412 (1953).
2. Ahlén, L., and O. Samuelson, *ibid.*, *25*, 1293 (1953).
3. Ambrose, D., *J. Sci. Instruments*, *32*, 323 (1955).
4. American Society for Testing Materials, *A. S. T. M. Standards*, Part 5, "Petroleum Products," D 664-52, Philadelphia, 1952, p. 253.
5. Ames, S. R., and S. B. Licata, *J. Am. Oil Chemists Soc.*, *25*, 203 (1948).
6. Anderson, K., E. S. Bettis, and D. Revinson, *Anal. Chem.*, *22*, 743 (1950).
7. Arragon, G., *Compt. rend.*, *211*, 558 (1940).
8. Asselineau, J., *Bull. soc. chim. France*, *19*, 884 (1952).
9. Baggesgaard-Rasmussen, H., *Z. anal. Chem.*, *105*, 269 (1936).
10. Baudet, P., and E. Cherbuliez, *Helv. Chim. Acta*, *38*, 841 (1955).
11. Bellamy, L. J., *The Infrared Spectra of Complex Molecules*, Wiley, New York; Methuen, London, 1954.
12. Bergerman, J., and J. S. Elliot, *Anal. Chem.*, *27*, 1014 (1955).
13. Berntsson, S., and O. Samuelson, *Acta Chem. Scand.*, *9*, 277 (1955).
14. Bhargava, P. M., and C. Heidelberger, C., *J. Am. Chem. Soc.*, *77*, 166 (1955).
15. Bhattacharya, S. N., and A. Ghose, *Anal. Chim. Acta*, *11*, 249 (1951).
16. Bighi, C., and G. Trabanelli, *Ann. chim.*, *Roma*, *45*, [2–3], 109 (1955); *Anal. Abstracts*, *2*, No. 2460 (1955).
17. Bishop, E. R., E. B. Kittredge, and J. H. Hildebrand, *J. Am. Chem. Soc.*, *44*, 135 (1922).
18. Block, R. J., E. L. Durrum, and G. Zweig, *A Manual of Paper Chromatography and Paper Electrophoresis*, 2nd ed., Academic Press, New York, 1955.
19. Blom, L., and L. Edelhausen, *Anal. Chim. Acta*, *13*, 120 (1955).
20. Bray, H. G., W. V. Thorpe, and K. White, *Biochem. J.*, *46*, 271 (1950).
21. Bray, H. G., W. V. Thorpe, and P. B. Wood, *ibid.*, *48*, 394 (1951).
22. Brice, B. A., M. L. Swain, S. F. Herb, P. L. Nichols, Jr., and R. W. Riemenschneider, *J. Am. Oil Chemists Soc.*, *29*, 279 (1952).
23. Brimley, R. C., and F. C. Barrett, *Practical Chromatography*, Reinhold, New York, 1953.
24. Brissaud, L., *Mém. poudres*, *28*, 43 (1938); *Chem. Abstracts*, *33*, 7559 (1939).
25. Brockmann, H., and E. Meyer, *Ber.*, *86*, 1514 (1953).
26. Brown, J. B., *J. Am. Oil Chemists Soc.*, *32*, 646 (1955).
27. Bryant, F., and B. T. Overell, *Nature*, *167*, 361 (1951).
28. Bryant, W. M. D., *J. Am. Chem. Soc.*, *60*, 1394 (1938).
29. Bryant, W. M. D., and J. Mitchell, Jr., *ibid.*, *60*, 2748 (1938).
30. Bueding, E., and H. W. Yale, *J. Biol. Chem.*, *193*, 411 (1951).
31. Bulen, W. A., J. E. Varner, and R. C. Burrell, *Anal. Chem.*, *24*, 187 (1952).
32. Burshtein, R. Kh., *Zavodskaya Lab.*, *6*, 825 (1937); *Chem. Abstracts*, *32*, 73 (1938).
33. Burton, H. S., *Nature*, *173*, 127 (1954).
34. Busch, H., R. B. Hurlbert, and V. R. Potter, *J. Biol. Chem.*, *196*, 717 (1952).
35. Caglioti, V., and G. Sartori, *Gazz. chim. ital.*, *66*, 741 (1936); *Chem. Abstracts*, *31*, 2956 (1937).
36. Carson, W. N., Jr., and R. Ko, *Anal. Chem.*, *23*, 1019 (1951).
37. Cason, J., and G. A. Gillies, *J. Org. Chem.*, *20*, 419 (1955).
38. Cavallini, D., N. Frontali, and G. Toschi, *Nature*, *163*, 568 (1949).

39. Cavallini, D., and N. Frontali, *Biochem. et Biophys. Acta, 13,* 439 (1954); *Chem. Abstracts, 48,* 6498 (1954).

40. Cheftel, R. I., R. Munier, and M. Macheboeuf, *Bull. soc. chim. biol., Paris, 35,* 1085 (1953).

41. Cheftel, R. I., R. Munier, and M. Macheboeuf, *ibid., 35,* 1091 (1953).

42. Clark, L. W., *J. Am. Chem. Soc., 77,* 6191 (1955).

43. Colthup, N. B., *J. Opt. Soc. Am., 40,* 397 (1950).

44. Consden, R., A. H. Gordon, and A. J. P. Martin, *Biochem. J., 38,* 224 (1944).

45. Corcoran, G. B., *Anal. Chem., 28,* 168 (1956).

45a. Cundiff, R. H., and P. C. Markunas, *ibid., 28,* 792 (1956).

46. Cuta, F., and Z. Kucera, *Chem. Listy, 47,* 1166 (1953); *Chem. Abstracts, 48,* 3850 (1954).

47. Dalin, G. A., and J. N. Haimsohn, *Anal. Chem., 20,* 470 (1948).

48. Dal Nogare, S., *ibid., 25,* 1874 (1953).

49. Davies, M. M., and G. B. B. M. Sutherland, *J. Chem. Phys., 6,* 755 (1938).

50. Deal, V. Z., and G. E. A. Wyld, *Anal. Chem., 27,* 47 (1955).

51. DeFord, D. D., J. N. Pitts, and C. J. Johns, *ibid., 23,* 938 (1951).

52. de Jonge, A. P., *Rec. trav. chim., 74,* 760 (1955).

53. Detoni, S., and D. Hadzi, *J. Chem. Soc., 1955,* 3163.

54. Donaldson, K. O., V. J. Tulane, and L. M. Marshall, *Anal. Chem., 24,* 185 (1952).

55. Duncan, R. E. B., and J. W. Porteous, *Analyst, 78,* 641 (1953).

56. Dustin, J. P., E. Schram, S. Moore, and E. J. Bigwood, *Bull. soc. chim. biol., Paris, 35,* 1137 (1953).

57. Elizer, L. H., *Ind. Eng. Chem., Anal. Ed., 14,* 635 (1942).

58. Elsden, S. R., *Biochem. J., 40,* 252 (1946).

59. Epstein, J. H., H. A. Sober, and S. D. Silver, *Anal. Chem., 19,* 675 (1947).

60. Erler, K., *Z. anal. Chem., 131,* 106 (1950).

60a. Ferguson, H. P., *Anal. Chem., 22,* 289 (1950).

61. Fewster, M. E., and D. A. Hall, *Nature, 168,* 78 (1951).

62. Flett, M. St. C., *J. Chem. Soc., 1951,* 962.

63. Fleury, P. F., *Chim. anal., 35,* 197 (1953).

64. Folin, O., and F. F. Flanders, *J. Am. Chem. Soc., 34,* 774 (1912).

65. Forziati, F. H., J. W. Rowen, and E. K. Plyler, *J. Research Natl. Bur. Standards, 46,* 288 (1951).

66. Freeman, N. K., *J. Am. Chem. Soc., 75,* 1859 (1953).

67. Frehden, O., and K. Fürst, *Mikrochemie, 25,* 256 (1938).

68. Fritz, J. S., *Anal. Chem., 24,* 306 (1952).

69. Fritz, J. S., and R. T. Keen, *ibid., 25,* 179 (1953).

70. Fritz, J. S., and N. M. Lisicki, *ibid., 23,* 589 (1951).

71. Fuchs, F., *Monatsh., 9,* 1132, 1143 (1888); *11,* 363 (1890).

72. Furman, N. H., *Anal. Chem., 14,* 367 (1942); *22,* 33 (1950); *26,* 84 (1954).

73. Furman, N. H., ed., *Scott's Standard Methods of Chemical Analysis,* 5th ed., Vol. 2, Van Nostrand, New York, 1939, p. 2246.

74. Glaser, R. J., and C. R. Estee, *Proc. S. Dakota Acad. Sci., 29,* 75 (1950); *Chem. Abstracts, 47,* 8586 (1953).

75. Goddu, R. F., and D. N. Hume, *Anal. Chem., 26,* 1679 (1954).

76. Goepfert, G. J., *Biochem. J., 34,* 1012 (1940).

77. Gran, G., *Acta Chem. Scand., 4,* 559 (1950).

78. Gran, G., and B. Althin, *Ibid.*, *4*, 967 (1950).
79. Grant, W. M., *Anal. Chem.*, *20*, 267 (1948).
80. Grove, J. F., and H. A. Willis, *J. Chem. Soc.*, *1951*, 877.
81. Hadzi, D., and N. Sheppard, *Proc. Royal Soc. (London)*, *A216*, 247 (1953).
82. Hanak, A., and K. Kürschner, *Z. Untersuch. Lebensm.*, *60*, 278 (1930).
83. Hall, N. F., *J. Am. Chem. Soc.*, *52*, 5115 (1930).
84. Hall, N. F., and J. B. Conant, *ibid.*, *49*, 3047 (1927).
85. Hall, N. F., and T. H. Werner, *ibid.*, *50*, 2367 (1928).
86. Hardy, T. L., D. O. Holland, and J. H. C. Nayler, *Anal. Chem.*, *27*, 971 (1955).
86a. Harlow, G. A., C. M. Noble, and G. E. A. Wyld, *ibid.*, *28*, 784 (1956).
86b. Harlow, G. A., C. M. Noble, and G. E. A. Wyld, *ibid.*, *28*, 787 (1956).
87. Harris, J. T., Jr., and M. E. Hobbs, *J. Am. Chem. Soc.*, *76*, 1419 (1954).
88. Heymann, E., and G. Robinov, *Trans. Faraday Soc.*, *38*, 209 (1942).
89. Hill, U. T., *Ind. Eng. Chem., Anal. Ed.*, *18*, 317 (1946).
90. Hillig, F., *J. Assoc. Official Agr. Chem.*, *34*, 782 (1951).
91. Horsey, L. H., *Azeotropic Data*, American Chemical Society, Washington, D. C., 1952.
92. Houston, D. F., and W. A. Van Sandt, *Ind. Eng. Chem., Anal. Ed.*, *18*, 538 (1946).
93. Hubacher, M. H., *Anal. Chem.*, *21*, 945 (1949).
94. Hunter, W. H., and J. D. Edwards, *J. Am. Chem. Soc.*, *35*, 452 (1913).
95. Isherwood, F. A., and D. H. Cruickshank, *Nature*, *173*, 121 (1954).
96. Isherwood, F. A., and C. S. Hanes, *Biochem. J.*, *55*, 824 (1953).
97. Ishidate, M., and M. Masui, *Pharm. Bull., Japan*, *2*, [1], 50 (1954); *Anal. Abstracts*, *2*, abstract 100 (1955).
98. Jaffé, H. H., *J. Am. Chem. Soc.*, *77*, 4451 (1955).
99. James, A. T., *Chem. & Process Eng.*, *36*, 95 (1955).
100. James, A. T., and A. J. P. Martin, *Analyst*, *77*, 915 (1952).
101. James, A. T., and A. J. P. Martin, *Biochem. J.*, *48*, 7 (1951).
102. James, A. T., and A. J. P. Martin, *ibid.*, *50*, 679 (1952).
103. James, A. T., and A. J. P. Martin, *Brit. Med. Bull.*, *10*, No. 3, 170 (1954).
104. Jensen, F. W., and A. L. Parrack, *Anal. Chem.*, *18*, 595 (1946).
105. Jones, R. N., A. F. McKay, and R. G. Sinclair, *J. Am. Chem. Soc.*, *74*, 2575 (1952).
106. Kalbe, H., *Z. physiol. Chem.*, *297*, 19 (1954).
107. Kamath, N. R., and V. B. Mainkar, *Anal. Chem.*, *22*, 724 (1950).
108. Katz, M., and R. A. Glenn, *ibid.*, *24*, 1157 (1952).
109. Kaufmann, H. P., and J. Budwig, *Fette u. Seifen*, *53*, 69, 253, 390, 408 (1951).
110. Kaufmann, H. P., and W. H. Nitsch, *ibid.*, *56*, 154 (1954).
111. Kaufmann, H. P., and W. H. Nitsch, *ibid.*, *57*, 473 (1955).
112. Kawamura, F., K. Momoki, and S. Suzuki, *Japan Analyst*, *3*, 29 (1954); *Chem. Abstracts*, *48*, 6914 (1954).
113. Kawerau, E., and T. Wieland, *Nature*, *168*, 77 (1951).
114. Kelley, H. M., *Anal. Chem.*, *23*, 1081 (1951).
115. Kirk, M. M., *Ind. Eng. Chem., Anal. Ed.*, *13*, 625 (1941).
116. Kirrmann, A., and N. Duane-Dubois, *Compt. rend.*, *236*, 1361 (1953).
117. Koepsell, H. J., and E. S. Sharpe, *Arch. Biochem. Biophys.*, *38*, 443 (1952).
118. Kolthoff, I. M., *Anal. Chem.*, *8*, 237 (1936); *22*, 65 (1950).
119. Kolthoff, I. M., and J. J. Lingane, *Polarography*, 2nd ed., 2 vols., Interscience, New York-London, 1952.

120. Kolthoff, I. M., and E. B. Sandell, *Textbook of Quantitative Inorganic Analysis*, 3rd ed., Macmillan, New York, 1952, p. 587.
121. Kolthoff, I. M., and V. A. Stenger, *Volumetric Analysis*, Vol. II, Interscience, New York-London, 1947, pp. 56–7.
122. Kuelemans, A. I. M., A. Kwantes, and P. Zaal, *Anal. Chim. Acta, 13*, 357 (1955).
123. Kunin, R., and R. J. Myers, *J. Am. Chem. Soc., 69*, 2874 (1947).
124. Kunin, R., and R. J. Myers, *Ion Exchange Resins*, Wiley, New York, 1950.
125. Lederer, E., and M. Lederer, *Chromatography*, Elsevier, Amsterdam-New York, 1953.
126. Lingane, J. J., *Electroanalytical Chemistry*, Interscience, New York-London, 1953.
127. Lingane, J. J., *Anal. Chim. Acta, 11*, 283 (1954).
128. Loebl, H., G. Stein, and J. Weiss, *J. Chem. Soc., 1951*, 405.
129. Long, C., *Biochem. J., 36*, 807 (1942).
130. Lykken, L., P. Porter, H. D. Ruliffson, and F. D. Tuemmler, *Ind. Eng. Chem., Anal. Ed., 16*, 219 (1944).
131. Mader, W. J., and H. A. Frediani, *Anal. Chem., 20*, 1199 (1948).
132. Malm, C. J., G. F. Nadeau, and L. B. Genung, *Ind. Eng. Chem., Anal. Ed., 14*, 292 (1942).
133. Markunas, P. C., and J. A. Riddick, *Anal. Chem., 23*, 337 (1951).
134. Maron, S. H., I. N. Ulevitch, and M. E. Elder, *ibid., 24*, 1068 (1952).
135. Martin, A. J. P., and R. L. M. Synge, *Biochem. J., 35*, 1358 (1941).
136. Marvel, C. S., and R. D. Rands, *J. Am. Chem. Soc., 72*, 2642 (1950).
137. Marvel, C. S., and J. C. Richards, *Anal. Chem., 21*, 1480 (1949).
138. Matheson, H., H. S. Isbell, and E. R. Smith, *J. Research Natl. Bur. Standards, 28*, 95 (1942).
139. McClure, J. H., T. M. Roder, and R. H. Kinsey, *Anal. Chem., 27*, 1599 (1955).
140. McCready, R. M., H. S. Swenson, and W. D. Maclay, *ibid., 18*, 290 (1946).
141. McNair, J. B., *J. Am. Chem. Soc., 54*, 3249 (1932).
142. Meesook, B. B., and C. B. Purves, *Paper Trade J., 123*, 35 (1946).
143. Meites, L., and T. Meites, *Anal. Chem., 28*, 103 (1956).
144. Meyer, H., and E. Riklis, *Nature, 172*, 543 (1953).
145. Micheel, F., and P. Albers, *Mikrochim. Acta, 1954*, 489.
146. Miner, R. W., ed., "Ion Exchange Resins in Medicine and Biological Research," *Ann. N. Y. Acad. Sci., 57*, Art. 3, 61–324 (1953).
147. Mitchell, J., Jr., *Anal. Chem., 21*, 448 (1949).
148. Mitchell, J., Jr., and B. A. Montague, unpublished results.
149. Mitchell, J., Jr., and D. M. Smith, *Aquametry*, Interscience, New York-London, 1948, p. 297 ff.
150. Mitchell, J., Jr., and D. M. Smith, *Anal. Chem., 22*, 746 (1950).
151. Mitchell, J., Jr., D. M. Smith, and W. M. D. Bryant, *J. Am. Chem. Soc., 62*, 4 (1940).
152. Mitchell, J., Jr., and A. L. Ryland, paper presented at microchemical meeting Vienna, Austria, July 12–17, 1955. *Mikrochim. Acta, 1-6*, 422 (1956).
153. Moore, S., and W. H. Stein, *J. Biol. Chem., 176*, 367 (1948).
154. Moore, S., and W. H. Stein, *ibid., 192*, 663 (1951).
155. Moretti, J., and R. I. Cheftel, *Bull. soc. chim. biol., 37*, 699 (1955).
156. Moss, M. L., J. H. Elliott, and R. T. Hall, *Anal. Chem., 20*, 784 (1948).
157. Moyle, V., E. Baldwin, and R. Scarisbrick, *Biochem. J., 43*, 308 (1948).

158. Nachod, F. C., ed., *Ion Exchange: Theory and Application*, Academic Press, New York, 1949.
159. Nadeau, G. F., and L. E. Branchen, L. E., *J. Am. Chem. Soc.*, *57*, 1363 (1935).
160. Nair, J. H., III, *Anal. Chem.*, *25*, 1912 (1953).
161. Neale, S. M., and W. A. Stringfellow, *Trans. Faraday Soc.*, *33*, 881 (1937).
162. Nerheim, A. G., and C. R. Estee, *Univ. S. Dakota Bull.*, *31*, 111 (1952); *Chem. Abstracts*, *48*, 8675 (1954).
163. Nichols, M. L., and B. H. Kindt, *Anal. Chem.*, *22*, 785 (1950).
164. Nicolet, B. H., and L. D. Shinn, *J. Biol. Chem.*, *139*, 687 (1941).
165. O'Connor, R. T., *J. Am. Oil Chemists Soc.*, *32*, 616 (1955).
166. O'Connor, R. T., *ibid.*, *32*, 624 (1955).
167. Ono, S., and T. Hayashi, *Bull. Chem. Soc. Japan*, *26*, 268 (1953).
168. Osburn, O. L., H. G. Wood, and C. H. Werkman, *Ind. Eng. Chem., Anal. Ed.*, *5*, 247 (1933).
169. Pagel, H. A., and F. W. McLafferty, *Anal. Chem.*, *20*, 272 (1948).
170. Palit, S. R., *ibid.*, *18*, 246 (1946).
171. Patton, H. W., J. S. Lewis, and W. I. Kaye, *ibid.*, *27*, 170 (1955).
172. Perila, O., *Acta Chem. Scand.*, *9*, 1231 (1955).
173. Peterson, M. H., and M. J. Johnson, *J. Biol. Chem.*, *174*, 775 (1948).
174. Pifer, C. W., E. G. Wollish, and M. Schmall, *Anal. Chem.*, *25*, 310 (1953).
175. Pohl, H. A., *ibid.*, *26*, 1614 (1954).
176. Pope, C. G., and M. F. Stevens, *Biochem. J.*, *33*, 1070 (1939).
177. Radell, J., and E. T. Donahue, *Anal. Chem.*, *26*, 590 (1954).
178. Ramsey, L. L., and W. I. Patterson, *J. Assoc. Official Agr. Chem.*, *31*, 139 (1948).
179. Reichl, E. R., and J. E. Löffler, *Mikrochim. Acta*, *1954*, 226.
180. Reid, J. D., and H. D. Weihe, *Ind. Eng. Chem., Anal. Ed.*, *10*, 271 (1938).
181. Reindel, F., and W. Hoppe, *Ber.*, *87*, 1103 (1954).
182. Roberts, E. J., *Anal. Chem.*, *19*, 616 (1947).
183. Roberts, E. J., and J. A. Ambler, *ibid.*, *19*, 118 (1947).
184. Roberts, E. R., *Trans. Faraday Soc.*, *37*, 353 (1941).
185. Roberts, J. D., and C. M. Regan, *Anal. Chem.*, *24*, 360 (1952).
186. Roland, J. F., Jr., and A. M. Gross, *ibid.*, *26*, 502 (1954).
187. Ruehle, A. E., *Ind. Eng. Chem., Anal. Ed.*, *10*, 130 (1938).
188. Ruziczka, K., *Z. anal. Chem.*, *126*, 94 (1943).
189. Ruziczka, W., *Chim. Anal.*, *32*, 33 (1950).
190. Safranski, L. W., and E. Segal, unpublished work.
191. Samson, S., and H. Zschuppe, *Chem. Weekblad*, *50*, 341 (1954).
192. Samuelson, O., *Ion Exchangers in Analytical Chemistry*, Wiley, New York, 1953.
193. Sandin, R. B., M. Kulka, and D. W. Woolley, *Ind. Eng. Chem., Anal. Ed.*, *8*, 355 (1936).
194. Schaefgen, J. R., and P. J. Flory, *J. Am. Chem. Soc.*, *72*, 689 (1950).
195. Schicktanz, S. T., W. I. Steele, and A. C. Blaisdell, *Ind. Eng. Chem., Anal. Ed.*, *12*, 320 (1940).
196. Schlenker, F. S., *Anal. Chem.*, *19*, 471 (1947).
197. Schnell, H., *Makromol. Chem.*, *2*, 172 (1948).
198. Schroeder, W. A., L. M. Kay and R. S. Mills, *Anal. Chem.*, *22*, 760 (1950).
199. Schwaer, L., *Chem. Listy*, *26*, 485 (1932); *Chem. Abstracts*, *27*, 707 (1933).

200. Schwaer, L., *Collection Czech. Chem. Commun.*, *7*, 326 (1935); *Chem. Abstracts*, *29*, 7826 (1935).
201. Seligson, G., and B. Shapiro, *Anal. Chem.*, *24*, 754 (1952).
202. Semerano, G., *Mikrochemie*, *24*, 10 (1938).
203. Semerano, G., and L. Sartori, *ibid.*, *24*, 130 (1948).
204. Shepard, A. F., N. R. Winslow, and J. R. Johnson, *J. Am. Chem. Soc.*, *52*, 2083 (1930).
205. Shreve, O. D., M. R. Heether, H. B. Knight, and D. Swern, *Anal. Chem.*, *22*, 1261 (1950).
206. Shreve, O. D., M. R. Heether, H. B. Knight, and D. Swern, *ibid.*, *22*, 1498 (1950).
207. Sideri, C. N., and A. Osol, *J. Am. Pharm. Assoc.*, *42*, 586 (1953).
208. Siggia, S., and N. A. Floramo, *Anal. Chem.*, *25*, 797 (1953).
209. Silk, M. H., and H. H. Hahn, *Biochem. J.*, *56*, 406 (1954).
210. Silverman, L., *Chemist Analyst*, *36*, 57 (1947).
211. Sinclair, R. G., A. F. McKay, G. S. Myers, and R. N. Jones, *J. Am. Chem. Soc.*, *74*, 2578 (1952).
212. Singh, B., and S. Singh, *J. Indian Chem. Soc.*, *16*, 343 (1939).
213. Slagle, F. B., and E. Ott, *J. Am. Chem. Soc.*, *55*, 4404 (1933).
214. Smith, E. L., *Biochem. J.*, *36*, 22 (1942).
215. Smith, F., and D. Spriesterbach, *Nature*, *174*, 466 (1954).
216. Sookne, A. M., and M. Harris, *J. Research Natl. Bureau Standards*, *26*, 205 (1941).
217. Stark, J. B., A. E. Goodban, and H. S. Owens, *Ind. Eng. Chem.*, *43*, 603 (1951).
218. Swann, M. H., *Anal. Chem.*, *21*, 1448 (1949).
219. Synge, R. L. M., *Analyst*, *71*, 256 (1946).
220. Takahashi, T., K. Kimoto, and H. Sakurai, "Organic Microanalysis by Cerimetry," *Report of Institute of Industrial Science, Univ. of Tokyo*, *5*, No. 6 (Nov. 1955).
221. Thompson, A. R., *Australian J. Sci. Res.*, *B4*, 180 (1951).
222. Tolliday, J. D., G. W. H. Thompson, and G. Forman, *J. Soc. Leather Trades' Chemists*, *32*, 291 (1948); *34*, 221 (1950).
223. Tsai, K. R., and Y. Fu, *Anal. Chem.*, *21*, 818 (1949).
224. Ultee, A. J., Jr., and J. Hartel, *ibid.*, *27*, 557 (1955).
225. *Ultraviolet Spectral Data*, American Petroleum Institute Research Project 44, Carnegie Institute of Technology, Pittsburgh, Pennsylvania.
226. Van de Kamer, J. H., K. W. Gerritsma, and E. J. Wansink, *Biochem. J.*, *61*, 174 (1955).
227. Van Slyke, D. D., and R. T. Dillon, *Compt. rend. trav. lab. Carlsberg, Ser. chim.*, *22*, 480 (1938).
228. Van Slyke, D. D., R. T. Dillon, D. A. MacFadyen, and P. Hamilton, *J. Biol. Chem.*, *141*, 627 (1941).
229. Van Slyke, D. D., and J. Folch, *ibid.*, *136*, 509 (1940).
230. Van Slyke, D. D., A. Hiller, and D. A. MacFadyen, *ibid.*, *141*, 681 (1941).
231. Van Slyke, D. D., D. A. MacFadyen, and P. Hamilton, *ibid.*, *141*, 671 (1941).
232. von Sydow, E., *Acta Chem. Scand.*, *9*, 1119 (1955).
233. Wagner, H., L. Abisch, and K. Bernhard, *Helv. Chim. Acta*, *38*, 1536 (1955).
234. Waltz, J. E., and G. B. Taylor, *Anal. Chem.*, *19*, 448 (1947).
235. Warshowsky, B., and M. W. Rice, *ibid.*, *20*, 341 (1948).
236. Webster, H. L., and A. Robertson, *Analyst*, *80*, 616 (1955).

237. Wegmann, R., P. F. Ceccaldi, and J. Biez, *Fette u. Seifen, 56*, 159 (1954).
238. Wenger, P. E., D. Monnier, and S. Faraggi, *Anal. Chim. Acta, 13*, 89 (1955).
239. Willard, H. H., and N. H. Furman, *Elementary Quantitative Analysis*, Van Nostrand, New York, 1940, p. 120.
240. Willard, H. H., and P. Young, *J. Am. Chem. Soc., 52*, 132 (1930).
241. Winter, H., *Z. Lebens.-Untersuch., 99*, 34 (1954); *Anal. Abstracts, 2*, abstract 3439 (1955).
242. Wiseblatt, L., and W. B. McConnell, *Can. J. Chem., 33*, 1452 (1955).
243. Wolff, J. P., *Anal. Chim. Acta, 1*, 90 (1947); *Ann. chim., 8*, (12), 201 (1953).
244. Woodward, C. C., and G. S. Rabideau, *Anal. Chem., 26*, 248 (1954).
245. Yackel, E. C., and W. O. Kenyon, *J. Am. Chem. Soc., 64*, 121 (1942).
246. Yemm, E. W., and E. C. Cocking, *Analyst, 80*, 209 (1955).
247. Zbinovsky, V., and R. H. Burris, *Anal. Chem., 26*, 208 (1954).

Determination of
ACID ANHYDRIDES

C. W. HAMMOND, *E. I. du Pont de Nemours & Co., Inc.*

I. INTRODUCTION

Acid anhydrides are hydrolyzed readily to their parent acids in the presence of basic or acidic catalysts. Therefore, most procedures for determining organic acids may be used in analyses for anhydrides, the simplest being direct titration with aqueous alkali or with sodium methylate in a nonaqueous system. Berger, Sela, and Katchelski (5) used the latter for titrations of N-carboxy-α-amino acid anhydrides. The sample was dissolved in a neutral or basic solvent such as benzene, dimethyl formamide, or butylamine and titrated with sodium methylate in methanol–benzene to the thymol blue end point (see pages 22 and 28 in the chapter in this volume on determination of organic acids). Usually, however, samples of anhydrides also contain significant percentages of free acids. Consequently, general methods of analysis must provide a means for determining the anhydride function, $-C(=O)OC(=O)-$, in the presence of the acid function, $-C(=O)OH$.

A majority of the few reported methods for determining anhydrides are volumetric in nature. They are based on (a) hydrolysis followed by titration of the acid, (b) a combination of hydrolysis with esterification or anilide formation and acidimetric titration, (c) amide formation followed by titration of excess base, and (d) hydrolysis with subsequent titration of excess water. Of the methods available, these are the only ones which have been generally applied to any diverse number of anhydrides; details of several procedures will be included in this chapter.

Several other interesting methods of a semiphysical nature have been described, all more or less specifically devised for acetic anhydride but which might be applicable to analyses for other anhydrides. These include gasometric, colorimetric, and solvent volume increase methods. Of these the thermometric methods based on acid catalyzed hydrolysis appear to offer the greatest potential for application to anhydrides other than acetic anhydride. Most of the semiphysical procedures are quite rapid and for specific systems are well suited for control analyses.

Infrared is one of few instrumental techniques which can be applied for the specific identification of the anhydride functional group. Quantitative methods employing infrared can be developed for specific anhydrides.

A colorimetric method has been described for determinations of small amounts of anhydrides. In this case the anhydride is converted to a hydroxamic acid, which in turn forms a highly colored chelate complex with ferric ions. Other instrumental techniques can be applied in special cases but for the most part methods must be based on other functions in the anhydride molecule. For further details the reader is referred to the chapter on determination of acids and to the chapter on microdetermination of carboxyl groups which appeared in Volume II of this series.

With few exceptions, procedures for determining acid anhydrides can also be used for determinations of acyl halides.

II. ACIDIMETRIC METHODS

1. Hydrolysis

In general the rate of reaction of anhydrides with water is quite slow unless catalyzed by basic or strongly acidic substances. With few exceptions, therefore, methods employing hydrolysis alone or in combination with a second reaction employ a suitable catalyst, e. g.:

$$\begin{array}{c} \text{O} \\ \parallel \\ \text{RC} \\ \diagdown \\ \text{O} + \text{H}_2\text{O} \xrightarrow{\text{Na}^+} 2\text{RC}\text{—OH} \\ \diagup \\ \text{RC} \\ \parallel \\ \text{O} \end{array} \tag{1}$$

Of course, when using sodium ions as catalyst the sodium salt of the acid results. In all cases the presence of free acid in the anhydride must be taken into account, and suitable correction be made for it.

One of the early methods devised for the analysis of anhydrides, and one which is still of considerable use, involves the decomposition of the anhydride with excess standard barium hydroxide or sodium hydroxide under reflux conditions (46).

Procedure (46). Into a 300 ml. erlenmeyer flask fitted with a ground joint, about 5 meq. of the anhydride is weighed and 100 ml. of standardized 0.1 N Ba(OH)$_2$ or carbonate-free NaOH is added. The flask is attached to a reflux condenser which has an efficient carbon dioxide trap on the top, and refluxed until all of the anhydride is hydrolyzed. The mixture is cooled to room temperature and the excess caustic titrated with 0.1 N HCl using phenolphthalein as indicator. The method assumes that no other weighable material will be in the sample except anhydride and the corresponding acid.

Only one titration is made by this method and the free acid is accounted for by calculation.

Calculation. Let x represent the weight of anhydride present in the sample and y represent the weight of acid present in the sample, then:

$$x + y = p, \text{ the sample weight}$$

and:

$$mx + y = q, \text{ the total weight of acid found by titration}$$

where:

$$m = \frac{2 \times \text{mol. wt. of acid}}{\text{mol. wt. of anhydride}}$$

$$x = \frac{q - p}{m - 1} \quad \text{and} \quad \frac{100x}{p} = \% \text{ anhydride}$$

Variations of this method as applied to acetic anhydride were given by Reclaire (30) and Radcliffe and Mendofski (28), who depended on hydrolysis by boiling with water alone followed by titration of the resulting acid.

While such single titration methods have utility for process control where speed and simplicity are of prime interest, their precision and accuracy, particularly where either component is quite small, are not as good as other methods of analysis.

2. Reaction with Aniline

Another approach to the determination of anhydrides is based on formation of anilides:

$$(RCO)_2O + C_6H_5 \cdot NH_2 \longrightarrow C_6H_5 \cdot NHCOR + RCOOH \qquad (2)$$

In early methods employing this reaction the acid formed was titrated acidimetrically. For example, Menshukin and Vasilieff (22) heated about 2 grams of sample with about 3 grams of aniline and then titrated the resulting acid with standard caustic solution. This method was limited to essentially pure anhydrides since no means was provided for correcting for free acid originally present in the sample. In addition under the conditions of analysis aniline also reacted with some of the free acid to form anilide:

$$RCOOH + C_6H_5 \cdot NH_2 \longrightarrow C_6H_5 \cdot NHCOR + H_2O \qquad (3)$$

Where only the single titration was employed results would tend to be low.

Kappelmeier and van Goor (19) also employed the one-step acidimetric method for analyses of essentially pure anhydrides of dibasic acids. They proposed the term "anilic acid number" for use in expressing relative purity of these anhydrides. In their method about 5 millimoles of the anhydride was dissolved in 10 milliliters of acetone and 5 milliliters of purified aniline was added. With anhydrides such as phthalic and maleic the mixtures were allowed to stand for thirty minutes at room temperature. Higher molecular weight anhydrides required up to thirty minutes reflux before reaction was complete. Total acidity after reaction was determined by titration with standardized 0.5 N alcoholic potassium hydroxide. These authors (19) reported essentially quantitative results on nearly pure samples of the following anhydrides: succinic, maleic, addition products of maleic with linseed oil, phthalic, and tetrachlorophthalic.

Direct analyses for anhydrides without interference from free acids have been made by titration of excess aniline rather than determination of total acidity. Through titration with a strong acid aniline combined as the weakly associated acid salt can be titrated quantitatively. Malm and Nadeau (21) employed this method for assaying the acetic anhydride content of cellulose esterification baths. They treated the sample with a standard anhydrous solution of aniline in glacial acetic acid and then determined excess aniline by titration with a strong mineral acid.

Siggia and Hanna (38) extended this procedure in applying it to other anhydrides. They found that an ethylene glycol–isopropanol system provided a better environment than acetic acid for detecting the end point in the titration for excess aniline. The lower anhydrides reacted quantitatively with purified aniline at room temperature; others required heating at 100°C.

Procedure (37,38). The sample, containing about 4 millimoles of anhydride, is weighed into a test tube (or condenser flask if heat is required to effect quantitative reaction). About 0.9 g. (9.5–10 millimoles) of purified aniline is added dropwise from a weighing buret. The amount of aniline added is determined accurately by weighing the buret before and after delivery into the tube containing the sample. The solution is allowed to stand 5 minutes at room temperature or heated in a water bath at 98–100°C. depending on the nature of the anhydride (see Table I). After reaction is complete the mixture is transferred quantitatively to a 150 ml. beaker with ethylene glycol–isopropanol (1 + 1) and diluted to about 50 ml. with this solvent. Then the resulting solution is titrated potentiometrically with 0.2 N hydrochloric acid (19 ml. concentrated HCl diluted to 1 liter with the glycol–isopropanol solution), using glass-calomel electrodes. A blank is run on an accurately weighed portion, about 0.4 g., of the aniline.

Calculation. This titer is calculated to that required to titrate the weight of aniline added to the sample of anhydride. The difference in millimoles between the calculated blank titer and the sample titer is equivalent to the millimoles of anhydride in the sample.

TABLE I

Analytical Data for Anhydrides by Aniline Method

| Anhydride | Reaction conditions | | Anhydride found, wt. %[a] | Acid-anhydride mix. | |
	Time, min.	Temp., °C.		Wt. % anhydride Added	Found
Acetic............	5	Room	(5) 99.7–100.2	77.8	77.5
Propionic..........	5	Room	(3) 99.5–100.1	60.9	60.6
Butyric............	5	Room	(2) 99.8–100.1	87.2	86.5
Maleic............	15	Room	(4) 99.4– 99.6	91.0	90.7
Phthalic..........	15	100	(3) 99.5–100.5	50.8	50.3
Camphoric........	45	100	(3) 100.0–100.3	87.5	88.0

[a] Figures in parentheses indicate number of individual determinations.

Results obtained on purified anhydrides and acid-anhydride mixtures, together with conditions, are noted in Table I (37,38).

Where applicable this one-step method is quite reliable. It requires a knowledge of the nature of the anhydride, however, since there is some tendency for the aniline to react with free acid according to equation (3), leading to high results. Maleic anhydride with aniline allowed to stand 90 minutes at room temperature or 15 minutes at 100°C. gave results of 100.3 and 110.4%, respectively. Succinic anhydride could not be analyzed by this method because of interference from the acid. Conditions for conversion of succinic anhydride to the anilide were sufficiently drastic to lead to partial reaction of the free acid.

3. Reaction with Morpholine

Morpholine, like aniline, has been recommended for use as a reagent in a direct method for determining acid anhydrides. A method employing morpholine was described by Hogsett, Kacy, and Johnson (17) for estimating chrysanthemum acid anhydride plus the acid chloride in allethrin, a synthetic insecticide. More recently Johnson and Funk (18) extended the method to analyses for other anhydrides. A measured excess of morpholine in methanol solution is added to the sample. The morpholine reacts mole for mole with the anhydride producing one mole each of amide and acid. After reaction is complete the excess base is determined by titration with standard methanolic hydrochloric acid to the methyl yellow–methylene blue end point. Most anhydrides studied reacted quantitatively with morpholine in five minutes at room temperature.

The method was found suitable for use over a wide range of concentrations of anhydride. It was not applicable, however, to anhydrides where the acids have ionization constants in water greater than 2×10^{-2}, e. g., maleic and citraconic anhydrides. The free acids are acidic to the indicator in the alcohol system. Accuracy and precision of the method are about 0.2% for samples containing high concentrations of anhydride.

Procedure (18). Precisely 50 ml. of 0.5 N morpholine reagent (44 ml. redistilled morpholine diluted to 1 liter with methanol) is delivered to a 250 ml. glass-stoppered flask. The reagent is most conveniently stored in a bottle fitted with a 50 ml. delivery pipet and protected from carbon dioxide and moisture. The sample, containing up to 20 meq. of anhydride, is added and the flask swirled to effect solution. After standing at room temperature for five minutes or more (see Table II), the solution is titrated with 0.5 N hydrochloric acid in methanol (84 ml. 6 N HCl diluted to 1 liter with methanol) to the methyl yellow–methylene blue end point represented by a change in color from green to amber. The mixed indicator is prepared by dissolving 1.0 g. of methyl yellow (p-dimethylaminoazobenzene) and 0.1 g. of methylene blue in 125 ml. of methanol.

Calculation. The difference in titer between a blank and the sample is a measure of anhydride.

The morpholine procedure appears to have an advantage over the previously described aniline method since the former is based on volumetric delivery of the reagent and visual titration. Where desirable the method can be scaled down to analyze for small quantities of anhydrides. For example, 10 ml. samples of acetic acid, containing 0.06 and 0.01% acetic anhydride, respectively, were treated with 50 ml. of 0.02 N morpholine in methanol. Excess morpholine was determined by titration with 0.1 N methanolic hydrochloric acid.

Results on several anhydrides, using 0.5 N reagents, are given in Table II (18). With the exception of 2-ethylhexanoic anhydride, which required a minimum of 30 minutes reaction time, the anhydrides listed reacted quantitatively with morpholine in 5 minutes at room temperature.

TABLE II

Analytical Data for Anhydrides by Morpholine Method

Anhydride	Anhydride found, wt. %[a]	Acid calc., wt. %	Total %
Acetic..................	(5) 99.7 ± 0.1	0.2	99.9
Propionic..............	(3) 99.5 ± 0.1	0.5	100.0
Butyric................	(4) 98.0 ± 0.2	1.9	99.9
2-Ethylhexanoic[b]........	(6) 98.9 ± 0.2	0.1	99.0
Succinic...............	(5) 96.9 ± 0.1	2.4	99.3
Glutaric...............	(3) 97.1 ± 0.1	3.4	100.5
Phthalic...............	(3) 99.6 ± 0.1	0.3	99.9
Chrysanthemum..........	(2) 98.6 ± 0.1	0.5	99.1

[a] Figures in parentheses represent number of individual determinations.
[b] Required 30 minutes reaction time; all others, 5 minutes.

4. Hydrolysis. Esterification

The most widely applicable methods for the determination of anhydrides are based on two separate titrations. One employs hydrolysis according to equation (1). The second depends on esterification or anilide formation. The former is based on the reaction:

$$(RCO)_2O + NaOCH_3 \longrightarrow RCOOCH_3 + RCOONa \qquad (4)$$

or:

$$(RCO)_2O + CH_3OH \longrightarrow RCOOCH_3 + RCOOH \qquad (5)$$

It is apparent that the difference in titer for acidity between reaction (1) and reaction (4) or (5) is equivalent to anhydride content of a sample. Free acids, of course, do not interfere since they will titrate mole for mole with caustic by all of these reactions.

One of the most versatile of the acidimetric procedures was described by Smith and Bryant (40). In their method one portion of the sample is titrated directly at room temperature with sodium methylate in methanol according to equation (4). A second portion of the sample is hydrolyzed with water, using pyridine as catalyst, and total acidity is determined by titration with aqueous caustic at room temperature. The addition of large amounts of pyridine just before titration greatly accelerates the hydrolysis of the anhydride. In most cases the hydrolysis is almost instantaneous, thus obviating the alkaline or neutral aqueous refluxing required by other methods. The measure of anhydride then becomes the equivalent difference between the titer for total acid and that for anhydride. The initial presence of free acids is without effect upon the determination.

Procedure (40). (*1*) The sample, containing up to 40 millimoles of anhydride plus acid, is weighed into a dry glass-stoppered 250 ml. volumetric or 300 ml. erlenmeyer flask. If the sample is a solid, 20–30 ml. of dry methanol or acetone is added, warming if necessary to complete solution. The solution is then titrated directly at room temperature with standardized 0.5 *N* sodium methylate in methanol to the phenolphthalein or thymol blue end point. (The coefficient of cubical expansion of methanol is considerably higher than that of water. Therefore, the actual normality of the methylate reagent must be known at the temperature at which the titration is made.) The titer is a measure of the millimoles of anhydride plus any free acid present in the sample.

(*2*) A second sample, containing up to 40 meq. of anhydride plus acid (1 millimole anhydride = 2 milliequivalents), is weighed into a glass-stoppered flask. Then 25 ml. each of pyridine and water are added and the solution titrated immediately with standardized 0.5 *N* aqueous sodium hydroxide to the same end point used in the first titration. (For this titration indicator in dioxane solution is recommended since alcohol might react with the anhydride. In the methylate titration either alcohol or dioxane can be used safely as solvent for the indicator.)

Calculation. The anhydride content is measured by the difference between the two titers expressed in milliequivalents per gram of sample. From part *1:*

$$\text{anhydride} + \text{acid, meq./g.} = \frac{\text{ml.} \times N \text{ NaOCH}_3}{\text{g. sample}} = a$$

From part *2:*

$$\text{total acidity, meq./g.} = \frac{\text{ml.} \times N \text{ NaOH}}{\text{g. sample}} = b$$

$$\text{anhydride, wt. \%} = (b - a) \times \text{M.W.}$$

Free acidity originally present in the sample also can be estimated from $b - (b - a)$ or $a - 2(b - a)$. Since this is derived from the difference between two large numbers, the accuracy and precision are poor for determinations of less than one per cent of free acid. Similarly samples having low anhydride contents are subject to relatively high errors.

A selected group of anhydrides with widely different structures were chosen for evaluation (40).   The results gave an average precision of 0.2% and in the case of glutaric, phthalic, and camphoric anhydrides, which were of high purity, gave an accuracy of the same value.   All of the compounds were titrated at room temperature with the exception of camphoric anhydride.   Due to steric hindrance arising from the presence of an adjacent tertiary carbon atom, the latter compound required thirty minutes of heating with excess reagent followed by back titration with standard acid. Table III summarizes the data obtained for this series of compounds and includes approximate free acidity values calculated by difference between titers.

TABLE III

Analysis of Anhydrides by Sodium Hydroxide–Sodium Methylate Method

| Anhydride | Millimoles per gram sample | | | Anhydride found, wt. %[a] | Free acid, % (calc.) |
	NaOH (a)	NaOCH₃ (b)	—CO—O—CO— (a − b)		
Acetic..........	19.61	9.88	9.73	(4) 99.3 ± 0.2	0.8
Propionic........	15.40	7.79	7.61	(3) 99.0 ± 0.2	1.2
n-Heptylic.......	8.21	4.21	4.00	(1) 96.9	2.7
Succinic.........	19.83	10.35	9.48	(4) 94.8 ± 0.2	5.1
Maleic.......	20.20	10.22	9.98	(2) 97.8 ± 0.0	1.4
Glutaric.........	17.57	8.80	8.77	(2) 100.0 ± 0.1	0.2
Glutaric.........	17.42	8.67	8.75	(2) 99.8 ± 0.1	−0.5
Glutaric.........	17.43	9.05	8.38	(2) 95.5 ± 0.0	4.4
Camphoric..	10.99	5.49	5.50	(2) 100.2 ± 0.4	−0.1
Benzoic.........	8.84	4.45	4.39	(2) 99.3 ± 0.1	0.7
Phthalic........	13.50	6.75	6.75	(2) 99.9 ± 0.3	0.0
Furoic..........	9.61	4.97	4.64	(4) 95.6 ± 0.2	3.7

[a] Figures in parentheses indicate number of individual determinations.

Crotonic anhydride could not be analyzed by this procedure. Some potential interfering substances in the form of lactones were investigated. The results obtained are tabulated in Table IV.

In this group of four lactones, glucono-δ-lactone gave a large net titer. If present in mixtures with anhydrides this compound would lead to ambiguous results because of its ease of hydrolysis in aqueous solution.   In the

TABLE IV

Analytical Data for Lactones

Lactone	Millimoles per gram sample		
	NaOH (a)	NaOCH$_3$ (b)	Δ (a − b)
Glucone-δ-lactone............	5.65	0.05	5.60
Phthalide..................	0.11	0.02	0.09
Coumarin..................	0.05	0.02	0.03
β-Methylumbelliferone.........	5.63	5.62	0.01

absence of anhydrides (which could be proved by one of the aquametric methods in Section IV), however, the nature of this compound and other readily hydrolyzed esters such as the formates would be evident. In anhydride-acid systems the millimoles from the methylate titer alone should be equivalent to 50% or more of the value with aqueous caustic.

The sodium hydroxide–sodium methylate procedure (40) is effective at room temperature for determinations of most anhydrides. The method, however, requires use of two standardized caustic reagents. Lukashevich (20) used uncatalyzed hydrolysis on one portion of the sample and esterification with methanol, according to equation (5), on a second portion. Acidic end products from both reactions could be titrated with standardized sodium hydroxide. In the absence of suitable catalysts both hydrolysis and esterification required relatively drastic conditions for all but the simplest anhydrides. The single caustic reagent approach is simplified through use of pyridine as catalyst for both the hydrolysis and esterification steps (11). In this case the severity of reaction conditions is a function of the rates of esterification and hydrolysis in the presence of pyridine as catalyst and of the solubility of the sample in methanol and in aqueous pyridine. For example, acetic, propionic, n-butyric, maleic, succinic, and phthalic anhydrides can be esterified and hydrolyzed at room temperature. Stearic anhydride, on the other hand, requires refluxing to complete reaction due primarily to its limited solubility in methanol and water–pyridine at 25°C. The analysis is more conveniently made on smaller quantities of sample than that used in the sodium hydroxide–sodium methylate method, employing 0.1 N caustic for the final titrations.

Procedure (11). (1) The sample, containing up to 4 millimoles of anhydride plus acid, is weighed into a dry 125 ml. glass-stoppered erlenmeyer flask. Then 20 ml. of dry methanol (<0.05% H$_2$O) and 10 ml. of dry pyridine (<0.1% H$_2$O) are added. For most anhydrides the stoppered flask is allowed to stand 30 minutes at room temperatures. (Samples which are only partially soluble at room temperature or which contain sterically hindered anhydrides are refluxed for 15 minutes.) At the end of this time the solutions are titrated with standardized 0.1 N aqueous sodium hydroxide to the phenolphthalein end point.

(2) A second sample, containing up to 2 millimoles of anhydride or 4 meq. of anhydride plus acid, is weighed into a 250 ml. erlenmeyer flask. Then 20 ml. of distilled water and 10 ml. of pyridine are added, after which the solution is titrated with standardized 0.1 N aqueous sodium hydroxide to the phenolphthalein end point.

Calculation. Anhydride and free acid contents are calculated in the same way as that described in the sodium hydroxide–sodium methylate method on page 104.

This single alkali reagent procedure has a precision and accuracy of 0.2%, relative, for samples containing more than 50% anhydride. For lesser quantities the reliability of the method decreases. Typical results obtained on a variety of anhydrides are given in Table V. The anhydride and acid data noted represent an average of duplicate determinations.

TABLE V

Analytical Data for Anhydrides by Hydrolysis–Methanol Esterification Method

Anhydride	Found, wt. %		
	Anhydride	Acid	Total
Acetic.	95.9	3.6	99.5
Acetic.	94.5	5.3	99.8
Propionic.	99.0	1.1	100.1
n-Butyric.	97.1	2.5	99.6
Maleic.	92.8	6.1	98.9
Succinic.	96.4	3.8	100.2
Stearic[a].	28.8	76.7	105.5
o-Phthalic.	99.3	0.7	100.0

[a] Sample probably contained several per cent of palmitic acid and/or anhydride.

Another variation in technique might be based on saponification of the ester formed by reaction with sodium methylate or methanol, according to equations (4) and (5) (11). Where applicable this approach would require only a single sample for anhydride (and acid) determinations. After titration with sodium methylate as on page 104 or esterification with methanol, as above, followed by neutralization of the free acid, the ester could be determined by one of the saponification methods described by Hall and Shaefer in Volume II of this series.

5. Hydrolysis. Anilide Formation

Two-step procedures also have been reported which combine reactions (1) and (2). Radcliffe and Mendofski (28) modified a method proposed by the British Export Committee, (Richmond (31) and Griffin (16)), who had recommended aqueous hydrolysis with the Menshukin and Vasilieff method (22, see p. 100) for determination of acetic anhydride. This modification called for use of 20 ml. instead of 2–3 ml. of aniline to act as a coolant, thereby minimizing the interfering anilide reaction (3). The following procedure was proposed for acetic anhydride by Radcliffe and Mendofski (28) and also by Allen (1).

Procedure (28). (*1*) About 50 meq. of acetic anhydride is weighed into a tared glass-stoppered erlenmeyer flask and 20 ml. of water added. A reflux condenser is attached and the solution boiled until the anhydride is hydrolyzed completely. The liberated acid is titrated with 1 *N* sodium hydroxide using phenolphthalein as indicator. This step yields total acid originating from both acid and anhydride.

(*2*) About 50 meq. of anhydride is introduced into a tared small glass-stoppered flask containing about 20 ml. of freshly distilled aniline. The flask is stoppered quickly and the contents mixed. After cooling, the flask is reweighed to obtain sample weight by difference. The contents of the small flask are washed with alcohol into a larger flask, where acidity is determined by titration with 1 *N* caustic to the phenolphthalein end point. This step yields all of the free acid plus one-half of the acid from the anhydride.

Calculation. The net titer between steps *1* and *2* is a measure of anhydride content of the sample. The calculations are the same as those given on page 104.

Although this method was satisfactory in analyses for acetic anhydride, it would appear to be more generally applicable by substituting room temperature alkaline hydrolysis (see p. 104) for the water refluxing step and using lower normality caustic.

Radcliffe and Mendofski (28) in a detailed study of methods for the assay of acetic anhydride critically evaluated several methods: (*a*) straight aqueous hydrolysis, (*b*) method of Treadwell (p. 99), (*c*) method of Menshukin and Vasilieff (p. 100), (*d*) British Export Committee procedure, a combination of *a* and *c*, and (*e*) their modified method above. They concluded that the methods *a*, *b*, *c*, and *d* were not satisfactory, whereas method *e* gave fairly consistent results.

III. METHODS BASED ON REACTION WITH 2,4-DICHLOROANILINE

Substituted anilines, particularly 2,4-dichloroaniline, have been suggested by several investigators as reagents for anhydrides. They were developed primarily for determinations of small amounts of acetic anhydride in acetic acid. Edwards and Orton (12) extracted the anilide formed by rapid reaction of 2,4-dichloroaniline with acetic anhydride, converted the anilide to the corresponding chloramine which was determined by iodine–sodium thiosulfate titration. This procedure was time consuming and required too many steps for high accuracy and precision in analyses. Other workers found that more reliable determinations were obtained through use of a measured amount of the substituted aniline followed by titration of the excess after the anilide reaction was complete. For example, Calcott, English, and Wilbur (8) determined excess 2,4-dichloroaniline with sodium nitrate using starch–potassium iodide paper to determine the end point. A similar method by I. G. Farbenindustrie A. G., using m-nitroaniline, was described in Berl-Lunge (6).

Procedure (8). Approximately 2 g. of 2,4-dichloroaniline is accurately weighed into a 300 ml. erlenmeyer flask and 25 ml. of glacial acetic acid added. About 6 meq. of anhydride is weighed into the flask and the mixture shaken, if necessary, to dissolve the sample. After standing at room temperature (25 °C.) for one hour to permit complete reaction, the contents of the flask are transferred to a 400 ml. beaker, washing the flask with 150 ml. of 5% hydrochloric acid at a temperature no higher than 20°C. The temperature of the acidified mixture is adjusted to between 20 and 25°C. and the excess substituted aniline is titrated with 0.1 N sodium nitrite solution. Starch–potassium iodide paper is used to determine the end point, which should persist for at least one minute. Blank determinations are made on weighed portions of 2,4-dichloroaniline. Also an end point blank is determined on a volume of distilled water approximately equal to the final titrated volume of sample to determine the amount of nitrite solution required to give the starch–iodide paper test. This amount is subtracted from all titration volumes.

The temperature of the solution during titration should be maintained below 26°C. to avoid interference by dichloroacetanilide and the titration must be completed within one hour of the time of dilution.

Calculation.

$$\text{Meq./g. aniline for blank} = \frac{\text{ml.} \times N \text{ NaNO}_2}{\text{g. aniline}} = a$$

$$\text{Meq. aniline in sample} = a \times \text{g. aniline in sample} = b$$

$$\text{Meq. excess aniline in sample} = \text{ml. from back titration} \times N \text{ NaNO}_2 = c$$

$$\text{Wt. \% anhydride} = \frac{(b - c) \times \text{M.W.}}{\text{g. sample}} \times 100$$

Orton and Bradfield (24) and Skrabal (39) used a comparable method for detecting small amounts of anhydride in acid but determined the excess 2,4-dichloroaniline by oxidation with bromide–bromate solution followed by reaction with potassium iodide and titration of the liberated iodine.

The following data were reported on recovery of acetic anhydride added to 75 ml. quantities of acetic acid:

Anhydride added, mg.	Anhydride found, mg.
95.5	93.6
47.8	47.9, 47.0
9.5	9.5, 9.4

Procedure (24).   To a measured quantity of acid (75–100 ml.) in 500 ml. iodine flasks is added 10 ml. of 2,4-dichloroaniline solution (0.4% in glacial acetic acid) and the mixture is allowed to stand overnight.   Then 85 ml. of distilled water is added followed by 10 ml. of 10% hydrochloric acid, and 10 ml. of 0.1 N bromide–bromate reagent.   After 5 minutes, 10 ml. of 10% potassium iodide is added and the solution titrated immediately with 0.1 N sodium thiosulfate solution using starch solution as an end point indicator.   Blanks are run on the 2,4-dichloroaniline solution.

Calculation.

$$\text{Wt. \% anhydride} = \frac{\text{blank titer} - \text{sample titer} \times N \text{ Na}_2\text{S}_2\text{O}_3 \times \text{M.W.}}{\text{g. sample}} \times 100$$

IV. AQUAMETRIC METHODS

Since hydrolysis is one of the simplest reactions of anhydrides, methods based upon measurement of water consumed in this reaction offer interesting potentialities for direct analyses.   The refinement of the Karl Fischer reagent as a specific for the determination of water has permitted exploitation of this idea.   Smith, Bryant, and Mitchell developed two methods for the determination of anhydrides by aquametric means (23,41,42).   Both procedures depend upon effecting hydrolysis of the anhydride in the presence of a known excess of water, followed by the determination of the unreacted water by titration with Karl Fischer reagent.   These procedures open up new fields of possibilities, because many of the interferences encountered in acidimetric methods do not exist in aquametric ones.   For example, free organic acids, mineral acids, buffer salts, and esters do not interfere.   Only those reactions involving the release or up-take of water have any influence upon the determination and in many cases, these can be eliminated by a proper blank.

1. Acid Hydrolysis

The hydrolysis of acid anhydrides by water alone is not easily achieved and with the exception of acetic anhydride cannot be done in any reasonable time even by boiling. Smith et al. (41) showed that the removal of small amounts of water from acetic acid with acetic anhydride was not completely effected in forty-eight hours at room temperature. Numerous catalysts for the hydrolysis have been proposed.

Acids have been shown to be effective catalysts in nearly anhydrous systems, based on extensive rate studies of the hydrolysis of acetic anhydride in glacial acetic acid (25,26,51). In this environment the reaction is second order but in essentially aqueous systems a first-order reaction is observed (13,27,33,39). Yvernault (51) found that the velocity of hydrolysis of acetic anhydride in acetic acid employing strong acid catalysis increased in the order: CCl_3COOH, HCl, H_2SO_4, $HClO_4$. In aqueous systems strong acids have little effect. This observation has been cited as evidence that HX and not H^+ is the active catalyst (25,33). Similar effects were observed in studies of the hydrolysis of succinic, methylsuccinic, itaconic, maleic, citraconic, and phthalic anhydrides (34). Even in organic media rate of reaction may depend on the nature of the solvent. Orton and Jones (25), for example, found that the rate of hydrolysis of acetic anhydride was slower in methyl acetate than acetic acid.

Orton and Bradfield (24) suggested the use of chromic acid and Cochrane and Smythe (9) used sulfuric acid as catalysts. Smith, Bryant, and Mitchell (41) investigated a catalyst mixture consisting of 100 g. of boron trifluoride per liter of glacial acetic acid, and containing 6.75 g. of water. Initial experiments using propionic anhydride indicated that, while hydrolysis was only 93% complete in one hour, it was 99.8% complete in two hours at 60°C. A method based upon this acid hydrolysis in the presence of boron trifluoride was found applicable to most aliphatic anhydrides.

Acid Hydrolysis Procedure (23,41). The sample, containing up to 4 millimoles of anhydride, is weighed into a 250 ml. glass-stoppered volumetric flask. Then 20 ml. of reagent (glacial acetic acid containing 100 g. BF_3 plus 6.5 ml. water per liter of solution) is added and an identical amount transferred to another flask for a blank (see reference 23, p. 275, for preparation of this reagent). The flasks are placed in a water bath at 60 ± 1°C. with the stoppers loosened momentarily to permit the enclosed air to expand and then tightened. After two hours, the flasks are removed from the bath and allowed to cool. After careful addition of 5 ml. portions of pyridine to each flask, the solutions are titrated with Karl Fischer reagent (see reference 23, p. 65 for preparation of this reagent; Karl Fischer reagent also can be purchased from laboratory supply houses).

Calculation. Anhydride is measured by the difference between water found in the blank and the water remaining in the sample solution. A correction must be made for any free water originally present in the sample as determined by titration

with Karl Fischer reagent.   The millimoles of water consumed plus the millimoles
of water in the sample are equivalent to the millimoles of anhydride.

Analytical results for a number of anhydrides are given in Table VI
where they are compared with data obtained by the acidimetric sodium hy-
droxide-sodium methylate method (23,41).

TABLE VI

Analytical Data for Anhydrides by Acid Hydrolysis

Anhydride		Anhydride found, wt. %	
		Acid hydrolysis[a]	Sodium hydroxide–sodium methylate method
Acetic............	(6)	100.0 ± 0.2	99.9
Propionic.........	(4)	97.0 ± 0.3	97.2
Butyric...........	(2)	85.5 ± 0.5	85.4
Crotonic..........	(2)	89.6 ± 0.0	
Valeric...........	(2)	2.0 ± 0.4	1.9
Caproic...........	(2)	78.6 ± 0.4	78.4
Heptylic..........	(2)	92.0 ± 0.3	92.1
Glutaric..........	(2)	95.3 ± 0.3	95.5
Benzoic...........	(4)	99.0 ± 0.3	99.2
Furoic............	(4)	95.1 ± 0.5	94.8

[a] Figures in parentheses represent number of individual determinations.

With the exception of the carefully distilled acetic anhydride the compounds were of C. P. quality containing varying amounts of free acid.
These results indicate that the method is suitable for quantitative determinations of the anhydrides of aliphatic acids and certain aromatic and
heterocyclic compounds.   Of several anhydrides of dibasic acids examined
only that of glutaric gave quantitative results.   Maleic, phthalic, and succinic anhydrides showed 0, 11, and 91% hydrolysis, respectively.

Aldehydes, acetals, and orthoesters interfere in the acid hydrolysis
method.   All react with acetic acid in the presence of boron trifluoride to
form water (23).   Nitriles interfere by absorbing water (23).   In all cases
the reactions are essentially quantitative.   Consequently, where the concentrations of these classes of compounds are known, suitable corrections
may be applied to the anhydride results.

2. Alkaline Hydrolysis

The fact that pyridine was a satisfactory catalyst for the hydrolysis of
anhydrides in the sodium hydroxide–sodium methylate procedure sug-

gested that it might serve equally well as a catalyst for an aquametric method (42). A number of anhydrides were treated directly with excess water in the presence of pyridine. The results indicated that, for most anhydrides, this treatment was inadequate, even at elevated temperatures and for extended periods of time. Other stronger amines such as tributylamine, triethylamine, and *n*-butylamine were equally unsuccessful (43). However, since another alkaline catalyst in the presence of an amine might be effective, sodium iodide was chosen for study because of its solubility in pyridine, its inertness toward Fischer reagent, and its alkalinity. This combination proved successful and formed the basis of an alkaline hydrolysis method for anhydrides employing Karl Fischer reagent for titrations of water.

Alkaline Hydrolysis Procedure (23,42). The sample, containing up to 10 millimoles of anhydride, is weighed into a 250 ml. glass-stoppered volumetric flask. Then 25 ml. of reagent is added (100 g. NaI + 8 ml. H_2O in 1 liter of pyridine solution; the added water, together with that normally found in pyridine, should result in a water concentration of about 1%). This quantity of reagent contains approximately 14 millimoles of water or about 40% excess over that required for hydrolysis. The flask, together with a blank, is placed in a water bath at $60 \pm 1\,°C$. with the stoppers loosened momentarily to permit expansion of the heated air. The flasks are left in the bath for one hour. At the end of this time, they are removed, allowed to cool to room temperature, and the contents titrated for water with Karl Fischer reagent.

Calculation. The difference in water found between blank and sample, plus water originally present, is equivalent to the anhydride content of the sample.

Typical results are given in Table VII. Comparative data by the acid hydrolysis or acidimetric sodium hydroxide–sodium methylate method are included.

It can be seen by comparison with Table VI that most dibasic acids give quantitative results by alkaline hydrolysis, whereas they do not by the acid hydrolysis method. Maleic anhydride cannot be determined by the alkaline hydrolysis method, since it reacts violently with the pyridine reagent. Camphoric anhydride failed to react completely, probably due to steric hindrance. The poor precision obtained for benzoic anhydride was caused by the formation of a coating of benzoic acid on the anhydride.

In general, the alkaline hydrolysis procedure is more widely applicable than the acid hydrolysis method. In common with the latter no interference is encountered from easily hydrolyzed esters. No interference is observed from most acetals, orthoesters, and nitriles. In favorable cases the presence of carbonyl compounds does not seriously affect the alkaline hy-

TABLE VII

Analytical Data for Anhydrides by Alkaline Hydrolysis Method

Anhydride		Anhydride found, wt. %		
		Alkaline hydrolysis[a]	Acid hydrolysis	Sodium hydroxide–sodium methylate
Acetic............	(8)	99.5 ± 0.4	99.2	99.5
Propionic..........	(4)	97.4 ± 0.2	97.2	
n-Butyric..........	(2)	98.3 ± 0.3		98.3
Crotonic...........	(2)	87.3 ± 0.1	87.1	
Caproic............	(4)	95.0 ± 0.2		94.8
Heptylic...........	(4)	89.1 ± 0.3	89.2	
Succinic...........	(4)	91.0 ± 0.5		90.9
Glutaric...........	(2)	100.1 ± 0.2	100.2	
Benzoic............	(5)	89.7 ± 1.0		89.8 ± 0.5
Phthalic...........	(2)	98.9 ± 0.2		98.4
Furoic.............	(2)	94.9 ± 0.2	94.9	

[a] Figures in parentheses represent number of individual determinations.

drolysis method.   Although small amounts of strong acids do not interfere, large quantities are likely to affect the alkaline catalyst activity.   Samples containing high concentrations of strong acids usually are best analyzed by acid hydrolysis.

V. MISCELLANEOUS CHEMICAL METHODS

1. Reaction with Oxalic Acid.   Permanganate Titration

Rosenbaum and Walton (35) described a permanganate method for the determination of the purity of acetic anhydride based upon a reaction of the anhydride with excess oxalic acid according to the following equation:

$$H_3CCOOOCCH_3 + HOOCCOOH \longrightarrow CO_2 + CO + 2CH_3COOH \qquad (6)$$

The excess oxalic acid was determined by titration with potassium permanganate.   Apparently this method has not been evaluated for other anhydrides, but might prove to be a useful and rapid procedure for analyses of systems free of easily oxidized materials.

Procedure for Acetic Anhydride (35).   1 g. of anhydride is weighed into a wide mouth glass-stoppered flask containing approximately 1 g. of anhydrous oxalic acid accurately weighed.   2 ml. of pyridine, dried over barium oxide and calcium hydride, is added.   The flask is stoppered and cooled in crushed ice for five minutes to prevent loss of anhydride.   Then the flask is gently warmed, loosening the stopper to vent the excess gas, and held at 50°C. for ten minutes. The mixture is diluted with water to dissolve the remaining oxalic acid and acidified and the excess oxalic acid titrated with permanganate. A blank is run containing a weighed portion of oxalic acid and 2 ml. of pyridine.

2. Reaction with Oxalic Acid. Gasometric Method

Whitford (49), in a paper antedating that of Rosenbaum and Walton, described an interesting variation of the oxalic acid method for acetic anhydride. In this procedure, the evolved carbon monoxide and carbon dioxide were collected and measured gasometrically. The reaction was complete in 15 minutes and an accuracy of 0.1–0.2% absolute was claimed. In Table VIII are noted results obtained by this method. The method was found best suited for samples containing less than 5% acetic acid. This procedure has potential for semimicro determinations using a gasometer similar to that used in the Dumas nitrogen method.

TABLE VIII
Analytical Results on Acetic Anhydride by Gasometric Method

Sample wt., g.	Gas, cc.	Calculated	
		Anhydride, g.	Anhydride, wt. %
Pure Acetic Anhydride			
0.1942	100.0	0.1944	100.1
0.1711	88.0	0.1710	99.9
0.1694	87.2	0.1695	100.0
Commercial 92% Acetic Anhydride			
0.1985	93.75	0.1823	91.9
0.1898	89.8	0.1749	92.1

Procedure for Acetic Anhydride (49). Approximately 25 ml. of anhydrous pyridine is introduced into a gasometer of the type described by Walton (47) and saturated with carbon dioxide and carbon monoxide. Approximately 1 g. of anhydrous oxalic acid is added and the mixture is shaken to dissolve. About 0.2 g. of anhydride is weighed accurately into a thin glass bulb. The sealed bulb is introduced into the gasometer and broken by shaking. The volume of collected gas is read after allowing the gasometer to return to initial temperature. Since the presence of water has a very powerful inhibitory effect upon the reaction, it is essential that all reagents be absolutely anhydrous.

VI. PHYSICAL METHODS

While very few physical methods have been described for determination of anhydrides in general, several very clever methods have been reported for acetic anhydride which may have some application to certain problems.

1. Thermometric Procedures

A number of analyses have been reported based upon the calorimetric measurement of heat liberated by reaction of anhydrides with aniline, water, and other reagents.   Richmond and Eggleston (32) estimated the anhydride by the heat liberated upon reaction with aniline, using toluene as a diluting medium to prevent combination with any free acid present. Cochrane and Smythe (9) measured the heat liberated when the anhydride was hydrolyzed by dilute acetic acid in the presence of sulfuric acid.   Berl and Türck (7) also measured the heat of reaction resulting from the hydrolysis of acetic anhydride by aqueous acetic acid using hydrochloric acid as catalyst.   Berl and Türck described a rapid method well suited to the routine examination of acetylation mixtures.   In the range of 50–100% anhydride, they reported an accuracy of 0.08%, based upon use of 10 ml. samples.   A summary of results obtained by this method are given in Table IX.

Procedure of Berl and Türck (7).   *Apparatus.*   The apparatus consisted of a dewar flask 40 × 200 mm. I. D. packed in a container filled with insulating material. A stirrer, thermometer, and inlet tube passed through a tightly fitting stopper with

TABLE IX

Analytical Data for Acetic Anhydride by Calorimetric Method

Anhydride added, wt. %	Temp. rise, °C.	Anhydride found, wt. %	
		Calorimetric	Nitroaniline method[a]
93.90	7.154	93.90	93.96
96.20	7.340	96.30	96.30
97.80	7.460	98.00	97.80
99.87	7.640	100.00	99.90
91.20	6.945	91.20	91.15
88.25	6.700	88.05	88.15
85.50	6.510	85.50	85.50
83.60	6.350	83.50	83.65
44.70	3.250	44.00	44.70

[a] Reference 6.   See also p. 109.

appropriately located holes. The stirrer was made from a piece of glass plate of such a size as to occupy completely the free cross section of the flask and was sealed to a glass rod. Mixing was obtained by reciprocating action. The calibrated thermometer had a range from 13 to 25° graduated in 0.02°C. Figure 1 shows the assembly of the apparatus.

Procedure. Sample and hydrolysis reagent (150 g. glacial acetic acid plus 72 g. of concentrated hydrochloric acid per liter of aqueous solution) in separate closed containers are thermstated in a water bath at 15°C.

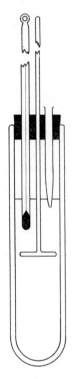

Fig. 1. Thermometric apparatus for determining acetic anhydride in acetic acid by hydrolysis (7).

Exactly 200 ml. of hydrolysis reagent is placed in the dewar flask. The flask is stoppered and stirring is begun. The temperature is recorded each minute until the temperature becomes constant (about 5 minutes). Then exactly 10 ml. of sample is added through the inlet tube. The temperature is recorded each minute until a constant maximum value is obtained. The difference between the initial and final constant temperatures is a measure of anhydride content. Actual percentages are taken from a curve prepared from data obtained on knowns analyzed in exactly the same way.

Greathouse, Janssen, and Haydel (15) employed perchloric acid as catalyst for the thermometric determination of up to 40% acetic anhydride in acetic acid and also for water in acetic acid. Perchloric acid has been shown to be one of the most effective catalysts for the hydrolysis (see p. 111). Two procedures were described depending on (a) measurement of the maximum temperature rise and (b) titration to cessation of temperature rise. In the former, 200 ml. of sample, 4 ml. of catalyst, and 25 ml. of water were mixed at constant temperature and the maximum temperature rise recorded. In the latter, 2 ml. of catalyst was added to 100 ml. of sample and the resulting solution was titrated with 2 M water in acetic acid, added in increments of 1 or 0.5 ml., until no further temperature rise was observed. This titration procedure will determine only excess anhydride over water present in the sample. The temperature rise procedure, described below, would appear to offer better potential for application to other anhydrides.

Procedure of Greathouse, Janssen, and Haydel (15). *Reagents.* A 1 to 20 dilution of 60% perchloric acid is prepared in acetic acid. A calculated amount of acetic anhydride is added to remove exactly the water present in this solution. (Water in the acetic acid used can be determined conveniently by titration with Karl Fischer reagent (23).) The anhydride must be added slowly and the solution kept below 30°C. by immersing it in ice water. The anhydrous reagent should be stored below its freezing point (about 5°C. is convenient) where it will retain its full catalytic activity for at least a week.

Apparatus. Greathouse and co-workers (15) used an assembly consisting of dewar flask, mechanical stirrer, thermometer, and burets protected with desiccants for delivering acetic acid, acetic anhydride, and perchloric acid. The complete apparatus was designed for use in determining anhydride or water in acetylating mixtures by the temperature rise and titration to cessation of temperature rise methods. For determinations of anhydride content by the temperature rise method the following are needed: (1) dewar flask having an internal volume of 400 to 500 ml., (2) aluminum foil covered cork stopper containing three holes to accommodate thermometer and stirrer and to permit introduction of sample and reagents, (3) calibrated thermometer, 0 to 100° graduated in 0.1°C., (4) mechanical stirrer to operate at 600 r.p.m. or slightly higher, (5) pipets for delivering sample, catalyst, and water.

Procedure. Sample, catalyst, and distilled water in separate closed containers are placed in a thermostatically controlled water bath set at 2°C. above room temperature. After temperature equilibrium has been obtained, 200 ml. of sample is transferred to the dewar flask. With the stirrer running, 4 ml. of catalyst solution is added and the temperature of the solution is recorded immediately. Then 25 ml. of distilled water is added in the following manner. In order to avoid too rapid dilution of the catalyst the water is added slowly until the temperature starts to rise sharply and then the remaining water is added quickly. The maximum temperature is recorded and the differential calculated as the difference in degrees Centigrade between the initial and maximum temperature. The anhydride content of the sample is read from a curve prepared from data obtained by analysis of known mixtures.

The known mixtures should be handled in the same apparatus and under the same conditions as the samples of unknown anhydride content. Then the calibration curve prepared from the observed temperature rise vs. concentration can be used directly for analyses of the samples.

For analyses of samples containing 10% or less anhydride only 10 ml. of water is used. Results must be taken from another calibration curve plotted from data obtained on knowns analyzed under the same conditions.

Greathouse and co-workers (15) calibrated their methods with known mixtures containing from about 9 to 26% anhydride. Through the use of such large samples temperature differentials of about 14°C. were observed at the low level and 50°C. for the knowns at the 26% level. Use of 25 ml. of water (ca. 1.4 moles) provides about a 75% excess over that required to hydrolyze 200 ml. of a sample containing 40% anhydride.

The procedure of Berl and Türck (7), on the other hand, employs a minimum of about a 90-fold excess of water over acetic anhydride. This great excess of water would reflect in a lower temperature rise.

The perchloric acid catalyzed procedure (15) would appear to be the more reliable where adequate quantities of sample are available. Also the greater catalytic activity of perchloric over hydrochloric acid would indicate that the former would be more likely to form the basis for determinations of other anhydrides. Possibly a method could be developed on a smaller scale using perchloric acid in acetic acid catalyst for the hydrolysis of 100 millimole or smaller quantities of anhydride with about a 100% excess of water. Small, well-insulated dewar flasks probably could be used which would permit reliable temperature measurements to about 0.01°C.

A variation in the calorimetric approach was proposed by Somiya (43–45) and Rybin (36) based on reaction with aniline. Acetic anhydride was allowed to react with excess aniline and the aniline remaining after acetylation was measured by titration with a standard solution of acetic anhydride. The course of the titration and the end point were followed thermometrically. Strong acids were found to retard the velocity of acetylation of aniline (44). Pyridine, however, was found beneficial. Analyses of acetic anhydride by the procedure described below showed a precision of about 0.1%. This procedure requires more time than the acid catalyzed hydrolysis methods but is useful for those cases where significant amounts of strong acids are undesirable.

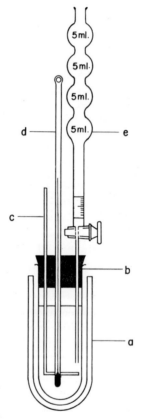

Fig. 2. Thermometric apparatus for determining acetic anhydride by reaction with aniline (43–45).

Procedure of Somiya (43–45). *Reagents*. Standard acetic anhydride reagent, ca. 2.5 M, is prepared by mixing 1.2 parts of anhydride with 1 part of glacial acetic acid and 2 parts of tetrachloroethane. Approximately 2.5 M aniline reagent is prepared by diluting 1 part of freshly distilled, dry aniline with 3 parts of tetrachloroethane.

Apparatus. The apparatus (Fig. 2) consists of a dewar flask (a) about 3.5 cm. in diameter and 10–15 cm. long with unsilvered stripe, a titration vessel (b), a ring stirrer (c), a 0–30°C. thermometer, graduated in 0.05°C. (d), and a buret (e) which has four 5 ml. bulbs and a 5 ml. graduated portion divided in 0.05 ml.

Procedure. *(1)* *Standardization.* The acetic anhydride reagent is standardized against pure freshly distilled aniline. First a preliminary titration is made for order of magnitude, by weighing about 250 mg. of aniline into the titration vessel. About 20 ml. of tetrachlorethane is added and the height of the thermometer adjusted so that the bulb is immersed. This solution is titrated with the acetic anhydride reagent, adding such increments as will give a temperature rise of between 0.4 and 0.6°C. This requires about 0.2 ml. increments. After each addition the solution is stirred until no further temperature rise is noted. The volume of reagent and temperature observed are recorded after each addition. A plot is made of temperature vs. volume of titrant on graph paper and the points joined with the best straight lines. The intersection of these lines represents the end point. The volume of titrant equivalent to this end point is read from the graph, and the approximate equivalency of the reagent is calculated.

For an accurate standardization 5 g. of aniline is weighed into the titration vessel and 15 ml. of tetrachloroethane added. Then from a buret is added slowly and with cooling an amount of acetic anhydride which is 0.8 ml. less than that required for the weight of aniline, using the preliminary standardization as a basis for calculation. After addition of 1 ml. of pyridine, the contents of the titration vessel are adjusted to room temperature. The solution is placed in the dewar flask and the titration and plot made as in the preliminary standardization.

Similarly, the aniline reagent is standardized against the anhydride reagent. Exactly 15 ml. of the aniline reagent is transferred to the titration vessel, 1 ml. of pyridine is added, and the solution is titrated with the anhydride reagent.

(2) *Analysis of the Sample.* A preliminary determination is made of the amount of aniline solution required per gram of sample. Then about 6 g. of anhydride is accurately weighed into the titration vessel. Aniline reagent is added slowly with cooling until about 0.7 ml. excess aniline solution is present. 1 ml. of pyridine is added and the solution adjusted to room temperature. The titration vessel is placed in the dewar flask and the excess aniline titrated thermometrically with standard anhydride solution. From the curve of temperature vs. volume of standard anhydride, the end point volume of anhydride required is determined. The aniline equivalent of this volume is subtracted from the total aniline added to obtain the net quantity of aniline required by the anhydride.

2. Infrared Analysis

The carbonyl group vibrations of the anhydride function lead to strong absorptions in the infrared region of the spectrum. Two absorption bands are observed which are usually separated by 0.1 to 0.2 micron (ca. 60 cm.$^{-1}$) (29). These bands are quite specific and are well suited for identifications of acid anhydrides. The actual location of the bands depends on the molecular configuration. In general, however, anhydrides with five-member rings show one carbonyl absorption band in the range 5.35–5.5 μ (1870–1820 cm.⁻¹) and a second between 5.55 and 5.7 μ (1800–1750 cm.⁻¹). Other types of anhydrides show the two absorptions at 5.4–5.55 μ (1850–1800 cm.⁻¹) and 5.58–5.75 μ (1790–1740 cm.⁻¹), respectively. In all cases there is a small shift to longer wave lengths in compounds having a double bond conjugated to the carbonyl group. Absorption bands for typical anhydrides are shown in Table X.

TABLE X

Carbonyl Absorptions of Acid Anhydrides

Anhydride	Type	Absorption bands		Ref.
		μ	cm.⁻¹	
Acetic	Open-chain	5.47	1827	
		5.70	1754	
Caproic	Open-chain	5.47	1825	29
		5.68	1760	
Glutaric	Six-member ring	5.55	1802	48
		5.68	1761	
Crotonic	Open-chain, conjugated	5.62	1780	3
		5.80	1725	
Benzoic	Open-chain, conjugated	5.58	1789	4
		5.84	1710	
Succinic	Five-member ring	5.35	1865	3
		5.61	1782	
Maleic	Five-member ring, conjugated	5.40	1848	
		5.60	1790	
Phthalic	Five-member ring, conjugated	5.42	1845	3
		5.64	1775	

Plyler and Barr (27) described an infrared method for the analysis of acetic anhydride–acetic acid–water mixtures. The intensity of the strong absorption band at 5.47 μ was proportional to anhydride concentration. Also bands at 5.75 and 6.15 μ were suitable for determinations of acetic acid and water, respectively. In similar fashion other anhydride systems also can be analyzed. Since the absorption bands shift slightly from compound to compound, each system must be calibrated for use in quantitative analyses.

In some cases the —C—O—C— group absorption may be useful for quantitative purposes. This also absorbs strongly but is not as selective as the carbonyl group absorptions of the anhydride function. Usually five-member ring anhydrides show absorption due to —C—O—C— group vibrations in the range 7.65–8.3 μ (1310–1200 cm.$^{-1}$) (4,10). Open-chain anhydrides, on the other hand, show this absorption between 8.5 and 9.55 μ (1175 and 1045 cm.$^{-1}$) (10).

The infrared region of the spectrum, therefore, forms the basis of a powerful means for identifying the anhydride group. Quantitative methods can be devised readily for known systems, making this approach valuable for control-type analyses.

3. Ultraviolet. Visual Procedures

The anhydride group, like the acid function, shows no marked absorption in the near ultraviolet. Consequently, methods based on ultraviolet absorption are feasible only for those anhydrides in which the carbonyl group is conjugated with a carbon-carbon double bond or which contain conjugated unsaturation elsewhere in the molecule. Examples of compound type absorptions are given in the chapter in this volume on the determination of acids.

In special cases anhydrides can be separated from admixture with acids and determined by ultraviolet absorption. Argawal and Spagnolo (2), for example, used chloroform to extract phthalic anhydride from mixtures with its parent acid. Anhydrides in the extract were determined by measurement at 291 or 300 mμ against a chloroform blank.

The hydroxamic acid reaction has been used for spectrophotometric determinations of anhydrides. Goddu, LeBlanc, and Wright (14) described procedures for estimations of esters, acid chlorides, and anhydrides. Each of these classes of compounds forms hydroxamic acids with relative ease on reaction with hydroxylamine and the resulting hydroxamic acid can be determined conveniently as the highly colored chelate with ferric ions. Anhydrides react with hydroxylamine as follows:

$$(\text{RCO})_2\text{O} + \text{H}_2\text{NOH} \longrightarrow \text{R}\overset{\text{O}}{\overset{\|}{\text{C}}}\text{NHOH} + \text{RCOOH} \qquad (7)$$

The resulting hydroxamic acid reacts with iron to form a red complex:

$$(1/n)\text{Fe}^{+3} + \text{R}\overset{\text{O}}{\overset{\|}{\text{C}}}\text{NHOH} \longrightarrow \text{RC—NH} + \text{H}^+ \qquad (8)$$
$$\underset{\underset{\searrow}{\underset{\text{Fe}/n}{}}}{\overset{\|}{\text{O}}\quad\overset{\|}{\text{O}}}$$

Absorption maxima vary among types of anhydrides. Consequently, for optimum accuracy calibration curves must be prepared from data obtained on the same anhydride as that present in the sample. In the absence of esters, the precision and accuracy are about 2%, based on use of alkaline hydroxylamine. To determine anhydrides in the presence of esters, neutral hydroxylamine is required. In this case the results are somewhat less accurate. The procedure described below utilizes the neutral reagent with added notes on use of alkaline hydroxylamine.

Hydroxamic Acid Procedure (14). *Reagents.* Approximately 1.8 M hydroxylamine hydrochloride is prepared by adding 12.5 g. of the C. P. salt to 100 ml. of methanol, refluxing if necessary to effect solution.

Stock solutions of iron reagent are made by dissolving 5.0 g. of ferric perchlorate (nonyellow) in 10 ml. of 70% perchloric acid plus 10 ml. of water. The solution is carefully diluted to 100 ml. with anhydrous 2B alcohol, cooling under a tap during addition of the alcohol. (Stock solution also can be prepared by carefully dissolving 0.8 g. of pure iron wire in 10 ml. of 70% perchloric acid in a small beaker. The mixture is heated cautiously on a hot plate until the iron has dissolved and then allowed to cool. Then the solution is transferred to a 100 ml. volumetric flask with 10 ml. of water and diluted to the mark with anhydrous 2B alcohol, cooling under a tap as the alcohol is added.)

Ferric perchlorate reagent solution is prepared by adding 40 ml. of stock solution to a 1 liter volumetric flask. Then 12 ml. of 71% perchloric acid is added and the solution diluted to volume with anhydrous 2B alcohol. The dilution should be carried out by adding the alcohol in 50 to 100 ml. increments and cooling between each addition until the perchloric acid has been diluted to about 10% of its original concentration. The ferric ion concentration of this reagent solution is 5.7 millimolar and the acid concentration is 0.16 M.

Procedure. Neutral hydroxylamine reagent is prepared to titrating a portion of the 1.8 M hydroxylamine hydrochloride solution with 12.5% (3.1 M) sodium hydroxide in dry methanol to the phenolphthalein end point. The mixture is filtered to remove the precipitated sodium chloride. The clear filtered reagent is stable for at least 4 hours.

The sample is dissolved at a concentration of 0.01 to 0.001 M anhydride in dry benzene. 5 ml. of this solution is transferred to a 25 ml. distillation flask and 3 ml. of filtered neutral hydroxylamine reagent added together with a boiling stone. A reflux condenser is attached and the solution is refluxed gently on a hot plate for 10 minutes. At the end of this time, the flask is removed from the hot plate (the condensers are not washed down) and the contents allowed to cool spontaneously to room temperature. The solution is transferred to a 50 ml. volumetric flask, washing with the ferric perchlorate reagent, finally making up to volume with additional reagent. The flask is shaken, if necessary, to dissolve ferric hydroxide. After several minutes the absorbance of the sample is read against a blank in a suitable spectrophotometer or colorimeter. The blank is run in the same way as the

sample, substituting 5 ml. of solvent for the sample solution. Anhydride content
of the sample is calculated after reference to a calibration curve prepared by analysis
of knowns (see Fig. 3). For maximum accuracy the calibration curve must be
prepared using the same anhydride as that present in the sample. The wave
length for measuring the absorption maximum varies among compounds and should
be determined for the particular anhydride to be analyzed. Most aliphatic hydrox-

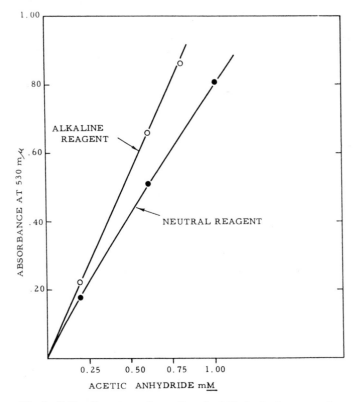

Fig. 3. Calibration curves for acetic anhydride in dry benzene using
alkaline and neutral hydroxylamine reagent (14).

amic acids show absorption maxima at 530 mμ while the aromatic compounds show
broad absorption at 550 to 560 mμ.

In the absence of esters, alkaline hydroxylamine reagent can be used conveniently
in place of the neutral solution. The alkaline reagent is prepared by mixing equal
volumes of the 12.5% hydroxylamine hydrochloride and 12.5% methanolic sodium
hydroxide. In this case only a 5 minute reflux is necessary.

A comparison of absorbance from reaction of acetic anhydride with neutral and alkaline hydroxylamine reagent is shown in Figure 3 (14). It is evident that a 5 minute reflux with alkaline reagent results in a more intense color than 10 minute reflux with neutral reagent. Possibly the latter could be improved by increasing reflux time.

The procedure is applicable to a variety of anhydrides. It is not subject to interference from acids, most amides, or nitriles. Acid chlorides react. Easily hydrolyzed esters interfere; these include the formates, some phenolic esters, peroxyesters, lactones, and probably esters of electronegatively substituted acids, e. g.. chloroacetic acids. High concentrations of free

TABLE XI

Analytical Data for Anhydride-Ester Mixtures

	Anhydride			Ester		
No.	Added, mg.	Found, mg.	Recovery, wt. %	Added, mg.	Found, mg.	Recovery, wt. %
	Acetic Anhydride–n-Butyl Acetate					
1	3.10	3.17	102	2.80	2.85	102
	3.10	3.20	103	2.80	2.80	102
	p-Toluic Anhydride–Methyl p-Toluate					
1	2.00	1.85	93	8.10	...	...
2	6.00	5.90	98	4.05	...	...
3	2.37	2.25	95	5.87	5.82	99
	2.37	2.13	90	5.87	5.94	101
4	3.01	2.95	98	5.06	5.30	105
	3.01	3.00	100	5.06	5.25	104

carbonyl compounds may interfere by consuming hydroxylamine but this probably can be eliminated through the use of higher concentrations of the hydroxylamine reagent. Transition elements such as copper, nickel, and vanadium interfere by forming colored chelates with hydroxamic acids. Ions which complex ferric iron such as chloride, tartrate, acetic acid, and water may affect the intensity of the color of the complex.

Applications of this colorimetric method are illustrated in Table XI, which gives results on the analysis of anhydride-ester mixtures (14). Total anhydride plus ester was determined by the alkaline hydroxylamine method and anhydride alone using neutral reagent. Further details on the method as applied to the determination of esters are given in the chapter on esters, p. 55 ff., in Volume II of this series.

4. Miscellaneous Physical Methods

Probably the simplest procedure, useful for very rough work, is based on the differential solubility of acetic anhydride in benzene and acetic acid in water. Wolgast (50) added a known volume of a sample of acetic anhydride in acetic acid to a measured volume of benzene and water. The mixture was shaken for a few seconds, after which the water layer was separated and its volume determined. The increase in volume represented acetic acid; acetic anhydride was estimated by difference.

Various physical measurements have been used in studies of the rate of hydrolysis of anhydrides. Philip (26) determined freezing points at frequent intervals as a means of following the reaction of acetic anhydride with water in acetic acid. Rivett and Sidgwick (34) measured electrical conductivity for estimating free acidity during hydrolysis of several anhydrides (see p. 111).

Doubtless other methods also can be employed for specific systems. For general applicability, however, the acidimetric chemical procedures are recommended.

References

1. Allen, A. H., *Commercial Organic Analysis.* Vol. I, 5th ed., Blakiston, Philadelphia, 1932, p. 680.
2. Argawal, M. M., and F. Spagnolo, *Anal. Chem., 25,* 1412 (1953).
3. Barnes, R. B., R. C. Gore, U. Liddel, and Van Zandt Williams, *Infrared Spectroscopy.* Reinhold, New York, 1944.
4. Bellamy, L. J., *The Infrared Spectra of Complex Molecules.* Methuen, London; Wiley, New York, 1954.
5. Berger, A., M. Sela, and E. Katchelski, *Anal. Chem., 25,* 1554 (1953).
6. Berl, E., and G. Lunge, *Chemische-technische Untersuchungsmethoden.* Vol. 3, 8th ed., Springer, Berlin, 1932, p. 770.
7. Berl, E., and H. Türck, *Z. anal. Chem., 95,* 143 (1933).
8. Calcott, W. S., F. L. English, and O. C. Wilbur, *Ind. Eng. Chem., 17,* 942 (1925).
9. Cochrane, J. R., and C. A. Smythe, *Proc. Soc. Chem. Ind. Victoria, 30,* 351 (1930); *Chem. Abstracts, 24,* 4732 (1930).
10. Colthup, N. B., *J. Optical Soc. Am., 40,* 397 (1950).
11. Dal Nogare, S., B. A. Montague, and J. Mitchell, Jr., paper presented before Division of Analytical Chemistry, 125th meeting, American Chemical Society, Kansas City, March 30, 1954.
12. Edwards, M. G., and K. J. P. Orton, *Analyst, 36,* 417 (1911); *J. Chem. Soc., 99,* 1181 (1911).
13. Felsenfeld, O., *Chem. Listy, 28,* 89 (1934); *Chem. Abstracts, 28,* 7126 (1934).
14. Goddu, R. F., N. F. LeBlanc, and C. M. Wright, *Anal. Chem., 27,* 1251 (1955).
15. Greathouse, L. H., H. J. Janssen, and C. H. Haydel, *ibid., 28,* 357 (1956).

16. Griffin, R. C., *Technical Methods of Analysis.* McGraw-Hill, New York, 1927, p. 107.
17. Hogsett, J. N., H. W. Kacy, and J. B. Johnson, *Anal. Chem.*, *25*, 1207 (1953).
18. Johnson, J. B., and G. L. Funk, *ibid.*, *27*, 1464 (1955).
19. Kappelmeier, C. P. A., and W. R. van Goor, *Verfkroniek*, *21*, 136 (1948); *Chem. Abstracts*, *42*, 7199 (1948).
20. Lukashevich, V. D., *J. Chem. Ind.*, *U. S. S. R.*, *8*, 1086 (1931).
21. Malm, C. J., and G. F. Nadeau, U. S. Patent 2,063,324 (December, 1936).
22. Menshukin, N., and M. Vasilieff, *J. Russ. Phys. Chem. Soc.*, *21*, 190 (1889).
23. Mitchell, J., Jr., and D. M. Smith, *Aquametry.* Interscience, New York-London, 1948.
24. Orton, K. J. P., and A. E. Bradfield, *J. Chem. Soc.*, *1927*, 983.
25. Orton, K. J. P., and M. Jones, *ibid.*, *101*, 1708 (1912).
26. Philip, J. C., *Proc. Chem. Soc.*, *28*, 259 (1913).
27. Plyler, E. K., and E. S. Barr, *J. Chem. Phys.*, *3*, 679 (1935).
28. Radcliffe, L. G., and S. Mendofski, *J. Soc. Chem. Ind.*, *36*, 628 (1917).
29. Randall, H. M., R. G. Fowler, R. G. Dangle, and N. Fuson, *Infrared Determination of Organic Structures.* Van Nostrand, New York, 1948.
30. Reclaire, A., *Perfumery Essential Oil Rec.*, *13*, 148 (1922).
31. Richmond, H. D., *Analyst*, *42*, 133 (1917).
32. Richmond, H. D., and J. A. Eggleston, *ibid.*, *51*, 281 (1926).
33. Rivett, A. C. D., and N. V. Sidgwick, *J. Chem. Soc.*, *97*, 732 (1910).
34. Rivett, A. C. D., and N. V. Sidgwick, *ibid.*, *97*, 1677 (1910).
35. Rosenbaum, C. K., and J. H. Walton, *J. Am. Chem. Soc.*, *52*, 3366 (1930).
36. Rybin, S. I., *Chem. Zentralblatt*, *1*, 3474 (1933).
37. Siggia. S., *Quantitative Organic Analysis via Functional Groups*, 2nd ed., Wiley, New York, 1954, p. 50.
38. Siggia, S., and J. G. Hanna, *Anal. Chem.*, *23*, 1717 (1951).
39. Skrabal, A., *Monatsh.*, *43*, 493 (1922).
40. Smith, D. M., and W. M. D. Bryant, *J. Am. Chem. Soc.*, *58*, 2452 (1936).
41. Smith, D. M., W. M. D. Bryant, and J. Mitchell, Jr., *ibid.*, *62*, 608 (1940).
42. Smith, D. M., W. M. D. Bryant, and J. Mitchell, Jr., *ibid.*, *63*, 1700 (1941).
43. Somiya, T., *Proc. Imp. Acad. (Japan)*, *3*, 79 (1927); *Chem. Abstracts*, *21*, 3030 (1927).
44. Somiya, T., *Proc. Imp. Acad. (Japan)*, *5*, 34 (1929); *Chem. Abstracts*, *23*, 1840 (1929).
45. Somiya, T., *J. Soc. Chem. Ind.*, *51*, 135T (1932).
46. Treadwell, F. P., and W. T. Hall, *Analytical Chemistry.* Vol. II, 3rd English ed., Wiley, New York, 1911, p. 584.
47. Walton, H., *Z. physik. Chem.*, *47*, 185 (1904).
48. Wassermann, H. H., and H. E. Zimmerman, *J. Am. Chem. Soc.*, *72*, 5787 (1950).
49. Whitford, E. L., *ibid.*, *47*, 2939 (1925).
50. Wolgast, K., *Svensk Kem. Tidskrift*, *32*, 110 (1920).
51. Yvernault, T., *Compt. rend.*, *233*, 411 (1951).

Determination of
AMINES AND AMIDES
and Related Compounds

E. F. HILLENBRAND, JR., AND C. A. PENTZ, *Carbide and Carbon Chemicals Company, South Charleston, West Virginia*

I. INTRODUCTION

Since Wöhler first prepared synthetic urea in 1828, thousands of new nitrogen-containing organic compounds have been synthesized, many of them achieving importance commercially. Of these the amines are the largest group, having found wide application as corrosion inhibitors, absorbents for acid gases, emulsifiers for polishes, paints, and cosmetics, and intermediates for the manufacture of dyes, detergents, pharmaceuticals, and many other products.

Amines are derivatives of ammonia in which one or more of the hydrogens are replaced by an organic radical. They are classified, respectively, as primary, secondary, and tertiary amines depending upon the number of hydrogens substituted.

Like ammonia, all three classes of amines are electron donors and hence exhibit an alkaline reaction in amphiprotic or acidic solvents, the basic strength depending upon the nature of the organic radical and the number of hydrogens substituted. Most aliphatic amines are stronger bases than ammonia and therefore can be readily titrated in aqueous solution with standard acid. On the other hand, aromatic amines such as aniline are generally much weaker than ammonia and can be titrated quantitatively only in more acidic solvents such as acetic acid.

Other chemical reactions of the amino group that are useful in quantitative analysis include acetylation, formation of Schiff bases by reaction with aldehydes, oxidation, and, in the case of aromatic amines, diazotization and nitrosation. Some of these reactions can be used to distinguish between the three classes of amines.

It is frequently necessary to determine primary, secondary, and tertiary amines in admixture. There are several ways to accomplish this by a combination of the type reactions referred to above. A recent procedure based on a differential potentiometric titration also permits the determination of mixtures of certain aliphatic and aromatic amines.

Spectroscopic and polarographic methods have proved of little value for the quantitative analysis of amine mixtures and, when applicable, the precision is very poor. In general, chemical methods provide the most dependable, rapid, precise methods of analysis presently available for these compounds.

Amides are very much weaker bases than amines and cannot be titrated as bases even in strongly acidic solvents. A saponification method, a dehydration procedure for primary amides, as well as a colorimetric procedure based on the formation of the corresponding hydroxamic acids, are applicable to some of these compounds.

Imides are actually weak acids and can be titrated as such in basic solvents such as ethylenediamine or dimethylformamide. Imines may be determined by hydrolysis and measurement of the aldehyde formed by one of the titrimetric methods available for carbonyl compounds. A general titrimetric method is available for quaternary ammonium salts; in addition, these compounds undergo a number of colorimetric reactions which are applicable to their determination.

II. AMINES AND AMIDES

1. Total Nitrogen

Procedures for the determination of the total nitrogen content of a compound are particularly helpful to the chemist because they provide a means for establishing the empirical formula of a compound and may aid in its identification. Then, too, when satisfactory functional group procedures are not available for the particular nitrogen compound, these procedures may provide the only satisfactory measurement of the nitrogen function. Among the classical methods for the quantitative determination of nitrogen, those due to Dumas and Kjeldahl are most widely used in the laboratory. A description of each of these procedures follows.

A. DUMAS METHOD

In principle this procedure consists of converting the combined nitrogen of the sample into elementary nitrogen, which is measured volumetrically

(21). Modifications and refinements have improved the usefulness of the basic technique. Pregl (78,79) pioneered the micro adaptation of the classical Dumas macro method and offered a procedure that gave excellent results in expert hands. However, there were two objectionable restrictions: (a) low results were obtained with compounds difficult to ignite and (b) high results were obtained in some cases due to the formation of carbon monoxide and, possibly, other associated gases (33,94). Various investigators tried to overcome these handicaps by the burning of oxygen-containing nitrogen-free compounds along with the material being analyzed. Spies and Harris (92) advocated the use of potassium chlorate together with high temperatures. Hayman and Adler (40) used copper acetate, while Kirsten (49) used nickel oxide to catalyze the reaction.

The procedure herein described was outlined by Unterzaucher (95). The sample is burned over copper oxide in a stream of moist carbon dioxide and oxygen. The gas current is produced by leading carbon dioxide from dry ice through a flask containing 30% hydrogen peroxide. The gas is led over heated copper at the far end of the combustion tube to remove the excess oxygen quantitatively and to reduce the oxides of nitrogen. The free nitrogen is collected in an azotometer over potassium hydroxide. The complete burning of those nitrogenous materials formerly difficult to ignite is effected by the availability of free oxygen at all times during the analysis. The water carried along by the gas from the oxygen generator has a favorable effect on the combustion process, since the conditions are thus provided for the gasification of the residual carbon. The constant automatic regeneration of the copper oxide prolongs the life of the tube and its filling. Under these conditions the combustion tube is left permanently in the furnace at the prescribed temperature. Consequently all parts of the apparatus remain permanently connected with each other during a series of analyses. This permits the use of ball-and-socket joint connections, thereby eliminating errors formerly caused by the use of rubber connections. The combustion tube projects beyond the furnace; a fall in temperature thus occurs in the projecting portion of the tube and facilitates the complete oxidation of any carbon monoxide formed during the analysis. This procedure is applicable to all types of organic nitrogenous materials.

Reagents. (1) *Cupric oxide*, wire form. (2) *Copper*. Place the required amount of wire-form cupric oxide in the exit end of the combustion tube. Place in a 400–500 °C. furnace and pass carbon dioxide gas, which has been scrubbed through acetone, over the tube filling in the furnace until the cupric oxide is reduced to metallic copper. Shut off the furnace control and continue passing carbon dioxide through the tube until the contents have cooled to room temperature. *(3) Copper gauze*, 120-mesh. *(4) Cupric oxide*, C. P. powdered. *(5) Hydrogen peroxide*, C. P. 30% Merck (Superoxol) or equivalent.

Apparatus. *(1)* Combustion boat, platinum; inside dimensions 37 by 9 by 9 mm. *(2)* Friedrich capsule. *(3)* Combustion tube, Vycor; prepare by using the items and dimensions indicated in Figure 1. *(4)* Azotometer; prepare by using the items and dimensions indicated in Figure 2. *(5)* Carbon dioxide generator. Fill a one-pint dewar flask with carbon dioxide snow and fit the flask with a one-hole rubber stopper. Insert the base of a glass T-tube through the stopper, sealing one arm to a delivery stopcock and connecting the other arm to a pressure-regulating valve consisting of a 200 ml. vented regulating bottle containing 100 ml. of mercury. Allow the generator to operate for at least 12 hours before any determinations are made. *(6)* Apparatus preparation. Assemble the apparatus as shown in Figure 3 and purge the system with carbon dioxide gas (reverse rinse) while the combustion

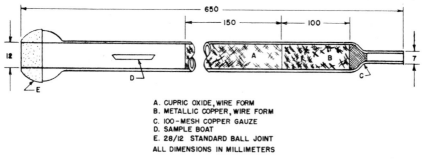

A. CUPRIC OXIDE, WIRE FORM
B. METALLIC COPPER, WIRE FORM
C. 100-MESH COPPER GAUZE
D. SAMPLE BOAT
E. 28/12 STANDARD BALL JOINT
ALL DIMENSIONS IN MILLIMETERS

Fig. 1. Combustion tube.

furnace is heated to 800–850 °C. This usually takes one and one-half to two hours. *(7)* Reverse rinse. Purge with carbon dioxide by adjusting the stopcocks so that the azotometer and oxygen generator are by-passed, with the gas entering the exit end of the combustion tube and continuing through the tube to the atmosphere. Introducing the sample into the tube against this counterflow of gas prevents much air from entering the apparatus during this operation. It also results in quicker air expulsion.

Sample Preparation. Use an amount of sample equivalent to an evolution of 3 to 8 ml. of nitrogen. Usually a 10 to 30 mg. portion of the sample is sufficient. Use a semimicro balance for all weighings. If the sample is a solid or nonvolatile liquid, weigh the sample into a tared platinum boat approximately one-third filled with powdered cupric oxide. Weigh to the nearest 0.01 mg. Cover the sample with a layer of the powdered cupric oxide. If the sample is a volatile liquid, fill a Friedrich weighing capsule to one-half of its volume with powdered cupric oxide, replace the cork, and weigh the capsule and contents to the nearest 0.01 mg. Remove the cork, introduce the sample, replace the cork and weigh the capsule and contents to the nearest 0.01 mg. Fill the capsule with additional cupric oxide, remove the cork, and insert into the combustion tube.

Procedure. While volatile samples are being weighed, cool that portion of the combustion tube in which the Friedrich capsule is to be placed by packing carbon dioxide snow around the exterior portions. Continue the reverse rinse with CO_2 gas and insert the boat or Friedrich capsule into the combustion tube so that it

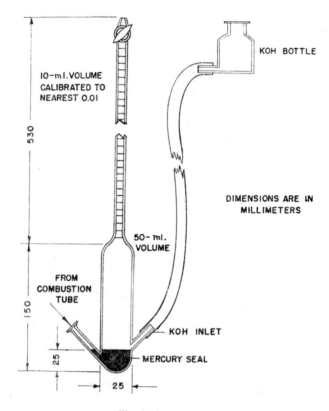

Fig. 2. Azotometer.

lies 60 to 70 mm. from the furnace. Replace the ball-joint connection at the inlet of the combustion tube. Continue reverse rinsing with CO_2 gas for approximately 10 minutes. Then adjust the stopcocks so the CO_2 gas flow by-passes the combustion tube and azotometer and purges through the hydrogen peroxide flasks to the air. When the entire system has been purged, adjust the stopcocks so the CO_2 gas bubbles through the hydrogen peroxide and combustion tube to the azotometer. Adjust the gas flow so approximately two bubbles per second will pass into the azotometer. Continue the gas flow until the bubbles become uniformly minute and

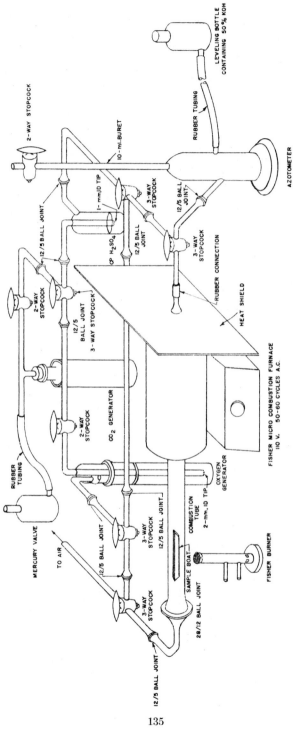

Fig. 3. Semimicro Dumas apparatus assembly.

135

about the size of a pinpoint. Close the azotometer inlet stopcock and fill the azotometer to the zero reading with the 40% potassium hydroxide solution; then open the stopcock. With volatile samples, remove the dry ice packing from around the combustion tube. Ignite the sample from left to right with a Precision high-temperature burner adjusted to a low flame. Allow the flame to approach the sample gradually and not directly in order to give slow decomposition. After the sample ignites apply the blast heat of the burner and gradually move it forward until it is adjacent to the furnace. This may take from 10 to 20 minutes. Remove the flame, continuing the gas rate of two bubbles per second into the azotometer until the bubbles have become uniformly minute and about the size of a pinpoint. Close the azotometer inlet stopcock. In approximately 15 minutes raise the leveling bottle so the liquid level in both the azotometer and leveling bottle is the same. Read the volume of nitrogen evolved. Record the temperature surrounding the azotometer and the barometric pressure.

Calculate the volume of nitrogen corrected to standard conditions:

$$0.98V \times \frac{273}{t + 273} \times \frac{p}{760} = V'$$

where V = milliliters of nitrogen evolved, V' = milliliters of nitrogen corrected to standard conditions, t = temperature, °C., p = pressure, mm. Hg, and 0.98 = correction factor, including adhesion of the KOH to the azotometer, vapor pressure of the solution, and the apparatus blank.

Calculate the nitrogen percentage:

$$\frac{V' \times 0.125}{\text{g. sample}} = \text{nitrogen, per cent by weight}$$

B. KJELDAHL METHOD

This procedure for the determination of nitrogen in organic compounds was originally proposed for use in the brewing industry, but soon met with widespread adoption because of its ease of operation, the simplicity of the apparatus, and because it is possible to carry out a large number of estimations simultaneously. The substance is decomposed with hot concentrated sulfuric acid and the nitrogen is fixed as ammonium sulfate. This operation is hastened by adding potassium sulfate to the mixture to raise the boiling point. The reaction mixture is treated with excess sodium hydroxide to liberate the nitrogen as ammonia, which is recovered by distillation and collected in standard acid (50). The excess acid is titrated with standard alkali solution.

As is the case with the classical procedures, many modifications and improvements have been offered since Kjeldahl first published his original method in 1883. To increase the severity of the reaction and reduce the digestion time, Gunning (34) proposed the use of potassium sulfate as a means of raising the boiling point of the digestion medium and this has now become standard practice. However, Self (85) and Carpiaux (11) have shown that in this case it is necessary to maintain the sulfuric acid content above a certain level to prevent loss of volatile ammonia. Various investigators have reported favorably on the use of sodium sulfate as a substitute for potassium sulfate. Under certain conditions phosphoric acid with sulfuric acid has proved a successful digestion medium (23).

It is often necessary to increase the severity of the reaction through the use of an oxidizing agent. Two substances that have merited a great deal of attention are potassium permanganate (17) and hydrogen peroxide (51). The permanganate has been shown to yield uncertain results and its use has largely been discontinued. Hydrogen peroxide is very acceptable as an oxidizing agent, although the reaction is more or less violent and must be handled cautiously. Mears and Hussey (64) have reported the successful use of perchloric acid as an aid to digestion.

Considerable effort has been expended in the search for catalysts to produce a further increase in the velocity of the reaction. We will not attempt to trace the various lines of endeavor here; the interested reader is referred to the literature (7). As old as the procedure itself is the use of mercury, either free or combined, as the catalyst. In 1885 Wilfarth (104) reported on a number of compounds used as catalysts, and mercury was stated to be most efficient. Other catalysts that have found acceptance are: copper, alone or as the oxide or sulfate; selenium, alone or as the dioxide (SeO_2) or oxychloride ($SeOCl_2$); and various mixtures of these. A digestion mixture of copper sulfate, potassium sulfate, and mercuric oxide in sulfuric acid has been given official status by the Association of Official Agricultural Chemists.

In 1913, Winkler (106) proposed collecting the ammonia from the steam distillation in 4% boric acid, rather than the standard acid called for in the original Kjeldahl method. The advantages of this were later confirmed by Markley and Hann (63). Boric acid is an extremely weak acid, and does not cause a color change with the indicators used. However, ammonia is fixed by it, and as such can be titrated directly with acid. This technique obviates the need for more than one standard solution.

Up to this point our discussion has considered only those compounds whose nitrogen is in basic form and easily split off during digestion to form ammonium sulfate. However, there are a number of compounds whose nitrogen is present in other than a basic form, such as nitrates, nitro, nitroso, and azo compounds, and ring nitrogen compounds. These compounds are refractory and require special treatment to convert the nitrogen to a more easily reducible form prior to the sulfuric acid digestion.   Further information on the Kjeldahl technique and on other methods for determining nitro, nitroso, and nitrate groups is given in Volume II of this series, p. 71 ff.

In 1886, Jodlbauer (43) made an approach to the problem by suggesting the addition of phenols to the digestion medium.   Phenols are readily nitrated, and subsequent treatment with a suitable reducing agent renders the nitrogen available for the acid digestion.   In 1916, Cope (15) stated that salicylic acid was a very satisfactory substitute for phenol.   This reagent is now generally accepted, although phenols still find some usage. The use of hydriodic acid and phosphorus (26) is useful in reducing hydrazine, nitro, nitroso, and azo derivatives:

$$RNO_2 + 6HI + 2P \longrightarrow RNH_2 + 2H_2O + 2PI_3 \tag{1}$$

The red phosphorus maintains a high concentration of hydriodic acid:

$$PI_3 + 3H_2O \longrightarrow 3HI + H_3PO_3 \tag{2}$$

Among the many reducing agents that have been successfully used are zinc, sodium thiosulfate, iron, stannous chloride, sodium hyposulfite, and sulfur (7).

The following semimicro procedure, which embraces many of the later modifications, is one that has been found most acceptable for general usage in determining amines, amides, imines, and imides in the Carbide laboratories.   Nitriles and cyano compounds may also be determined easily by this procedure without need for special treatment.

The compounds are hydrolyzed by hydrogen peroxide and sulfuric acid to ammonium acid sulfate:

$$RCN + 2H_2O_2 \longrightarrow RCONH_2 + H_2O + O_2 \tag{3}$$

$$RCONH_2 + H_2SO_4 + H_2O \longrightarrow NH_4HSO_4 + RCOOH + 2H_2O \tag{4}$$

Reagents.   (*1*) *Concentrated sulfuric acid*, C. P.   (*2*) *Hydrogen peroxide*, *30%*.   (*3*) *Potassium hydroxide*, *50%* aqueous solution.   (*4*) *Boric acid*, 1.0% aqueous solution.   (*5*) *Standard 0.01 N hydrochloric acid*.   (*6*) *Mixed indicator* (61). Prepare separate solutions of 0.1% bromocresol green and 0.1% methyl red in methanol.   Mix, using 5 parts of the bromocresol green and 1 part of the methyl red solutions.   Prepare a fresh solution of each indicator and a new mixture every two weeks.

Apparatus.   The distillation apparatus is an adaptation of that suggested by Hallet (38) and is readily adapted to either semimicro or macro determinations.   See Figure 4.

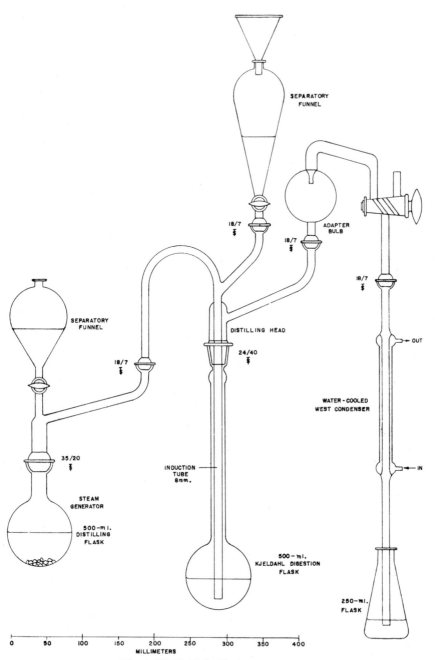

Fig. 4. Kjeldahl distillation apparatus.

Digestion.   Prepare a sufficient number of 500 ml. 24/40 glass-stoppered Kjeldahl digestion flasks to make all blank and sample determinations in duplicate. Into each sample flask introduce an amount of sample calculated to contain not more than 0.4 mg. of nitrogen.   If the sample is an aliquot of a dilution, add an equivalent amount of the diluent to each blank.   Add 5 ml. of concentrated sulfuric acid and boil the contents of each flask gently for the length of time indicated in Table I.   From a buret add exactly 2.0 ml. of the hydrogen peroxide *dropwise*, swirling each flask constantly during the addition.   Again heat the contents of the flasks to the appearance of dense white fumes, continue to boil gently for 15 minutes, and then allow the flasks and contents to cool to room temperature.

Distillation.   Add 100 to 150 ml. of distilled water to the digestion flask and connect the flask to the distillation apparatus as shown in Figure 4.   Make all connections with ground-glass joints.   Transfer 50 ml. of the boric acid solution into the 250 ml. erlenmeyer flask used for the receiver, as shown.   Add 5 or 6 drops of the mixed indicator.   Be sure the lower tip of the condenser extends below the liquid level in the flask.   Transfer 25 ml. of the potassium hydroxide to the separatory funnel above the digestion flask.   Pass cold water through the condenser and allow the potassium hydroxide to drop slowly into the digestion flask.   Shake the

TABLE I

Total Nitrogen by Kjeldahl Method

Compound	Sample, mg.[a]	Digestion time, min.
Acetamide...........................	15 to 30[b]	30
Acetoacetanilide.....................	35 to 50[b]	30
Aniline..............................	20 to 35	30
Dibutylamine.......................	25 to 40	60
Diethanolamine.....................	20 to 40	30
Di(2-ethylhexyl)amine...............	40 to 50	60
Ethylethanolamine...................	20 to 35	30
Ethyldiethanolamine.................	25 to 40	30
Methyldiethanolamine................	25 to 40	30
Methylethanolamine..................	20 to 35	30
Monoethanolamine...................	15 to 25	30
Monoisopropanolamine................	20 to 35	60
Morpholine..........................	20 to 35	30
Phenyldiethanolamine................	35 to 50	60
Phthalimide.........................	35 to 50[b]	30
Thialdine...........................	35 to 50[b]	30
Triethanolamine.....................	25 to 40	30
Urea................................	5 to 12[b]	30

[a] Introduce 1 to 3 g. of the sample, weighed to the nearest 0.1 mg., into a 500 ml. volumetric flask.   Dilute to the mark with distilled water or methanol, depending on the miscibility of the sample.   Use a 10 ml. aliquot for the analysis.

[b] Weigh to the nearest 0.1 mg. using tared watch glasses or cigarette paper.

apparatus during this addition to prevent layering of the alkali, which may result in a violent reaction. Close the three-way stopcock and apply heat to the steam generator in such a manner that a minimum of steam condensation takes place in the digestion flask. If necessary, additional water may be added to the steam generator through the separatory funnel above the distillation flask. Collect the distillate for 10 minutes, lower the receiver slightly, and continue the distillation for 5 additional minutes. Remove the receiver and titrate the contents with standard 0.01 N hydrochloric acid just to the disappearance of the blue color and the first appearance of a faint pink color.

Calculate the nitrogen percentage:

$$\frac{(A - B)N \times 1.401}{\text{g. sample}} = \text{nitrogen, per cent by wt.}$$

where A = milliliters of N normal HCl required for the sample and B = average milliliters of N normal HCl required for the blank.

Table I shows the proper sample size and reaction conditions for a number of compounds for which this procedure has been found satisfactory. The sample size is based on the nitrogen content of the pure compound equivalent to 20 to 40 ml. of 0.01 N hydrochloric acid.

III. AMINES

1. Total Primary, Secondary, and Tertiary Amines

The basic properties of primary, secondary, and tertiary amines offer a functional approach to their determination by acid-base titrations. Although the reactions as exhibited below do not permit differentiation between the different types of amines, they do effect quantitative estimation of their alkaline properties:

$$RNH_2 + HX \longrightarrow RNH_2 \cdot HX \tag{5a}$$

$$R_2NH + HX \longrightarrow R_2NH \cdot HX \tag{5b}$$

$$R_3N + HX \longrightarrow R_3N \cdot HX \tag{5c}$$

The titrations are often performed in aqueous medium although application may be made to only a limited number of compounds. Not only are solubility limitations imposed by use of water as a solvent, but also the end point may be difficult to observe. To extend the application of the titration to a larger number of compounds, alcohol is often used to increase the solubility of certain amines.

In order to enhance the alkaline characteristics of weakly basic amines, it is often necessary to use nonaqueous solvents to give sharp end points. Fortunately, these procedures are accurate and precise and require no special equipment. The techniques required are easily learned.

A. TITRATION WITH HYDROCHLORIC ACID IN WATER

Certain water-soluble amines exhibit sufficiently strong alkaline dissociation in aqueous solution to insure a satisfactory end point using either indicator or potentiometric means. These compounds react stoichiometrically with hydrochloric acid in water to form the corresponding amine hydro-

TABLE II
Titration of Amines with Hydrochloric Acid in Water

Compound	K_b	Sample, g.[a]	End point, pH
Butylamine	4.1×10^{-4b}	0.18 to 0.29	6.4
N-Butyldiethanolamine	5.4×10^{-6c}	0.40 to 0.65	5.4
Diethanolamine	6.0×10^{-6c}	0.26 to 0.42	5.4
Diethylamine	1.3×10^{-3b}	0.20 to 0.28	—
Diisopropanolamine	2.0×10^{-5c}	0.36 to 0.44	—
Diisopropylamine	3.7×10^{-4c}	0.30 to 0.38	—
Dimethylethanolamine	1.3×10^{-5c}	0.26 to 0.34	—
Ethylamine	5.6×10^{-4b}	0.16 to 0.22[d]	—
Ethylenediamine	8.5×10^{-5b}	0.08 to 0.14	4.5
Hexylamine	1.3×10^{-4c}	0.25 to 0.40	6.3
N-(2-Hydroxyethyl)morpholine	6.5×10^{-8c}	0.33 to 0.52	4.5
Isopropylamine	4.3×10^{-4b}	0.18 to 0.22	—
N-Methylmorpholine	1.7×10^{-7c}	0.25 to 0.40	4.6
Monoethanolamine	2.8×10^{-5b}	0.15 to 0.25	6.1
Morpholine	3.3×10^{-6c}	0.22 to 0.35	5.1
γ-Picoline	6.3×10^{-9c}	0.23 to 0.37	4.0
Piperazine	$K_1 = 6.4 \times 10^{-5a}$ $K_2 = 3.7 \times 10^{-9b}$	0.11 to 0.17	4.0
Triethanolamine	3.1×10^{-7c}	0.37 to 0.60	5.0
Triethylamine	5.7×10^{-4b}	0.36 to 0.44	—
Triethylene glycol 3-aminopropyl ether	6.6×10^{-5c}	0.52 to 0.83	6.0

[a] Weigh the samples to the nearest 0.1 mg. in the most convenient manner.
[b] From Lange, *Handbook of Chemistry*, Handbook Publishers, Sandusky, Ohio.
[c] From Carbide and Carbon Chemicals Co., unpublished data.
[d] Use a sealed-glass ampule.

chloride. The amount of standard hydrochloric acid required for the titration is a direct measure of the amine originally present.

Mixed Indicator. Prepare separate solutions of 0.1% bromocresol green and 0.1% methyl red in methanol. Mix, using 5 parts of the bromocresol green solution, and 1 part of the methyl red solution. Prepare fresh solutions of each indicator and a new mixture every two weeks.

Procedure. Transfer 50 ml. of water to each of a sufficient number of 250 ml. glass-stoppered erlenmeyer flasks to make all sample determinations in duplicate. Add 6 to 8 drops of bromocresol green–methyl red mixed indicator and make neutral by the dropwise addition of hydrochloric acid to the disappearance of the green color. Into each flask introduce an amount of sample containing 3 to 4 meq. of amine. Swirl the flask to effect solution. Titrate with standard 0.1 N hydrochloric acid to the disappearance of the green color. If, because of sample color, it is desirable to titrate potentiometrically, consult Table II for the pH at the end point for several representative amines.

Calculate the amount of amine present:

$$\frac{AN \times \text{E. W.}}{\text{g. sample} \times 10} = \text{amine, per cent by wt.}$$

where A = milliliters of N normal HCl required and E. W. = equivalent weight of the amine.

Table II shows the proper sample size for a number of compounds for which this procedure was found satisfactory. Also included are some ionization constants, K_b, and the pH of the end point if a potentiometric titration is required. Of course, the potentiometric data can be plotted and the end point calculated. The sample size is based upon the amount of pure amine equivalent to 25 to 40 ml. of 0.1 N hydrochloric acid.

Although the above procedure is not as generally applicable as the titration of amines with perchloric acid in acetic acid medium (see Section III.1C), the method is often used as a control of the quality of commercially available materials.

B. TITRATION WITH HYDROCHLORIC ACID IN METHANOL

In order to extend the range of application of titration of amines with hydrochloric acid, alcohol often is used as a solvent. However, the basic strength of methanol is about the same as acetonitrile (slightly less than water) and the procedure is limited therefore to amines having pK_b values (in water) of approximately 8.8 or less. The advantage of using methanol lies in its ability to dissolve many organic amines which are not soluble in water.

Indicator. Dissolve 0.15 g. of methyl orange and 0.08 g. of xylene cyanol FF in 100 ml. of distilled water.

Procedure. Transfer 25 to 50 ml. of methanol to each of a sufficient number of 250 ml. glass-stoppered erlenmeyer flasks to make all sample determinations in duplicate. Add 3 to 5 drops of methyl orange–xylene cyanol mixed indicator and make neutral by the dropwise addition of hydrochloric acid in methanol to an amber-brown end point. Into each flask introduce an amount of sample containing 3 to 4 meq. of amine. Swirl the flask to effect solution. Titrate with standard 0.1 N hydrochloric acid in methanol to the original amber-brown color. If, because of sample color, it is desirable to titrate potentiometrically, a complete titration curve must be obtained. From the plot of milliliters of titrant versus apparent pH, the end point may be ascertained. Soak the electrodes in methanol for 15 to 30 minutes prior to the titration.

Calculate the amount of amine present:

$$\frac{AN \times \text{E. W.}}{\text{g. sample} \times 10} = \text{amine, per cent by wt.}$$

where A = milliliters of N normal HCl required and E. W. = equivalent weight of the amine.

The normality of the hydrochloric acid–methanol reagent may vary from day to day, and it should be standardized before using by titrating exactly 40 ml. of the reagent with standard 0.1 N sodium hydroxide using phenol-

TABLE III
Titration of Amines with Hydrochloric Acid in Methanol

Compound	Sample, g.[a]
Butylamine	0.18 to 0.29
N-Butyldiethanolamine	0.40 to 0.65
N,N'-Di(α-methylbenzyl)ethylenediamine	0.34 to 0.54
Dibutylamine	0.32 to 0.52
Diethanolamine	0.26 to 0.42
Ethylenediamine	0.08 to 0.14
Monoethanolamine	0.15 to 0.25
γ-Picoline	0.23 to 0.37
Piperazine	0.11 to 0.17
Pyridine	0.20 to 0.32
o-Toluidine	0.27 to 0.43
Tributylamine	0.46 to 0.75
Triethanolamine	0.37 to 0.60
Triethylene glycol 3-aminopropyl ether	0.52 to 0.83

[a] Weigh the sample to the nearest 0.1 mg. in the most convenient manner.

phthalein indicator. Appreciable amounts of water affect the titration adversely; thus, efforts should be made to maintain an essentially anhydrous condition during titration. Table III shows the proper sample size for a number of compounds for which this method was found satisfactory. The sample size is based upon the amount of amine equivalent to 25 to 40 ml. of 0.1 N hydrochloric acid.

C. TITRATION WITH PERCHLORIC ACID IN ACETIC ACID

The use of perchloric acid in acetic acid medium stems from the discovery of Conant, Hall, and Werner (12,13,35,36) that organic amines give excellent end points when titrated with a strong mineral acid in acetic acid solution. Based on the measurement of conductivity of several acids in acetic acid solution, Kolthoff and Willman (52) found that perchloric acid has the greatest acid strength of all the mineral acids in this medium. Considerable effort has been reported for the investigation of a proper solvent to be used as a titration medium (30,76). The choice of solvent may often be prompted by the application in view. Most commonly used solvents, however, remain acetic acid or dioxane or a mixture of the two. The end point may be detected either by visual indicator or potentiometrically. Most often used of the indicators is crystal violet or methyl violet (71). Of the many types of electrode systems investigated (12,30,62,74,84,101), the use of a glass indicating electrode together with a reference electrode consisting of a silver wire coated with a thin layer of silver chloride as suggested by Fritz (27) is most convenient. An excellent review of the theoretical aspects of nonaqueous titrations has been published by Riddick (80).

Reagent. Measure 8 ml. of 70 to 72% perchloric acid in a graduate and transfer to a 1000 ml. volumetric flask containing approximately 500 ml. of glacial acetic acid. Swirl the flask to effect solution and dilute to the mark with additional glacial acetic acid. Allow the reagent to stand overnight before using, and standardize against Bureau of Standards potassium acid phthalate using crystal violet indicator. If necessary, heat the solution to dissolve the standard and cool before titrating.

Procedure. Transfer 50 ml. of glacial acetic acid to each of a sufficient number of 250 ml. glass-stoppered erlenmeyer flasks to make all sample determinations in duplicate. Add 2 or 3 drops of a 1.0% solution of crystal violet indicator in glacial acetic acid and make neutral by the dropwise addition of perchloric acid in acetic acid to the first green color. Into each flask introduce an amount of sample containing 3 to 4 meq. of amine. Swirl the flask to effect solution. Titrate with standard 0.1 N perchloric acid to the green color of the neutral acetic acid.

Calculate the amount of amine present:

$$\frac{AN \times \text{E. W.}}{\text{g. sample} \times 10} = \text{amine, per cent by wt.}$$

where A = milliliters of N normal $HClO_4$ required and E. W. = equivalent weight of the amine.

Typical data obtained from the analysis of samples of specially purified organic bases are shown in Table IV.

TABLE IV

Analysis of Organic Bases by Direct Titration (62)

Compound	Determined purity, %	
	Indicator method	Potentiometric method
Diethylaniline....................................	99.17	99.36
8-Hydroxyquinoline.............................	99.45	99.78
Diphenylguanidine...............................	—	99.91
Aniline..	99.41	—
n-Butylamine..................................	99.32	—
Tris(hydroxymethyl)aminomethane.................	—	99.94
Benzocaine.....................................	—	99.20
2-"Nonyl"-4,4-bis(hydroxymethyl)-2-oxazoline.........	99.85	100.00

Table V gives the proper sample size for a number of compounds for which this procedure was found satisfactory. The sample sizes are based upon the amount of amine equivalent to 20 to 40 ml. of 0.1 N perchloric acid under the conditions of the analysis specified.

Among the many applications of the perchloric acid in acetic acid titration are the determination of basic impurities in refined hydrocarbons (105) and hydrocarbon oils (107), pyridine carboxylic acids (47), and amine salts (75). The procedure has also been modified by application to micro analysis (48). In general, a reproducibility of $\pm 0.2\%$ or better has been reported for a majority of the amine compounds investigated (62,74).

2. Primary Amines

Although primary amines react with a large number of compounds and reagents, attempts to develop quantitative applications have produced few satisfactory procedures. Ones most often used depend upon the reaction with nitrous acid or with aldehydes. Van Slyke (96,97) adapted the nitrous

TABLE V

Determination of Amines by Titration with Perchloric Acid in Acetic Acid

Compound	Sample, g.[a]
β-Alanine (β-aminopropionic acid)	0.17 to 0.35
Aminoacetic acid (glycine)	0.15 to 0.30
Aminoethyldiethylamine	0.12 to 0.23
α-Aminovaleric acid	0.23 to 0.46
Aniline	0.19 to 0.38
Diamylamine	0.31 to 0.62
1,4-Dicyanopiperazine	0.33 to 0.66
Diethanolamine	0.21 to 0.42
Diethylenetriamine	0.07 to 0.14
Di(2-ethylhexyl)amine	0.48 to 0.97
Dimethylaniline	0.24 to 0.48
Dimethylethanolamine	0.18 to 0.36
Dipropylenetriamine	0.09 to 0.18
2-Ethylhexylamine	0.26 to 0.52
5-Ethyl-2-pentenylpyridine	0.34 to 0.68
5-Ethyl-2-(pentenyl-1-butenyl)pyridine	0.45 to 0.90
Hydroxyethylaminoethylethanolamine	0.15 to 0.30
5-Hydroxy-3-picoline	0.22 to 0.44
2-Methyl-5-butenylpyridine	0.29 to 0.59
2-Methyl-5-ethylpyridine	0.24 to 0.48
Methylphenylethanolamine	0.30 to 0.60
Monoethanolamine	0.12 to 0.24
Morpholine	0.17 to 0.34
N-Phenylmorpholine	0.33 to 0.65
β-Picoline	0.19 to 0.37
Piperazine	0.09 to 0.18
Pyridine	0.16 to 0.32
Salicylalethanolamine	0.33 to 0.66
o-Tolyldiethanolamine	0.39 to 0.78
o-Tolylethanolamine	0.30 to 0.60
o-Toluidine	0.21 to 0.42
Triethanolamine	0.30 to 0.60

[a] Weigh the sample to the nearest 0.1 mg. in the most convenient manner.

acid reaction in his classical method in which the nitrogen released by primary amines is collected and measured volumetrically:

$$RNH_2 + HNO_2 \longrightarrow ROH + N_2\uparrow + H_2O \tag{6}$$

$$R_2NH + HNO_2 \longrightarrow R_2N-N=O + H_2O \tag{7}$$

$$R_3N + HNO_2 \longrightarrow R_3N \cdot HNO_2 \tag{8}$$

The reaction with aldehydes to form Schiff bases also has been adapted to provide a convenient method for the determination of the —NH₂ group:

$$RNH_2 + R'CHO \longrightarrow RN{=}CHR' + H_2O \qquad (9)$$

The reaction has been studied not only from the amount of aldehyde consumed but also from the viewpoint of the quantity of water released in the reaction.

A. VAN SLYKE METHOD

The first quantitative adaption of the nitrous acid reaction with aliphatic amino groups was presented by Van Slyke (96) in 1911. Although it was used primarily in protein studies to determine amino groups in amino acids, the method may be extended to many primary amines.

Nitrous acid reacts with certain primary amines and ammonia to liberate a quantitative volume of nitrogen. Any other volatile reaction products are removed by scrubbing through the proper solvents. The low molecular weight ethers formed as reaction products from methyl- and ethylamine are sufficiently water soluble that they may be removed by scrubbing through distilled water. However, as the molecular weight of the amine increases, the volatile reaction products must be scrubbed through solvents such as tributyl phosphate or dimethoxytetraglycol (see Table VI). The volume of nitrogen, which is measured in a gas buret, is a direct measure of the primary amine or ammonia originally present.

Reagents. (1) *Cylinder nitrogen*, Linde or equivalent, convenient for purging. (2) *Sodium nitrite*, 25% aqueous solution. *Prepare fresh daily.* (3) *Glacial acetic acid*, Grasselli reagent grade or equivalent. (4) *Alkaline potassium permanganate*. Dissolve 25 g. of C. P. sodium hydroxide and 60 g. of potassium permanganate in one liter of distilled water.

Apparatus. Assemble the apparatus as shown in Figure 5. Make certain that all stopcocks are carefully greased and all connections vapor-tight. The stopcock at the base of the buret C should be open. Transfer sufficient alkaline potassium permanganate to the autobubbler pipet B to fill one bulb, and add 30 ml. additional. If auxiliary scrubbing is required, transfer sufficient liquid to the auxiliary autobubbler pipet B' to fill one bulb, and add 30 ml. additional. If not required, set stopcock R' to by-pass the scrubber completely.

Set the stopcocks as follows: X and Y to connect sample tube D with reaction chamber A; R to connect pipet B with both sides of the manifold; R' to close pipet B' from the header; S and T to connect buret C with both vent and nitrogen supply. When B and B' are closed from the system, stopcocks R and R' should be positioned so that the manifold is open from stopcock Y to stopcock S. Raise the mercury bottles F and G sufficiently to just fill the reaction chamber A and the gas buret C with mercury. Rinse the reaction chamber A with two 50 ml. portions of distilled water. Introduce the water into sample tube D, and lower mercury bottle F to draw the water into the chamber.   Set X to connect A with the sewer vent E and raise mercury bottle F to force the water to the sewer.   After the rinses, chamber A should be full of mercury and stopcocks X and Y should be closed.

Set stopcock S to connect buret C to the manifold and carefully adjust the height of mercury bottle G until the permanganate solution in B rises to the inlet tube just to the side arm containing the check valve.   Turn stopcock R to close B from the manifold.   If auxiliary scrubbing is required, set stopcock R' to connect pipet B' with buret C and carefully adjust the height of the mercury in bottle G until the

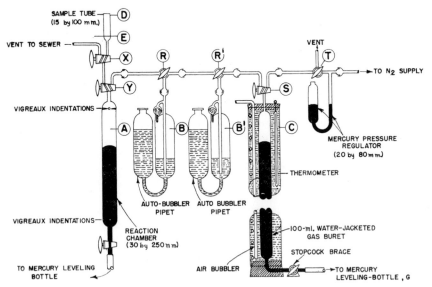

Fig. 5. Modified Van Slyke apparatus.

liquid in B' rises in the inlet tube just to the side arm containing the check valve. Turn stopcock R' to close B' from the manifold.

Set S to connect buret C with the vent-nitrogen header and raise bottle G to fill the buret with mercury.   Turn on a gentle stream of nitrogen, set T to by-pass the vent, and slowly lower bottle G to draw 100 ml. of the nitrogen into buret C.   Turn stopcock S to connect the buret with the manifold and T to permit the nitrogen to pass out the vent.   Set Y to connect reaction chamber A with the manifold, lower bottle F, and raise   ottle G to force nitrogen from buret C into A.

Turn X and Y to connect A with sample tube D and raise bottle F until mercury rises just above X, forcing the nitrogen out through D.   Repeat this operation twice to purge the system thoroughly, after which stopcocks X and Y should be closed.   The right bore of stopcock Y should be full of mercury.

Draw 100 ml. of nitrogen into buret C and turn off the nitrogen. Slowly raise bottle G until the mercury in C is at the 50 ml. mark. Vent the excess nitrogen in buret C through buret A out sample tube D.

Hold bottle G at the top of buret C and set stopcock R to connect pipet B with C, forcing the nitrogen into B. Lower bottle G slowly to draw the gas back into buret C. Repeat this scrubbing operation twice, and close B from the manifold. If auxiliary scrubbing is required, scrub the nitrogen through pipet B' by proper manipulation of stopcock R', as directed for B and R. Close B' from the manifold. Read the volume of gas in buret C by leveling the mercury column.

Scrub the gas twice again through the permanganate solution and read the volume of gas in the buret. If this volume is lower than that read previously, the system has a leak and the apparatus must be reassembled and prepared as described above. Set stopcock S to connect buret C with the vent-nitrogen header and raise bottle G until the mercury in C is between the 18 and 25 ml. marks, venting the excess gas through stopcock T. Immediately turn stopcock S to connect C with the manifold and read the initial volume of gas in the buret by leveling the mercury column.

Van Slyke equipment also is available from commercial sources.

Procedure.   Run a blank on the apparatus and reagent as described below except to omit the addition of sample. After preparation of the apparatus as described above, the stopcocks should be as follows: R and R' with pipets B and B' closed from the manifold; S with buret C connected with the manifold; T so that vent-nitrogen header is vented; X and Y closed, with Y having its right bore (side toward the manifold) full of mercury.

Into the sample tube D introduce an aliquot of the sample sufficient to evolve not more than 75 ml. of nitrogen. Turn X and Y to connect sample tube D with reaction chamber A and lower bottle F to draw the sample into A until the level of the sample is just at the top of stopcock X. Close the stopcocks. Add 10 ml. of the sodium nitrite solution into sample tube D from a graduate. Turn X and Y to connect D with A and lower bottle F to draw the solution into the reaction chamber until the level is just at the top of stopcock X. Again close the stopcocks.

Add, in order, 5 ml. of distilled water and 10 ml. of the glacial acetic acid to sample tube D. Keep stopcocks X and Y *closed* and lower bottle F so the mercury level is quite near the bottom of the reaction chamber. PRECAUTION! *Perform the following step slowly and carefully because the ensuing reaction may be somewhat violent if a considerable amount of primary amine is present. The sudden evolution of a large volume of nitrogen may develop sufficient pressure to force the gas out through stopcock Y.* Open stopcock X to connect sample tube D with Y and slowly turn stopcock Y to connect X with A, allowing the acid to be drawn into the reaction chamber until the level of the acid is just at the top of stopcock Y. *Close Y immediately.*

Raise and lower bottle F to provide thorough mixing of the sample and reactants and allow the reaction to proceed for 30 minutes. If necessary, allow gas to flow into pipet B during the reaction. Level the mercury column in buret C and record the initial volume of gas in the buret.   Except for slight changes due to temperature and pressure, this volume should be the same as that read in preparation of the apparatus.   Record the barometric pressure and the temperature indicated by the thermometer in the water jacket.

Open stopcock Y to connect reaction chamber A with the manifold and slowly raise bottle F until the level of the liquid in the reaction chamber just reaches the bottom of Y, forcing the vapor from A into buret C.   With bottle G at the top of buret C, turn stopcock R to connect C with pipet B and lower G until the permanganate solution in B rises in the inlet tube just to the side arm containing the check valve.   Scrub the gas through the permanganate solution until a constant volume is obtained in the buret.

If auxiliary scrubbing is required, scrub the gas in buret C through pipet B' by proper manipulation of stopcock R'.   Scrub the gas through the permanganate solution again until constant volume is obtained.   If it is necessary to repeat the auxiliary scrubbing, always make a final pass through the permanganate solution. Level the mercury column and record the final volume of gas in C.   Turn stopcocks X and Y to connect chamber A with the sewer vent, and raise bottle F to force the used reagents through vent E to the sewer.

Additional Instructions.   Never make more than three determinations without changing the alkaline potassium permanganate scrubber solution.   The autobubbler pipets and any other equipment which become fouled by the permanganate solution may be effectively cleaned by washing with a solution of 2% oxalic acid to which has been added 2 to 3% by weight sulfuric acid.   Ordinarily the only cleaning of the reaction chamber necessary is rinsing with distilled water.   If sufficient care is not exercised in the manipulation of the leveling bottles, however, the entire assembly may become fouled, necessitating complete dismantling for cleaning.

At all times keep a drop of distilled water floating on the mercury in the gas buret so that the theoretical correction for the vapor pressure of water is applicable.

In the manipulation of the mercury leveling bottles it is best not to make too sudden or extreme changes in the level of the mercury, because this brings unnecessary strain to bear on points of possible weakness.

Calculations.   Correct the net volume evolved by the blank to standard conditions:

$$\frac{P_b - P_v}{760} \times \frac{273}{273 + t_b} \times (B_f - B_i) = B$$

where B = milliliters of gas, at standard conditions, evolved by the blank, B_f = final milliliters of gas in buret, B_i = initial milliliters of gas in buret, P_b = atmospheric pressure, mm. Hg, P_v = vapor pressure of water at t_b°C., mm. Hg, and t_b = temperature of water jacket, °C.

Correct the net volume evolved by the sample to standard conditions:

$$\frac{P_a - P_w}{760} \times \frac{273}{273 + t_a} \times (A_f - A_i) = A$$

where A = milliliters of gas, at standard conditions, evolved by the sample, A_f = final milliliters of gas in buret, A_i = initial milliliters of gas in buret, P_a = atmospheric pressure, mm. Hg, P_w = vapor pressure of water at t_a °C., mm. Hg, and t_a = temperature of water jacket, °C.

Calculate the primary amine as milliequivalents:

$$(A - B)/22.4 = C$$

where A = milliliters of gas, at standard conditions, evolved by the sample, B = milliliters of gas, at standard conditions, evolved by the blank, and C = primary amine, milliequivalents.

Calculate the primary amine as per cent by weight:

$$\frac{C \times \text{E. W.}}{\text{g. sample} \times 10} = \text{primary amine, per cent by wt.}$$

where C = primary amine, milliequivalents, and E. W. = equivalent weight of the amine.

Table VI shows the proper sample size and reaction conditions for each of several compounds for which this method has been found satisfactory. The sample size is calculated from the amount of pure compound theoretically equivalent to not more than 75 ml. of nitrogen at standard conditions. Because of the relatively small amounts involved, the original samples should be diluted so that a 5 or 10 ml. aliquot contains the proper amount of sample.

TABLE VI
Primary Amines by the Van Slyke Method

Compound	Auxiliary scrubber liquid	Maximum sample[a]
Monomethylamine	Distilled water	0.078
Monoethylamine	Distilled water	0.12
Monoisopropylamine	Tributyl phosphate	0.15
Monobutylamine	Dimethoxytetraglycol	0.19
Monoisobutylamine	Tributyl phosphate	0.19
Monoethanolamine	—	0.16
Monoisopropanolamine	—	0.20
Ammonia	—	0.044

[a] Use an aqueous dilution such that a 5 or 10 ml. aliquot contains the amount indicated.

Table VI also lists the proper auxiliary scrubber liquid for each compound. This liquid, if required, is placed in pipet B' and used as described in the method.

The Van Slyke procedure is applicable to the determination of aliphatic primary amines and alcoholamines in the presence of the corresponding secondary and tertiary amines. Ammonia reacts quantitatively with the reagent and, if present, may be determined independently by a suitable procedure, such as the cobaltinitrite method (69), and a suitable correction applied. The procedure is not applicable to the determination of amino nitrogen in alcoholic solution, because the alcohol reacts with nitrous acid reagent to form alkyl nitrites, which are difficult to remove, and also depletes the excess nitrous acid reagent, thus resulting in incomplete amine reaction. This method has not been found suitable for the determination of complex aliphatic amines or the higher simple aliphatic amines.

The first and most often used application of the Van Slyke procedure is the determination of amino nitrogen in amino acids and proteins (96,97). Later investigators modified and applied the method to insoluble proteins (98); the polypeptides of glycine (81); and glycine and glycyl peptides (91).

B. KARL FISCHER REAGENT METHOD

The rapid reaction of primary amines with benzaldehyde in pyridine medium to release one mole of water, followed by the determination of the water formed, provides an indirect method for the determination of primary amines. Hawkins, Smith, and Mitchell (39) have applied the use of the Karl Fischer reagent for the determination of the water formed in the reaction after the excess aldehyde has been deactivated by reaction with hydrogen cyanide (8). The procedure is applicable to the determination of aliphatic, alicyclic, and aromatic primary amines and amino alcohols containing only primary amine groups.

Reagents. (1) *Pyridine*, freshly distilled. (2) *Benzaldehyde*, freshly distilled, inhibited with 0.1% hydroquinone. (3) *Sodium cyanide*, desiccated C. P. grade. (4) *Hydrogen cyanide*, 6.0% in pyridine. Carefully add 85 ml. of liquid hydrogen cyanide to 915 ml. of cold C. P. pyridine. Prepare and store the reagent in a well-ventilated hood. (5) *Karl Fischer reagent*, prepared and standardized as described below.

Karl Fischer reagent (68). Dissolve 762 g. of iodine in 2420 ml. of pyridine contained in a 9 liter glass-stoppered bottle and add 6 liters of methanol. Transfer 3 liter quantities of the stock solution to 4 liter buret bottles and cool in a suitable chopped-ice bath. Collect 135 ml. of liquid sulfur dioxide in a calibrated cold trap, add carefully to the contents of the buret bottle, and stopper Thoroughly mix the reagent and allow it to sit at room temperature for 2 days before calibration and use The Karl Fischer reagent, as well as electrometric titration apparatus, can be purchased through several laboratory supply houses.

To standardize the reagent transfer 25 ml. of anhydrous methanol to each of two 125 ml. glass-stoppered erlenmeyer flasks. From the buret add the reagent to each flask until a permanent light reddish-brown color is obtained. Match the colors of the solutions by the dropwise addition of reagent. Reserve one of the flasks as a blank. Into the second flask introduce 0.08 to 0.10 g. of distilled water weighed to the nearest 0.1 mg. by means of a hypodermic syringe. Immediately titrate with the reagent until the light reddish-brown color persists, using the blank as a guide to the proper color at the end point. Reserve the titrated solution as a blank and use the untitrated blank for a check determination, again matching the colors of the two solutions. Duplicate standardizations should agree within 0.001 g. water per 100 ml. of reagent.

Standardization.

$$\frac{\text{g. water} \times 100}{\text{ml. titration}} = \begin{array}{l}\text{factor, g. water consumed} \\ \text{by 100 ml. of reagent}\end{array}$$

Sodium tartrate dihydrate also can be used as a satisfactory stable source of water for standardizing the Karl Fischer reagent.

Procedure. Into each of two 250 ml. glass-stoppered volumetric flasks transfer 10 ml. of dry pyridine. Introduce an amount of sample equivalent to 10 meq. of primary amine into one of the flasks and reserve the other flask as a blank. If the sample is added as a 10 ml. aliquot of a pyridine solution, an equivalent amount of pyridine should be used as a blank.

To each flask add 3 ml. of benzaldehyde and place the sample together with the blank in a water bath at 60 ± 1°C. Momentarily loosen the stoppers to permit expulsion of the expanded air, restopper, and allow them to stand at 60° C. for 30 minutes. Remove the flasks from the bath and allow them to cool in air to room temperature.

Transfer the flasks to a well-ventilated hood, add 0.2 g. of dry sodium cyanide, and add 30 ml. of 6% hydrogen cyanide in pyridine. Shake the flasks vigorously for 1 minute and allow them to stand in the hood for 45 minutes. Titrate the sample and blank by the rapid addition of the Karl Fischer reagent to the first light reddish-brown color.

Determine the amount of water in the original sample by titrating a portion of the material with the Karl Fischer reagent after neutralizing the amine with glacial acetic acid. If a pyridine dilution was used, determine the amount of water in the pyridine dilution and in an equivalent volume of the pyridine solvent. Even very small quantities of water in the original sample or the pyridine solvent have a very substantial effect upon the calculated amine content and therefore cannot be neglected for accurate results.

Calculations.

$$\left[A - \left(B + \frac{S_1}{S_2} \right) C \right] F \times \frac{\text{E. W.}}{18.02} = \text{primary amine, per cent by wt.}$$

or, if a pyridine dilution of the sample is used,

$$\frac{[(A - D) - (B - E)] F \times \dfrac{\text{E. W.}}{18.02}}{S_1 V_1 / V_2} = \text{primary amine, per cent by wt.}$$

where A = milliliters Karl Fischer reagent required to titrate sample, B = milliliters required for blank, C = milliliters required to titrate water in original sample, D = milliliters required to titrate V_1 milliliters of pyridine dilution (before benzaldehyde reaction), E = milliliters required to titrate V_1 milliliters of pyridine solvent, E. W. = equivalent weight of amine, F = factor = g. $H_2O/100$ ml. reagent (see standardization of Karl Fischer reagent), S_1 = grams sample used for benzaldehyde reaction, S_2 = grams sample used in determination of water content, V_1 = volume of aliquot taken for analysis, ml., and V_2 = total volume of diluted sample, ml.

The results obtained by Hawkins, Smith, and Mitchell for different primary and primary-secondary amines are given in Table VII. Also, data determined for several amino alcohols are given in Table VIII. In most cases the precision and accuracy are within ±0.2%.

TABLE VII
Analytical Data for Primary Amines with the Karl Fischer Reagent (39)

Amine	Anal. for amine by other methods, wt. %	Amine[a]	Water	Total
Propylenediamine................	—	(2) 86.3 ± 0.2	14.1	100.4
Butylamine....................	—	(6) 98.2 ± 0.2	1.7	99.9
Diethylenetriamine..............	—	(4) 96.7 ± 0.1	1.3	98.0
Hexamethylenediamine..........	—	(4) 97.2 ± 0.1	2.7	99.9
Decamethylenediamine...........	—	(2) 97.0 ± 0.5	1.8	98.8
Laurylamine...................	98.1[b]	(2) 98.2 ± 0.2	0.6	98.8
Cyclohexylamine................	100.2[b]	(4) 99.7 ± 0.2	0.3	100.0
2-Aminomethylcyclopentylamine...	—	(2) 94.2 ± 0.3	5.4	99.6
o-Aminobicyclohexylamine........	96.7[c,d]	(2) 94.2 ± 0.1	0.1	94.3
Aniline.......................	98.8[a]	(2) 98.8 ± 0.1	0.1	98.9
m-Aminophenol.................	—	(2) 99.5 ± 0.1	0.0	99.5
p-Bromoaniline.................	99.4[c]	(6) 94.8 ± 0.3	0.0	94.8
p-Phenylenediamine.............	99.6[c]	(4) 99.9 ± 0.0	0.0	99.9
Benzylamine...................	92.8[b]	(5) 92.5 ± 0.2	0.7	93.2
Toluidine......................	—	(2) 97.1 ± 0.3	0.0	97.1
o-Aminodiphenylamine...........	99.0[c]	(2) 92.6 ± 0.2	0.0	92.6
β-Naphthylamine................	97.3[c]	(4) 97.2 ± 0.1	0.0	97.2

[a] Figures in parentheses represent number of individual determinations.
[b] By titration to bromophenol blue.
[c] By acetylation procedure for primary plus secondary amines.
[d] 96.2% by Kjeldahl analysis.

TABLE VIII

Analytical Data for Primary Amino Alcohols with the Karl Fischer Reagent (39)

Amino alcohol	Found, wt. %
Monoethanolamine[a]	100.1 ± 0.2
2-Amino-2-methylpropanol	91.1 ± 0.2
2-Amino-2-methyl-1,3-propanediol	91.6
2-Amino-1-butanol	88.9 ± 0.2
Tris(hydroxymethyl)aminomethane	96.1 ± 0.2

[a] Purified by fractionation, all others technical grade.

Heterocyclic amines react with the reagent to release one mole of water for every two moles of amine, thus causing interference. Also, amino alcohols having a secondary amine usually react nearly quantitatively.

C. SALICYLALDEHYDE METHOD

The reaction of primary amines with aldehydes to form Schiff bases not only has been adapted as described in Section III.3B, but also is used to determine secondary and tertiary amines as described in Section III.4. In addition, a unique method based upon measuring the excess aldehyde reagent has been developed by Johnson (44). The reaction with salicylaldehyde is conducted in pyridine medium in which the reaction products are neutral to phenolphthalein or thymolphthalein indicator and the excess salicylaldehyde is acidic. The amount of salicylaldehyde consumed, which is determined by titration of the excess with standard sodium methylate in pyridine, is a direct measure of the primary aliphatic amine present.

Phenolphthalein or thymolphthalein indicators in pyridine medium may be used interchangeably to detect the end point; however, in the presence of diethylamine only thymolphthalein may be used.

Reagents. (1) *Methanol*, anhydrous. (2) *Sodium methylate*, approximately 4 N; carefully add sodium metal or wire to anhydrous methanol until hydrogen is no longer evolved. (3) *Pyridine*, freshly distilled. (4) *Benzoic acid*, certified by Bureau of Standards. (5) *Phenolphthalein indicator*, 1.0% in pyridine; or thymolphthalein indicator, 1.0% in pyridine. (6) *Salicylaldehyde*, approximately 0.5 N; dilute 5 ml. of reagent-grade salicylaldehyde to 100 ml. with redistilled pyridine.

Standard 0.1 N Sodium Methylate–Pyridine. Transfer 120 ml. of the 4 N sodium methylate to a 4 liter bottle having a 29/42 ground-glass neck and containing 250 ml. of anhydrous methanol. Dilute the contents of the bottle to one gallon with redistilled pyridine. Standardize this reagent daily. The reagent readily absorbs carbon dioxide from the air, and is best preserved and used in a 50 ml. automatic buret; all vents open to the air must have protective Ascarite tubes.

Transfer 50 ml. of freshly distilled pyridine to each of a sufficient number of 250 ml. glass-stoppered erlenmeyer flasks to make all sample and blank determinations in duplicate. Reserve two of the flasks for the blanks. Into each of the other flasks introduce 0.35 to 0.40 g. of Bureau of Standards benzoic acid weighed to the nearest 0.1 mg. Stopper the flasks and swirl to effect complete solution. Add 2 or 3 drops of the thymolphthalein–pyridine indicator to each flask and titrate immediately with the sodium methylate–pyridine reagent to the first blue end point. During the titration direct a gentle stream of nitrogen into the flask through a short piece of 6 mm. glass tubing fastened near the tip of the buret.

Calculate the normality of the reagent as follows:

$$\frac{\text{g. benzoic acid}}{0.1221 \times (A - B)} = \text{normality of sodium methylate–pyridine}$$

where A = milliliters required for the sample and B = average milliliters required for the blank.

Procedure.

PRECAUTION! Amine samples readily absorb carbon dioxide from the air and must be protected from atmospheric contamination.

Prepare a sufficient number of pressure bottles to make all blank and sample determinations in duplicate. Add exactly 10 ml. of the 0.5 N salicylaldehyde to each of the bottles using the same pipet for each transfer. Reserve two of the bottles as blanks. If the sample is an aliquot portion of a dilution, add an equivalent amount of the diluent to each of the blanks.

Into each of the other bottles introduce an amount of sample calculated to contain not more than 3 meq. of primary amine. If a sealed-glass ampule is used, add several pieces of 8 mm. glass rod and shake the bottle vigorously to break the ampule. Allow the samples to stand together with the blanks at room temperature for 15 minutes.

Carefully remove the stopper and wash any adhering material into the bottle with a few milliliters of redistilled pyridine. To each bottle add approximately 1 ml. of the phenolphthalein indicator and titrate with standard 0.1 N sodium methylate–pyridine solution to the first red end point. During the titration direct a gentle stream of nitrogen into the bottle.

Calculation.

$$\frac{(B - A)N \times \text{E. W.}}{\text{g. sample} \times 10} = \text{amine, per cent by wt.}$$

where A = milliliters of N normal sodium methylate required for the sample, B = average milliliters of N normal sodium methylate required for the blank, and E. W. = equivalent weight of the amine.

Primary aromatic amines do not react quantitatively under the described conditions and, if present, are a source of error. Ammonia interferes and must be removed from the sample before accurate results may be obtained. Although ammonia may be removed by a technique similar to that described in Section III.4, generally more satisfactory results would be obtained by the separate determination of ammonia by the cobaltinitrite method (69) and the primary amine plus ammonia by the Van Slyke procedure. Alcohols and water do not interfere. Amine salts interfere quantitatively and a suitable correction must be applied if present. Because amine carbonates form easily, care must be exercised to prevent atmospheric contamination of the sample. Because heterocyclic secondary amines, such as piperidine, piperazine, and morpholine, react partially under the specified reaction conditions, they are a source of error and must be absent from the sample. Alcoholamines cannot be analyzed by this procedure and, if present, are a source of error.

TABLE IX

Determination of Primary Amines by the Salicylaldehyde Reagent

Compound	Sample, g.[a]
Methylamine	0.06 to 0.09[c]
Ethylamine[b]	0.09 to 0.14[c]
Isopropylamine	0.12 to 0.18[c]
Butylamine	0.15 to 0.22[c]
Hexylamine	0.20 to 0.30
Diethylaminoethylamine	0.23 to 0.35
2-Ethylhexylamine	0.26 to 0.39

[a] Weigh to the nearest 0.1 mg. using a suitable weighing pipet unless otherwise specified.
[b] Use thymolphthalein indicator only if diethylamine is present.
[c] Use a sealed glass ampule or an aliquot from a pyridine dilution.

Table IX shows the proper sample size for a number of compounds for which this procedure has been found satisfactory. The sample size is based on the amount of primary amine equivalent to 20 to 30 ml. of 0.1 N sodium methylate. For lower concentrations in noninterfering solvents proportionately larger samples may be used.

D. COPPER–SALICYLALDEHYDE METHOD

The primary amine-aldehyde reaction also has been adapted to a colorimetric procedure by Critchfield and Johnson (15a). The Schiff base formed with salicylaldehyde is reacted with cupric chloride in the presence of triethanolamine, a proton acceptor, to form a complex soluble in hexanol:

$$2 \quad \begin{array}{c} H \\ | \\ -C{=}NR \\ | \\ -OH \end{array} \quad + \; CuCl_2 \; + \; 2(HOCH_2CH_2)_3N \longrightarrow$$

$$\begin{array}{c} H \qquad\qquad H \\ -C{=}N{-}R \;\; R{-}N{=}C{-} \\ \searrow Cu \swarrow \\ -O \qquad\qquad O{-} \end{array} \quad + \; 2(HOCH_2CH_2)_3N \cdot HCl \quad (10)$$

The copper complex, which is extracted into hexanol, is colored; however, the absorption maximum occurs in a region that cannot be measured satisfactorily in the presence of excess salicylaldehyde. Therefore an aliquot of the hexanol layer is removed and the amount of copper present is determined colorimetrically by reaction with N,N-di(hydroxyethyl)dithiocarbamate (108).

Reagents. (*1*) *Triethanolamine.* Redistill 98% triethanolamine, under 1 to 2 mm. of pressure using a column 6 in. long and 30 mm. in diameter packed with glass beads and heated by means of resistance wire. Use a 3 liter round-bottom distillation flask fitted with a thermometer well. Stir the contents of the flask by means of a magnetic stirrer. Do not allow the kettle temperature to exceed 185°C. during the distillation. An optical density of 0.65 ± 0.02 for 0.372 mg. of ethanolamine should be obtained when this material is used in the following reagent.

(*2*) *Copper–salicylaldehyde reagent.* Into a 100 ml. glass-stoppered graduated cylinder add 15.0 ml. of the redistilled triethanolamine, 0.5 ml. salicylaldehyde, and 0.25 g. cupric chloride ($CuCl_2 \cdot 2H_2O$). Dilute to 100 ml. with distilled water and mix the contents.

(*3*) *N,N-di(hydroxyethyl)dithiocarbamic acid reagent.* Prepare a 2% by volume solution of reagent-grade carbon disulfide in methanol and a 5% by volume solution of diethanolamine in methanol. Prepare the reagent fresh daily by mixing equal volumes of the two components.

(*4*) *n-Hexanol.*

Procedure. By means of a suitable transfer pipet, add 2.0 ml. of the copper–salicylaldehyde reagent to each of three 25 ml. glass-stoppered graduated cylinders. Reserve one of the cylinders as a blank. Into each of the other cylinders add an amount of sample calculated to contain not more than the maximum amount of primary amine listed in Table X. The sample must not contain more than 0.01 mg. of ammonia or 0.5 g. of secondary and tertiary amine. For samples of less than 0.1 g. use a suitable dilution in water such that a 2.0 ml. aliquot contains not more than the maximum amount of primary amine listed in Table X. Dilute the contents of each graduate to the 10 ml. mark with distilled water, stopper, and mix thoroughly. Allow the samples to react for the length of time and at the temperature specified in Table X. After the reaction is complete add sufficient hexanol to bring the total volume of liquid to 25 ml. Stopper the cylinders, shake each vigorously 15 or 20 times, and allow the layers to separate.   Add 5 ml. of the N,N-di(hydroxyethyl)dithiocarbamic acid reagent to each of three additional 25 ml. glass-stoppered graduated cylinders.   The graduates and stoppers must be cleaned with cleaning solution, rinsed several times with tap and distilled water, and finally with methanol prior to each use.   By means of a suitable transfer pipet add 5.0 ml. of the hexanol layer from each reaction graduate to the respective graduates containing the dithiocarbamic acid reagent.   Add the hexanol dropwise to prevent the material from clinging to the walls of the pipet.   Dilute each cylinder to the 25 ml. mark with methanol, stopper, and mix the contents. Transfer portions of the samples and blank to respective cells of a spectrophotometer and obtain the optical density at a wave length of 430 mμ for the sample based on a reading of zero for the blank.   From a previously prepared calibration curve read the concentration of primary amine corresponding to the optical density.

A few primary amines do not react quantitatively with this reagent. In general, aromatic amines such as aniline, compounds that contain more than one primary amine group, and primary amines branched in the 2-position cannot be determined.   Propylenediamine and 2-ethylhexylamine are exceptions to this generalization.

Ammonia interferes if more than 0.01 mg. is present in the sample aliquot used for analysis.   The combined secondary and tertiary amine content of the sample aliquot used for analysis must not exceed 0.5 g. because of their solubilizing effect on the copper complex in the aqueous layer.   Strong oxidizing or reducing agents interfere by depleting the reagent.   Also,

TABLE X

Determination of Primary Amines by the Copper–Salicylaldehyde Reagent (15a)

Compound	Primary amine, mg., maximum	Temp., °C.	Time, min.
Aminoethylethanolamine..........	1.10	20 to 30	30 to 60
N-Aminoethylmorpholine.........	0.85	20 to 30	15 to 60
Butylamine....................	0.70[a]	20 to 30	15 to 60
Ethanolamine..................	0.50	20 to 30	15 to 60
Ethylamine....................	0.53	20 to 30	15 to 60
2-Ethylhexylamine..............	1.40	20 to 30	15 to 60
Hexylamine....................	1.10	20 to 30	15 to 60
Isobutanolamine................	0.60	20 to 30	60 to 120
Isopropanolamine...............	0.60	20 to 30	15 to 60
Methylamine...................	0.30	20 to 30	15 to 60
Propylenediamine...............	0.42[b]	98 ± 2	10 to 20

[a] Make dilutions using a 10% solution of methanol in water.
[b] Use 50 ml. glass-stoppered graduated cylinders.   Do not stopper during reaction.

compounds forming complexes with copper which are soluble in hexanol will give high results.

Table X gives the proper sample size and reaction conditions for a number of compounds for which this procedure has been found satisfactory. The maximum sample size is based on the amount of pure primary amine corresponding to an optical density of 0.9 under the conditions of the method.

3. Primary and Secondary Amines

A. ACETIC ANHYDRIDE–PYRIDINE REAGENT

Primary and secondary amines are readily acetylated, thereby providing a convenient and precise method for the analysis of amine mixtures. The reagent usually used for the acetylation is acetic anhydride in pyridine, which reacts as follows:

$$\begin{matrix} CH_3CO \\ CH_3CO \end{matrix}\!\!>\!\!O \;+\; \langle\;\rangle N \longrightarrow \langle\;\rangle N\!\!<\!\!\begin{matrix} COCH_3 \\ OCOCH_3 \end{matrix} \tag{11}$$

Acetylpyridinium acetate

$$R\!-\!NH_2 \;+\; \langle\;\rangle N\!\!<\!\!\begin{matrix} COCH_3 \\ OCOCH_3 \end{matrix} \longrightarrow \langle\;\rangle N\!\!<\!\!\begin{matrix} H \\ OCOCH_3 \end{matrix} \;+\; \underset{RNHCCH_3}{\overset{O}{\|}} \tag{12}$$

Primary
amine

$$\begin{matrix} R \\ R' \end{matrix}\!\!>\!\!NH \;+\; \langle\;\rangle N\!\!<\!\!\begin{matrix} COCH_3 \\ OCOCH_3 \end{matrix} \longrightarrow \langle\;\rangle N\!\!<\!\!\begin{matrix} H \\ OCOCH_3 \end{matrix} \;+\; \begin{matrix} R \\ R' \end{matrix}\!\!>\!\!N\overset{O}{\overset{\|}{C}}CH_3 \tag{13}$$

Secondary
amine

The excess acetylpyridinium acetate is then decomposed with water:

$$\langle\;\rangle N\!\!<\!\!\begin{matrix} COCH_3 \\ OCOCH_3 \end{matrix} \;+\; HOH \longrightarrow \langle\;\rangle N\!\!<\!\!\begin{matrix} H \\ OCOCH_3 \end{matrix} \;+\; CH_3COOH \tag{14}$$

The amount of amine reacted may be determined either by titrating the liberated acid or by measuring the amount of water consumed in hydrolyzing the excess acetylpyridinium acetate.

A second reaction of significance for the determination of primary and secondary amines is the formation of dithiocarbamic acids with carbon disulfide (42a):

$$RNH_2 \;+\; CS_2 \longrightarrow R\!-\!NH\!-\!\overset{S}{\overset{\|}{C}}\!-\!SH \tag{15}$$

$$R_2NH + CS_2 \longrightarrow R_2-N-\overset{\overset{\displaystyle S}{\|}}{C}-SH \qquad (16)$$

Recent application of these reactions show considerable promise in simplifying the analysis of amine mixtures (15b).

(1) **Titration of Liberated Acid.**   This procedure is similar to the method of Ogg, Willits, and Porter (72) for the determination of hydroxyl groups.

The acetylpyridinium acetate reagent reacts quantitatively with primary and secondary amines to form one equivalent of titratable acid and with water to form two equivalents.   The total acid liberated is determined by titration with standard alcoholic potassium hydroxide.   A blank is run in which the reagent is allowed to react with water under the same conditions and, from the difference in the amount of alkali consumed by the sample and the blank, the amount of primary or secondary amine may be calculated.

Hydroxyl compounds react with the reagent and in many cases the reaction is quantitative (see Volume I of this series, p. 26).   Ammonia reacts quantitatively with the reagent in 30 minutes at room temperature. Water decomposes the anhydride but, if the amount present is not excessive, interference is negligible.   Tertiary amines do not react.   Certain diacyl and pyrrole-type secondary amines do not react quantitatively and therefore interfere.   As the determination is based on an acidimetric titration, a suitable correction must be applied if the sample is not neutral to cresol red–thymol blue indicator in a medium similar to that resulting from the analysis for the amino function.

Reagents.   (*1*) *Acetic anhydride–pyridine reagent.*   Add 57 to 58 ml. of acetic anhydride to 450 ml. of pyridine containing 0.3 to 0.5% water to inhibit resin formation (see Volume I, p. 23).   Shake vigorously to obtain complete reaction. For best results, prepare the reagent fresh daily.   Preserve the solution in a dark-colored glass-stoppered bottle.   *Do not use the reagent if it becomes discolored.*   For specifications and a method for preparing a satisfactory grade of pyridine see Volume I, p. 25.   (*2*) *Mixed indicator.*   Add 1 part of 0.1% aqueous solution of cresol red, which has been neutralized with standard 0.1 N sodium hydroxide, to 3 parts of a 0.1% neutral aqueous solution of thymol blue.   (*3*) *Standard 0.5 N potassium hydroxide in methanol;* standardize against Bureau of Standards potassium acid phthalate using the mixed indicator.

Procedure.   Prepare a sufficient number of heat-resistant pressure bottles to make all blank and sample determinations in duplicate.   Carefully pipet 10 ml. of the acetic anhydride–pyridine reagent into each of the bottles, using the same pipet for each transfer.   Place the bottles in a crushed-ice bath and chill for approximately 10 minutes.   Reserve two of the bottles as blanks.

Prepare a pyridine dilution of the sample such that a 10-ml. aliquot will contain not more than 10 meq. of primary and secondary amine. For substantially pure material weigh the sample to the nearest 0.1 mg. using the amount specified in Table XI. If hydroxyl compounds or ammonia are present the sample size and reaction conditions must be adjusted accordingly.

Into each of the sample bottles transfer a 10 ml. aliquot of the sample dilution using a suitable transfer pipet. Immediately fit the bottles with pressure stoppers. Into each of the blanks introduce 10 ml. of pyridine using a suitable transfer pipet, and fit each bottle with a pressure stopper. Remove the bottles from the ice bath and allow the samples and blanks to react under the conditions specified in Table XI.

Reaction at 98 ± 2°C. Wrap each bottle securely in a canvas bag. Place the samples and blanks as close together as possible in a steam bath at 98 ± 2°C. for

TABLE XI

Determination of Primary and Secondary Amines by Acetylation and Titration of Liberated Acid

Compound	Maximum sample, g.[a]	Time, min.[b]	Temp., °C.
N-Aminoethylmorpholine	1.3	15	25
Ammonia	0.2	30	25
Aniline	0.9	15	25
Butylamine	0.73	15	25
N,N'-Di(α-methylbenzyl)ethylenediamine	1.3	60	98
Dibutylamine	1.3	15	25
Diethylamine	0.73	15	25
Diethylaminoethylamine	1.2	15	25
Diethylenetriamine	0.34	15	25
Diisopropylamine	1.0	15	25
Ethylamine	0.45	15	25
Ethylenediamine	0.30	15	25
2-Ethylhexylamine	1.3	15	25
Hexylamine	1.0	15	25
Isopropylamine	0.60	15	25
α-Methylbenzylamine	1.2	15	25
N-Methylaniline	1.0	60	98
Morpholine	0.87	15	25
Propylenediamine	0.37	15	25
Tetraethylenepentamine	0.38	15	25
o-Toluidine	1.0	60	25
Triethylenetetramine	0.38	15	25

[a] Prepare a pyridine dilution of the sample such that a 10 ml. aliquot will contain the amount of sample specified.

[b] If ammonia is present in the sample, a minimum reaction time of 30 minutes at room temperature is necessary.

the time specified.   Maintain sufficient water in the bath to just cover the liquid in the bottles.   Remove the bottles from the bath and allow them to cool in air to room temperature.   When the bottles have cooled, loosen the wrappers, uncap to release any pressure, and then remove the wrappers.

Reaction at room temperature.   Allow the samples to stand together with the blanks at room temperature for the length of time specified.   If ammonia is present a minimum reaction time of 30 minutes at room temperature is required.   Cool each of the bottles slightly under tap water and uncap carefully to prevent any loss of the contents.

To each of the bottles add 10 ml. of distilled water and allow the bottles to stand together for 5 to 10 minutes.   If samples are warm, cool to room temperature.   Add 20 ml. of the butanol and 3 to 5 drops of the mixed indicator to each of the bottles and titrate immediately with standard 0.5 N alcoholic potassium hydroxide to the appearance of a definite blue color.   Match the color of the sample with that of the blank.

Calculate the amount of primary and secondary amines.

$$\frac{(B - A) \times N}{\text{g. sample}} = \text{meq./gram primary and secondary amine}$$

If only one primary or secondary amine is present:

$$\frac{(B - A)N \times \text{E. W.}}{\text{g. sample} \times 10} = \text{amine, per cent by wt.}$$

where A = milliliters of N normal KOH required for the sample, B = average milliliters of N normal KOH required for the blank, and E. W. = equivalent weight of amine.

Table XI shows the proper sample size and reaction conditions for a number of compounds for which this procedure has been found satisfactory. The sample size is calculated from the amount of pure compound equivalent to approximately 20 ml. of 0.5 N KOH.   For lower concentrations in non-interfering solvents, a proportionately larger sample should be used.

(2) Titration of Excess Water.   Mitchell, Hawkins, and Smith (67) describe a procedure in which the acetylation products are hydrolyzed with a known excess of water and the excess determined by titration with Karl Fischer reagent.   This technique, which is independent of acid-base titrimetry, is applicable to primary and secondary amines generally, including aliphatic, alicyclic, heterocyclic, and aromatic types.

No interference is encountered from amides, urethans, nitriles, and tertiary amines.   In the presence of primary alcoholic hydroxyl the procedure may be modified to effect quantitative acetylation of both the amine and alcohol. Most secondary and tertiary alcohols react incompletely and hence interfere. Diaryl secondary amines and pyrrole fail to react.

Reagents. *(1) Acetylating reagent;* mix 1.5 moles (142 ml.) of pure acetic anhydride with sufficient dry pyridine to make one liter of solution. *(2) Hydrolysis reagent;* dissolve 100 g. of J. T. Baker C. P. or Merck A. R. grade dry sodium iodide and 22 ml. of water in 1 liter of pyridine. *(3) Karl Fischer reagent;* see Section III.2B for preparation of this reagent.

Procedure. Transfer a size sample equivalent to 10 meq. of primary and secondary amine to a 250 ml. glass-stoppered volumetric flask containing exactly 20 ml. of the acetylating agent. The sample may be weighed directly or added volumetrically in pyridine solution. If primary hydroxyl is present limit the sample size to 10 meq. of amine plus hydroxyl.

Run at least one blank on 20 ml. of the acetylating reagent. If a pyridine dilution of the sample is used add an equivalent volume of the pyridine solvent to each blank.

Stopper and shake each of the flasks and allow them to stand for 30 minutes at room temperature. In the presence of primary hydroxyl heat an additional 30 minutes at 60 ± 1 °C. to effect complete esterification.

At the end of this time add, by means of a calibrated pipet, 25 ml. of the hydrolysis reagent to each flask. Place in a water bath at 60 ± 1 °C. and, after raising the stopper momentarily to allow for expansion of the included air, stopper firmly and maintain at that temperature for 30 minutes. Allow the flasks to cool spontaneously to room temperature, and titrate the contents of each with Karl Fischer reagent.

Determine the amount of water in the original sample by titrating a portion of the material with the Karl Fischer reagent after neutralizing the amine with glacial acetic acid. If a pyridine dilution was used, determine the amount of water in the pyridine dilution and in an equivalent volume of the pyridine solvent. Even very small quantities of water in the original sample or the pyridine solvent have a very substantial effect upon the calculated amine content and therefore cannot be neglected for accurate results.

Calculations.

$$\frac{A - \left[\left(B + \frac{S_1 C}{S_2}\right)\right] F \times \frac{\text{E. W.}}{18.02}}{S_1} = \text{amine, per cent by wt.}$$

or, if a pyridine dilution of the sample is used.

$$\frac{[(A - D) - (B - E)] F \times \frac{\text{E. W.}}{18.02}}{S_1 V_1 / V_2} = \text{amine, per cent by wt.}$$

Where A = milliliters Karl Fischer reagent required to titrate sample, B = milliliters required for blank, C = milliliters required to titrate water in original sample, D =

TABLE XII. Analytical Data for Primary and Secondary Amines Using the Karl Fischer Reagent (67)

Primary amines	Equiv. wt.	Acidi-metric	Found, wt. %		
			Acetylation[a]	H_2O	Total
n-Butylamine	73.1	97.7	98.0 ± 0.5 (10)	1.7	99.7
Propylenediamine	37.1	—	84.1 ± 0.2 (2)	13.9	98.0
Hexamethylenediamine	58.1	—	99.9 ± 0.1 (4)	0.1	100.0
Cyclohexylamine	99.2	—	100.2 ± 0.2 (2)	0.0	100.2
o-Aminodicyclohexylamine	180.3	96.2[b]	96.7 ± 0.3 (2)	0.0	96.7
Benzylamine	107.2	92.8	92.7 ± 0.2 (2)	0.2	92.9
Aniline	93.1	—	100.8 ± 0.1 (4)	0.0	100.8
p-Toluidine	107.2	—	99.2 ± 0.1 (2)	0.0	99.2
p-Phenylenediamine	54.1	—	99.6 ± 0.1 (4)	0.0	99.6
p-Bromoaniline	172.0	—	99.4 ± 0.1 (4)	0.0	99.4
β-Naphthylamine	143.2	97.5	97.1 ± 0.2	0.0	97.1
o-Aminodiphenylamine	169.2	—	99.0 ± 0.2 (2)	0.0	99.0
2-Aminopyridine	94.1	—	100.0 ± 0.3 (2)	0.0	100.0
Diethylamine	73.1	99.7	99.7 ± 0.1 (2)	0.3	100.0
Di-n-butylamine	129.2	98.3	98.4 ± 0.2 (10)	0.1	98.5
Di-sec-butylamine	129.2	99.5	83.5 ± 0.2 (4)	0.1	83.6[c]
Diisobutylamine	129.2	100.1	100.1 ± 0.1 (2)	0.0	100.1
Methylaniline	107.2	—	98.8 ± 0.1 (4)	0.0	98.8
Morpholine	87.1	—	104.1 ± 0.2 (2)	0.0	104.1
Piperidine	85.2	99.4	99.8 ± 0.2 (2)	0.0	99.8
Piperazine hydrate	97.1	—	45.8 ± 0.2 (2)	53.8	99.6
Hydroxyamines					
Monoethanolamine	30.5	—	99.5 ± 0.1	0.2	99.7
Diethanolamine	52.6	—	99.6 ± 0.1	0.0	99.6
Hydroxyethylethylenediamine	34.7	—	99.1 ± 0.2	0.0	99.1

[a] Numbers in parentheses represent the number of determinations.
[b] Calculated from Kjeldahl nitrogen value.
[c] Low results probably due to presence of some tertiary amine.

milliliters required to titrate V_1 milliliters of pyridine dilution (before acetylation), E = milliliters required to titrate V_1 milliliters of pyridine solvent, E. W. = equivalent weight of amine, F = factor = g. $H_2O/100$ ml. reagent (see standardization of Karl Fischer reagent), S_1 = grams sample used for acetylation reaction, S_2 = grams sample used in determination of water content, V_1 = volume of aliquot taken for analysis, ml., and V_2 = total volume of diluted sample, ml.

The results obtained by Mitchell, Hawkins, and Smith are given in Table XII. In most cases the precision and accuracy are within ±0.2%.

B. CARBON DISULFIDE REACTION

Critchfield and Johnson (15b) found the dithiocarbamic acids formed by the reaction of carbon disulfide with primary and secondary amines could be titrated directly in an essentially nonaqueous medium. This method is unique in that primary and secondary amines are converted to acids and titrated with a base. Because of this fact, these amines can be determined in the presence of strong inorganic bases, ammonia, tertiary amines, and most acids. The equilibrium reaction with carbon disulfide is approximately 95% complete and is forced to completion by means of the sodium hydroxide titrant.

Reagents. (1) *Pyridine*, freshly distilled. (2) *Isopropanol*, 99%. (3) *Carbon disulfide*, reagent grade. (4) *Phenolphthalein*, 1.0% solution in pyridine. (5) *Sodium hydroxide*, standard 0.5 N carbonate free.

Procedure. To each of three 250 ml. glass-stoppered erlenmeyer flasks add the solvent mixture recommended in Table XIII. Reserve one of the flasks for a blank determination. Into each of the other flasks introduce an amount of sample containing not more than 15 meq. of primary or secondary amine. The combined ammonia and tertiary amine content of the sample aliquot used for analysis should not exceed 30 meq. For substantially pure material weigh the sample to the nearest 0.1 mg., using the amount specified in Table XIII. If more than 2.0 meq. of ammonia is present in the sample aliquot, cool the samples and blank to −10°C. using a brine bath. Do not use a dry ice–acetone bath as carbon dioxide interferes in the titration. By means of a suitable pipet add 5 ml. of carbon disulfide to each flask and swirl to effect complete solution. Add 5 or 6 drops of the phenolphthalein indicator to each flask and titrate with standard 0.5 N sodium hydroxide. For sample aliquots that contain more than 2.0 meq. of ammonia, conduct the titration below 0°C. This is best done by placing the flask in a 1000 ml. beaker containing a slurry of crushed ice in methanol. Stir the contents of the flask by means of a magnetic stirrer. During the titration swirl or stir the contents of the flasks to prevent an excess of titrant in the titration medium. The end point selected should be the first definite pink color stable for at least one minute.

Calculate the amount of primary and secondary amines.

$$\frac{(A - B) \times N}{\text{g. sample}} = \text{meq./gram primary and secondary amine}$$

If only one primary or secondary amine is present:

$$\frac{(A - B)N \times \text{E. W.}}{\text{g. sample} \times 10} = \text{amine, per cent by wt.}$$

where A = milliliters of N normal NaOH required for the sample, B = milliliters of N normal NaOH required for the blank, and E. W. = equivalent weight of amine.

The amount of tertiary amine that can be tolerated in the procedure is dependent upon the basicity of the amine and the solvent composition.

TABLE XIII

Primary and Secondary Amines, Determination
by Reaction with Carbon Disulfide

Compound	Maximum sample, g.[a]
2-Aminoethylethanolamine	0.78[b]
N-Aminoethylmorpholine	1.95[b]
Butylamine	1.10[c]
Butylamine, secondary	1.10[d]
Dibutylamine	1.93[c]
Diethanolamine	1.58[d]
Diethylamine	1.10[c]
Diethylenetriamine	0.52[b]
Di(2-ethylhexyl)amine	3.62[d]
Dihexylamine	2.78[c]
Dimethylamine	0.68[c]
2,6-Dimethylpiperazine	0.86[b]
Ethylamine	0.68[c]
Ethylenediamine	0.45[b]
2-Ethylhexylamine	1.93[d]
Hexylamine	1.52[c]
Isobutylamine	1.10[c]
Isopropanolamine	1.13[d]
Isopropylamine	0.89[d]
Methylamine	0.47[c]
Monoethanolamine	0.92[d]
Morpholine	1.31[b]
Propylenediamine	0.56[b]

[a] Weigh the sample to the nearest 0.1 mg. in the most convenient manner.

[b] Use a mixture containing 50 ml. of pyridine, 25 ml. of water, and 50 ml. of isopropanol as solvent.

[c] Use 75 ml. of isopropanol as solvent. If more than 2.0 meq. of ammonia is present add sufficient pyridine to suppress its basicity.

[d] Use a mixture containing 25 ml. of pyridine and 75 ml. of isopropanol as solvent.

In general, concentrations up to 20 meq. of tertiary amine will not be basic under the conditions of the titration. Approximately 30 meq. of ammonia can be tolerated provided the reaction and subsequent titration are performed at reduced temperatures. For reactions at room temperature, ammonia tends to react with carbon disulfide, and samples should contain not more than 2.0 meq. at this reaction temperature

Because the method is based upon an alkalimetric titration, compounds that are acid or basic to phenolphthalein under the conditions of the titration interfere and suitable corrections must be made. Acids with ionization constants in water greater than 1×10^{-7} and bases with ionization constants greater than 1×10^{-2} interfere quantitatively. Thus, with one sample, both acid (or base) and amine may be determined in one titration by quantitative neutralization before addition of the reagent carbon disulfide.

Aromatic amines do not react quantitatively and may interfere. Tertiary butylamine and diisopropylamine do not react quantitatively with the reagent, although the latter can be determined by a suitable modification of the method.

Table XIII shows the proper sample size for a number of compounds for which this method has been found satisfactory. Also included is the recommended solvent composition for the reaction and subsequent titration. The sample size is based upon the amount of pure amine equivalent to approximately 30 ml. of 0.5 N sodium hydroxide.

4. Secondary Amines

The reactions of primary amines with aldehydes and secondary amines with carbon disulfide previously described (see Sections III.2C and D and III.3C) afford a novel approach to the direct determination of secondary amines. The titration of the dithiocarbamic acid of the secondary amines after forming the imines of primary amines has recently been reported by Critchfield and Johnson (15c). Recent work also has been published on the determination of secondary amines by means of the formation of the nickel dithiocarbamate of primary and secondary amines which may be separated by an alkaline distribution of the salts between benzene and aqueous sodium hydroxide (71a).

A. 2-ETHYLHEXALDEHYDE–CARBON DISULFIDE METHOD

Primary amines react with a large excess of 2-ethylhexaldehyde to form the corresponding imine and water according to the following equation:

$$R\!-\!NH_2 + C_4H_9\!-\!\overset{\overset{\displaystyle C_2H_5}{|}}{CH}\!-\!CH\!=\!O \longrightarrow R\!-\!N\!=\!\overset{\overset{\displaystyle C_2H_5}{|}}{CH}\!-\!CH\!-\!C_4H_9 + H_2O \quad (17)$$

Secondary amines do not take part in the above reaction and are reacted with carbon disulfide as follows:

$$\overset{R}{\underset{R}{>}}NH + CS_2 \longrightarrow \overset{R}{\underset{R}{>}}N\!-\!\overset{\overset{\displaystyle S}{||}}{C}\!-\!SH \quad (18)$$

The dithiocarbamic acids formed in equation (18) can be titrated with standard aqueous sodium hydroxide using phenolphthalein indicator. Tertiary amines and ammonia do not react under the conditions of the reaction (within certain limits) and are not basic to the indicator in the titration medium.   The method of Critchfield and Johnson follows (15c).

Reagents.   (1) *Pyridine*, freshly distilled.   (2) *Isopropanol*, anhydrous.   (3) *Carbon disulfide*, reagent grade.   (4) *2-Ethylhexaldehyde reagent*.   Prepare 50% by volume solution of 2-ethylhexaldehyde in redistilled pyridine.   Add approximately 0.5% of phenyl-α-naphthylamine inhibitor.   Store the reagent in brown bottles and discard if the blank titration exceeds 0.5 ml. when used in the procedure, or if the color becomes too dark for satisfactory use.   (5) *Phenolphthalein*, 1.0% solution in pyridine.   (6) *Sodium hydroxide*, standard 0.5 N carbonate-free.

Procedure.   To each of three 250 ml. glass-stoppered erlenmeyer flasks add 10.0 ml. of the 2-ethylhexaldehyde solution by means of a suitable pipet.   If specified in Table XIV add 50 ml. of isopropanol to each flask.   Reserve one of the flasks for a blank determination.   Into each of the other flasks introduce an amount of sample containing not more than 15 meq. of secondary amine.   The combined ammonia and tertiary amine content of the sample aliquot should not exceed 30 meq.   The primary amine content of the sample aliquot should be less than 18.0 meq.   For substantially pure material weigh the sample to the nearest 0.1 mg. using the amount specified in Table XIV.   Allow the samples and blank to stand for 5 minutes at room temperature and add the amount of solvent specified in Table XIV.   Cool the contents of the flask to $-10 \pm 2°C$. using a brine bath.   Do not use a solid carbon dioxide–acetone bath because carbon dioxide interferes in the titration.   Remove the flasks from the bath and add 5 ml. of carbon disulfide to each by means of a suitable pipet.   Add 5 or 6 drops of the phenolphthalein indicator to each flask and immediately titrate with standard 0.5 N sodium hydroxide at below 0°C.   This is best done by placing the flask in a 1000 ml. beaker containing a slurry of crushed ice and methanol.   Stir the contents of the flask by means of a magnetic stirrer.   The end point selected should be the first definite pink color permanent for at least one minute.

Calculate the amount of secondary amine.

$$\frac{(A - B)N \times \text{E. W.}}{\text{g. sample} \times 10} = \text{secondary amine, per cent by wt.}$$

where A = milliliters of N normal NaOH required for the sample, B = milliliters of N normal NaOH required for the blank, and E. W. = equivalent weight of amine.

The amount of tertiary amine that can be tolerated in the procedure is dependent upon the basicity of the amine and the solvent composition. In general, concentrations up to 20 meq. of tertiary amine will not be basic under the conditions of the titration. Approximately 30 meq. of ammonia can be tolerated provided the reaction and subsequent titration are carried out at reduced temperatures. For reactions at room temperature, ammonia tends to react with carbon disulfide and samples should contain not more than 2.0 meq. at this reaction temperature.

Because the method is based upon an alkalimetric titration, compounds that are acidic or basic to phenolphthalein under the conditions of the titration interfere and suitable corrections must be made. Aromatic amines do not react quantitatively and may interfere. Approximately 18 meq. of most simple aliphatic amines can be present in the sample without interference. Primary alcoholamines, polyamines, aromatic amines, and amines highly branched in the 2-position do not react completely with 2-ethylhexaldehyde and will interfere. Diisopropylamine and secondary aromatic amines do not react quantitatively with carbon disulfide and cannot be determined by this method.

TABLE XIV

Determination of Secondary Amines by the
2-Ethylhexaldehyde–Carbon Disulfide Method

Compound	Sample, g.[a]
Dibutylamine	1.93[b]
Diethylamine	1.10[b]
Di(2-ethylhexyl)amine	3.62[c]
Dihexylamine	2.78[b]
Dimethylamine	0.68[d]
2,6-Dimethylpiperazine	0.86[e]
Morpholine	1.31[e]

[a] Weigh the sample to the nearest 0.1 mg. in the most convenient manner.
[b] Use 75 ml. of isopropanol as solvent. If more than 2.0 meq. of ammonia is present add sufficient pyridine to suppress its basicity.
[c] Use 25 ml. of pyridine and 75 ml. of isopropanol as solvent.
[d] Perform the reaction with 2-ethylhexaldehyde in the presence of 50 ml. of isopropanol. Add 25 ml. of isopropanol before the reaction with carbon disulfide.
[e] Use 50 ml. of pyridine, 25 ml. of water, and 50 ml. of isopropanol as solvent.

Table XIV shows the proper sample size for a number of compounds for which this method has been found satisfactory. Also included is the recommended solvent composition for the reaction and subsequent titration. The sample size is based upon the amount of pure amine equivalent to 30 ml. of 0.5 N sodium hydroxide.

B. NICKEL DITHIOCARBAMATE METHOD

The procedure of Nebbia and Gurrieri (71a) for the determination of secondary amines is based upon the selective solubility of the nickel dithiocarbamates of primary amines in alkaline medium. Depending upon the quantity of amine present the subsequent secondary amine determination may be performed either colorimetrically by converting to the highly colored copper dithiocarbamate or by liberating the nickel salt with silver nitrate and titrating with ethylenebisiminodiacetic acid using murexide as indicator (22a). For large quantities of secondary amines, a gravimetric separation of the nickel dithiocarbamates is effected and the nickel titrated as above. Because the method was applied to the analysis of methyl and ethylamines only, a detailed procedure is not given here. Studies to extend the method to secondary amines of higher molecular weight are in progress.

5. Secondary and Tertiary Amines

A. AZOMETHINE-ACIDIMETRIC METHOD

The previously described reaction of primary amines with aldehydes (see Section III.2) has been adopted by Wagner, Brown, and Peters (100) to determine a measure of secondary plus tertiary amines in a mixture of primary, secondary, and tertiary amines. The azomethine formed in the reaction of salicylaldehyde with a primary amine is a much weaker base than the secondary amine and the total secondary plus tertiary amine content of the reaction mixture may be titrated potentiometrically in nonaqueous medium. In the absence of ammonia, water in the sample does not interfere even in amounts up to 95%. Ammonia, in the absence of water, analyzes as primary amine. However, when both ammonia and water are present in large quantities, ammonia must be removed. Wagner *et al.* make use of the sodium cobaltinitrite precipitation to remove ammonia from the sample.

Reagents and Apparatus. *(1) Standard 0.5 N hydrochloric acid in isopropanol.* Add 1 volume of concentrated C. P. hydrochloric acid to isopropanol and dilute to 24 volumes with additional alcohol. Standardize against standard 0.5 N sodium hydroxide. (2) *Salicylaldehyde*, reagent grade, salicylic acid-free. (3) *Sodium cobaltinitrite-sodium nitrite reagent.* Dissolve 25 g. of sodium cobaltinitrite and 25 g. of sodium nitrite in distilled water and dilute to 200 ml. with additional water. (4) *Beckman Model M or equivalent titrimeter* equipped with glass and calomel electrodes.

Procedure. Transfer 80 ml. of methanol and 5 ml. of salicylaldehyde to each of two titration beakers. Into each beaker introduce an amount of sample containing 3 to 4 meq. of secondary plus tertiary amine. Cover each beaker with a watch glass, swirl the contents to mix thoroughly, and allow to stand at room temperature for 30 minutes. Titrate the mixture potentiometrically to the first end point with standard 0.5 N hydrochloric acid in isopropanol.

Calculate the amount of secondary and tertiary amine:

$$\frac{A \times N}{\text{g. sample}} = \text{meq./gram secondary and tertiary amine}$$

where A = milliliters of N normal HCl required.

Procedure for Removal of Ammonia. If ammonia is present in the sample transfer an amount of sample containing 15 to 20 meq. of amine to a suitable container. Immerse the container in an ice bath, neutralize the sample with hydrochloric acid, and dilute the contents to approximately 25 ml. with distilled water. Add 25 ml. of the cobaltinitrite reagent and allow the mixture to stand in an ice bath for 1.5 hours. Add 40 ml. of methyl Cellosolve and allow the mixture to stand for an additional 30 minutes in the ice bath. Filter the yellow sodium diammonium cobaltinitrite precipitate through an asbestos filter using suction. Wash the precipitate thoroughly with 50 ml. of 50% methyl Cellosolve previously cooled to 0°C. and transfer the precipitate and asbestos filter to a distilling flask. Add an excess of sodium hydroxide solution, distil the liberated ammonia into boric acid, and titrate in the usual manner.

If both water and ammonia are present in the original sample in large amounts, so that direct analysis for secondary amine is not possible, remove the ammonia as described above and recover the filtrate for analysis of amines. Transfer the filtrate to a distilling flask immediately after filtering, add an excess of sodium hydroxide, and collect 50 ml. of distillate in a 100 ml. volumetric flask containing 45 ml. of methanol previously cooled to 0°C. Dilute a 10 to 15 ml. aliquot of the methanol solution to 100 ml. and determine secondary plus tertiary amine content using the azomethine method.

Compounds and mixtures to which the procedure was applied satisfactorily are given in Table XV. Average error amounted to ±0.7% of the quantity of secondary amine present (100).

A typical titration curve is illustrated in Figure 6, which indicates the sharp end point of the secondary amine titration as well as the less distinct

TABLE XV.   Application of Azomethine Method to Known Mixtures of Amines (100)

Components in mixture	1° amine present, eq. × 10³	2° + 3° amine present, eq. × 10³	2° + 3° amine found, eq. × 10³	Error, %
Diethylamine, ethylamine	1.86	2.691	2.672	−0.7
Triethylamine, diethylamine, ethylamine[a]	3.72	4.56	4.60	+0.9
Di-n-butylamine, n-butylamine	2.75	2.756	2.742	−0.5
Tri-n-butylamine, di-n-butylamine, n-butylamine[b]	2.75	5.36	5.30	−1.1
Di-n-amylamine,[c] n-amylamine	1.92	1.812	1.801	−0.6
Dimethylamine, n-butylamine	2.75	3.993	3.930	−1.6
Dioctylamine, n-amylamine	1.92	3.402	3.352	−1.5
Diisopropylamine,[c] isopropylamine	4.226	3.983	4.000	+0.4
Diisobutylamine, isobutylamine	3.60	3.639	3.555	−2.3[c]
Bis-(1,3-dimethylbutyl)amine,[c] 1,3-dimethylbutylamine[c]	3.44	3.480	3.525	+1.2
Dicyclohexylamine,[c] cyclohexylamine[c]	3.52	1.890	1.867	−1.2
Diisopropylamine,[c] β-phenylethylamine	2.645	3.949	3.934	−0.4
Diisopropylamine,[c] 1-isobutyl-3-methylbutylamine[c]	3.47	3.983	3.958	−0.7
Piperidine, ethylamine	3.72	4.000	3.987	−0.3
Diethanolamine, ethanolamine[d]	3.74	4.133	4.065	−1.6
Diallylamine,[c] allylamine[c]	3.92	3.884	3.901	+0.4
Dimethallylamine,[c] methallylamine[c]	4.26	3.807	3.788	−0.5
Diethylenetriamine[c]	2.624	1.312	1.320	+0.6

[a] Triethylamine, 4.02 meq., and diethylamine, 0.538 meq.   [b] Tributylamine, 3.88 meq., and dibutylamine, 1.48 meq.   [c] Sample of diisobutylamine contained about 2.5% primary amine, as shown by application of the azomethine method to the diisobutylamine sample itself.   [d] 5 ml. of water added to the titration mixture and readings delayed after each addition of acid until further potential change due to hydrolysis of the diethanolamine–salicylaldehyde product was almost imperceptible.   [e] Purified commercial and laboratory samples; all others are unpurified commercial samples obtained mainly from Eastman Kodak Company and Sharples Solvents Corporation.

end point occurring as the azomethine is converted to its salt. Although this second inflection may be used to calculate primary amine content, more accurate results may usually be obtained using other procedures. This is especially true if water and ammonia are present in the sample.

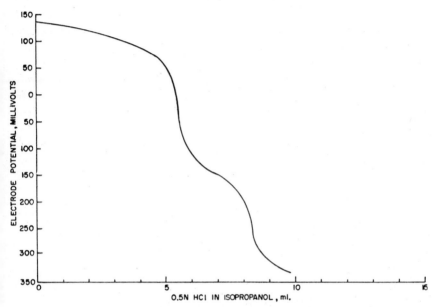

Fig. 6. Azomethine titration curve of secondary amine (100). Sample contains 2.77 milliequivalents of dibutylamine and 1.39 milliequivalents of butylamine. Zero on the electrode potential scale is equivalent approximately to a pH of 7 when the electrode system is used in aqueous solution.

6. Tertiary Amines

A. TITRATION WITH HYDROCHLORIC ACID IN METHANOL AFTER REACTION
OF PRIMARY PLUS SECONDARY AMINES WITH ACETIC ANHYDRIDE OR
PHENYLISOTHIOCYANATE

The direct determination of tertiary amines in the presence of primary and secondary amines is possible by preliminary reaction of the latter with acetic anhydride (or in special cases with phenylisothiocyanate). In an alcoholic medium the basic properties of the reaction products are negligible so that the residual basicity is due only to the unreactive tertiary amine, which may be titrated either potentiometrically or by using indicators with standard alcoholic hydrochloric acid.

This principle was originally employed by Blumrich and Bandel (6) for the analysis of di- and triethylamine mixtures. It was incorporated in a general procedure devised by Wagner, Brown, and Peters (99) for the analysis of primary, secondary, and tertiary aliphatic amine mixtures and later extended to aromatic amine mixtures by Siggia, Hanna, and Kervenski (88).

All of these investigators determined the residual basicity by a potentiometric titration. The following procedure, which employs an indicator, has been developed in the Carbide Laboratories.

Certain sterically hindered secondary amines, such as diisopropylamine or butylisopropylamine, which do not acetylate readily, are best reacted with phenylisothiocyanate. Inasmuch as this reagent is a lachrymator and difficult to handle, its use should be limited to those cases in which acetic anhydride does not react quantitatively. Appreciable amounts of water cannot be tolerated because of its deleterious effect upon the end point and because it reacts with the reagent and depletes the amount available for complete reaction of the primary and secondary amine.

Reagents. (*1*) *Hydrochloric acid*, 0.5 N alcoholic solution. Transfer 20 ml. of 6 N hydrochloric acid to a 250 ml. volumetric flask and dilute to the mark with methanol. Standardize the solution daily as follows: Measure exactly 40 ml. from a buret into a 250 ml. erlenmeyer flask and wash down the walls with a few milliliters of neutral distilled water. Add 6 to 8 drops of phenolphthalein indicator and titrate with standard 0.5 N aqueous sodium hydroxide to a pink end point permanent for at least 15 seconds. (*2*) *Methyl yellow-methylene blue mixed indicator.* Dissolve 0.5 g. of methyl yellow (*p*-dimethylaminoazobenzene) and 0.05 g. of methylene blue in 100 ml. of methanol. (*3*) *Acetic anhydride*, C. P., *or phenyliso-thiocyanate*, reagent grade. The latter material is a lachrymator and should be handled only under a fume hood.

Procedure. Transfer 100 ml. of methanol to each of a sufficient number of 500 ml. glass-stoppered erlenmeyer flasks to make all blank and sample determinations in duplicate. Use suitable pressure bottles if sealed-glass ampules are required.

Reserve two of the flasks as blanks. Into each of the other flasks introduce an amount of sample containing not more than 15 meq. of tertiary amine. For substantially pure material weigh the sample to the nearest 0.1 mg., using the amount and procedure specified in Table XVI. If a sealed-glass ampule is used, add several pieces of 8 mm. glass rod to each bottle, fit with a pressure stopper, and shake the bottle vigorously to break the ampule.

To each flask cautiously add 20 ml. of acetic anhydride measured from a 25 ml. graduate. If secondary amines are present (such as diisopropylamine or butylisopropyl amine, which acetylate with difficulty), use 10 ml. of phenylisothiocyanate in place of the acetic anhydride. Swirl the flasks to effect solution.

Allow the samples to stand together with the blanks at room temperature for 30 minutes. Maintain the samples at room temperature during this period by immersing the flasks in cold water when evidence of heat rise is noticed.

Add 6 to 8 drops of the mixed indicator and titrate with standard hydrochloric acid until the color changes from green to red-brown when viewed by reflected light. *Calculate* the normality of the standard hydrochloric acid.

$$(R \times S)/40 = N$$

where N = normality of alcoholic HCl, and R = milliliters of S normal NaOH required for the standardization.

Temperature correction:

$$\Delta N/\Delta T = 0.0005/°C. \text{ rise in temperature for } 0.5 \ N \text{ HCl in methanol}$$

Calculate the amount of tertiary amine:

$$\frac{(A - B)N \times E. W.}{g. \text{ sample} \times 10} = \text{tertiary amine, per cent by wt.}$$

where A = milliliters of N normal HCl required for the sample, B = milliliters of N normal HCl required for the blank, and E. W. = equivalent weight of amine.

Table XVI shows the proper sample size for a number of compounds for which this procedure has been found satisfactory. The sample size is based upon the amount of pure tertiary amine equivalent to 25 to 30 ml. of 0.5 N hydrochloric acid. For lower concentrations in noninterfering

TABLE XVI

Determination of Tertiary Amines by Direct
Titration with Hydrochloric Acid in Methanol

Compound	Sample, g.[a]
Diethylethanolamine	1.4 to 1.8
Di(2-ethylhexyl)ethanolamine	3.0 to 4.0
Dimethylethanolamine	0.8 to 1.1
Dimethylisopropanolamine	1.0 to 1.6
N-Ethylmorpholine	1.4 to 1.8
Methyldiethanolamine	1.5 to 1.9
N-Methylmorpholine	1.2 to 1.5
Tributylamine	2.0 to 3.0
Triethanolamine	1.5 to 2.5
Triethylamine	1.2 to 1.5[b]
Tri(2-ethylhexyl)amine	4.0 to 5.0
Triisopropanolamine	2.0 to 3.0
Trimethylamine	0.7 to 0.9[b]

[a] Weigh to the nearest 0.1 mg. using a suitable weighing pipet unless indicated otherwise.
[b] Use a sealed-glass ampule.

solvents a proportionately larger sample should be used. In no case should the sample contain more than 0.3 mole of total amine.

7. Separation of Aliphatic and Aromatic Amines

A. DIFFERENTIAL TITRATION IN ACETONITRILE

As has been discussed in Section III.3C concerning the determination of amines by titration in acetic acid medium, the apparent basic strength of

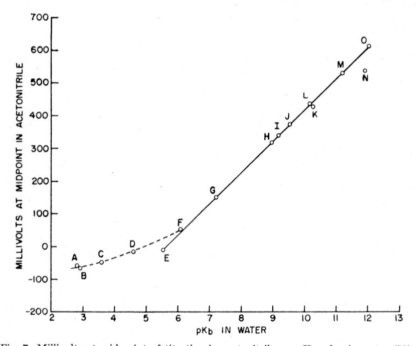

Fig. 7. Millivolts at mid-point of titration in acetonitrile vs. pK_b value in water (29):

A. Dibutylamine
B. Diethylamine
C. Butylamine
D. Ethanolamine
E. Hydrazine
F. Brucine
G. 2,6-Diaminopyridine

H. Pyridine
I. N-Methylaniline
J. Aniline
K. p-Bromoaniline
L. α-Naphthylamine
M. o-Chloroaniline
N. Anthranilic acid

amines may be enhanced by the use of nonaqueous solvents. By proper choice of solvents Fritz (29) has shown that amines of different basic strength may be titrated individually and has applied this technique to the analysis of aliphatic and aromatic amine mixtures as well as to the separate determination of certain aromatic amine and weaker base mixtures. By using acetonitrile as a solvent and perchloric acid in p-dioxane as a titrant, he noted that the potentials at the midpoints of the titration curves of amines when plotted against the pK_b values of these amines in water produced a straight line curve which had a slope of 100 mv. per pK_b unit (Fig. 7). This is almost double the value obtained for similar data in aqueous medium, thus enabling one to determine separately amines having less differences in basic strength.

The use of acetonitrile as a solvent is recommended because of its high dielectric constant, which permits easy potentiometric titration, and because it has no acidic properties. Dioxane also has been used (76) in obtaining titration curves for certain dibasic compounds and may be used as a suitable solvent. However, because of low dielectric constant, special cells are required to overcome electrical resistance. Acetic acid exhibits too great a leveling effect on the amines to permit differentiation of the aliphatic and aromatic amine character.

Reagents and Apparatus. (1) *Perchloric acid in p-dioxane.* Dissolve 8.5 ml. of 72% perchloric acid in 1 liter of p-dioxane. (2) *Perchloric acid in glacial acetic acid.* Dissolve 8.5 ml. of 72% perchloric acid in 50 ml. of glacial acetic acid. Add 22 ml. of acetic anhydride and let stand overnight. Dilute to 1 liter with glacial acetic acid. (3) *Methyl violet,* 0.2% solution in chlorobenzene. (4) *Eosin Y*, saturated solution in acetonitrile. (5) *Beckman pH meter or equivalent,* equipped with glass and calomel electrodes.

Standardization. Dissolve 100 mg. of primary-standard grade potassium acid phthalate in 25 ml. of hot glacial acetic acid. Cool, add 2 drops of methyl violet, and titrate with the perchloric acid in p-dioxane to a light blue-green end point.

Procedure A (potentiometric). Dissolve an amount of sample containing from 0.6 to 1.0 mg. of total amines in 20 ml. of acetonitrile. Using the millivolt scale of the pH meter, titrate potentiometrically with 0.1 N perchloric acid in p-dioxane. Determine a blank on each lot of acetonitrile by titrating a 20 ml. portion of acetonitrile potentiometrically with 0.1 N perchloric acid in dioxane.

Calculations.

$$\frac{(A - B)N \times \text{E. W.}_{\cdot a}}{\text{g. sample} \times 10} = \text{amine } a, \text{ per cent by wt.}$$

$$\frac{(C - D)N \times \text{E. W.}_{\cdot b}}{\text{g. sample} \times 10} = \text{amine } b, \text{ per cent by wt.}$$

Procedure B (indicator).   Dissolve an amount of sample containing from 0.6 to 1.0 mg. of total amines in 20 ml. of acetonitrile.   Add 6 drops of eosin Y indicator and titrate with 0.1 N perchloric acid in dioxane to a pale yellow end point.   Add 2 drops of methyl violet indicator and 20 ml. of acetic acid, and continue the titration until a blue-green end point is reached.   Determine a blank by the method given in Procedure A.

Calculations are identical with those in Procedure A.

Procedure C.   Follow Procedure A except to use 0.1 N perchloric acid in acetic acid as the titrant.   Determine the blank by titrating a 20 ml. portion of acetonitrile with perchloric acid in acetic acid.   This blank is subtracted from the first end point only.

Calculations

$$\frac{(A - E)N \times \text{E. W.}_a}{\text{g. sample} \times 10} = \text{amine } a, \text{ per cent by wt.}$$

$$CN \times \text{E. W.}_b = \text{amine } b, \text{ per cent by wt.}$$

where A = milliliters of N normal $HClO_4$ required to first end point, B = milliliters of N normal $HClO_4$ required to first end point in blank, E. W.$_a$ = equivalent

TABLE XVII

Titration of Amine Mixtures with Perchloric Acid in Dioxane (29)

Procedure	Compounds	Added, mg.	Found, mg.	Difference, mg.
A........	Di-*n*-butylamine	25.4	25.3	−0.1
	Pyridine	37.9	37.8	−0.1
A........	Di-*n*-butylamine	38.0	38.2	+0.2
	Pyridine	35.9	36.2	+0.3
C........	Aniline	36.2	36.3	+0.1
	o-Chloroaniline	30.0	30.4	+0.4
C........	Aniline	20.1	19.9	−0.2
	o-Chloroaniline	23.3	22.9	−0.4
B.......	β-Phenylethylamine	21.5	21.5	±0.0
	Aniline	26.7	—	—
B........	β-Phenylethylamine	42.8	42.7	−0.1
	Aniline	22.7	22.7	±0.0
B........	β-Phenylethylamine	44.5	44.3	−0.2
	Aniline	50.2	50.5	+0.3
C........	Pyridine	18.7	18.7	±0.0
	Caffeine	57.2	57.7	+0.5
C........	Pyridine	18.8	18.4	−0.4
	Caffeine	89.6	89.5	−0.1
C........	Aniline	24.1	23.1	−1.0
	Sulfathiazole	65.2	65.1	−0.1
C........	Aniline	25.5	25.6	+0.1
	Sulfathiazole	61.5	60.8	−0.7

weight amine of greater basic strength, E. W.$_b$ = equivalent weight amine of lesser basic strength, C = milliliters of N normal $HClO_4$ required for first to second end point, D = milliliters of N normal $HClO_4$ required for first to second end point in blank, and E = milliliters of N normal $HClO_4$ in acetic acid required for blank end point.

Table XVII presents the data obtained for a number of amine mixtures for which the above procedures were found to give satisfactory results. Also, to illustrate the potentiometric curve usually obtained, an example is presented in Figure 8. Procedure C is recommended for use when mix-

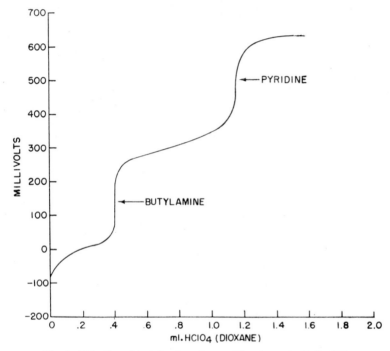

Fig. 8. Titration of butylamine plus pyridine in acetonitrile (29).

tures of aromatic amines and weaker bases such as aniline–o-chloroaniline, aniline–sulfathiazole, and pyridine–caffeine are encountered. The indicator Procedure B may often be used after a specific mixture has successfully been titrated potentiometrically.

Because water causes a decrease in sharpness of the end point, it must be absent from the sample. Also, basic impurities likely to be present in the acetonitrile must be corrected for by the determination of the blanks.

A study of the titration curves of some 55 amines published by Hall (35) will aid in predicting which mixture of amines may be successfully titrated.

8. Aromatic Amines

A. DIAZOTIZATION AND NITROSATION

Because of reaction of nitrous acid with primary and secondary aromatic amines to form diazo salts and nitroso compounds, respectively, this reaction has been used for many years as a means of determination of aromatic amines (the reaction also has been modified for use in determining primary aliphatic amines; see Section III.2):

$$\text{NH}_2 \cdot \text{HCl} \quad + \text{HONO} \longrightarrow \left[\overset{+}{\text{N}} \equiv \text{N} \right] \text{Cl}^- + 2\text{H}_2\text{O} \tag{19}$$

$$\text{NHR} \quad + \text{HONO} \longrightarrow \overset{\text{N}=\text{O}}{\underset{\text{N}-\text{R}}{|}} + \text{H}_2\text{O} \tag{20}$$

The reaction has been followed quantitatively both by direct titration with a standard solution of sodium nitrite (60,82,87) and also by titration of excess reagent with a standard solution of easily diazotized amine (55,56, 103). In the direct titration procedure, difficulty may be experienced in slow and incomplete reaction. Efforts to speed the reaction often cause loss of nitrous acid, which in turn produces high and inconsistent results.

By the addition of excess nitrous acid the equilibrium may be shifted toward complete reaction and the procedure thus may be applied to a greater number of compounds. Nitric acid is also added to prevent decomposition of the nitrous acid by shifting the equilibrium:

$$3\text{HNO}_2 \rightleftharpoons \text{HNO}_3 + 2\text{NO} + \text{H}_2\text{O} \tag{21}$$

Either p-nitroaniline or nitrocresidine (55) has been recommended for use in the back-titration of the excess reagent. The end point may be determined either potentiometrically, using a platinum electrode and a standard calomel cell as the reference electrode, or by using starch–iodide paper as an external indicator. "Deadstop" end point modifications also have been used successfully in the potentiometric titration (20,83). The procedure of Wild (103) follows.

Reagents. (*1*) *Hydrochloric acid,* concentrated. (*2*) *Hydrochloric acid,* 5% solution. (*3*) *Sodium nitrite,* 0.1 *N;* standardized against sulfanilic acid of known purity. (*4*) *Nitric acid,* concentrated, nitrogen tetraoxide-free. (*5*) *p-Nitroaniline.* Dissolve 14.0 g. of *p*-nitroaniline in 200 ml. of hot distilled water and 150 ml. of concentrated hydrochloric acid. Allow to stand overnight, filter, and dilute the filtrate to 1 liter. Standardize 10 ml. of the solution with the standard sodium nitrite following the procedure for the sample determination. This solution is stable for at least two weeks.

Procedure. Dissolve an amount of sample containing up to 4 meq. of amino compound in 5% hydrochloric acid and dilute to 500 ml. with acid of the same strength. Transfer a 50 ml. aliquot of the sample dilution to a beaker and add 250 ml. of distilled water and 25 ml. of concentrated hydrochloric acid. Cool the beaker and contents to 0 to 5 °C. in a suitable ice bath and add a little crushed ice to the beaker. While continuously stirring the contents of the beaker add 50 ml. of the 0.1 *N* sodium nitrite and immediately add 10 ml. of concentrated nitric acid, nitrogen tetraoxide-free. Cover the beaker with a watch glass and allow it to stand in the ice bath for 30 minutes with occasional stirring. Determine the excess sodium nitrite by titration with standard *p*-nitroaniline using either starch–iodide paper as an external indicator or a pH meter.

Calculate the amount of aromatic amine:

$$\frac{[(50 \times N) - AM] \times \text{E. W.}}{\text{g. sample} \times 10} = \text{aromatic amine, per cent by wt.}$$

where A = milliliters of M normal *p*-nitroaniline required, E. W. = equivalent weight of amine, and N = normality of $NaNO_2$.

If starch–iodide paper is used to determine the end point, a few titrations will provide the experience necessary to obtain accurate values. The blue color develops slowly and at the end point appears in about 2 seconds. In colored samples the blue-black color which develops may be seen in the area above the immersion depth on the starch–iodide paper.

If a platinum electrode is used as an indicating electrode, a standard calomel cell is used as the reference electrode. The solution should be stirred for 2 to 5 minutes after each addition of sodium nitrite and a microburet should be used for the addition of the reagent near the end point.

Table XVIII lists the compounds that have been found to give satisfactory results when using diazotization and nitrosation procedures (42,-89,90,103). In general an accuracy of ±0.1% is claimed (103).

Diazotization also has been applied colorimetrically to determine aromatic amines (54) and provides a basis for the separation of certain primary and tertiary aromatic amines by formation of diazo dyes and yellow nitroso compounds, respectively (18).

TABLE XVIII

Determination of Aromatic Amines by Diazotization and Nitrosation

	Back-titration	
Direct titration	Starch–iodide end point	Potentiometric
Aniline	Aniline	Aniline
4-Nitroaniline	Toluidines	Toluidines
p-Toluidine	Xylidenes	m-Xylidene
1-Amino-2-naphthol-4-sulfonic acid	Dehydrothioamino-sulfonic acids	o-Aminobenzoic acid
4-Aminoazobenzene	Primuline and similar bases	p-Aminobenzoic acid
1-Amino-8-naphthol-3,6-disulfonic acid		p-Aminochlorobenzene
Benzidine		p-Aminobenzenesulfonic acid
4,4'-Diaminodiphenyl-amine-2'-sulfonic acid		1,2,4-Nitroethoxyaniline
4-Aminophenol		1,2,4-Aminonitrophenol
1-Naphthylamine		Sodium azobenzene-disulfonamide
o-Aminodiphenyl		o-Phenylenediamine
Acetoacetanilide		
N-Ethyl-1-naphthylamine		
Diphenylamine		
N-Methylaniline		
N-Ethylaniline		
2,6-Tolylenediamine-4-sulfonic acid		

B. MISCELLANEOUS

There are several miscellaneous procedures for the determination of amino compounds which, because of their limited application or because of their nonfunctional approach, should be mentioned only briefly.

(1) **Picryl Chloride Method.** The reaction of picryl chloride with aniline, o- and p-toluidine, o- and p-anisidine, and benzidine to form sodium chloride, which may be determined either gravimetrically or volumetrically, has been used successfully (57). The sample is dissolved in ethyl acetate and added to an ester solution of picryl chloride containing sodium bicarbonate. After standing one hour at room temperature (15 minutes for aniline (58)) water is added and the reaction mixture heated in a hot-water bath for 15 minutes. The sample is allowed to stand at room temperature for 3 hours and the sodium chloride is then either filtered off and deter-

mined gravimetrically or is determined volumetrically without filtration using the Mohr titration method.

In the case of benzidine, both amino groups react. Interferences include the presence of negative substitution in aromatic amines which apparently hinders the reaction, i.e., anthranilic acid reacts incompletely and o-nitro-aniline does not react at all. Secondary amines also react only slightly. Although β-naphthylamine reacts erratically, the α-compound reacts nearly quantitatively.

(2) **Bromination.** Although the reaction of bromine with amino compounds is not based upon a functional group determination, the reaction because of its wide application is often used as a measure of certain aromatic amines. The presence of an amino group in the benzene ring activates the ortho and para hydrogens so that they are easily replaced with bromine:

$$\text{NH}_2 \quad + \quad 3\text{Br}_2 \quad \longrightarrow \quad \text{NH}_2(\text{Br})(\text{Br})(\text{Br}) \quad + \quad 3\text{HBr} \qquad (22)$$

The reaction may be performed either by direct titration or by the addition of a known excess of reagent and back titration of the excess. The bromine for the reaction may be conveniently supplied by the reaction of potassium bromate, potassium bromide, and hydrochloric acid, in situ:

$$\text{KBrO}_3 + 5\text{KBr} + 6\text{HCl} \longrightarrow 6\text{Br} + 6\text{KCl} + 3\text{H}_2\text{O} \qquad (23)$$

The direct titration method (9), though necessary for the determination of certain amines (o- and p-toluidines), requires the use of an outside indicator. In addition, the titration is time consuming because the reaction mixture is titrated until a drop of the solution produces a blue spot on starch–iodide paper, which persists for 2 to 4 minutes after the addition of the last drop of the titrant (bromate solution).

The indirect (or excess) method, first described by Koppeschaar (53), is the technique usually applied for the determination of aromatic amines. The modification of Day and Taggart (16) follows:

Reagents. (1) *Bromide–bromate reagent,* 0.2 N; dissolve 75 g. of potassium bromide and 5.6 g. of potassium bromate in distilled water and dilute to 1000 ml. (2) *Concentrated hydrochloric acid.* (3) *Potassium iodide,* 40% aqueous solution. (4) *Standard 0.1 N sodium thiosulfate.* (5) *Starch indicator,* 0.5% aqueous solution.

Procedure. Transfer 0.5 to 0.6 g. of the sample, weighed to the nearest 0.1 mg., to a 250 ml. volumetric flask. Dissolve the sample with a minimum quantity of dilute hydrochloric acid·and dilute to the mark with distilled water. Transfer a 25 ml. aliquot of the sample dilution to a 500 ml. iodine flask. Reserve a second flask as a blank. To both sample and blank introduce exactly 25 ml. of the 0.2 N bromide–bromate solution and add 50 ml. of distilled water. Add 5 ml. of concentrated hydrochloric acid to each flask and stopper immediately. Allow the sample to stand together with the blank at room temperature for the length of time specified in Table XIX. Cool the flasks in an ice bath and place 5 ml. of the 40% potassium iodide solution in the trough. Partly dislodge the stoppers and allow the iodide solution to be drawn into the flasks. Shake the flasks thoroughly and wash down the neck of the stopper and sides of the flask with distilled water. Titrate both blank and sample with the standard 0.1 N sodium thiosulfate, using 5 ml. of the starch indicator near the end of the titration.

Calculate the amount of amine:

$$\frac{(B - A)N \times \text{E. W.}}{W} = \text{amine, per cent by wt.}$$

where A = milliliters of N normal $Na_2S_2O_3$ required for the sample, B = milliliters of N normal $Na_2S_2O_3$ required for the blank, E. W. = equivalent weight of amine

$$= \frac{\text{molecular weight of amine}}{\text{number of bromine equivalents (see Table XIX)}}$$

and W = grams sample in dilution.

The reaction conditions and number of bromine equivalents consumed of a number of compounds for which this procedure gave satisfactory results are given in Table XIX. Note that, because aniline and deriva-

TABLE XIX

Aromatic Amines by Bromination

Amino compound	Reaction time, min.	Bromine equiv.
Aniline............................	5 to 10	$3Br_2$
p-Chloroaniline.....................	10	$2Br_2$
o-Nitroaniline......................	30	$2Br_2$
m-Nitroaniline......................	30	$3Br_2$
Acetanilide[a].......................	5 to 10	$3Br_2$
Sulfanilic acid[b].....................	30	$3Br_2$
Metanilic acid[b].....................	5 to 15	$3Br_2$
Anthranilic acid[b]....................	30	$3Br_2$
m-Aminobenzoic acid[b]..............	10 to 15	$3Br_2$
m-Toluidine........................	5 to 10	$3Br_2$

[a] Hydrolyze the sample in boiling 6 N hydrochloric acid for 10 to 15 minutes, neutralize with sodium hydroxide, acidify with hydrochloric acid, and dilute to 250 ml. Use 25 ml. aliquot for analysis.

[b] Dissolve the sample using dilute sodium hydroxide.

tives yielding aniline upon hydrolysis are susceptible to oxidation with bromine, the reaction with these compounds is conducted at reduced temperatures.

p-Aminobenzoic acid brominates to form a mixture of the di- and tribromo derivatives, and therefore cannot be determined using this procedure. p-Nitroaniline also cannot be determined, probably due to occlusion of the sample in the bulky precipitate formed.

IV. AMIDES

The usual basic properties of the nitrogen atom, upon which many of the nitrogen functional group analyses are based, are effectively neutralized by the presence of the acyl group in the amide compounds. This of course prohibits their titration as bases; for similar reasons the nitrogen basicity neutralizes the acidic properties of the acid radical. Also the acetylation and nitrosation type procedures are not applicable to their determination.

Some measure of success in the determination of amides has been obtained, however, by application of rigorous saponification reactions and by formation of the hydroxamic acids followed by complexing with ferric iron. In addition, the reaction of acylating agents with amides to form nitriles has been found applicable to the determination of unsubstituted amides. The estimation of amides by determination of total nitrogen has been described previously (see Section II).

1. Colorimetric Determination as Hydroxamic Acids

The reaction of acetamide with hydroxylamine hydrochloride to form acethydroxamic acid has long been known (42). Several authors have presented procedures for the conversion of many carboxylic acid derivatives to hydroxamic acids followed by the formation of a violet ferric iron complex and determination of the intensity of the color formed (41,45,59). By a combination of these reactions, satisfactory procedures have been developed and applied to the detection and estimation of amides (4,77,93).

$$
\begin{array}{c}
\underset{\substack{\parallel\\ \text{O}}}{\text{R—C—NX}} + \text{NH}_2\text{OH} \;\rightleftharpoons\; \underset{\substack{\parallel\\ \text{O}}}{\text{R—C—NHOH}} + \text{NX} \qquad (24)\\[2mm]
\underset{\substack{\mid\\ \text{OH}}}{\text{R—C=NOH}}
\end{array}
$$

$$X = H_2; \ H,R'; \ \text{or} \ R',R''$$

$$3R—C—NHOH + Fe^{+++} \rightleftharpoons (R—C—NHO)_3Fe + 3H^+ \qquad (25)$$
$$\underset{O}{\|} \qquad\qquad\qquad \underset{O}{\|}$$

Other derivatives of carboxylic acids such as esters, anhydrides, acid chlorides, imides, and nitriles react with the hydroxylamine reagent and interfere.   The procedure of Bergman (4) follows.

Reagents and Apparatus.   (*1*) *Hydroxylamine sulfate*, 2 *N*.   (*2*) *Sodium hydroxide*, 3.5 *N*.   (*3*) *Hydrochloric acid*, 3.5 *N*.   (*4*) *Ferric chloride*, 0.74 *N* in 0.1 *N* hydrochloric acid.   (*5*) *Photoelectric colorimeter*.

Procedure.   Prepare an aqueous dilution of the sample so that the amide concentration is 5 to 10 $\times$ 10^{-3} *M*.   Mix equal volumes of the 2 *N* hydroxylamine sulfate and 3.5 *N* sodium hydroxide.   Transfer 2.0 ml. of the alkaline hydroxyla-

TABLE XX

Optimum Conditions for Conversion of Amides into Hydroxamic Acids (4)

Compound	Temp., °C.	Reaction time, min.
Acetamide	60	120
	26	480
N-Methylacetamide	60	420
Acetanilide	60	180
N^4-Acetylsulfanilamide	60	240
Acetylglycine	60	240
Fluoroacetamide	26	60
Formamide	26	60
	60	10
Dimethylformamide	26	240
Succinimide[a]	60	120
Caprolactam	60	420
Asparagine	60	180
Glutamine	60	180
Glutathione	60	120
Glycylglycine	60	120
Nicotinamide	26	480
N^1-Methylnicotinamide methosulfate	26	360
Nicotinic acid methylamide	60	240
Coramine (nicotinic acid diethylamide)	60	480
Pantothenic acid, calcium salt	26	300
Barbitone	100	45
Pentobarbitone	60	300
Phenolbarbitone	100	120
Evipan, sodium	100	30

[a] Alkaline reagent converts compound into sodium salt of monoamido acid.

mine reagent to a suitable glass-stoppered graduate. Introduce 1.0 ml. of the sample dilution. Allow the solution to stand for the length of time and at the temperature specified in Table XX. Rapidly cool the contents of the graduate to room temperature and introduce 1.0 ml. of 3.5 N hydrochloric acid and 1.0 ml of the 0.74 M ferric chloride. Immediately determine the absorbance of the sample at its maximum absorption in the spectral range of 500 to 570 mμ. Determine the concentration of amide by reference to a calibration curve previously prepared from aqueous solutions of the pure amide.

Table XX shows the proper reaction conditions for a number of compounds for which this procedure was found satisfactory. In all cases a linear relationship was found between absorbance and amide concentration.

The rate of reaction between amides and hydroxylamine is affected not only by temperature but also by pH. Thus, if the reaction medium is made too strongly basic or if the reaction time at elevated temperature is increased, hydrolysis of the amide may occur, which decreases the yield of hydroxamic acid. Because the hydroxamic acid formed is also susceptible to decomposition, the reaction times specified should be followed closely. For similar reasons, the color should be determined immediately after generation.

2. Saponification

During a series of investigations of the hydrolysis of N-substituted fatty acid amides Olsen (73) found that, although normal saponification with alcoholic caustic did not effect complete cleavage of the amide bonding, if the reaction temperature were raised to the boiling point of ethylene glycol the amide could be hydrolyzed:

$$\text{RCONHR}' + \text{KOH} \longrightarrow \text{RCOOK} + \text{R}'\text{NH}_2 \tag{26}$$

If the resulting mixture were titrated with hydrochloric acid using bromophenol blue indicator, a measure of the excess reagent and the salt and amine formed could be determined. In the case of acetanilide and o-acetotoluidide, where the amines liberated are aniline and o-toluidine, thymol blue indicator is recommended because of their weak dissociation.

In the case of mixtures of both an amide and an ester of a fatty acid, by using the usual saponification techniques in conjunction with the ethylene glycolic potassium hydroxide hydrolysis, a measure of both the ester and the amide may be obtained. Olsen's procedure for the determination of amides, which eliminates interference of esters, follows.

Reagents. *(1) Potassium hydroxide,* 1.0 *N* solution in ethylene glycol. *(2) Hydrochloric acid,* standard 0.5 *N.* *(3) Ethyl ether,* C. P. *(4) Bromophenol blue,* 1.0% alcoholic solution.

Procedure. Into each of two 250 ml. glass-stoppered erlenmeyer flasks introduce exactly 50 ml. of the 1.0 *N* potassium hydroxide solution. Reserve one of the flasks as a blank. Into the other flask introduce an amount of sample, containing up to 6 meq. of the amide. Fit each flask with a suitable reflux condenser and place the sample and blank on a hot plate. Bring the contents of the flasks to a boil and allow to reflux for 6 hours. Remove the flasks from the source of heat and rinse down the condenser with 25 ml. of distilled water, collecting the rinsings in the flask. Remove the condenser and add 30 ml. of ethyl ether to each flask. Add 8 to 10 drops of the bromophenol blue indicator and titrate with standard 0.5 *N* hydrochloric acid to a yellow-green end point. If acetanilide or acetotoluidides are being analyzed, use thymol blue indicator and titrate from a yellow to a red end point.

Calculate the amount of amide:

$$\frac{(A - B)N \times \text{E. W.}}{\text{g. sample} \times 10} = \text{amide, per cent by wt.}$$

where A = milliliters of N normal HCl required for the sample, B = milliliters of N normal HCl required for the blank, and E. W. = equivalent weight of amide.

Compounds for which this procedure was found to give satisfactory results include: N-(2-hydroxyethyl)oleamide; acetanilide; p-acetotoluidide; and N-(2-hydroxyethyl)lauramide (73).

Because of the excessive reaction time required and the possible loss of reagent by reaction with the glass container, determinations of amides using saponification reactions are seldom used. However, because of the limited number of procedures available for the determination, the method has value. In the case of primary amides where one of the hydrolysis products is ammonia, the saponification has been modified by evolving the ammonia formed into excess standard acid and the excess acid determined by titration (86).

3. Dinitrobenzoyl Chloride–Pyridine Method

Amides are often used as the starting material in the preparation of nitriles by reaction with acid chlorides. Mitchell and Ashby (66) successfully developed a quantitative procedure for the determination of unsubstituted amides, based on the above reaction, using 3,5-dinitrobenzoyl chloride in the presence of pyridine. They found the procedure was applicable to the analysis of primary amides of mono- and dibasic aliphatic and aromatic amides. A measured excess of the reagent is reacted with the amide as follows:

$$RCONH_2 + \underset{NO_2 \diagdown \diagup NO_2}{\overset{COCl}{\bigcirc}} \longrightarrow RCN + \underset{NO_2 \diagdown \diagup NO_2}{\overset{COOH}{\bigcirc}} + HCl \qquad (27)$$

The excess reagent is decomposed by the addition of methanol:

$$\underset{NO_2 \diagdown \diagup NO_2}{\overset{COCl}{\bigcirc}} + CH_3OH \longrightarrow \underset{NO_2 \diagdown \diagup NO_2}{\overset{COOCH_3}{\bigcirc}} + HCl \qquad (28)$$

A blank is run in which the reagent is allowed to react with methanol under the same conditions, and from the difference in the amount of alkali consumed by the sample and blank, the amount of amide may be calculated.

Reagents. (1) *3,5-Dinitrobenzoyl chloride*, 2 *M*. Dissolve 461 g. and 3,5-dinitrobenzoyl chloride in sufficient purified anhydrous 1,4-dioxane to make 1 liter of solution. To remove the dark brown color, treat with activated charcoal and filter rapidly, protecting the solution from exposure to moisture. The final solution should be no more than light yellow in color. (2) *Dry pyridine*, C. P. (3) *Dry methanol*, C. P. (4) *Sodium methylate*, 0.5 *N* in methanol; prepare directly from sodium and anhydrous methanol.

Procedure. Into each of two 250 ml. glass-stoppered volumetric flasks introduce 15 ml. of the 3,5-dinitrobenzoyl chloride reagent and 5 ml. of pyridine. Reserve one of the flasks as a blank. Into the other flask introduce an amount of sample weighed to the nearest 0.1 mg. which contains 10 meq. of amide. Place the sample and blank flasks in a water bath maintained at 60°C. for 30 minutes. (If amides of dibasic acids are being determined, react at 70°C. for 1 hour.) Remove the flasks from the hot-water bath and cool in a suitable ice bath. To each flask add 2 ml. of dry methanol and after 5 minutes add an additional 25 ml. of methanol. Add 3 or 4 drops of a 1.0% solution of phenolphthalein indicator in methanol and titrate both sample and blank with the standard 0.5 *N* sodium methylate to a faint pink end point. A saturated solution of ethyl bis-2,4-dinitrophenyl acetate in 1:1 acetone–ethanol solution may be used as indicator in highly colored solutions.

Calculate the amount of amide:

$$\frac{(A - B)\ N \times E.\ W.}{g.\ sample \times 10} = amide, per\ cent\ by\ wt.$$

where A = milliliters of N normal $NaOCH_3$ required for the sample, B = milliliters of N normal $NaOCH_3$ required for the blank, and E. W. = equivalent weight of the unsubstituted acid amide.

The procedure was found satisfactory for the determination of the following primary amides: formamide; acetamide; diacetamide hydrochloride; propionamide; butyramide; isobutyramide; n-valeramide; heptamide; succinamide; glutaramide; adipamide; benzamide; salicylamide; p-nitrobenzamide; phthalamide; furoamide. In general, the precision and accuracy were about ±0.3%.

Water reacts quantitatively with the reagent to produce two moles of acidity similarly to the amides and must be corrected for. Similarly, correction for any free acidity in the sample must be made. N-Substituted amides, urethans, and anilides do not interfere. Although amines and alcohols react with the reagent, no interference is observed beyond depletion of the reagent.

V. IMIDES, IMINES, AND QUATERNARY AMMONIUM COMPOUNDS

1. Imides

The determination of imides is, in general, limited to the determination of the weakly acidic properties of these compounds. Some measure of success in the determination of imides has, however, been reported in the determination of the active hydrogen (46) and in hydriodic acid reaction (22). Fortunately, nonaqueous techniques again offer a solution which could not be approached by the usual titration methods.

Ethylenediamine was one of the first solvents used to increase the acidic properties of weakly acidic compounds (70). The nonaqueous approach was further extended to include the use of many other organic solvents (31). Later, Fritz (28) published a procedure based upon a nonaqueous titration which was applicable to a wide number of imides. The sample is dissolved in dimethylformamide and titrated with a standard solution of sodium methoxide in benzene–methanol solvent. For very weakly acidic imides, ethylenediamine is recommended as the solvent. Being able to determine the end point by using visual indicators also is an advantage of the procedure. The procedure of Fritz follows.

Reagents. (1) *Dimethylformamide*, technical grade. (2) *Ethylenediamine*, 95 to 100%. (3) *Azo violet* (p-nitrobenzeneazoresorcinol), saturated solution in reagent-grade benzene. (4) *o-Nitroaniline*, 0.15 g. in 100 ml. of benzene. (5) *Thymol blue*, 0.3 g. in 100 ml. of methanol. (6) *Sodium methoxide*, standard 0.1 N solution. Wash 6 g. of sodium in methanol and dissolve immediately in 100 ml. of methanol. Protect the solution from carbon dioxide contamination; if necessary, cool the solution to prevent too violent a reaction. When reaction ceases, add 150 ml. of methanol and 1500 ml. of benzene. Store the reagent in borosilicate glassware protected from carbon dioxide. Standardize every few days by titration against primary standard-grade benzoic acid dissolved in benzene–methanol mixture.

Procedure. Transfer 10 to 20 ml. of the recommended solvent (see Table XXI) to a 100 ml. erlenmeyer flask and add 2 drops of the specified indicator. Titrate with the sodium methoxide to a clear blue color to neutralize the acid impurities present (if o-nitroaniline indicator is used, titrate to an orange-red color). Introduce an amount of sample containing 1 to 2 meq. of imide. Titrate with the standard 0.1 N sodium methoxide to the proper end point.

Calculate the amount of imide present:

$$\frac{AN \times \text{E. W.}}{\text{g. sample} \times 10} = \text{imide, per cent by wt.}$$

where A = milliliters of N normal $NaOCH_3$ required and E. W. = equivalent weight of imide.

Table XXI lists the proper solvent and indicator for a number of imides and related thio compounds for which this procedure was found to give satisfactory results.

TABLE XXI

Titration of Imides and Related Thio Compounds (28)

Compound	Solvent	Indicator
S-Diphenylthiourea	DMF[a]	Azo violet
Dithiobiuret	DMF	Azo violet
Dithiooxamide	DMF	Azo violet
Hydantoin	DMF	Azo violet
1-Phenyl-3-cyclohexylthiourea	EN[b]	o-Nitroaniline[c]
1-Phenyl-3-naphthylthiourea	DMF	Azo violet
1-Phenyl-3-(2-pyrimidyl)thiourea	DMF	Azo violet
Phthalimide	DMF	Azo violet
Succinimide	DMF	Azo violet
Theobromine	Pyridine	Azo violet
Thiobarbituric acid	DMF	Thymol blue

[a] Dimethylformamide.
[b] Ethylenediamine.
[c] In the Carbide laboratories we have found benzopurpurin 4B and orange IV indicators to give a more easily discernible end point in ethylenediamine medium. The color changes from acid to base are red to blue and orange-yellow to blue, respectively.

Compounds that may cause interference include acids, phenols, amine salts, thiols, active halogens, and esters which will condense under the reac-

tion conditions to form acidic compounds.   Water interferes in titrations
in dimethylformamide; however, small amounts of water may be tolerated
when using ethylenediamine solvent.

It has been found that, if one of the substituents on the imide nitrogen
group is either $NH_2C(=O)$— or $RNHC(=O)$—, successful titration is uncertain.   For example, acetylurea gives a very poor end point yet hy-
dantoin may be determined successfully.   Also, the position of aryl groups
affects the acidity of the imide.   For instance, acetylacetanilide may be
satisfactorily determined, whereas acetylurea cannot be titrated.   Substitution of a thiocarbonyl group for a carbonyl group, however, appears to
increase the acidity of imides.   Significantly, caffeine is not sufficiently
acidic to be titrated although similar to theobromine in structure.   Therefore, the method permits titration of theobromine in the presence of caffeine if ethylenediamine is used to solubilize the sample.

2. Imines

Except for a limited amount of infrared (14), Raman (10), and ultraviolet (19,32) absorption spectra, no data of general application to the determination of imines have been reported.   The problem of the determination of imine becomes more difficult because of the tendency of these compounds to cyclize, thus losing the characteristic —CH=NH grouping.

Both imines and N-substituted imines (Schiff bases), however, are easily
hydrolyzed to form the corresponding aldehyde and ammonia or amine:

$$RCH{=}NH + H_2O \xrightarrow{\ H^+\ } RCH{=}O + NH_3 \tag{29}$$

$$RCH{=}NR' + H_2O \xrightarrow{\ H^+\ } RCH{=}O + R'NH_2 \tag{30}$$

Therefore, by determining the amount of aldehyde released the amount
of imine originally present may be determined.   For a complete discussion
of the determination of carbonyl compounds the reader is referred to Volume
I of this series, page 243.   A procedure found effective in the Carbide and
Carbon Chemicals Company laboratories is based upon the above hydrolysis
and determination of the carbonyl by using either the sodium bisulfite reaction or free hydroxylamine reagent (3).   Imines and N-substituted imines
have been estimated in the presence of primary, secondary, and tertiary
amines, ammonia, alcohol, and water mixtures.

Reagents.   (1) *Sulfuric acid*, approximately 6 *N*.   (2) *Sodium bisulfite*,
0.2 *N* aqueous solution.   (3) *Methyl red indicator*, 0.2% aqueous solution.   (4)
Starch indicator, 1.0% aqueous solution.   (5) *Standard 0.1 N iodine*.

Procedure. Add 25 ml. of distilled water to each of four 500 ml. glass-stoppered erlenmeyer flasks. Reserve two of the flasks for a blank determination. Into each of the other flasks introduce an amount of sample containing 1 to 2 meq. of imine. Place the flasks in an ice bath at 0 to 5°C. for 10 minutes. Add 2 drops of the methyl red indicator and neutralize by adding 6 N sulfuric acid from a buret. Swirl the flasks sufficiently to make sure the sample is completely neutralized but do not add an excess of acid. Return the flasks to the ice bath and allow them to stand 10 minutes. Introduce 25 ml. of 0.2 N sodium bisulfite into each flask using a pressure-type pipet. Keep the tip of the pipet just at the surface of the solution. Space the addition of the reagent to allow equal reaction time for all blanks and samples. Remove the flasks from the ice bath, swirl the contents gently, and allow them to stand at room temperature for exactly 30 minutes. Swirl the flasks occasionally during this time. Replace the flasks in the ice bath for exactly 5 minutes. Remove the flasks from the ice bath and add approximately 25 g. of crushed ice. Add 2 ml. of the starch indicator and titrate immediately with 0.1 N iodine to the first appearance of a blue end point.

Calculate the amount of imine present:

$$\frac{(B - A)N \times \text{E. W.}}{\text{g. sample} \times 10} = \text{imine, per cent by wt.}$$

where A = milliliters of N normal iodine required for the sample, B = milliliters of N normal iodine required for the blank, and E. W. = equivalent weight of imine.

Compounds for which this procedure was found to give satisfactory results include: ethylimine polymer, butylimine; N-butylidenebutylamine; N-decylidenedecylamine; amylimine; N-amylideneamylamine; N-(2-butyloctylidene)-3-butyloctylamine; N-ethylideneaniline; and N-butylideneaniline. In cases in which solubility difficulties occur the procedure is modified to use a 15:10 mixture of isopropanol and water as the solvent medium.

Because the procedure is based upon the determination of the aldehyde released by hydrolysis, it is obvious no differentiation between the cyclized polymer (if it is formed) and the imine is obtained. However, inasmuch as the —CH=NR group has a strong absorption band in the 6 micron region, a true measure of the monomer may be determined using an infrared spectrophotometer. Thus both a measure of the true imine content and amount of cyclized imine may be determined by applying both procedures.

In cases in which the aldehyde released by the neutralization (hydrolysis) reaction cannot be determined using sodium bisulfite reagent, the free hydroxylamine reaction may often be applied. Using this procedure the sample is added to 15 ml. of isopropanol and 10 ml. of water. 1 ml. of 0.04% solution of bromophenol blue indicator in methanol is added and the sample is nearly neutralized with 6 N hydrochloric acid; the final neutralization is completed with 0.5 N hydrochloric acid. To both a blank and the sample is added 35 ml. of 0.5 N hydroxylamine hydrochloride which has been neutralized with 0.5 N sodium hydroxide to bromophenol blue indicator. Exactly 3 ml. of 0.5 N hydrochloric acid is introduced and the blank and sample are allowed to stand at room temperature for 60 minutes. Both blank and sample are then titrated with standard 0.5 N sodium hydroxide to a blue-green end point.

This method has been applied successfully to the following imines and N-substituted imines: ethylimine; N-isopropylideneisopropylamine; butylimine; N-butylidenebutylamine; 2-ethylbutylimine; 2-ethylhexylimine; N-(2-ethylbutylidene)-2-ethylbutylamine; and α-methylbenzylimine.

A recent publication by Freeman (25) presents a nonaqueous method he has found applicable to the determination of Schiff bases. The sample is dissolved in acetic acid and titrated potentiometrically with standard 0.1 N perchloric acid in acetic acid. Methyl violet indicator may also be used to determine the end point. Coupled with the differential titration technique described in Section III.6A, satisfactory determination of the N-substituted imide as well as the amine impurity is reported.

3. Quaternary Ammonium Compounds

The analysis of quaternary ammonium compounds did not receive a great deal of attention until the relatively recent appreciation of the usefulness of some of these compounds as antiseptics and germicides. The usual approach to their analysis has been through the formation of a colored complex followed by a spectrophotometric measurement of the color intensity. In general, few methods have been reported applicable to the whole field of quaternary ammonium compounds, but rather procedures are presented applicable to certain types or even individual compounds.

A gravimetric method of analysis has been used for the estimation of quaternary ammonium compounds based on their reaction with Reinecke salt, $NH_4 + [Cr(NH_3)_2(SCN)_4]^- H_2O$, to precipitate a complex (102). The complex can be weighed as chromic oxide, or the percentage of nitrogen can be determined by combustion.

Nitrogen may be quantitatively recovered as ammonia from tetramethylammonium compounds using the Kjeldahl procedure (see Section II.1B) with a mercury catalyst (65).

An interesting technique for the determination of quaternary ammonium salts by titration with perchloric acid has been published by Pifer and

Wollish (74). In this procedure, the salts are dissolved in acetic acid, mercuric acetate is added to convert the salts to acetates, and the resulting quaternary ammonium acetates are titrated with perchloric acid in dioxane. The end point may be determined either potentiometrically or by using indicators. Salts other than chlorides, bromides, and iodides may be determined directly eliminating the need for the addition of the mercuric acetate. The method was found applicable to the determination of the following compounds: neostigmine bromide; choline chloride; (3-hydroxyphenyl)ethyldimethylammonium chloride; cetylpyridinium chloride; triphenyltetrazolium chloride; tetraethylammonium bromide; 3-(hydroxyphenyl)ethyldimethylammonium bromide; (2-hydroxy-3-cyclohexylbenzyl)methylpiperidinium bromide; dimethyl carbamate; choline dihydrogen citrate; and choline dihydrogen tartrate.

Bickerman (5) has reported the determination of tetramethylammonium sulfate or nitrate by heating the compound with sodium hydroxide in a nickel retort. Trimethylamine is distilled off, absorbed in standard sulfuric acid, and the excess acid is titrated with standard alkali. The original solution is evaporated to dryness, the residue is heated to redness, cooled, taken up in a little water, and the heating repeated to recover the last traces of the amine.

Fogh, Rasmussen, and Skadhauge (24) recently reported a method for the determination of cetylpyridinium chloride that holds great promise for the micro determination of other quaternary ammonium compounds. It is based on the ability of bromocresol purple indicator to produce a blue color (not associated with this indicator at any known pH) with different quaternary ammonium compounds. This spectrophotometric procedure provides for the determination of concentrations ranging from 0 to 25 gamma (0.001 mg.) per milliliter. The results are independent of variations in temperature within certain limits, and uninfluenced by the presence of calcium, magnesium, ferrous, ferric, and cupric ion up to concentrations of 1.0%. All measurements are made on a Beckman DU spectrophotometer at a wave length of 620 mμ, using 1 cm. cells. The sample absorbance is compared to a calibration curve determined on a series of standard solutions.

This technique followed along the lines of the earlier investigation reported by Auerbach in 1943 (1,2) in which alkyl benzyldimethylammonium chloride was successfully determined in concentrations up to 2 g. per liter. Auerbach found the benzyl type quaternary ammonium compounds form colored salts with bromothymol blue (dibromothymolsulfonephthalein) and bromophenol blue (tetrabromophenolsulfonephthalein) indicators.

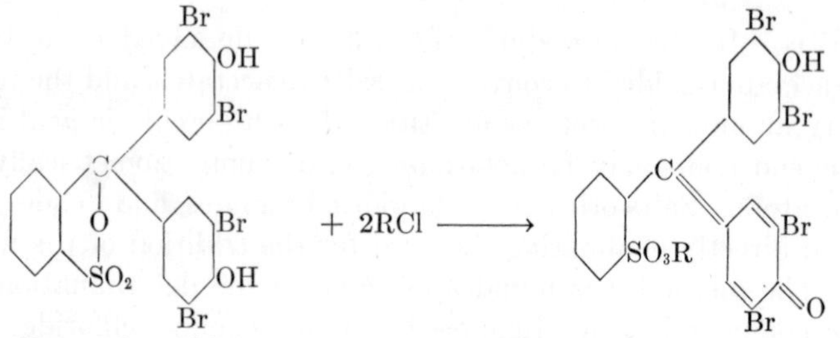

Bromophenol blue

R = quaternary ammonium cation

He extracted the colored salts from aqueous alkaline solution with benzene and measured the intensity of the color developed in a photoelectric colorimeter. By means of a factor previously derived from a standard solution, the concentration of quaternary ammonium compound was readily calculated. While it is not claimed that only quaternary ammonium compounds respond to this procedure, some 50 or 60 of the more common non-quaternary amines all give negative tests.

The successful determination of the tetrazolium salts employing a colorimetric measurement of the deviation from the equivalence point has been reported by Hall (37).

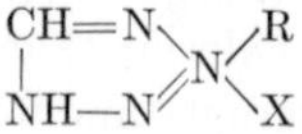

Tetrazolium salt

A dilute solution of the salt is titrated nearly to, or just beyond, the equivalence point with picric acid. The titrated salt solution is chilled to 0°C., filtered, and the optical density measured at a wave length of 430 mμ. The presence of strong acids cannot be tolerated, and there must be no significant color absorption by any other materials present.

References

1. Auerbach, M. E., *Ind. Eng. Chem., Anal. Ed.,* *15*, 492 (1943).
2. Auerbach, M. E., *ibid.,* *16*, 739 (1944).
3. Barrett, S. J., and D. H. Whitehurst, unpublished data, Carbide and Carbon Chemicals Company, South Charleston, West Virginia.
4. Bergman, F., *Anal. Chem.,* *24*, 1367 (1952).
5. Bickerman, J. J., *Z. anal. Chem.,* *90*, 335 (1932); *Chem. Abstracts, 27,* 480 (1933).
6. Blumrich, K., and G. Bandel, *Angew. Chem.,* *54*, 374 (1941).
7. Bradstreet, R. B., *Chem. Revs., 27,* 331 (1940).
8. Bryant, W. M. D., J. Mitchell, Jr., and D. M. Smith, *J. Am. Chem. Soc., 62,* 3504 (1940).

9. Callin, T., and J. A. R. Henderson, *J. Soc. Chem. Ind.*, *41*, 161 (1922).
10. Cantarel, R., *Compt. rend.*, *210*, 480 (1940).
11. Carpiaux, E., *Bull. soc. chim. Belg.*, *27*, 13; *Chem. Abstracts*, *7*, 3463 (1913).
12. Conant, J. B., and N. F. Hall, *J. Am. Chem. Soc.*, *49*, 3047, 3062 (1927).
13. Conant, J. B., and T. H. Werner, *ibid.*, *52*, 4436 (1930).
14. Colthup, N. B., *J. Optical Soc. Am.*, *40*, 397 (1950).
15. Cope, W. C., *J. Ind. Eng. Chem.*, *8*, 592 (1916).
15a. Critchfield, F. E., and J. B. Johnson, *Anal. Chem.*, *28*, 436 (1956).
15b. Critchfield, F. E., and J. B. Johnson, *ibid.*, *28*, 430 (1956).
15c. Critchfield, F. E., and J. B. Johnson, *ibid.*, *28*, 432 (1956).
16. Day, A. R., and W. T. Taggart, *Ind. Eng. Chem.*, *20*, 545 (1928).
17. Dowell, C. T., W. G. Friedemann, and D. C. Cochrane, *ibid.*, *13*, 358 (1921).
18. English, F. L., *Anal. Chem.*, *19*, 457 (1947).
19. Ferguson, L. N., and G. E. K. Branch, *J. Am. Chem. Soc.*, *66*, 75 (1944).
20. Ferrero, P., and J. Brehain, *Ind. chim. belge*, *16*, 103 (1951).
21. Fischer, F., *Chem. Fabrik.*, 154–6 (1950); *Chem. Abstracts*, *34*, 5015 (1940).
22. Fierz-David, H. E., E. Pfanner, and F. Oppliger, *Helv. Chim. Acta*, *28*, 1463 (1945).
22a. Flaschka, H., *Mikroch. Acta*, *38*, 34 (1952).
23. Folin, O., and L. E. Wright, *J. Biol. Chem.*, *38*, 461 (1919).
24. Fogh, J., P. O. H. Rasmussen, and K. Skadhauge, *Anal. Chem.*, *26*, 392 (1954).
25. Freeman, S. K., *ibid.*, *25*, 1750 (1953).
26. Friedrich, A., E. Kühass, and R. Schnürch, *Z. physiol. Chem.*, *216*, 68 (1933).
27. Fritz, J. S., *Anal. Chem.*, *22*, 1028 (1950).
28. Fritz, J. S., *ibid.*, *24*, 674 (1952).
29. Fritz, J. S., *ibid.*, *25*, 407 (1953).
30. Fritz, J. S., *Acid-Base Titrations in Non-aqueous Solvents*. G. Frederick Smith Co., Columbus, Ohio.
31. Fritz, J. S., and N. M. Lisicki, *Anal. Chem.*, *23*, 589 (1951).
32. Grammaticakis, P., *Compt. rend.*, *225*, 684 (1947).
33. Grant, J., *Quantitative Organic Microanalysis*. 4th ed., Churchill, London, 1945.
34. Gunning, J. W., *Z. anal. Chem.*, *28*, 188 (1899).
35. Hall, N. F., *J. Am. Chem. Soc.*, *52*, 5115 (1930).
36. Hall, N. F., and T. H. Werner, *ibid.*, *50*, 2367 (1928).
37. Hall, W. T., *Chem. Anal.*, *42*, 9 (1953); *Chem. Abstracts*, *47*, 4249 (1953).
38. Hallet, L. T., *Ind. Eng. Chem.*, *Anal. Ed.*, *14*, 977 (1942).
39. Hawkins, W., D. M. Smith and J. Mitchell, Jr., *J. Am. Chem. Soc.*, *66*, 1662 (1944).
40. Hayman, D. F., and S. Adler, *Ind. Eng. Chem.*, *Anal. Ed.*, *9*, 197 (1937).
41. Hestrin, S., *J. Biol. Chem.*, *180*, 249 (1949).
42. Hoffman, C., *Ber.*, *22*, 2854 (1889).
42a. Hofman, A. W., *ibid.*, *1*, 169 (1868).
43. Jodlbauer, M., *Chem. Zentr.*, *57*, 433 (1886).
44. Johnson, J. B., *Anal. Chem.*, received for review.
45. Johnston, R. B., M. J. Mycek, and J. S. Fruton, *J. Biol. Chem.*, *185*, 629 (1950).
46. Jureček, M., *Chem. Listy*, *40*, 239 (1946).
47. Kahane, E., *Bull. soc. chim. France*, *18*, 92 (1951).
48. Keen, R. T., and J. S. Fritz, *Anal. Chem.*, *24*, 564 (1952).
49. Kirsten, W., *ibid.*, *19*, 925 (1947).

50. Kjeldahl, J., *Z. anal. Chem.*, *22*, 366 (1883); *Compt. rend. Lab. Carlsberg*, *2* (1), 12 (1883).

51. Koch, F. C., and T. L. McMeekin, *J. Am. Chem. Soc.*, *46*, 2066 (1924).

52. Kolthoff, I. M., and A. Willman, *ibid.*, *56*, 1007, 1014 (1934).

53. Koppeschaar, W., *Z. anal. Chem.*, *15*, 233 (1876).

54. Langecker, H., *Biochem. Z.*, *324*, 214 (1953).

55. Lee, H. R., and D. C. Jones, *Ind. Eng. Chem.*, *16*, 930 (1924).

56. Lee, H. R., and D. C. Jones, *ibid.*, pp. 948–9.

57. Linke, B., H. Preissecker, and J. Stadler, *Ber.*, *65*, 1282 (1932).

58. Linke, B., H. Preissecker, and J. Stadler, *ibid.*, pp. 1280–2.

59. Lippman, F., and L. C. Tuttle, *J. Biol. Chem.*, *159*, 21 (1945).

60. Lunge, G., and E. Berl, *Chemische-technische Untersuchungsmethoden*, Springer, Berlin, 1931; Edwards, Ann Arbor, Mich.

61. Ma., T. S., and G. Zuazaga, *Ind. Eng. Chem., Anal. Ed.*, *14*, 280 (1942).

62. Markunas, P. C., and J. A. Riddick, *Anal. Chem.*, *23*, 337 (1951).

63. Markley, K. S., and R. M. Hann, *J. Assoc. Official Agr. Chem.*, *8*, 455 (1925).

64. Mears, B., and R. E. Hussey, *J. Ind. Eng. Chem.*, *13*, 1054 (1921).

65. Middleton, G., and R. E. Stuckey, *J. Pharm. Pharmacol.*, *3*, 829 (1951); *Chem. Abstracts*, *46*, 1387 (1952).

66. Mitchell, J., Jr., and C. E. Ashby, *J. Am. Chem. Soc.*, *67*, 161 (1945).

67. Mitchell, J., Jr., W. Hawkins, and D. M. Smith, *ibid.*, *66*, 782 (1947).

68. Mitchell, J., Jr., and D. M. Smith, *Aquametry*. Interscience, New York-London, 1948, p. 19.

69. Mizuch, K. G., and A. Ya. Savchenko, *Org. Chem. Ind., U. S. S. R.*, *7*, 24 (1940).

70. Moss, M. L., J. H. Elliott, and R. T. Hall, *Anal. Chem.*, *20*, 784 (1948).

71. Nadeau, G. F., and L. E. Branchen, *J. Am. Chem. Soc.*, *57*, 1363 (1935).

71a. Nebbia, L., and F. Gurrieri, *Chimica e industria (Milan)*, *35*, 896 (1953).

72. Ogg, C. L., W. L. Porter, and C. O. Willits, *Ind. Eng. Chem., Anal. Ed.*, *17*, 394 (1945).

73. Olsen, S., *Die Chemie*, *56*, 202 (1943).

74. Pifer, C. W., and E. G. Wollish, *Anal. Chem.*, *24*, 300 (1952).

75. Pifer, C. W., and E. G. Wollish, *ibid.*, p. 519.

76. Pifer, C. W., E. G. Wollish, and M. Small, *ibid.*, *25*, 310 (1953).

77. Polya, J. B., and P. L. Tardew, *ibid.*, *23*, 1036 (1951).

78. Pregl, F., *Die quantitative Organische*. Springer, Berlin, 1920.

79. Pregl, F., *Die quantitative Mikroanalyse*. 2nd ed., Springer, Berlin, 1923.

80. Riddick, J. A., *Anal. Chem.*, *24*, 41 (1952).

81. Rutherford, H. A., M. Harris, and A. L. Smith, *Proceedings of the American Textile Chemists and Colorists*, 650 (Nov. 1, 1937).

82. Sabalitschka, T., and H. Schrader, *Z. anal. Chem.*, *34*, 45 (1921).

83. Scholten, H. G., and K. S. Stone, *Anal. Chem.*, *24*, 749–50 (1952).

84. Seaman, W., and E. Allen, *ibid.*, *23*, 592 (1951).

85. Self, P. A. W., *Pharm. J.*, *88*, 384 (1912).

86. Siggia, S., *Quantitative Organic Analysis via Functional Groups*. 2nd. ed., Wiley, New York, 1954, p. 47.

87. Siggia, S., *ibid.*, p. 109.

88. Siggia, S., J. G. Hanna, and I. R. Kervenski, *Anal. Chem.*, *22*, 1295 (1950).

89. Singh, B., and G. Ahmad, *J. Indian Chem. Soc.*, *15*, 416 (1938).

90. Singh, B., and A. Rehmann, *ibid.*, *19*, 349 (1942).
91. Sluyterman, L. A. Ae., and M. Kooistra, *Rec. trav. chim.*, *70*, 1045 (1951); *Chem. Abstracts*, *46*, 6549 (1952).
92. Spies, J. R., and T. H. Harris, *Ind. Eng. Chem.*, *Anal. Ed.*, *9*, 304 (1937).
93. Soloway, S., and A. Lipschitz, *Anal. Chem.*, *24*, 898 (1952).
94. Thornburg, H. L., and J. S. Bodenschatz, unpublished data, Carbide and Carbon Chemicals Co., South Charleston, West Virginia.
95. Unterzaucher, J., *Mikrochemie ver. Mikrochim. Acta*, *36/37*, 706 (1951).
96. Van Slyke, D. D., *J. Biol. Chem.*, *9*, 185 (1911).
97. Van Slyke, D. D., *ibid.*, *12*, 275 (1912).
98. Viscontini, M., *Helv. Chim. Acta*, *29*, 1491 (1946).
99. Wagner, C. D., R. H. Brown, and E. D. Peters, *J. Am. Chem. Soc.*, *69*, 2609 (1947).
100. Wagner, C. D., R. H. Brown, and E. D. Peters, *ibid.*, *69*, 2611 (1947).
101. Wagner, W. F., and W. B. Kauffman, *Anal. Chem.*, *25*, 538 (1953).
102. Wild, F., *Estimation of Organic Compounds*. University Press, Cambridge, England, p. 171.
103. Wild, F., *ibid.*, p. 178.
104. Wilfarth, H., *Chem. Zentr.*, *56*, 17, 113 (1885).
105. Wilson, H. N., *J. Soc. Chem. Ind. (London)*, *67*, 237 (1948).
106. Winkler, Z., *Angew. Chem.*, *26*, 231 (1913).
107. Wittman, G., *ibid.*, *A60*, 330 (1948).
108. Woelfel, W. C., *Anal. Chem.*, *20*, 722 (1948).

Determination of
OLEFINIC UNSATURATION

A. Polgár and J. L. Jungnickel, *Shell Development Company*

CONTENTS (*continued*)

I. INTRODUCTION

Unsaturation shared by two adjacent carbon atoms, commonly represented by a double bond, is termed olefinic or ethylenic unsaturation. Two or more such linkages may be present in the same molecule. When separated by two or more single bonds, they are termed isolated double bonds; when they alternate with single bonds, they form conjugated systems; when twinned at a common carbon atom, they are called allenic systems or cumulenes.

The remarkable chemical reactivity of organic compounds possessing these groups accounts for the existence of a wide variety of analytical methods for determination of unsaturation. Probably no other functional group is represented by such a large number of published analytical methods and procedural variations. Over two thousand articles in the chemical literature pertaining to the subject have come to the authors' attention; doubtless many more exist. Considering the large amount of older work on the "classical" methods such as halogenation (much in need of review) and the recent development of powerful newer analytical tools such as the various chromatographic and spectroscopic techniques, the authors believe that a rather comprehensive survey of the present status of unsaturation analysis should prove useful to many analytical and organic chemists. Because many of the wide variety of analytical methods available possess particular advantages in regard to scope, specificity, convenience, or other features, it does not seem possible to limit the present discussion to a selected small number of analytical procedures. Moreover, some procedures have never been adequately studied; further investigation of the potentialities of some of these methods seems justified. For these reasons, a rather large number of methods and variations in procedure are referred to in this chapter. However, detailed procedures and discussions are included only for the more important methods.

Nearly all chemical methods for determination of unsaturation involve the addition of a reagent to the double bond. (In fact, the ability of an unsaturated molecule to undergo addition reactions is a primary characteristic of the species.) Methods based on halogenation, hydrogenation, epoxidation, nitration, thiocyanation, mercuration, or on addition of mercaptans, bisulfite, amines, etc., are of this type. Most of these chemical methods depend on a titrimetric or volumetric procedure for measuring the amount of reagent consumed in the addition reaction. Only a few methods are based on the measurement of the reaction products. Of these, certain oxidation methods involving rupture of the carbon chain at the position of the ethylenic bond are important because they provide information on structure as well as on the extent of unsaturation.

Instrumental methods cover a variety of procedures based on physical or physicochemical properties of unsaturated compounds. Structural information often can be obtained also from these properties. Infrared and Raman spectra arise from characteristic vibrations of the atoms, yielding both qualitative and quantitative information on the structure in the vicinity of the double bond. Ultraviolet and visible absorption spectra produced by excitation of electrons in unsaturated compounds provide additional analytical results, especially on conjugated systems. Mass spectrometry uses the characteristic patterns of ionized molecular fragments to furnish quantitative structural analysis. Polarography, usually classed as an instrumental method, depends primarily on chemical reactivity; conjugated and allenic double bonds are polarographically reducible.

The chromatographic methods depend on differences in adsorbability on solid surfaces or distribution between two fluid phases. Unlike most chemical methods, which measure only the extent of unsaturation, chromatographic methods actually separate the olefinic compounds out of the sample, thus making them available for more detailed examination.

II. CHEMICAL METHODS

Although the graphic representation of a double bond suggests a binding of special strength, in many respects such a bond in a molecule is rather a point of weakness. This weakness accounts for the difference in type of reactions which olefins undergo, as compared to compounds with only single bonds. Whereas the latter group of organic molecules can yield derivatives only by a process of substitution, compounds with double bonds can also yield derivatives by a process of addition. This ability to combine directly with certain atoms or groups is a characteristic property of olefinic substances on which almost all chemical methods for their quantitative determination are based.

Electronically, an ethylenic linkage is represented by the sharing of two electron pairs by the adjacent carbon atoms. It is believed that one of these pairs has the properties of the σ-electrons of an "ordinary" single carbon-carbon bond, and that the second pair, termed π-electrons, represents a bond of lower energy content. This latter pair of electrons is less firmly held between the carbon nuclei and is responsible for the high chemical reactivity of olefinic compounds.* Several observations suggest that the addition to an olefinic linkage takes place in two steps and involves an ionic intermediate. The initial step is the attack by a positive fragment of the reagent on the double bond to form a cation which then may combine with the negative fragment of the reagent formed in the first step, or may add any other anion available in the reaction mixture. The intermediate ion is considered as a π-complex in which the cationic portion of the reagent is linked to the π-electrons of the carbon-carbon double bond (144). The corresponding reaction with an anion is impossible since the ethylenic linkage cannot act as an electron acceptor without the actual fission of the

---

* For detailed discussions of the electronic theory of the olefinic double bond, refer to the several excellent monographs published recently, e. g., references 144, 284, 498 and 517.

π-bond. In the case of fission of the π-bond the exclusive *trans* addition of halogen to olefins could not be satisfactorily explained.

This reaction mechanism, confirmed by a large number of experimental facts, classifies olefins as anionoid (nucleophilic) substances and explains why reactions with cationoid (electrophilic) substances, such as halogens, ozone, and strong acids, proceed readily, while reactions with anionoid substances, such as weak acids and ammonia and its salts, in general do not occur.

Thus, in the reaction of Br_2 with a symmetrical olefin in, say, acetic acid, the initial partial polarization of the bromine molecule (a) is followed by the formation of the intermediate positively charged π-complex (b). Next the

$$\begin{matrix} \diagdown\diagup \\ C \\ \| + \overset{\delta+}{Br} \ \overset{\delta-}{Br} \\ C \\ \diagup\diagdown \\ (a) \end{matrix} \longrightarrow \begin{bmatrix} \diagdown\diagup \\ C \\ \| \to Br \\ C \\ \diagup\diagdown \end{bmatrix}^{+} + Br^{-} \longrightarrow \begin{matrix} | \\ Br-C- \\ | \\ -C-Br \\ | \end{matrix}$$

$$(a) \hspace{3cm} (b) \hspace{3cm} (c)$$

π-electron bond is rearranged into a σ-bond to join the bromine atom to either carbon atom of the original double bond, with the result that the other carbon is now available to form another σ-bond with the negatively charged bromine atom to yield the dibromide (c).

As a further illustration of this reaction mechanism, the addition of an unsymmetrical reagent, such as ICl, to an unsymmetrical olefin may be considered. Such an olefin carries minute electrical charges ($\delta+$, $\delta-$) on the doubly bound carbon atoms, the sign and intensity of these charges being determined by the relative electron-withdrawing ability of the groups attached to these carbon atoms. Therefore, the I^+ cation will be attached unsymmetrically, being closer to the more negative end of the bond. The reaction with the Cl^- anion will then occur more readily at the other end of the bond:

$$\begin{matrix} \diagdown\diagup \\ C \ \delta+ \\ \| \\ C \ \delta- \\ \diagup\diagdown \end{matrix} + I^+Cl^- \longrightarrow \begin{bmatrix} \diagdown\diagup \\ C \\ \| \to I \\ C \\ \diagup\diagdown \end{bmatrix}^{+} + Cl^- \longrightarrow \begin{matrix} | \\ Cl-C- \\ | \\ -C-I \\ | \end{matrix}$$

In addition to this orienting effect, radicals attached, or adjacent, to the doubly bound carbon atoms have a decisive influence on the ease with which addition can occur. It follows from the π-complex theory that increasing substitution of groups more electropositive than hydrogen (e. g., methyl or phenyl groups) is accompanied by an increase in rate of addition, whereas less electropositive groups (e. g., halogens or a carboxyl group) retard the addition. Correspondingly, an actual charge on the molecule is important in determining the rate. Thus, the ion $CH_2=CH-COO^-$ is approximately 300 times more reactive than the undissociated acid (664). Relative rates of addition of bromine to a few substituted ethylene derivatives, determined in CH_2Cl_2 solution at $-78°C$. (25), are:

$$(CH_3)_2C=C(CH_3)_2 \quad (CH_3)_2C=CH_2 \quad C_6H_5CH=CH_2 \quad CH_3CH=CH_2$$
$$14.0 \qquad\qquad 5.5 \qquad\qquad 3.4 \qquad\qquad 2.0$$

$$CH_2=CH_2 \quad CH_3CH=CH-COOH \quad CH_2=CH-COOH \quad CH_2=CHBr$$
$$1.0 \qquad\qquad 0.3 \qquad\qquad\qquad small \qquad\qquad small$$

Addition to conjugated double bonds presents a more complex picture. Here, again, the addition proceeds in a stepwise manner and is initiated at one end of the conjugated system, usually by the positive fragment of the reagent. If the two ends are different, the electronically more favorable end will be attacked. With a conjugated diene the resulting intermediate ion will offer two positions where the other fragment of the reagent (or an ion of corresponding sign present in the reaction mixture) may enter. Of these, the position leading to a 1,4-addition is favored, 1,2-addition occurring to a lesser extent. The remaining 3,4-double bond in this latter case, but especially the newly formed 2,3-bond in the 1,4-addition, as a result of the proximity of electronegative groups, show a marked decrease in reactivity toward adding a second molecule of the reagent. Prolonged reaction times and severe reaction conditions are necessary to effect addition to this remaining double bond. Trienes and longer conjugated systems behave in a like manner giving primary products of larger complexity.

Certain exceptions have been observed to these generalizations. Acrolein, for example, adds bromine more easily than does ethylene (and crotonaldehyde more easily than propylene); the increase in reactivity is greater than would be predicted from the electronegative properties of the aldehyde group. However, this increased reactivity can be easily understood if it is considered that the strongly electronegative carbonyl group changes the character of the conjugated carbon-carbon double bond from anionoid to cationoid (25):

$$\overset{\delta+}{C}=C-\overset{\delta-}{C}=O$$

In accordance with this view, acrolein adds two moles of $NaHSO_3$, a typical anionoid reagent, one mole of which adds irreversibly to the double bond. It would follow that the β-carbon is attacked first leading to the product:

$$\overset{\displaystyle SO_3Na}{\underset{\displaystyle CH_2-CH_2-CH=O}{|}}$$

Markownikoff's rule states that, in the addition of a hydrogen halide to an ethylene derivative at normal temperatures, the halogen is attached to the carbon atom of the double bond that carries the lesser number of hydrogen atoms (413). Exceptions to this rule have been observed in the addition of HBr to certain olefins. In the absence of oxygen or peroxides, "normal" addition takes place, but in their presence a much faster "abnormal" reaction proceeds. The mechanism proposed by Kharasch and his collaborators for this "peroxide effect" involves a radical chain reaction with bromine atoms (423). The product of such an addition has the halogen atom attached to the less substituted carbon, violating Markownikoff's rule, e. g.:

$$BrCH_2-CH=CH_2 + HBr \begin{cases} \xrightarrow{no\ O_2} BrCH_2-CHBr-CH_3 \\ \\ \xrightarrow{+\ O_2} BrCH_2-CH_2-CH_2Br \end{cases}$$

It is known that many other compounds add readily to olefins under conditions of radical catalysis. Thus CCl_4 will add to olefins in the presence of a peroxide (343), but in its absence no reaction takes place. Other compounds containing several chlorine atoms attached to one carbon atom are known to add likewise to olefins (e. g., $CHCl_3$, $CHCl_2-COOC_2H_5$). In addition to peroxides, ultraviolet light (sunlight) can also initiate these chain reactions.

The above highlights of the electronic theory of olefinic double bonds have been presented to provide a better understanding of the scope of chemical methods designed for the determination of olefinic unsaturation. It seems evident that the desirable course is addition by the ionic mechanism. Actually, this is the course utilized in the majority of methods, those which employ polar or ionizing solvents. In nonpolar solvents, such as CCl_4, the presence of small amounts of polar materials (added purposefully or present incidentally in the reaction mixture) may successfully conduct the reaction along ionic lines. In contrast to the ionic type of addition reaction, the radical chain reaction presents many unknown features; it should therefore be prevented by careful selection of the experimental conditions. Peroxides, formed readily from many of the olefinic compounds, or exposure of the reaction mixture to intense light, seem to be the chief initiators of this course of reaction. The result may be analytically useless products. This certainly will be the case when solvent molecules participate in a radical-type addition reaction.

Of course, many of these points have been clearly recognized and utilized by alert analytical chemists. However, several of the unsaturation methods presently in use suffer from fundamental defects and place an unnecessary burden on the analyst who wishes to arrive to an unequivocal interpretation of results.

1. Halogenation

A. GENERAL

Most of the classical methods for the determination of olefinic unsaturation involved halogenation and were developed primarily for the analysis of animal and vegetable fats. It was found, in general, that these halogenation methods were unsatisfactory when applied to complex petroleum mixtures; consequently new methods or modifications of earlier methods were developed for petroleum products. It is generally acknowledged that the position of analytical halogenation, although considerably improved, is still far from satisfactory, as evidenced by the multiplicity of methods in use at the present time and the continual search for new ones.

It was a relatively simple matter to design methods for the characterization of individual compounds or simple mixtures, but the difficulties to overcome became significant when the application of many of these halogenation methods to complex mixtures of natural origin, especially to petroleum hydrocarbons, was attempted. The molecular intricacy of these materials, wide differences in reactivity, and the presence of interfering configurations all add to the complexity of the problem of developing a single, or at best a few, methods of rather universal applicability.

(1) **Nature of the Halogenation Reaction.** Bromine is the most useful halogen reagent and has enjoyed the most widespread application in analytical procedures. Chlorine is so reactive that its use is often accompanied by severe substitution, while iodine adds rather reluctantly and only to a few ethylenic compounds. Two interhalogen compounds, iodine monochloride and iodine monobromide, have also found considerable use. The relative reactivity of these compounds (659) may be associated with increasing polarizability (211):

Halogen	I_2	IBr	Br_2	ICl
Relative rate of addition	1	3×10^3	10^4	10^5

The interpretation of halogenation values as giving a quantitative measure of olefinic unsaturation is based upon the assumptions that addition takes place rapidly, giving rise to stable addition products, and that halogen substitution is a slow process (likewise other types of secondary reactions). Unfortunately, these postulates are not necessarily true. Thus it was shown by Bartlett, Fraser, and Woodward (42) that addition of bromine in CCl_4 solution to 1,1-dineopentylethylene:

$$\begin{array}{c} (CH_3)_3CCH_2 \\ \diagdown \\ (CH_3)_3CCH_2 \diagup \end{array} C{=}CH_2$$

was a slow process and could not be applied quantitatively; however, substitution with a corresponding evolution of HBr readily occurred.

Equations (1) through (7) represent types of reactions that may occur.

$$-CH{=}CH{-} \qquad + X_2 \longrightarrow \underset{\underset{X}{|}}{\overset{\overset{X}{|}}{-CH{-}CH{-}}} \qquad (1)$$

$$-CH{=}CH{-}CH_2{-} + X_2 \longrightarrow -CH{=}CH{-}CHX{-} + HX \qquad (2)$$

$$-CH{=}CH{-} \qquad + X_2 \longrightarrow -CH{=}CX{-} + HX \qquad (3)$$

$$-CH{=}CH{-} \qquad + HX \longrightarrow \underset{\underset{H}{|}}{\overset{\overset{X}{|}}{-CH{-}CH{-}}} \qquad (4)$$

$$-CH{=}CH{-} + X_2 + AB \longrightarrow \underset{\underset{X}{|}}{\overset{\overset{B}{|}}{-CH{-}CH{-}}} + X^- + A^+ \qquad (5)$$

$$-CHX{-}CHX{-} \longrightarrow -CH{=}CH{-} + X_2 \qquad (6)$$

$$-CHX{-}CHX{-} \longrightarrow -CH{=}CX{-} + HX \qquad (7)$$

Only reaction (1) represents true addition and is, therefore, the most useful for analytical purposes. On the other hand, a knowledge of the extent of other possible reactions may permit their analytical utilization. Thus, some methods apply a correction for the acidity (HX) formed by reactions such as (2). This correction leads to theoretical results only if the final product of halogenation contains one mole of halogen per mole, i.e., only if reactions (3), (4), (5), and (7) do not occur. However, total halogen absorption due to a combination of reactions (1) and (3) has been used successfully (see Section II.1.C(3)). Reaction (5) represents the participation of the negatively charged portion of the solvent (or another suitable component of the reaction mixture) in the addition. The loss of free halogen due to this reaction is a correct measure of the double bond content; however, correcting for the halogen acid formed would give only half of the true value (see Section II.1.B(4)).

Subsequent hydrolysis of either added or substituted halogen (or both) is an important reaction and it is difficult, if not impossible, to eliminate or correct for it. The reactions of the ethylenic bond are much more complex when X_2 in the above equations is an interhalogen compound.

The number and nature of substituents on the doubly bound carbon atoms, as discussed earlier, have very specific influences on the rate of addition. A generalization is that bromine will react with any ethylenic linkage where each ethylenic carbon atom holds at least one atom of hydrogen, but it will rarely react with completely substituted ethylenic linkages. This rule is a very gross approximation because it does not take into account the chemical nature of the substituents. As discussed earlier, the proximity of electronegative groups retards the rate of addition and in certain instances addition does not occur at all. In general, chain branching promotes substitution reactions, and the ease of substitution also increases with increasing molecular weight.

Further complications arise when the olefinic compound contains two or more conjugated linkages. In general, only one mole of halogen adds readily, and addition of the second or third mole of halogen may be effected only under drastic reaction conditions (at high temperature or prolonged reaction time).

(2) Catalytic Effects. It was pointed out earlier that addition in a completely nonpolar environment (e. g., sample solvent CCl_4, reagent Br_2 in CCl_4) may start out as a free radical reaction, but traces of polar compounds (water, HBr, etc.) could cause the reaction to proceed by a polar mechanism if peroxides and strong light are excluded. Induction periods observed in such nonpolar systems point to an autocatalytic effect by halide ions produced during the initiation of the reaction. This catalytic effect of halide ions on halogen addition to the ethylenic linkage received considerable attention from several investigators (e.g., Nozaki and Ogg (465)), but these kinetic studies failed to result in a clear-cut elucidation of the mechanism involved. The importance of excess KBr in the bromide–bromate titration seems to be an analytical manifestation of this phenomenon. An empirical approach, however, seems to have been proved quite profitable to the analytical chemist. More than seventy years ago, it was found by Hübl (280,281) that $HgCl_2$ exerted a beneficial effect on the addition of iodine to fatty materials. Since then catalysis by mercuric salts has been a favored resource whenever reluctantly reacting substances had to be analyzed.

Undoubtedly, the major catalytic role is played by the medium of the addition reaction. Although the double bond in a molecule containing sufficiently polar groups may be polar enough to initiate addition even in nonpolar solvents, it is reasonable to expect that the polarizing effect on the double bond, as well as on the halogen molecule, will be significantly greater in polar or dissociating solvents. Interaction between the reagent molecules or the ionic intermediate and the solvent molecules should also be considered at this point. The appearance of solvent fragments in the final product of addition has already been discussed.

Halogenation methods employ a wide variety of solvents; water, acetic acid, methanol, chloroform, and carbon tetrachloride are the most common. In most instances, the solubility properties of the sample for which the method was intended determine the selection of the reaction medium.

It has been shown that halogen addition reactions of olefinic substances are governed by four major factors: (1) structural features of the olefin, (2) variations of the halogen, (3) solvent, and (4) catalytic solutes. Decreasing electronegativity of the substituents (e. g., —COOH > —CH$_3$ > —C$_6$H$_5$), and increasing electronegativity of halogen (e. g., I$_2$ < Br$_2$ < ICl) increase the anionoid reactivity of the olefin. A negative charge in the molecule produces a similar effect by its polarizing action on the double bond. (All these effects should be reversed if the olefin reacts by the less common cationoid mechanism, e. g., α,β-unsaturated aldehydes.) Addition rates will be greater in acids or bases, but other catalytic effects may override differences in the polarity of reaction medium.

These points may be illustrated by a set of examples in Table I.

TABLE I

Catalytic Effects in Halogenation
(All reactions were carried out in the dark at room temperature)

Olefin	Reagent	Solvent	Catalyst	Reaction	Ref.
1-Pentene..............	Br$_2$	CCl$_4$	None	Quant.	Table VIII
Methyl maleate or methyl fumarate.....	Br$_2$	CCl$_4$	None	No reaction	(241)
Maleic acid or fumaric acid...............	Br$_2$	AcOH	None	Unmeasurably slow	(471)
	Bromide–bromate	Water	None	2% reaction in 7 min.	(391)
	Bromide–bromate	Water	HgSO$_4$	Quant. in 7 min.	(391)

(3) Halogenation of Complex Mixtures. Interferences. These problems are less acute when a single olefinic compound in a relatively uniform medium is to be halogenated, and conditions can usually be found under which quantitative results are obtained. With complex mixtures, however, such as oils of vegetable and animal origin, or especially petroleum distillates, the unsaturation values obtained using different halogens generally show considerable variation. Similar discrepancies are encountered when the same halogen source is used in different solvents, in different concentrations, or when the reaction time, temperature, or light intensity is varied. Each of these factors may exert differing effects according to the type of double bond present and the nature of other components of the sample mixture. It is possible, however, to obtain reproducible reactions by rigorous control of these reaction conditions. For specification purposes, reproducibility may be all that is needed; this has been the case with unsaturation values of oils used by the paint and varnish industry. However, good reproducibility does not necessarily imply that the amount of halogen consumed is a correct measure of the olefinic double bond content of the material examined.

In petroleum distillates, the presence of aromatic hydrocarbons is a serious complicating factor. Although simple homologs of benzene are inert, mesitylene and isodurene have been found to undergo substitution by halogens quite readily (675). Polynuclear aromatics give substitution as well as addition when treated with halogens. Mair, Willingham, and Streiff (403), as a result of their research under A. P. I. Project No. 6, were forced to conclude that determination of halogen numbers are without significance for estimating olefinic unsaturation when applied to petroleum mixtures containing aromatic hydrocarbons of high molecular weight.

Certain sulfur and nitrogen compounds, common constituents of petroleum and shale oil fractions, also react readily with halogen (137,149,576). Mercaptans form disulfides, which may be oxidized further to the corresponding alkyl sulfonyl halides; the halogen is reduced to the corresponding halogen acid:

$$2RSH \xrightarrow[-2HX]{+ X_2} RSSR \xrightarrow[-8HX]{+ 5X_2 + 4H_2O} 2RSO_2X$$

Excess reagent produces complex substitution reactions as well. Organic sulfides are readily oxidized through an intermediate addition product to sulfoxides, and in the presence of excess halogen the reaction may proceed to the corresponding sulfones:

$$R_2S \xrightarrow{+X_2} R_2SX_2 \xrightarrow[-2HX]{+ H_2O} R_2SO \xrightarrow[-2HX]{+ X_2 + H_2O} R_2SO_2$$

Thiophenes, benzothiophenes, and dibenzothiophenes, the predominant

TABLE II

Interference of Some Sulfur and Nitrogen Compounds

Compound	Bromine Number found		No. of Br atoms reacting per molecule
	Method of DuBois and Skoog (155)[a]	Method of Johnson and Clark (308)[b]	
Sulfur compounds:			
Ethanethiol	125.5	—	1.0
2-Propanethiol	87.2	—	0.8
2-Methyl-2-propanethiol	158.1	—	1.8
2-Butanethiol	162.6	—	1.8
Pentanethiol	88.0	—	1.1
Phenylmethanethiol	—	76.6	1.2
2-Thiapropane	263.9	—	2.1
2-Thiabutane	201.5	—	1.9
2-Methyl-3-thiapentane	161.8	—	2.1
2,4-Dimethyl-3-thiapentane	141.1	—	2.1
4-Thiaheptane	144.4	—	2.1
5-Thianonane	113.1	—	2.1
2,8-Dimethyl-5-thianonane	—	103.4	2.4
Thiacyclopentane	181.0	—	2.0
2-Methylthiacyclopentane	146.0	—	1.9
Thiacyclohexane	127.5	—	1.6
2-Methylthiacyclohexane	158.0	—	2.3
Thiophene	66.8	—	0.7
2-Methylthiophene	166.3	—	2.0
2-Methylthiophene	—	161.2	2.0
3-Methylthiophene	151.8	—	1.9
3,4-Dithiahexane	42.3	—	0.6
5-Methyl-3,4-dithiaheptane	65.2	—	1.2
2,2,5,5-Tetramethyl-3,4-dithiahexane	71.1	—	1.6
2,9-Dimethyl-5,6-dithiadecane	—	11.9	0.3
4,5-Dithiaoctane	136.0	—	2.6
Nitrogen compounds:			
Pyrrole	—	700	5.9
N-Ethylpyrrole	—	528	6.3
2,5-Dimethylpyrrole	—	635	7.5
Pyridine	—	0.0	—
4-Methylpyridine	—	0.1	—
2-(5-Nonyl)pyridine	—	1.5	—
2,4,6-Trimethylpyridine	—	1.4	—

[a] Determined by Rampton (507).
Determined by Dinneen, Smith, and Ball (149).

representatives of sulfur compounds in high-boiling petroleum fractions, react readily with halogens under the conditions of most analytical methods.   Of the two predominant nitrogen compound types in shale oils, pyrroles were found to add 6 to 7 atoms of bromine per molecule, while pyridines showed no significant reaction.   Data for the interference of some typical sulfur and nitrogen compounds are shown in Table II.

Halogenation methods are not applicable to motor fuels containing tetraethyllead; this additive reacts with halogens according to the equation:

$$Pb(C_2H_5)_4 + X_2 \longrightarrow Pb(C_2H_5)_3X + C_2H_5X$$

(4) **Titration Techniques.** Only a few of the halogenation methods involve the gravimetric determination of the product of reaction.   Most methods are titrimetric and, with a few exceptions, the amount of reagent used is obtained by back-titrating the excess added to the reaction mixture. Iodine is titrated directly with standard sodium thiosulfate solution:

$$I_2 + 2S_2O_3^{--} \longrightarrow 2I^- + S_4O_6^{--}$$

but reagents containing the more volatile interhalogen compounds (iodine monochloride or iodine monobromide), or especially bromine, are first reacted with excess potassium iodide to liberate the equivalent amount of iodine:

$$Br_2 + 2I^- \longrightarrow 2Br^- + I_2$$

Prepare standard 0.1 N sodium thiosulfate solution as follows: For each liter of solution, dissolve 25 g. of sodium thiosulfate pentahydrate in 500 to 600 ml. of distilled water and dilute to 1 liter.   Add 0.01 g. of sodium carbonate and 0.4 ml. of chloroform as preservative.   Mix thoroughly by shaking or by bubbling nitrogen through the mixture for 15 minutes, and store in a glass-stoppered bottle.   This reagent is commonly standardized against potassium dichromate or iodine.

The end point is usually determined visually by the disappearance of the well-known blue color which starch gives with iodine in the presence of iodide ions.

Prepare a 1% starch solution as follows: For each liter of solution, suspend 10 g. of soluble starch in 50 ml. of distilled water and add 15 g. of potassium hydroxide dissolved in 50 ml. of distilled water.   Dilute with 900 ml. of distilled water and let stand for about 1 hour.   Neutralize the alkali with concentrated hydrochloric acid, using indicator paper, then add 2 ml. of glacial acetic acid as a preservative.

This starch solution shows satisfactory stability and sensitivity for long periods.   Other preparations are given in the literature (46,373,461).

Arsenic trioxide also has been proposed (673), and employed occasionally, for the back-titration of bromine.   The reaction:

$$As_2O_3 + Br_2 + 2H_2O \longrightarrow As_2O_5 + 4HBr$$

is quantitative if the concentration of the halogen acid is below 24%. Usually solutions of 0.1 N As_2O_3 in alkali bicarbonate or in a mineral acid are used.   Both reagents are stable; however, the latter combination is considered more satisfactory due to its better resistance to atmospheric oxygen (671).   Usually an excess of the reagent is employed and a back-titration is carried out with the bromination reagent in the presence of a redox indicator (e. g., indigo carmine).   Direct titration with an arsenite solution is not recommended (533).

Sensitive instrumental methods are also available for detection of the end point; these may be used to advantage when dark reaction mixtures are to be titrated and in micro or trace methods.   Kolthoff and Bovey (359) determined the end point amperometrically, using a rotating platinum electrode for titrating with a bromide–bromate solution.   The amperometric method of Knowles and Lowden (355) is based on titrating, with potassium iodate solution, the excess thiosulfate added to the reaction mixture containing iodine.   The deadstop electrometric technique of Foulk and Bawden (194) has been used by DuBois and Skoog (155) for direct titration of olefins with bromide–bromate solution.   The deadstop method was also used by Braae (70) for direct titration with bromine in carbon tetrachloride and by Duke and Maselli (159) for back-titration of iodine monochloride, iodine monobromide, and pyridinium sulfate dibromide with thiosulfate.   A differential polarographic method has also been proposed for this purpose (515).   Witter, Newcomb, and Stotz (679) made use of a spectrophotometer at a wave length of 430 mμ in order to determine the iodine liberated by the excess bromine.   A spectrophotometric end point determination was also used by Sweetser and Bricker (605), who titrated directly with bromide–bromate reagent and observed the appearance of tribromide ions in a titration cell specially designed for the Beckman model DU spectrophotometer.

(5) **Evaluation of Results.   Reporting.**   Results of halogenation are usually expressed as Bromine Number, or Iodine Number, these values representing the amount of free halogen, in grams, which is consumed in reaction with 100 grams of the sample:

$$\text{Bromine Number, g./100 g.} = \frac{\text{(milliequivalents of } Br_2) \times (8.0)}{\text{(weight of sample, g.)}}$$

$$\text{Iodine Number, g./100 g.} = \frac{\text{(milliequivalents of } I_2) \times (12.7)}{\text{(weight of sample, g.)}}$$

Knowledge of the molecular weight of the olefin permits the calculation of olefin content of the sample. For a monoolefin:

$$\text{Olefin content, \% by wt.} = \frac{\text{(milliequivalents of halogen)} \times \text{(molecular weight of olefin)}}{\text{(weight of sample, g.)} \times (20)}$$

In complex natural products, the per cent olefin content must, unless specific knowledge of the nature of the olefins is available, be calculated on the basis of assumed average molecular weight of the olefins. In the case of petroleum fractions, the latter is customarily estimated from an average curve representing the relation between molecular weight and boiling point of monoolefins (Table III). Kurtz, Mills, Martin, Harvey, and

TABLE III

Relation of Olefin Molecular Weight to 50% Boiling Point (18)

A. S. T. M. 50% b. p., °F.	Mol. wt. of olefins
100	72
150	83
200	96
250	110
300	127
350	145

Lipkin (370) have stated that this average molecular weight may be estimated with reasonable accuracy for gasoline cuts of 25°C. boiling range but may be in considerable error for a complete gasoline because of unequal distribution of the olefins. Such a calculation entails another serious uncertainty. Assuming that the halogenation value determined for such a material is a correct measure of the double bond content (which, in view of the interferences discussed above, is seldom the case), the formula above does not reflect the presence of more than one double bond in any one olefinic molecule. Conjugated diolefins may be determined by maleic anhydride addition and an approximate estimate of their contribution to the halogenation value can be made; however, there is no method available to determine and correct for the nonconjugated diolefins and the polyolefins. Another practical consideration should be mentioned at this point. In the halogenation methods, aromatic compounds with olefinic side groups are determined as olefins, although for various evaluation purposes they should rather be regarded as aromatics. In view of these effects the calculated olefin content is generally excessively high as compared with values determined by silica gel adsorption. Materials with high olefin content would fare worst. As an extreme case, a discrepancy of 38%, obtained on a shale oil naphtha (149), may be mentioned.

B. IODINATION

Iodine without any catalyst adds only with difficulty in the cold to ethylenic linkages. According to the investigation of van der Steur (598), if an oil or fat is dissolved in carbon tetrachloride containing excess iodine, a condition of equilibrium is attained only after several days. From the low equilibrium constants found (e.g., 1.05×10^{-2} for oleic acid at $0°C$.) it is evident that one cannot expect complete conversion to the iodine addition product. At higher temperatures these constants increase but the reaction becomes irregular (629). Thus the Margosches procedure (reagent, iodine in ethanol) should merit little consideration as a quantitative method; it was shown to be inapplicable to substances containing electronegative groups near the olefinic bond (142) (such as in ricinoleic acid).

The active agent in the Hübl and Wijs reagents is iodine monochloride, both parts of which participate in the addition. Only the Wijs reagent (iodine monochloride in glacial acetic acid) is retained in present-day practice. The Hübl reagent (iodine and mercuric chloride in ethanol) has been found to be too unstable and applicable only to edible fats and oils containing no conjugation. The Wijs method received numerous thorough studies which showed that this reagent, too, adds incompletely to conjugated double bonds. Addition to one double bond of a conjugated diene and to two double bonds of a conjugated triene goes rather rapidly, but the saturation of the remaining double bond is extremely slow. This characteristic behavior of the Wijs reagent was utilized by von Mikusch and Frazier (436) to develop a difference determination for the conjugated acid content of an oil. The total unsaturation is determined by a modified Hanus reagent (IBr) under specified reaction conditions. The partial iodine value, corresponding to one out of two, or two out of three, double bonds is obtained by the standard Wijs solution (ICl in acetic acid) with a 2 minute reaction time. The difference between the two results is a measure of the conjugated diene content of the sample. Discrepancies between this value and the maleic anhydride addition value, determined according to the method of Kaufmann and Baltes or that of Ellis and Jones (see Section II.8), were later shown to be largely due to incomplete reaction of maleic anhydride with conjugated systems containing one or more of the double bonds in the *cis* configuration (431).

Low results are also encountered when certain electronegative groups are present in the molecule if the reaction time is not lengthened considerably (58,206). Low values and recurring end points in the back-titration of iodine may be the result of the liberation of halogen from the addition product by the re-forming of the original double bond, as shown in equation (6) (see Section II.1.A(1)). According to van Duin (158), the rate of this reaction depends on the group ($—COCH_3$ > $—C_6H_5$ > $—COOC_2H_5$ > $—COOH$, etc.) adjacent to the double bond. In ionizing solvents (acetic acid, alcohol), decomposition proceeds to a greater extent than in nonionizing media (carbon tetrachloride, chloroform, benzene). Occasional high results with the Wijs reagent are attributed to the substitution that occurs with ease when both doubly bound carbon atoms carry an alkyl substituent (e.g., 3,4-diethyl-3-hexene) (356). Examples in Table IV illustrate these observations.

TABLE IV

Analytical Results by the Standard Wijs Method

Compound	Iodine Number		% of theor.	Ref.
	Theor.	Found[a]		
Ethyl linoleate..............	164.7	162.4	98.6	(394)
Methyl linolenate..........	260.6	257.3	98.8	(394)
Ethyl elaidate..............	81.8	80.9	98.8	(394)
Elaidic acid................	89.9	88.8	98.8	(394)
2-Pentene..................	362.2	362.1	100.0	(356)
2-Methyl-2-butene..........	362.2	360.5	99.5	(356)
1-Hexene..................	301.8	302.6	100.3	(356)
3- and 4-Methyl-1-pentene...	301.8	302.2	100.1	(356)
2,3-Dimethyl-2-butene.......	301.8	366.3, 359.1	120.1	(356)
Cyclohexene...............	309.5	306.8	99.1	(356)
3- and 5-Methyl-1-hexene....	258.7	262.2	101.4	(356)
4-Methyl-1-hexene..........	258.7	258.6	100.0	(356)
Diisobutylene.............	226.4	255.3, 259.0	113.5	(356)
3,4-Diethyl-3-hexene........	181.3	214.8, 239.4	125	(356)
Cetene...................	113.2	113.2	100.0	(356)
β-Eleostearic acid..........	273.7	183.0	66.9	(436)
9,11-Octadecadienoic acid....	181.0	91.2	50.4	(436)
Isoprene..................	747.1	377.5	50.5	(356)
Cyclopentadiene...........	769.2	327.0	42.5	(356)

[a] Most values are the average of two determinations.

The Hanus reagent (iodine bromide in acetic acid) is similar in its behavior to the Wijs solution.

The reaction with both the Wijs and Hanus reagents can be catalyzed by mercuric acetate and these rapid methods give good agreement with values by the standard procedures. In some instances, however, this increased reactivity may result in disturbing side reactions. Castor oil, for instance, which reacts normally by the standard methods, gives high values in the rapid procedures (265,462). Skell and Radlove (582) showed that this irregular behavior is due to the presence of the free hydroxyl group in ricinoleic acid. From a practical point of view, the results of mercuric acetate iodine number determinations should be critically examined if the presence of free hydroxyl groups is suspected.

(1) **Iodine.** The Margosches reagent (410,411) is iodine (0.2 N) in absolute alcohol. The sample, dissolved in alcohol, is briefly shaken with excess reagent; then a large volume of water is added to the reaction mixture, which, after a few minutes standing is titrated with standard thiosulfate. Margosches found that, with sufficient excess of reagent, the agreement with Hübl and Hanus iodine values was satisfactory. DeGrotte, Keiser, Wirtel, and Monson (142), however, concluded that the method was not suitable for castor oil, but, because it gave concordant results on many fatty modifications derived from castor oil, preferred it for its rapidity to the more elaborate (although more reliable) Hübl method for control work.

The applicability of the method to petroleum products was greatly handicapped by its solvent system. Modifications suggested by Galle (200), which included the use of acetone–ether (2:1), ethanol–amyl alcohol (4:1), or an emulsifier, did not seem to have overcome these difficulties. With carefully controlled sample sizes and more than 100% halogen excess, Grosse-Oetringhaus (229) obtained low values. In many cases cleavage of free halogen from a dihalide occurred, as shown by recurring titration end points.

Scotti (562) proposed mercuric acetate as an accelerator in conjunction with a solution of iodine in benzene. The mercury salt is dissolved in glacial acetic acid and added to the fatty sample directly after the addition of the reagent. Practically instantaneous reaction is reported. The reagent was tested by Hoffman and Green (267), but the Wijs solution was found more satisfactory.

A rapid and reproducible test for determining the relative unsaturation of isoprene-isobutylene polymers was introduced by Gallo, Wiese, and Nelson (201). This procedure, involving a reaction between the polymer and iodine in the presence of mercuric acetate and trichloroacetic acid, was also used, after a slight modification, by Currie (135).

(2) **Iodine Monochloride.** While iodine in ethanol adds with difficulty to olefinic double bonds, Hübl (280,281) found that in presence of $HgCl_2$ the reaction becomes more regular and is not accompanied by substitution. The active agent in this reaction is assumed to be iodine monochloride formed in the reaction of iodine with the excess mercuric chloride:

$$HgCl_2 + 2I_2 \longrightarrow HgI_2 + 2ICl$$

However, because the reagent is very unstable and requires long reaction time (3 to 18 hours) to ensure complete addition, Hübl's method has been largely replaced by the Wijs method. Graefe (225) attempted to apply Hübl's method to mineral oils, but the results were greatly dependent on reaction time and temperature, suggesting substitution. The Wijs method gave better reproducibility (224).

The Wijs method may be considered as a modification of the original Hübl procedure. The reagent is iodine monochloride in acetic acid and it is considerably more stable than the Hübl solution. This reagent may be prepared from iodine monochloride or from iodine trichloride plus iodine (156), but the original directions of Wijs can also be followed. The reaction time originally suggested by Wijs (685) was 3 to 10 minutes. Now it is usually 0.5 hour; however, even longer times are necessary for drying oils. For most samples a large excess of reagent is used.

The procedure given below is essentially identical with those adopted by the American Chemical Society (A. C. S.) (151), the Association of Official Agricultural Chemists (A. O. A. C.) (31), the American Oil Chemists' Society (A. O. C. S.) (13), the American Society for Testing Materials (A. S. T. M.) (16), and the Institute of Petroleum (I. P.) (290).

Reagent. (a) This is preferably prepared by dissolving separately 7.9 g. of reagent-grade iodine trichloride and 8.7 g. of resublimed iodine in glacial acetic acid by heating on a water bath. The two solutions are mixed and made up to 1 liter with glacial acetic acid. (b) Alternatively, the solution may be prepared by dissolving 13 g. of resublimed iodine in 1 liter of glacial acetic acid and passing dry chlorine gas through the solution until its normality, as determined by titration against sodium thiosulfate solution, is doubled. At this stage, the solution suddenly lightens in color. If too much chlorine has been added, a solution of iodine in glacial acetic acid should be added to compensate.

In preparing the reagent by either method, it is recommended that glacial acetic acid which passes the dichromate test for at least 30 minutes be used. The reagent should be stored in a dark bottle.

Procedure. A quantity of sample such that 70 to 90% of the reagent remains unconsumed is weighed into a dry 500 ml. "iodine flask" and dissolved in carbon tetrachloride or chloroform (15 to 20 ml.). The following sample sizes are recommended:

Drying or marine animal oils........................ 0.15–0.18 g.
Semidrying oils.................................... 0.2 –0.3 g.
Nondrying fatty oils............................... 0.3 –0.4 g.
Petroleum products............................... 0.2 –1.0 g.

Then the reagent (25 ml.) is added from an automatic pipet and the flask is stoppered, shaken, and allowed to stand in the dark for 30 minutes or longer. At the end of the reaction period, potassium iodide (20 ml. of 15%) and water (100 ml.) are added and the liberated iodine is titrated with standard 0.1 N sodium thiosulfate solution. Two blank determinations are run under identical conditions.

Although standard references caution against using a Wijs reagent that is older than 30 days, Norris and Buswell (463) found that their reagent stock, prepared in a standard manner and containing 1.5% excess equivalent of iodine over chlorine, did not change measurably over a period of 505 days. A similar observation was made by Hiscox (265).

Some typical results by the standard Wijs method are shown in Table IV.

An early modification of the Wijs solution, proposed by Marshall (417), involved the use of carbon tetrachloride as reagent and sample solvent. Other nonpolar solvents have also been employed, especially when the solubility of the sample in acetic acid was unsatisfactory or when back-titration of the acid, formed in the reaction mixture by substitution or splitting out, was desired. Thus, Kemp and co-workers used chloroform or carbon disulfide (337) for natural rubber hydrocarbons, and p-dichloro-benzene (338) for butadiene and related polymers in combination with the Marshall reagent. The procedure, which consisted of back-titrating the excess iodine monochloride after a reaction period of one hour, appeared to give reproducible values for the various types of polymers examined; however, these results did not always correspond to the true unsaturation values.

The reasons for this behavior were critically examined by Lee, Kolthoff, and Mairs (378). This extensive investigation revealed that 90 to 95% of the double bonds in the polymer add iodine monochloride within several minutes at room temperature and that after this time the remaining double bonds react at a much slower rate. Almost all the splitting out (of HX or X_2) also occurs within these first few minutes. Consequently, any additional acid formed after this time may be assumed to form by substitution only. Based upon these principles, a procedure was developed that yielded values of unsaturation which are corrected for substitution and are independent of the reaction time within wide limits. For polymers, studied previously by this rather complex procedure, a simple method is also available. A third method for routine use is also given. Carbon disulfide and chloroform are used as sample solvents; the iodine monochloride reagent is 0.11 M in chloroform. A more recent procedure of Lee, Kolthoff, and Johnson (377) takes advantage of the more rapid addition to the original olefin than to the decomposition products. Excess reagent (0.02 to 0.05 M iodine monochloride in carbon tetrachloride) was varied and a plot of 5 to 8 results obtained after 1 hour reaction time gave good unsaturation values for several branched olefins and polymers.

Another modification, involving the addition of mercuric acetate to the reaction mixture, was proposed by Hoffman and Green (267). This catalyst (10 ml. of 2.5% mercuric acetate in glacial acetic acid) is added directly to the sample after adding the Wijs solution. Reaction times of 3 minutes at room temperature were found satisfactory to obtain good agreement with standard Wijs values. In testing this method, Hiscox (265) found that the volume of Wijs reagent could also be reduced to 10 ml., providing great saving on solution, without affecting the reliability of results.

A micro titration method, employing a specially designed reaction flask and iodine monochloride (or bromine) in carbon tetrachloride, was reported by Phillips and Wake (487). Another micro method by Whalley and Ellison (658), primarily designed for oils, uses standard Wijs reagent and a special titration unit with a dead stop apparatus.

(3) **Iodine Monobromide.** Iodine bromide, dissolved in acetic acid, was introduced by Hanus (242) as a halogenation reagent. This reagent has very good keeping qualities and is often preferred to the Wijs solution. However, the application of the Hanus Method as an iodine number procedure seems to have been handicapped by the great popularity of the Wijs method.

The reagent preparation and procedure given below are essentially those of the Association of Official Agricultural Chemists (30).

Reagent. 13.2 g. of resublimed iodine is dissolved in 1 liter of acetic acid (99.5%) which shows no reduction with dichromate and sulfuric acid; then enough bromine (about 3 ml.) is added to double the halogen content as determined by titration. The iodine may be dissolved by heating, but the solution should be cold when the bromine is added.

This solution is about 0.2 N. It can also be prepared by dissolving 20 g. of iodine monobromide in 1 liter of glacial acetic acid. When stored in an amber glass-stoppered bottle, the reagent is stable for a long time.

Procedure. The sample is weighed into a dry glass-stoppered flask and dissolved in chloroform or carbon tetrachloride (10 ml). Hanus solution (25 ml., at least 60% excess) is added and the flask is let stand in the dark for 30 minutes, shaking occasionally. After this time, potassium iodide (10 ml. of 15%) and water (100 ml.) are added, and the liberated iodine is titrated with standard 0.1 N sodium thiosulfate solution. For the approximate sample size, the following schedule is recommended (100):

Drying or marine animal oils	0.15–0.18 g.
Semidrying oils	0.2 –0.3 g.
Nondrying oils	0.3 –0.4 g.
Solid fats	0.8 –1.0 g.
Petroleum mixtures	0.2 –1.0 g.

This method gives precise results on nonconjugated fatty materials but the results are a few per cent lower than those obtained by the standard Wijs method. On the conjugated oils, such as tung oil, the results vary greatly, and the standard Hanus method is considered inapplicable to such materials.

The method has received considerable attention also from petroleum chemists. Faragher, Gruse, and Garner (183) concluded that the reagent did not cause any appreciable substitution on a variety of paraffins, straight, branched, or cyclic olefins, diolefins, and aromatics of the gasoline boiling range. The results with olefins indicated the true unsaturation, and even diolefins gave iodine values approaching theory on increasing the excess of the Hanus solution. Good checks were also obtained by Morrell and Egloff (443) on various cracked distillates when the reaction conditions were kept constant. Richter (520) reached similar conclusions from his comparison of the Hanus method with the Wijs, Hübl, McIlhiney, and Kaufmann procedures and praised the stable end point of the reaction. However, with higher boiling petroleum distillates, the method gave erratic results (641). It was later shown by Winward and Garner (675) that this dependency on reagent excess is mainly due to substitution of certain aromatic types. It was concluded that substitutions on the benzene ring in the 1,3,5-positions make the molecule especially sensitive to the reagent (examples, mesitylene and isodurene). Naphthalene and two substituted naphthalenes also showed a small interference. Some of these results are shown in Table V.

The first modification of the Hanus method involved the replacement of acetic acid with carbon tetrachloride. Marshall (417) tried this solvent with good results for iodine monochloride but found that iodine monobromide in 10 minutes did not react to a sufficient extent. Hunt (282) also

TABLE V

Hanus Iodine Numbers of Some Nonolefinic Hydrocarbons (675)

Hydrocarbon	Iodine Number	
	20 min. reaction	6 hr. reaction
2,2,4-Trimethylpentane...............	Nil	Nil
n-Hexadecane......................	Nil	Nil
Methylcyclohexane..................	Nil	—
Decalin...........................	Nil	Nil
p-Xylene..........................	Nil	—
m-Xylene..........................	Nil	Nil
Mesitylene........................	37–12	68.5
Diphenyl..........................	Nil	Nil
Pseudocumene[a]...................	Nil	Nil
Isodurene.........................	50–15	—
Naphthalene......................	1.0–1.5	3.5
α-Methylnaphthalene[a].............	6–5	—
β-Methylnaphthalene[a].............	3–2	—
Hexaethylbenzene..................	Nil	—
Tetralin[a].........................	Nil	Nil

[a] "Not pure."

tried this combination and, by allowing 1 hour for the reaction, obtained satisfactory results on some animal and vegetable oils. However, when Johansen (306a) tried to apply it to petroleum products, the results were unsatisfactory.

Von Mikusch and Frazier (435) were primarily concerned with the iodine values obtainable on oils containing conjugated systems. The most important examples are eleostearic acid and licanic acid, major components of tung oil and oiticica oil. All standard halogenation methods saturate, at best, only two of the three conjugated double bonds of these compounds. Extreme impractical conditions, such as reaction time of up to one week with 700% reagent excess, were needed with the standard Wijs reagent to saturate the third double bond. With the Hanus method, the results obtained on tung oil vary even more than most of the others with time, temperature, and sample weight. The extensive investigation of these reaction conditions by von Mikusch and Frazier showed that by reacting with 500 to 800% excess reagent of double strength (0.4 N) at 0°C. for 3 hours, quantitative addition to all three double bonds can be effected. A somewhat less concentrated reagent (0.32 N) in 1 hour at 20°C. was recommended for materials containing only isolated double bonds. Typical results by this so-called Woburn iodine method are shown in Table VI.

Except in the case of tall oil and sardine oil, these values agree with Wijs iodine values within 1 to 5 units. The discrepancy with tall oil is ascribed to the presence of rosin acids, sterols, etc., which react incompletely with Wijs reagent. The value on castor oil shows that the hydroxyl group of ricinoleic acid is not attacked by 0.32 N iodine bromide solution.

TABLE VI

Iodine Values on Some Fatty Materials by the Woburn Iodine Method (435)

Sample	Normality of IBr soln.	Halogen excess, %	Temp., °C.	Time, hrs.	Iodine Number	
					IBr soln.	Wijs soln.
Soybean oil.............	0.36	500–800	20	1	126.5	130.5
Soybean pentaerythritol ester.................	0.40	500–800	20	1	128.4	127.6
Soybean fatty acids.......	0.40	500–800	20	1	136.0	137.8
Linseed oil..............	0.36	500–800	20	1	185.5	186.8
Linseed fatty acids........	0.40	500–800	20	1	196.4	194.2
Sardine oil..............	0.36	500–800	20	1	189.2	196.9
Tall oil.................	0.40	500–800	20	1	203.8	169.5
Walnut oil..............	0.32	500–800	20	1	156.0	155.2
Castor oil...............	0.32	500–800	20	1	88.9	87.4
Tung oil.................	0.40	545 ± 30	0	1 / 2.5 / 3 / 5	219.9 / 225.4 / 226.6 / 226.8	224.2[a]
β-Eleostearic acid.........	0.32	550–600	20	1	272.7	273.7[a]
	0.40	600–2000	0	3	273.8	
9,11-Linoleic acid.........	0.32	400–500	20 / 0 / 0	1 / 3 / 5	183.3 / 182.6 / 183.7	181.2[b]
Oiticica oil..............	0.40	800–1000	0	3	203.9	—

[a] Probable value from hydrogenation.
[b] Theoretical iodine value.

In a further modification of the Hanus method, Norris and Buswell (462) found that in the presence of mercuric acetate the reaction time can be shortened to 3 to 5 minutes. This reagent gave values identical with those obtained in the standard Hanus method on nonconjugated fats. On castor oil, however, the values were high, indicating substitution of ricinoleic acid in the presence of the mercury salts. This "rapid" method is also unsatisfactory on conjugated oils.

Micro methods utilizing the Hanus reagent have been published by Ralls (506) and by Grunbaum and Kirk (233).

(4) **Other Iodination Reagents.** Kaufmann and Grosse-Oetringhaus (328) recommended thiocyanogen iodide to replace the promising but unstable thiocyanogen reagent (see Section II.6). The iodide behaves similarly to the mother compound in its reactivity; however, it has better stability and yields more reproducible results. It is assumed that both the iodine and thiocyanogen fragments add to the double bond:

$$\text{>C=C<} + \text{NCSI} \longrightarrow \begin{array}{c} \text{I} \\ | \\ -\overset{|}{\underset{\underset{\text{NCS}}{|}}{\text{C}}}-\overset{|}{\underset{|}{\text{C}}}- \end{array}$$

The reagent is prepared from lead thiocyanate, $Pb(SCN)_2$, by the addition of iodine in benzene or carbon tetrachloride solution. A 0.2 N reagent and 15 to 20 hour reaction times were recommended. The excess reagent is back-titrated, after addition of potassium iodide, with thiosulfate. The authors applied the method also to a number of gasolines and lubricating oils and obtained results (329,330) which were similar to those by the thiocyanogen method. Other standard halogenation methods (Wijs, Hanus, Kaufmann, etc.) gave, in general, higher values on the same samples.

Aqueous iodine in the presence of methanol was used by Siggia and Edsberg (575) for the analysis of vinyl alkyl ethers. It was shown that the product of the addition reaction was the corresponding iodoacetal (cf. equation (5) in Section II.1.A(1)):

$$\text{RO—CH=CH}_2 + \text{I}_2 + \text{CH}_3\text{OH} \longrightarrow \begin{array}{c} \text{I} \\ | \\ \text{RO—CH—CH}_2 \\ | \\ \text{OCH}_3 \end{array} + \text{HI}$$

The reaction time for the analysis is only 10 minutes and the results showed less than 0.5% deviation from theoretical (with an average deviation of 0.2%). This method is of particular value for samples which contain acetals or acetaldehyde. In previous methods, based on hydrolysis, these common impurities of vinyl ethers interfered, but they have no effect in this procedure. The method is not applicable to vinyl ethers which are insufficiently soluble in aqueous methanol.

Crotonaldehyde has been determined by adding standard iodine (0.01 N) and sodium hydroxide (1 N) solutions to an aqueous solution of the sample; after 45 minutes the iodine liberated by hydrochloric acid is titrated with thiosulfate (627).

C. BROMINATION

The addition of bromine to olefinic compounds has been used extensively as a method for the quantitative measurement of unsaturation. Allen (10) was probably the first to describe (in 1881) an analytical method employing this halogen (liberated from an aqueous sodium hypobromite solution with hydrochloric acid) for the determination of unsaturation in shale and petroleum products. Since this time, bromine has remained the almost exclusive analytical halogenation reagent of the petroleum industry.

That a universal bromination method is not yet available is evidenced by the large number of procedures that have been proposed, many of which are still being used in various laboratories. However, a compromise of the variables involved enables several of these methods to give accurate analysis in specific cases. In other instances, knowledge of limitations of the various procedures should make possible an intelligent choice of the method most suitable for a particular purpose.

Methods discussed below are grouped according to the nature of the reagent employed. Bromine in acetic acid (Uhrig-Levin reagent) and in carbon tetrachloride (McIlhiney reagent), or its tribromide complex in methanol (Kaufmann reagent), in water (Shell Development reagent), and especially the unusual hydrogen perbromide complex in chloroform furnish solutions which display rather limited stability on standing. The addition compound of bromine with sulfuric acid and pyridine in glacial acetic acid (Rosenmund-Kuhnhenn reagent) provides a solution that is stable in the dark, while aqueous potassium bromide–bromate (Francis reagent) keeps indefinitely. Catalysis by mercuric salts, primarily to effect addition to hindered olefinic bonds has been employed in conjunction with several of these reagents.

Almost all bromination methods are titrimetric in nature. Only a few methods measure gravimetrically the bromine absorbed by the olefinic sample. Of these the Rossmann bromine vapor procedure has shown promise to avoid at least some of the common shortcomings of the liquid phase methods.

In general, bromine reacts vigorously with most olefinic bonds. As a result of this high reactivity, its use is more frequently accompanied by undesirable side reactions than was found with iodination reagents. Some other side effects, such as reaction between the sample and the solvent, and interference by peroxidized components of the sample, stem rather from the nature of the reaction conditions and of the materials examined than from the characteristics of the reagent itself.

These side effects may be grouped as follows: (a) substitution in a position removed from the olefinic bond; (b) spontaneous elimination of hydrogen bromide from the addition product; (c) elimination of hydrogen bromide from the addition product under the influence of water; (d) reaction of the sample with the solvent; and (e) effect of peroxidized samples.

Effect (b) may be considered as substitution at the double bond. Before the second halogen fragment adds, the intermediate complex re-forms the original double bond with the elimination of a proton from one of the olefinic carbon atoms.

If it could be assumed the all ethylenic linkages are stoichiometrically brominated and that all substitution occurred at other points in the molecule (or in some nonolefinic components of the sample), a correction for the hydrogen bromide content of the reaction mixture should furnish an accurate measure of unsaturation in the sample. This assumption was made in the method of McIlhiney (reagent, bromine in carbon tetrachloride), but an examination of data by this procedure (Tables VII, IX, XI, XX) shows that the corrected values are nearly always low and in some cases even negative. The explanation may be that addition does not occur to the full extent or that other side reactions which also produce hydrogen bromide are prominently present. Of course, if some of the acid was formed in side reactions (b) or (c), subtracting the corresponding halogen from the total bromine consumption will lead to low results. Side reaction (c) produces hydrogen bromide from the addition product by hydrolysis during back-titration in aqueous medium. This effect was considered by Buckwalter and Wagner (91).

Side reaction (d) as a probable source of high total absorption values in the McIlhiney procedure was pointed out by Hofmann (268). Various mineral oils, when dissolved in carbon tetrachloride and kept at room temperature in diffuse daylight, liberated hydrochloric acid. The quantity of acid liberated from one of the oils studied, determined in the manner recommended by McIlhiney (iodate addition and thiosulfate titration), corresponded to 11.2 "substituted" bromine number in 30 minutes contact time. This effect was studied later by Kharasch, Jensen, and Urry (343) and was classified as a photochemical or peroxide-induced free radical chain reaction.

While the sum of the "addition" and "substitution" figures in the McIlhiney method is nearly always high (as much as 200% above theoretical), for the Kaufmann method (reagent, tribromide in absolute methanol) Jordan (311) and later Wilson (669) found total absorption values quite close to theoretical bromine consumption. However, subsequent titration of the acidity formed in the reaction showed that in some instances (styrene, indene) as much as half of the total bromine consumed was used up in "substitution." Wilson concluded that addition and substitution on an olefinic carbon atom are mutually exclusive; it appears that hydrogen bromide formation in these reactions is due to side reactions (b) or (c). Obviously, acidity originating from these effects should not be corrected for.

Nearly theoretical values were also observed by Lewis and Bradstreet (383) (reagent, bromide–bromate in the presence of sulfuric acid) for several of the olefins studied, although "substitution," as determined by the acidity formed, accounted for the major part of the bromine consumption in all cases. Definite reaction conditions yielded constant end points indicating that the bromine-substituted products are relatively indifferent to further bromination either by substitution or by addition. Lewis and Bradstreet used an aqueous medium; it is possible that the hydrobromic acid found was chiefly due to hydrolysis (effect (c)).

The participation of the reagent solvent (methanol) in the reaction by the Kaufmann method was proved by Earle and Milner (162), who isolated some monobromo-monomethoxy derivative in addition to the dibromide and observed the formation of hydrogen bromide during their studies of soybean oil. This reaction was reported earlier by Bartlett and Tarbell (43).

An extreme case was presented by Schulek and Boyer (558). These authors determined allyl alcohol by titrating the acid produced on reacting with bromine water. One equivalent of acid was found per molecule of alcohol and it was suggested that the addition product hydrolyzed quantitatively to give 1-bromo-2,3-propanediol.

These observations and other evidence point to the complexity of bromination reactions and suggest the conclusion that substitution corrections based on acidity determinations are fundamentally incorrect. Undeniably, when correction is applied to certain pure compounds in the McIlhiney method, improved addition values result. The failure of this principle, however, is clearly shown by the negative values obtained in some other instances, especially on petroleum distillates.

It seems more fruitful to eliminate recognized sources which lead to these disturbing effects. Many efforts have been directed along such lines by investigators of the field, resulting in definite improvements. Inherent characteristics in olefinic molecules are the major source of discrepancies. While certain olefinic types may be satisfactorily analyzed by most methods, some other types yield excessively low or excessively high results in all methods. Certain chlorinated unsaturated compounds and branched olefins, respectively, are examples for these types.

Direct titration has been frequently recommended to avoid large reagent excess and long contact time. Results by the popular DuBois-Skoog
method (reagent, bromide–bromate in acidic medium) show that the nature
of the sample remains the dominating factor in the course of the reaction
(Table XV). An objection by Francis (195) to direct titration emphasizes
the fact that, in direct titration with bromide–bromate solution, bromine is
generated in high local concentration with the result that substitution is
promoted rather than avoided.

Since it has been shown conclusively (58,158) that splitting-off of hydrogen halide in dissociating solvents is greater than in nondissociating solvents, carbon tetrachloride gained an early prominence in bromination reactions as well as a solvent for the various iodinating reagents. Observations
by Hofmann (268), however, showed clearly that carbon tetrachloride reacts with the sample and, to suppress this undoubtedly free radical type
reaction, halogenation in the presence of carbon tetrachloride or chloroform
must be carried out in the dark.

The dependence of results on the reaction temperature in the McIlhiney
method was shown by Buckwalter and Wagner (91). Molecular configuration seemed to be the determining factor. Some compounds brominated normally at 75°C., others only at room temperature, while some others
yielded entirely meaningless results unless brominated near, or below,
0°C.

The influence of peroxides on halogenation results was considered by
Wilson (669). In some instances, he observed that, when insufficient reagent was added to the sample and the reaction mixture became completely
colorless, iodine was liberated on the addition of sodium iodide solution.
He ascribed this reaction to peroxidized hydrocarbons interacting with the
sodium iodide in the presence of the acid released by the substitution action
of the reagent on the hydrocarbon. Depending on the nature of this reaction, the halogen liberated by one molecule of peroxidized hydrocarbon
could amount to three times that which would have been absorbed by the
hydrocarbon had it not been peroxidized. Thus the presence of peroxides in
the sample leads to low results; therefore, they should be either eliminated
before halogenating the sample, or corrected for on the basis of an independent determination.

(1) **Bromine in Acetic Acid.** An early application of bromine in acetic
acid (0.1 N) for the determination of olefinic unsaturation in vegetable
oils was reported by Manchot and Oberhauser (407). The unconsumed
excess reagent was determined bromometrically with arsenious acid after
moderate (0.5 to 2 hours) reaction times.

Employing direct titration to avoid side reactions, Uhrig and Levin (623) later proposed a somewhat more concentrated reagent (2%) for olefinic hydrocarbons; the orange-yellow color of free excess bromine was used to indicate the end point. The authors tried various reaction solvents such as olefin-free naphtha, benzene, and carbon tetrachloride, and finally chose chloroform. An obvious drawback of the method is that end points with colored samples are difficult to observe. In such cases, testing a drop of the reaction mixture on a spot plate with potassium iodide–starch solution was found helpful.

Working with chloroform solutions, Uhrig and Levin found that results on olefins such as cyclohexene, diisobutylene, triisobutylene, styrene, and oleic acid were reproducible and accurate within 3 to 4 bromine number units. These results indicated to the authors the absence of substitution in the individual compounds examined, but this question was not studied further on petroleum distillates.

Direct titration with bromine in acetic acid was also used for the estimation of C_3 and C_4 monoolefins absorbed in cold ($-48°C.$) chloroform (595). When hydrogen sulfide, mercaptans, and butadiene were removed prior to the titration, the analysis of a C_4 olefin mixture showed only 0.3% absolute deviation from the theoretical value. With the less reactive propylene, somewhat low recoveries were observed. Ethylene reacts only to a slight extent and is not determined in this method. However, employing excess reagent and back-titration, Miller and Pearman (439) determined ethylene with an accuracy of ±0.02%.

Dienes of certain configuration (e.g., α-dienesterol) could also be determined rapidly and quantitatively in acetic acid solutions containing sodium acetate by direct titration with bromine in acetic acid (375).

Reid and Beddard (514) successfully applied bromine in acetic acid to the determination of low bromine absorption values (1.0 to 0.0001 g./100 g.). Excess 0.01 N bromine solution is added to the sample at ice water temperature and the unused reagent is back-titrated after 3 minutes reaction time. Less than 2% errors were obtained on allyl alcohol and crotonaldehyde solutions with bromine numbers as low as 0.001. No substitution seemed to occur. A micro method for cis-2-butene in cyclobutane, reported by Benson (49), is an adaptation of the Uhrig-Levin procedure.

Several investigators felt that direct titration with bromine in acetic acid can be reliably accomplished only in the presence of a catalyst. Winkler (674) employed mercuric chloride, added in powder form to the reaction mixture, and titrated with 0.1 N solution of bromine. On a number of vegetable oils, this method gave precise results that checked well with

values obtained by Winkler's bromide–bromate method (see Section II.1.-
C(7)). Reproducible results, which were in good agreement with those by
the Wijs method, were obtained by Jasperson (306) on a number of partially hydrogenated vegetable oils, titrated in the presence of mercuric acetate with a 0.5 to 1.0% (by volume) solution of bromine in glacial acetic acid.
On drying oils, however, the results were low, indicating that the method is
not applicable to samples containing significant conjugated unsaturation.
A modification of this method was applied by Pardun (477) for the determination of the olefin content of extraction naphtha in the 0.001 to 2%
range.

(2) **Bromine in Carbon Tetrachloride.** Bromine in carbon tetrachloride
was recommended originally by McIlhiney (396) to replace the less stable
and slowly reacting Hübl reagent. An excess of the standard solution is
added to the sample dissolved in carbon tetrachloride and the unused portion of bromine is determined by adding an aqueous solution of potassium
iodide to the reaction mixture and titrating with standard thiosulfate solution. Any hydrogen bromide which may have been formed is determined
in the aqueous phase iodometrically after addition of iodate to liberate additional iodide:

$$6HBr + KIO_3 + 5KI \longrightarrow 6KBr + 3I_2 + 3H_2O$$

This bromine substitution figure is multiplied by two and subtracted from
the first titration to yield the bromine addition figure.

The use of this method has almost exclusively been limited to petroleum
products. The following details are essentially from the standard method
of the Institute of Petroleum (289).

Reagent. About 27 g. (9 ml.) of bromine is dissolved in 1 liter of dried
carbon tetrachloride and stored in a dark bottle. This approximately 0.33 N
solution should be iodometrically standardized daily against thiosulfate.

Procedure. A measured volume (10 to 15 ml., at least 50% excess) of
reagent is added to a dry, cooled flask, which is then closed and immediately
cooled in an ice-water bath. The sample, or preferably an aliquot of a previously prepared dilution in carbon tetrachloride, is added. The flask is
quickly stoppered, vigorously shaken, and replaced in the cooling bath. After
2 minutes standing, aqueous potassium iodide solution (20 ml. of 10%) is
added, the mixture is shaken and rapidly titrated with 0.1 N sodium thiosulfate
solution to the starch indicator end point. Potassium iodate solution (5 ml.
of 2%) is added and the mixture is again titrated to the starch end point.

The principle of the McIlhiney method of correcting for substitution was
warmly received and was subsequently utilized in combination with other

halogenating agents (e.g., iodine chloride, iodine bromide). However, it soon became evident that in many instances neither the addition nor the substitution values could be regarded as a correct measure of the reaction they were expected to indicate. The method gives satisfactory values for certain pure compounds, but in general the results tend to be low. Corrected values on gasolines, although fairly reproducible, are invariably low, and on gas and lubricating oils even negative values have been obtained (91,643).

Buckwalter and Wagner (91) showed that the temperature plays a significant role in the course of these reactions. With increase of temperature, the total bromine consumption increases, but at higher temperatures (e.g., 75°C.) all of it may be substitution (example abietic acid). Some compounds, on the other hand, yield close to theoretical addition values only at an elevated temperature (example, crotonic acid). The authors called attention also to the spontaneous cleavage of hydrogen bromide (from the dibromide product) which occurs especially easily in the presence of water. To avoid these errors, they modified the McIlhiney method by working at a definite temperature and by transferring the excess bromine and hydrogen bromide in a current of nitrogen into aqueous potassium iodide. This method seemed to be useful in the case of some acidic samples (e.g., cinnamic acid, crotonic acid) for which the corrected McIlhiney values were very low or negative, but failed to give satisfactory results in several instances (e.g., abietic acid). Some of these results are shown in Table VII.

A method similar in principle to that of Buckwalter and Wagner was also published by Pöll (489).

To eliminate secondary reactions in the McIlhiney method, Casimir and Dimitriu (102) recommended 50 to 70% excess halogen, 15 to 30 minutes reaction in the dark and at low temperature, and immediate titration after iodate addition. It seems, however, that these good points have remained largely unnoticed by subsequent investigators.

In other attempts to eliminate substitution, direct titration with bromine in carbon tetrachloride was also tried. Morrell and Levine (444) titrated with a 4% solution to an orange color that persisted for 30 seconds. A solution containing a known olefin in a known concentration was titrated simultaneously. George, Wechsler, and Mark (207,208) determined styrene and α-methylstyrene in the presence of their polymers in nitrobenzene-carbon tetrachloride solution by direct titration with bromine in carbon tetrachloride. Direct titration at 20°C., catalyzed with mercuric chloride, and using the deadstop electrometric technique for the end point determination is the basis of a procedure published by Braae (70). Methanol containing hydrobromic acid, hydrochloric acid, and the mercury salt was used as sample solvent. Since different olefins react at different rates, titration was

TABLE VII

Analytical Data by Buckwalter and Wagner (91)

Compounds	Method[a]	Temp., °C.	Percentage of theoretical		
			Total absorption	Substitution	Addition
Octene...............	A	Room	136	42	94
		Room	132.5	36	96.5
	B	20	106.5	7	99.5
Cyclohexene...........	A	Room	108	19	89
		Room	104	12	92
	B	75	106	17	89
		0	99.5	3	96.5
Limonene..............	A	Room	115	15.5	99.5
		Room	117	17.5	99.5
	B	75	139	36	103
Styrene...............	A	Room	98	2	96
		Room	103.5	2	101.5
	B	75	102	0	102
Indene................	A	Room	195.5	107	88.5
		Room	214.5	126	88.5
	B	75	206	121	85
		0	115.5	21	94.5
Crotonic acid...........	A	Room	24.5	0	24.5
	B	75	103	5	98
		20	15.5	0	15.5
Undecylenic acid........	A	Room	115.5	28	83.5
	B	60	102	12	90
Cinnamic acid.........	A	Room	100	109	−9
		Room	99.5	97	2.5
	B	75	101	0	101
Abietic acid...........	A	Room	272	328	−56
		Room	243	268.5	−25.5
	B	75	251.5	335	−83.5
		0	124.5	82.5	42

[a] Method A, McIlhiney method; reaction time, 18 hours. Method B, nitrogen-sweeping method; time of bromination, 0.5 to 4 hours; time of sweeping, 0.5 to 8 hours.

continued until the excess reagent did not disappear for 2 minutes. The precision of the method in multiple determinations using varying sample sizes was approximately 3% on several monoolefins. The accuracy of the method could not be estimated since the purity of the samples was unknown. Titrations performed at $-10°C$. on olefinic samples containing thiophene showed no effect by this easily substituted sulfur compound.

A variation of the McIlhiney method, developed in the authors' laboratories in 1940 (483), has given satisfactory results on a large number of pure hydrocarbons and cracked distillates of the gasoline and kerosine boiling ranges. Conjugated diolefins do not brominate completely, and the method is not generally applicable to unsaturated chlorinated compounds or to unsaturated oxygen-containing materials. The method (567) involves the reaction of the sample in the dark at ice temperature with a measured excess of bromine in carbon tetrachloride in the presence of water, following which the excess bromine is determined iodometrically. One or two additional determinations are made at increased reaction times and the results are extrapolated to zero time if there is significant change in bromine absorption with time. The extrapolation procedure is primarily necessary with cracked petroleum distillates. It is based on the assumption that addition, although rapid at first, decreases in rate, and a slow substitution begins, as the saturation of the double bonds of diverse reactivity is approached. If the addition is complete when the first value is obtained and the rate of side reactions remains constant, extrapolation to zero time should give the correct addition value.

The application of this method to a large number of pure olefins has given very close agreement with the theoretical values. The extrapolated values in general are slightly on the lower side. Typical results are shown in Table VIII. The value for pinene is high, in agreement with published figures (91). This compound appears to undergo rupture of the bridge ring in addition to saturation of the double bond. Details of the procedure are given below.

Reagent. For each liter of solution, 17.2 g. (5.5 ml.) of bromine is dissolved in carbon tetrachloride. This reagent (0.2 N) is standardized daily as follows: Carbon tetrachloride (25 ml.) and water (100 ml.) in a glass-stoppered flask are cooled in an ice bath for 10 minutes. Reagent (15 ml.) is added and the flask is stored in the dark for 10 minutes. Potassium iodide solution (15 ml. of 20%) is added, and the titration is made with standard 0.1 N sodium thiosulfate solution to the starch end point.

Procedure. The sample is dissolved in carbon tetrachloride (25 ml.) in a glass-stoppered flask, water (100 ml.) is added, and the flask cooled in an ice bath for 10 minutes. A light shield is placed around the neck of the flask, reagent in 65 to 70% excess is added, and the flask (kept in the ice bath) is stored in the dark. Exactly 10 minutes after the addition of the reagent, potassium iodide solution (15 ml. of 20%) is added and the liberated iodine titrated with 0.1 N sodium thiosulfate solution to the starch end point. The

TABLE VIII

Analytical Data by the Extrapolation Method (567)
(Bromine in carbon tetrachloride)

Compound	Extent of reaction, % of theor.
1-Pentene	101
2-Pentene	97
2-Methyl-2-butene	100
2,2-Dimethylpropene	100
1-Hexene	100
2,3-Dimethyl-2-butene	99
1-Heptene	99
4-Methyl-2-pentene	101
2,3,3-Trimethyl-1-butene	99
1-Octene	100
2,3,4-Trimethyl-2-pentene	96
Diisobutylene	101
1-Decene	99
Triisobutylene	99
1-Tetradecene	100
1-Hexadecene	97
1-Octadecene	99
Styrene	99
α-Methylstyrene	100
4-Phenyl-1-butene	97
Stilbene	ca. 60
Cyclohexene	99
3-Methylcyclohexene	99
Pinene	ca. 150
2,5-Dimethyl-1,5-hexadiene	101
d-Limonene	100
2-Methyl-1,3-butadiene	100
4-Methyl-1,3-pentadiene	54
2,3-Dimethyl-1,3-butadiene	54

determination is repeated with 20 minutes reaction time. If these two results differ by 2% or more, a third determination is made with 30 minutes reaction time, and the results are extrapolated to zero time.

A similar procedure has been described for determination of traces of olefins in butane (95).

(3) **Tribromide Complex in Methanol.** Bromine in absolute methanol which has been saturated with sodium bromide was introduced by Kaufmann (321,322,331) and was originally intended for the determination of unsaturation in fatty oils. Kaufmann claimed that this reagent was more

stable than any other bromine solution tested, due to the fact that the halogen did not exist in the free state but was apparently loosely attached to the sodium bromide or methanol or both. (The solution is yellow in color, whereas a bromine solution of equivalent strength in methanol alone is reddish-brown.)

The reagent (0.2 N) is made up by dissolving 16 g. (5.2 ml.) of bromine in 1 liter of absolute methanol containing 120 to 150 grams of dry sodium bromide. The sample (0.1 to 1.0 g., depending on the extent of unsaturation), dissolved in chloroform, is reacted with 25 ml. of the reagent for 0.5 to 2 hours. The excess reagent is then back-titrated, after the addition of potassium iodide (15 ml. of 10%), with 0.1 N sodium thiosulfate (697). Kaller (315) found that the back-titration is more practical to carry out bromometrically with either titanous chloride using methylene blue indicator:

$$2Ti^{+++} + Br_2 \longrightarrow 2Ti^{++++} + 2Br^-$$

or with standard arsenite solution to methyl red after the addition of aqueous hydrochloric acid to the reaction mixture.

Earle and Milner (162) applied this method to the determination of unsaturation of soybean oil and observed that values differed but little from those found by the Wijs and Hanus methods. Results were not affected by moderate changes in temperature and illumination. Half-hour reaction time was not enough and even at two hours of reaction a large excess (ca. 300%) of reagent was necessary. Conjugated oils (tung and oiticica) gave low values.

Savary (554) preferred the Kaufmann method to other procedures for α,β-unsaturated acids and Petrova (485) applied it also to α,β-unsaturated aldehydes and ketones, back-titrating the excess bromine with a standard solution of anethole in methanol to the disappearance of color. The Kaufmann method was also successfully adapted to the determination of methallyl chloride as a liquid, and as a vapor in air, or in fumigated grain (170). On some allyl esters and ethers, however, results by the Kaufmann method were approximately 10% lower than theoretical, or than the average by some other methods (Wijs, Rosenmund-Kuhnhenn) (69).

In the application of the Kaufmann method to olefinic hydrocarbons, Garre and Grosse-Oetringhaus (205) found good values for cyclohexene and 1,5-hexadiene, and recommended the method for gasolines, assuming the absence of any substitution reaction. It was shown by Uhrig and Levin (623), however, that triisobutylene gave bromine numbers between 94 and 120 (theory, 95) depending on the reagent excess used. These high values clearly indicated the presence of substitution.

In contrast to these observations, Wilson (669) found low bromine values on several C_6 to C_{10} olefins. Titration of the hydrobromic acid content of the reaction mixture showed that substitution was present in each case and with two branched olefins only a small portion of the bromine consumption was due to addition. However, the total absorption values, when corrected for peroxides (see Section II.1.C), were near theoretical, rendering Wilson's modification probably the best halogenation method for multiply branched olefins. These results, compared with values by the standard McIlhiney method, are shown in Table IX.

TABLE IX

Analytical Data by the Modified Kaufmann Method (669)

	Percentage of theoretical			
	Modified Kaufmann method[a]			Standard McIlhiney method
Compound	Total absorption	Substitution	Addition	
1-Octene....................	99.1	25.3	73.8	96.6
1-Hexene..................	97.2	26.3	70.9	98.0
1,5-Hexadiene..............	99.7	19.3	80.4	96.1
2,4,4-Trimethyl-1-pentene......	98.6	72.8	25.8	84.1
2,4,4-Trimethyl-2-pentene......	90.9	89.4	1.5	45.8

[a] Corrected for small amounts of peroxides.

(4) **Tribromide Complex in Water.** An aqueous bromination reagent, containing bromine and excess potassium bromide, has been in use in the authors' laboratories for some time (483). This reagent is easy to prepare and has displayed very satisfactory keeping qualities. Since the potassium bromide is in excess, all the bromine content is assumed to be in the loose Br_3^- form. This brominating agent has been found to be especially applicable to oxygen-containing olefinic compounds which react incompletely in some other halogenation methods. Phenol reacts quantitatively to give tribromophenol, but most saturated alcohols, ketones, aldehydes, esters, and acids do not interfere to any appreciable degree. The normal procedure involves the shaking of the sample in the presence of ice with a 65 to 70% excess of reagent for 20 minutes and back-titrating the unreacted bromine iodometrically with sodium thiosulfate. To avoid loss of bromine, the reaction is carried out in an evacuated bottle (Procedure A). With difficultly reacting samples, the reaction is carried out at room temperature for 1 hour (Procedure B).

Reagent.   For each liter of solution, 35.8 g. of potassium bromide is dissolved in about 100 ml. of water and 17.2 g. (5.5 ml.) of bromine is added.   The solution is mixed until bromine is dissolved, then diluted to volume.   This reagent (0.2 N) is standardized daily in an evacuated bromination bottle (Fig. 1) by drawing in reagent (15 ml.), potassium iodide solution (15 ml. of 20%), and water (about 100 ml.) through a piece of rubber tubing;   then the vacuum

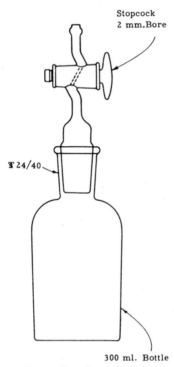

Fig. 1. Bromination bottle.

is released, the stopper is removed, and the titration is made with standard 0.1 N sodium thiosulfate to the starch end point.

Procedure A.   The bromination bottle is filled two-thirds full with crushed ice, stoppered, and evacuated.   An aliquot of diluted sample (in alcohol or acetone) and the reagent (65 to 70% in excess) are introduced, and the bottle is shaken for 20 minutes in a mechanical shaker.   Potassium iodide solution (15 ml. of 20%) is added, the vacuum is released, and the mixture is titrated with standard 0.1 N sodium thiosulfate solution to the starch end point.   If the result of a duplicate determination with 90% reagent excess differs by more than 1%, the method should be considered not applicable to the sample.

Procedure B. Procedure A is followed but with these differences: Ice is omitted, 80% reagent excess is used, and the shaking is continued for 1 hour.

Typical results obtained by these procedures are shown in Table X.

TABLE X

Results by the Aqueous Tribromide Method (483)

Compound	Extent of reaction,-% of theoretical	
	Proc. A	Proc. B
Allyl alcohol....................	99	—
β-Chloroallyl alcohol...............	98	100
Methallyl alcohol.................	102	—
Methylvinylcarbinol...............	97	—
Crotyl alcohol....................	100	—
4-Hydroxy-2-methyl-1-pentene........	96	—
Acrolein.........................	100	—
α-Chloroacrolein..................	10	92
Acrolein dimer....................	100	—
Methacrolein.....................	100	—
Methyl isopropenyl ketone...........	99	—
Mesityl oxide.....................	99	—
Acrolein diacetate.................	100	—
Methacrolein diacetate..............	99	—
1,1,3-Triallyloxypropane............	101	—
Acrylic acid......................	86	97
Sodium acrylate...................	—	100
Methacrylic acid..................	99	99
Tetrahydrobenzoic acid.............	99	—
Vinyl acetate.....................	100	—
Vinyl propionate..................	—	103
Vinyl butyrate....................	—	99
Vinyl crotonate...................	—	64
Vinyl oleate......................	—	100
Allyl acetate.....................	98	—
Allyl propionate..................	100	—
Chloroallyl propionate..............	ca. 40	93
Allyl butyrate....................	101	—
Allyl caproate....................	98	—
Allyl caprylate...................	100	—
Allyl hexahydrobenzoate............	99	—
Diallyl adipate...................	91	97
Diallyl phthalate..................	ca. 60	101
Allyl crotonate...................	77	100
Methyl α-chloroacrylate............	<1	66
Ethyl acrylate....................	10	101
α-Allyl glycerol ether..............	100	—

| | Extent of reaction, % of theoretical | |
Compound	Proc. A	Proc. B
Allyl glycidyl ether...................	100	—
Allyl 1,3-dichloro-2-propyl ether.......	99	—
Allyl sulfolanyl ether................	100	—
Dimethallyl ether....................	86	101
Vinyl chloride......................	100	—
Dichloroethylene....................	—	36
1,1-Dichloro-1-propene...............	—	(low)
1,3-Dichloro-1-propene...............	(low)	96
2,3-Dichloro-1-propene...............	(low)	99
3-Chloro-1-butene...................	2	103
1-Chloro-2-butene...................	101	—
1,4-Dichloro-2-butene................	80	97
Allyl N-ethyl carbamate..............	100	—
Dibutyl allyl phosphate..............	100	—
2,4-Dimethyl-3-sulfolene.............	98	100

An aqueous bromine–bromide method for the determination of vinyl acetate was also reported by Gurvits and Mel'nikova (235).

(5) **Hydrogen Perbromide Complex in Chloroform.** Gal'pern and Vinogradova (202) used a solution of bromine in chloroform to determine the unsaturation values of olefins. They state that, when bromine is dissolved in chloroform, a series of reactions occur, finally to yield bromine in loose chemical combination with hydrogen bromide:

$$5Br_2 + 2CHCl_3 \longrightarrow HBr_3 + HBr_5 + 2CBrCl_3$$

This gives a solution almost deprived of free bromine. The loose addition compounds react with the olefinic double bonds with the formation of dibromo products and the liberation of hydrogen bromide, which is the by-product of addition and does not apparently result from substitution. (The addition of bromine from HBr_3 to α,β-unsaturated acids, with the elimination of hydrogen bromide, was later studied by Morton and Robertson (446).)

The freshly made reagent (approximately 0.2 N) undergoes an initial rapid change in titer; for this reason, it should not be used until it is at least two days old. Beyond this time, it should be standardized twice daily. The initial decrease in normality of the reagent is presumably due to the interaction of free dissolved bromine and chloroform to give hydrogen per-bromides and monobromotrichloromethane. After a few days, the reagent does not have the characteristic odor of bromine.

The procedure followed by Gal'pern and Vinogradova involved the use of a calculated 60 to 70% excess of the reagent and 1 to 10 minute reaction times, without using any substitution correction. This method has been applied to a number of synthetic olefins with very satisfactory results. Some of these data, compared with addition values by the McIlhiney method obtained by the same authors, are given in Table XI. The value for styrene is unaccountably high. The abnormal behavior of pinene was mentioned in Section II.1.C(2).

TABLE XI

Bromine Addition Data by the Method of Gal'pern and Vinogradova (202)

| Compound | Percentage of theoretical addition | |
	Hydrogen perbromide complex in CHCl₃	Br₂ in CCl₄ (McIlhiney method)
2-Methyl-1-butene....................	101.4	76.1
n-Octene.............................	100.9	84.4
Diisobutylene........................	98.6	68.7
Cyclohexene..........................	99.5	86.8
Limonene.............................	98.2	79.1
Amylene..............................	101.4	76.1
Styrene..............................	113.3	80.8
Pinene...............................	138.6	80.1

(6) **Pyridinium Sulfate Dibromide.** For the determination of unsaturation in fatty oils, Rosenmund, Kuhnhenn, Rosenberg-Gruszynski, and Rosetti (536) suggested that pyridinium sulfate dibromide ($C_6H_5N.H_2SO_4.-Br_2$) might be used as a reagent capable of providing a more active halogen than the iodination reagents that were currently in use. In discussing the chemistry of this reagent, Rosenmund and Kuhnhenn (534) showed that the compounds of bromine with pyridine or quinoline are active bromine addition agents and that they do not participate in secondary reactions of substitution or oxidation. The reagent, approximately 0.1 N in respect to bromine in glacial acetic acid, was very easy to prepare and remained stable over a long period of time. The general procedure was essentially the same as that of the Wijs method. Several applications of the method were presented (531,535). It was shown that the reaction was complete in 2 minutes and that the results for fatty materials did not depend on the reagent excess. The preparation of the reagent (544) is given below.

Reagent. A 40 ml. portion of glacial acetic acid is placed in each of three glass-stoppered flasks. To the first, 16 ± 0.2 g. of pyridine is added slowly with cooling and gentle agitation. In the same manner, 20 ± 0.2 g. of concentrated sulfuric acid is added to the second flask. These solutions are combined with further cooling. To the third flask, 16 ± 0.2 g. of bromine is added; then this solution is added to the mixture of the first two solutions. This mixture is then diluted with glacial acetic acid to 2 liters and stored in a dark bottle.

Bolton and Williams (63) applied this reagent to sterols and to the unsaponifiable fraction (mainly squalene) of olive oil with satisfactory results. Angell (27) found that pyridinium sulfate dibromide effected complete saturation of the ring with such compounds as furan, sylvan, and furfuryl alcohol. Little if any substitution occurred. However, furfural, furoic acid, and furyl cyanide reacted only to a slight extent. The Rosenmund-Kuhnhenn reagent was also found to be applicable to the quantitative determination of allyl group in methallyl chloride (170) and in several mono- and polyallyl esters and ethers (69). Modifications of the original procedure were presented by Rosenmund and Grandjean for the estimation of very low unsaturation values in medicinal paraffin oils (533).

The use of pyridinium sulfate dibromide in conjunction with mercuric acetate catalyst was suggested by Rowe, Furnas, and Bliss (544). Consistently good results were obtained on several samples of tall oil using approximately 70% excess reagent in the dark with a 16 hour reaction time. The unsaturation values obtained indicated complete reaction with the conjugated systems in the oil. An exaggerated test showed no trace of bromide ions in the reaction mixture, substantiating the claim of Rosenmund and Kuhnhenn.

Benham and Klee (48) found that the modification of Rowe, Furnas, and Bliss gives quantitative results on all ordinary nonconjugated oils and fats (dissolved in 5 ml. of carbon tetrachloride) in 1 minute when 10 ml. of 2.5% mercuric acetate in glacial acetic acid solution is added to the mixture. These authors claimed (349) that the true iodine value of oils containing conjugated double bonds (tung, oiticica) is obtained with 30 to 120 minute reaction times. However, Lips (385) found that, on polymerized oils, this modification of Klee and Benham gave apparent values which tended to increase with increased reaction time and reagent excess. Erroneous results due to the action of mercuric acetate on the reagent and on the samples were also observed in reactions prolonged over a day. Chloroform caused partial deterioration of the reagent and should not be used in place of carbon tetrachloride as a sample solvent; this effect was greater in the presence of the mercuric salt.

The applicability of the Benham-Klee method to conjugated oils and acids was also studied by Planck, Pack, and Goldblatt (488). These authors found that, if the mercuric acetate is added to the sample before, rather than after, the reagent is added as directed by Benham and Klee, values on tung oil samples agree with catalytic hydrogenation values, and values on α- and β-eleostearic acid agree with the theoretical values. A reagent excess of 200 to 250% and a 1 hour reaction time were proved to be optimum. Light was found to affect the values greatly. Consequently, the use of low actinic glass flasks, addition of the reagent in partially darkened room, and storage in complete darkness during the reaction period were recommended. Some results by this procedure are shown in Table XII.

TABLE XII

Analytical Data by the Method of Planck, Pack, and Goldblatt (488)
(Reagent excess 200–250%; reaction time 1 hour)

	Iodine Number	
Sample	Modified pyridinium sulfate dibromide method	Catalytic hydrogenation
α-Eleostearic acid (100%).............	273.8[a]	272.8
β-Eleostearic acid (98%)..............	272.8[a]	270.2
Tung oil, domestic...................	232.1[b]	232.3
Tung oil, Chinese....................	228.5[a]	227.9
Tung oil, isomerized.................	230.8[a]	229.2

[a] Average of three determinations.
[b] Average of two determinations.

The good success of the Rosenmund and Kuhnhenn reagent for fatty materials could not be duplicated for branched-chain olefins that occur in petroleum distillates. Wilson and Nisbet (670) applied this reagent to the analysis of synthetic mixtures of saturated and unsaturated hydrocarbons and showed that, in the case of straight-chain compounds, the bromine number increased only to a slight degree when the reaction time was increased up to 1 hour. However, two branched-chain olefins examined in the continuation of this work by Wilson (669) gave abnormal results even after the short reaction period of 5 minutes (Table XIII).

(7) **Bromide–Bromate in Water.** An aqueous solution of bromide and bromate ions, acidified with a mineral acid, was one of the earlier of the bromination reagents for the determination of olefinic unsaturation (626, 650). The Winkler method (672) employed crystalline potassium bromide and an excess of 0.1 N potassium bromate solution. The unused portion of the reagent was determined either iodometrically or bromometrically by means of acidic arsenite solution (671).

TABLE XIII

Analytical Data by the Rosenmund-Kuhnhenn Method (669)

Compound	Extent of reaction, % of theoretical	
	5 min. reaction time	1 hr. reaction time
1-Octene............................	99.7[a]	101.3[a]
1-Hexene...........................	100.1[a]	100.6[a]
1-Cetene............................	99.8[a]	104.6[a]
1,5-Hexadiene......................	100.2[a]	100.4[a]
Cyclohexene.........................	100.4	—
2,4,4-Trimethyl-1-pentene.............	118.0	130.0
	117.0	130.9
	122.2	131.3
	118.9	131.0
2,4,4-Trimethyl-2-pentene.............	124.8	178.2
	124.1	177.5
	122.7	181.5
	125.9	182.3

[a] Average of four determinations.

The first bromide–bromate procedure published in the English literature is attributed to Francis (195). The original Francis method used an excess of potassium bromide–bromate reagent in acid solution as the brominating agent, and the unused excess was determined iodometrically. During subsequent years, this procedure went through numerous modifications to emerge as the most widely applied bromination method.

Bacon (36) modified the Francis method for dark colored samples. The excess reagent was back-titrated past the thiosulfate end point, the aqueous phase was separated from the benzene phase containing the sample, and the excess thiosulfate in the aqueous phase was titrated with standard iodine solution.

Both these procedures gave reasonably good results for straight-chain compounds, but were unreliable for certain ring structures. To correct this shortcoming of the method, Cortese (118) used excess reagent but a smaller volume of sulfuric acid and continued the shaking after the addition of a second portion of the acid. Mulliken and Wakeman (451), voicing the same criticism as Cortese, presented a modification which required adding the reagent in two portions to the sample. The total shaking period was also shortened to 2 minutes. Generally low results were obtained, supporting the claim of these authors that by this procedure substitution was reduced.

Further modifications were made on the Francis method by Thomas,

Bloch, and Hoekstra (613), who found that substitution could be reduced by cooling the reaction mixture at several stages.

The modification of Lewis and Bradstreet (382) employed n-heptane as sample solvent and titration in the presence of excess potassium bromide in the reaction mixture. Direct titration of this mixture was continued to a faint yellow color; then 1 ml. excess reagent was added. After 2 minutes shaking the unused reagent was back-titrated with thiosulfate. This procedure, considerably more rapid than the previous ones, gave theoretical values for 1-heptene, diisobutylene, and trimethylethylene, but erratic results were obtained for tri- and tetraisobutylene. The same authors (383) later proposed a further modification of their procedure, by means of which it is possible to determine the bromine addition and substitution values separately. It was recognized that bromine numbers, although reliable for many straight-chain and some branched olefins, should be expected to be in error on mixtures containing highly branched unsaturated compounds.

A critical examination of the advantageous points of the above methods by Johnson and Clark (308) resulted in a procedure that was subsequently incorporated into the A. S. T. M. Standards (21) and adopted also by the Institute of Petroleum (291). Details of the method are given below:

Reagent. 51.0 g. of potassium bromide and 13.92 g. of potassium bromate are dissolved in water and diluted to 1 liter. This approximately 0.5 N solution is standardized as follows: 50 ml. of glacial acetic acid and 1 ml. of concentrated hydrochloric acid are placed in a glass-stoppered flask and chilled in an ice bath for approximately 10 minutes. With constant swirling of the flask, 5.00 ml. of reagent is added at a rate of 1 to 2 drops per second. The stoppered flask is shaken and replaced in the ice bath for 5 minutes, potassium iodide solution (5 ml. of 15%) is added, and the flask is shaken again. After the addition of about 100 ml. of water, the solution is titrated with standard 0.1 N sodium thiosulfate solution to the starch end point.

Procedure. The sample is weighed into a 50 ml. volumetric flask containing some carbon tetrachloride and diluted to the mark. A 5 ml. aliquot of this solution is pipetted into a glass-stoppered flask containing 50 ml. of glacial acetic acid. With constant swirling, reagent is added at a rate of 1 to 2 drops per second until a faint yellow color is reached that remains for at least 5 seconds. An additional 1 ml. of the reagent is added, the flask stoppered and shaken for 40 seconds, then potassium iodide solution (5 ml. of 15%) is added. The stopper is again replaced, the flask is shaken vigorously, and 100 ml. of water is added. After being shaken again for 1 minute, the solution is titrated with 0.1 N sodium thiosulfate solution to the starch end point. The test is discarded if the back-titration is less than 5 ml. or greater than 10 ml. of thiosulfate solution.

The following sample sizes are recommended:

Bromine Number	Sample size, g.
0 to 10	20 to 16
10 to 20	10 to 8
20 to 50	5 to 4
50 to 100	2 to 1.5
Over 100	1 to 0.5

A large number of pure compounds have been analyzed according to this method by A. S. T. M. cooperators. Some of these data are given in Table XIV. These results show that values are close to theoretical for straight-chain and cyclic monoolefins and generally slightly high for most branched-chain monoolefins. Certain highly branched olefins gave results which were 16 to 20% above theoretical. Nonconjugated diolefins showed normal reaction, but conjugated diolefins reacted only to the extent of approximately one double bond. Substituted benzenes, naphthalenes, and phenanthrenes generally do not react with bromine under the conditions of the method. However, mesitylene and isodurene undergo substitution, as was found earlier by Winward and Garner (675) for the Hanus method.

The use of a mercury salt in combination with a measured excess of bromide–bromate reagent was proposed by Lucas and Pressman (391). These authors found that bromine addition by their method can be quantitatively performed within 3 minutes, even in the presence of conjugated double bonds which react slowly with bromine (e.g., maleic and fumaric acids). In some cases, however, substitution as well as addition was found to take place (e.g., propiolic acid, 2,3-dimethylbutadiene, and cinnamic acid).

DuBois and Skoog (155) found that the catalytic action of a mercury salt is strong enough to effect extremely rapid reaction between bromine and an olefinic double bond. Their method involves direct titration with standard potassium bromide–bromate reagent in the presence of mercuric chloride, the end point being determined by the deadstop electrometric technique (194). The presence of dark colored materials causes no difficulty. Errors due to substitution are reduced to a minimum in this titration technique by keeping the reaction mixture cooled to 0 to 5°C. The amount of judgment required in the use of this procedure is considerably less than with most other methods and the time required per analysis is short.

This procedure has also been accepted as a tentative standard by the

TABLE XIV

Analytical Data by the A. S. T. M. Color-Indicator Bromide–Bromate
Method (24)

Compound	Purity, %	Extent of reaction, % of theor.
1-Pentene	95+	102.4
1-Octene	98+	99.4
2-Octene	98+	99.9
1-Decene	97+	97.5
1-Dodecene	95+	96.7
1-Tetradecene	99.7	100.1
1-Hexadecene	97	99.7
2-Methyl-1-pentene	95	102.3
2-Ethyl-1-butene	95	97.3
4-Methyl-*cis*-2-pentene	99.7	98.7
4-Methyl-*trans*-2-pentene	99.4	99.6
2,3-Dimethyl-1-butene	99.8	117.1
2,3-Dimethyl-2-butene	99.7	102.6
4,4-Dimethyl-2-pentene	98+	98.9
2-Ethyl-1-hexene	95+	118.7
2,3,3-Trimethyl-1-butene	98.6	119.4
Diisobutylene	*a*	101.8
2,4,4-Trimethyl-1-pentene	98+	102.3
2,4,4-Trimethyl-2-pentene	98+	101.5
3,4,4-Trimethyl-2-pentene	98+	119.8
3-Methyl-2-isopropyl-1-butene	97+	116.3
Triisobutylene	—	101.6
Tetraisobutylene	*b*	100.8
Cyclohexene	98+	99.4
Indene	95+	99.8
1,4-Dihydronaphthalene	98.1	100.0
4-Vinyl-1-cyclohexene	98+	100.7
Terpinolene	—	95.6
d-Limonene	*b*	101.4
Dipentene	—	101.2
Cyclopentadiene	95+	49.8
cis-1,3-Pentadiene	96	54.9
2-Methyl-1,3-butadiene	99	55.0
2-Methyl-1,3-pentadiene	95+	58.3
Styrene	98+	99.5
Stilbene	93–95	15.5

a Purified by silica gel percolation.
b Eastman white label product.

A. S. T. M. (22) and is included in the Standard Methods of the Institute of
Petroleum (292). Details of the method are given below.

Titration Solvent. 1 liter of titration solvent is prepared by mixing the following volumes of materials: 714 ml. of glacial acetic acid, 134 ml. of carbon tetrachloride, 116 ml. of methanol, 18 ml. of sulfuric acid (1:5), and 18 ml. of a 10% methanolic solution of mercuric chloride.

Reagent. The standard 0.5 N reagent is prepared by dissolving 51.0 g. of potassium bromide and 13.92 g. of potassium bromate in 1 liter of water. This reagent is standardized as described earlier for the color-indicator procedure.

Procedure. A 5 ml. aliquot of a 50 ml. solution of sample in carbon tetrachloride is pipetted into the cooled (0 to 5°C.) titration vessel containing 110 ml. of titration solvent. A mechanical stirrer and the two electrodes are placed in this solution, the stirring is started, and, when the temperature of the solution is below 5°C., the electric "eye" of the titration apparatus is adjusted to a nearly closed position. (A suitable indicating meter can be used as a substitute for the electric "eye" instrument.) The reagent is added dropwise at first, and if the "eye" does not flicker appreciably, the rate of addition may be increased until the electric "eye" opens. Small additions are then made, noting the action of the "eye" which when open shows the presence of unabsorbed bromine. The end point is indicated when 2 drops of reagent cause the "eye" to remain open for at least 30 seconds. A blank determination on the solvents should be negligible. The recommended sample sizes (in 50 ml. carbon tetrachloride solution) are the same as given for the color-indicator procedure.

Some results obtained by this procedure are given in Table XV. A comparison of these results for olefins with those by the color-indicator bromide–bromate procedure (Table XIV) shows very little difference between the two methods. Straight-chain olefins give nearly theoretical results, but some branched olefins react excessively. However, anthracene and its derivatives, in contrast to the color-indicator method, show only slight reactivity toward bromine in the electrometric procedure. Because sulfur compounds and pyrroles react in these A. S. T. M. procedures, erroneously high results are obtained on many naphthas of petroleum, or especially shale oil, origin if not treated prior to the bromine number determination (149, 507).

Other instrumental techniques for detection of end points in titrations with bromide–bromate have been published. In a direct titration procedure, Sweetser and Bricker (605) used a Beckman DU spectrophotometer, equipped with a special titration cell, to determine the end point. Absorbance readings at a selected wave length (270 to 360 mμ) were plotted against volume of titrant; the end point was indicated by the sudden increase in absorbance at the appearance of tribromide ions in the reaction mixture. Kolthoff and Bovey (359) determined the end point amperometrically, using a rotating platinum electrode, in the titration of dilute aqueous solutions of styrene.

TABLE XV

Analytical Data by the A. S. T. M. Electrometric
Bromide–Bromate Method (24)

Compound	Purity, %	Extent of reaction % of theor.
1-Hexene.............................	99	100.5
2-Hexene.............................	95	100.2
1-Tetradecene.......................	99.7	101.6
1-Hexadecene.......................	97	101.2
1-Octadecene........................	95	96.8
2-Methyl-1-pentene..................	95	94.4
4-Methyl-1-pentene..................	95	99.5
4-Methyl-cis-2-pentene..............	99.7	101.9
4-Methyl-trans-2-pentene............	99.4	101.0
2,3-Dimethyl-1-butene...............	99.8	114.6
2,3-Dimethyl-2-butene...............	99.7	101.5
2-Ethyl-1-butene....................	95	106.3
2,3,3-Trimethyl-1-butene............	98.6	117.9
Diisobutylene.......................	a	99.4
Cyclopentene........................	99	99.9
Cyclohexene.........................	100	102.0
d-Limonene..........................	b	99.3
2-Methyl-1,3-butadiene..............	99	51.0
Styrene.............................	—	99.1
α-Methylstyrene.....................	—	98.3

ᵃ Purified by silica gel percolation.
ᵇ Eastman white label product.

Many special applications of the bromide–bromate reagent have been reported. Butadiene dimer was determined in admixture with 1,3-butadiene by quantitatively distilling out butadiene with chloroform and brominating the residue, following Johnson and Clark's procedure with special conditions (237). A bromide–bromate procedure was found to be applicable for determination of Dimalone, an insect repellant with a bicycloheptene structure; recoveries were better than 99% (216). Another modification of the Francis method was reported for the determination of unsaturation of terpenes known to be easily substituted in most halogenation methods (181). Styrene has been determined in the presence of 1,4-divinyl-2,3,5,6-tetrachlorobenzene by titration with standard bromide–bromate solution in carbon tetrachloride (538). Under the conditions used, the substituted divinylbenzene does not react because of the presence of the *ortho*-chlorines. Bromide–bromate reagent was also applied to partially polymerized acrylic and allyl esters after several other standard halogenation procedures were found to be inapplicable (7). The determination of 2,3-dihydropyran required a special procedure involving the use of mercuric chloride and carefully controlled reaction conditions (393).

(8) Gravimetric Bromination Methods. The bromine vapor methods involve the use of an enclosed system in which bromine is allowed to act on a thin layer of the unsaturated material in the dark. The excess bromine vapor is removed by evacuation, or with a stream of inert gas, preferably at an elevated temperature. The increase in weight is taken as a measure of unsaturation. It seems that this principle was first employed by Hehner (252). Improved procedures were presented later by Becker (44), Toms (617), Rossmann (541), and others. This technique has not found extensive use, although it offers several advantages. The reaction with simple olefins is complete in a few minutes, but longer reaction times and large excesses of bromine do not influence the results. Conjugated systems (β-eleostearic acid), as well as some usually inactive double bonds (e. g., —COOH on the adjacent carbon atom), react quantitatively. It was claimed by several investigators that substitution is absent if the determination is made in the dark. However, castor oil gave abnormally high values and Böeseken and Pols (59) concluded that the bromine vapor methods are unsuitable in the presence of hydroxyl groups (as in ricinoleic acid). The complete removal of bromine from the reacted sample may present difficulties, but Rossmann (540) devised a procedure by which the excess bromine can be titrated, making superfluous the drying of the film to constant weight. These methods were primarily designed for nonvolatile samples, but a titrimetric variation of the procedure by Rossmann (539) permits the analysis of volatile materials by means of a special apparatus.

Stieglitz, Andress, and Demediuk (599) examined the applicability of the Rossmann method to hydrocarbons. Several olefinic types reacted normally, but the type, —C(CH$_3$)=CH—, gave high values. This error was avoided in a modified procedure operating at $-18°$C.

While most of the bromine vapor methods are micro or semimicro procedures, Atmore and Hawke (33) found that equally reliable results can be obtained on fatty materials (except castor oil) if the procedure is scaled up to about 0.1 gram sample sizes. A similar procedure was published by Burden and Grindley (93).

Another group of gravimetric bromination methods involves precipitating the olefinic components of the sample with excess bromine, followed by washing, drying, and weighing the isolated precipitate. There are numerous references in the literature to the estimation of the percentage of various unsaturated fatty acids in admixtures by this technique. These methods are based upon the formation of di-, tetra-, and hexabromides by reaction of bromine with oleic, linoleic, and linolenic acids, respectively. Solubility differences in certain solvents (660) permit the fractionation of these products from each other and from products of conjugated acids. The quantitative analytical value of these methods is highly doubtful (72). Yields are low, requiring the use of empirical correction factors (316). Occlusion is not uncommon and even moderate pretreatment of the oil may destroy the ability of the oil to form polybromides. The chief value of these methods is probably that of providing useful means of isolating pure fatty acids from crude mixtures since the polybromides crystallize, and can be readily purified and debrominated to regenerate the unsaturated acid in a good state of purity.

Precipitation-gravimetric procedures have also been employed in the rubber industry for the determination of unsaturated hydrocarbons in crude rubber and latex. A benzene or carbon tetrachloride solution of the rubber is brominated for one hour, the brominated product is precipitated with alcohol, washed, dried, and weighed (665). Gravimetric factors for converting weights of bromide to weights of rubber vary from one plant source to another, such as 0.290 for kok-saghyz, 0.292 for guayule, and 0.303 for *Cryptostegia*, instead of the theoretical 0.299 calculated for an isoprene unit. A critical investigation of the variables of the above procedure was presented by Gowans and Clark (223). These authors proposed a modified procedure that was claimed to furnish accurate and precise results. A factor of 0.301 was obtained for guayule rubber; for *Hevea* smoked sheet, the conversion factor was identical with the theoretical value (0.299).

(9) Other Bromination Reagents. *Pyridinium Bromide Perbromide.* The perbromide of pyridine hydrobromide is a relatively stable, crystalline molecular complex of variable composition, but can be prepared with the approximate composition of $C_5H_5NHBrBr_2$ (178). This reagent was first proposed for the addition of bromine to the double bond by Rosenmund and Kuhnhenn (534) and was recently studied by Lombard and Heywang (387). The latter authors found that the hydrogen bromide portion of the complex does not take part in the addition reaction, which is usually free of undesirable side effects.

Pyridine Methylbromide Dibromide. This compound, $C_5H_5NCH_3BrBr_2$, was proposed recently by Rosenmund and Grandjean (532) as a more versatile reagent than pyridinium sulfate dibromide (see Section II.1.C(6)). The compound can be readily recrystallized and thus provides a satisfactorily pure source of halogen. It is employed in glacial acetic acid solution supersaturated with anhydrous sodium acetate. It was found advantageous to include anhydrous sodium acetate in the reaction mixture to suppress radical reactions by removing water from the solution (pyridinium sulfate dibromide precipitates sodium sulfate under similar conditions). Several novel steps, designed to suppress side reactions, are incorporated in the procedure when essential oils are analyzed. Prior to the addition of the saturated sodium acetate and the reagent solutions, the sample is first treated with hydroxylamine to tie up peroxides and aldehydes, then with acetic anhydride to acetylate amines, phenols, alcohols, and the excess hydroxylamine. Theoretical and constant unsaturation values were obtained on a number of essential oils by this procedure in 2 to 12 hour reaction times.

Saponification Method of Volmar and Samdahl (628). The method involves the bromination of the sample, in ether solution, at $-10°C.$, saponification of the isolated addition product, and determination of the bromine content by the Volhard method. The excess bromine is washed out of the reaction mixture with sodium hyposulfite and water.

Bromine on Carbon. Wirth (678) brominated ethylene in the presence of acetylene and ethane on the surface of carbon impregnated with bromine. Ethylene brominates at $-78°C.$ in 1.5 minutes while acetylene is almost completely inert at this temperature. This observation is utilized in a volumetric gas analysis method.

Electrolytic Bromine. A novel way of brominating gaseous olefins was proposed by Bratzler and Kleemann (75). Bromine is generated electrolytically in a continuous manner while the olefin-containing gas stream flows by. The electrolyte, a dilute sulfuric acid solution of potassium bromide, also flows through the electrode vessel. The overflow is continuously collected in another vessel in which it is mixed with a potassium iodide–starch solution. The amount of bromine liberated is calculated from the intensity of the current, and the amount of gas sample is measured by a flow meter. A gas sample containing approximately 2% ethylene was analyzed with a precision of $±5\%$.

D. CHLORINATION

Chlorine and some of its compounds, although extensively used as vapor-phase chlorinating reagents (94,217), have been applied to the analytical halogenation of unsaturated compounds only to a very limited extent.

Chlorine itself is excessively reactive and easily leads to substitution and other side reactions. Such a side reaction, observed by Kraus and Reynolds (364), resulted in the isolation, by a cyclization process, of the ethylenic units in polyisoprenes. However, chlorine generated electrolytically from hydrogen chloride, was successfully employed in a coulometric titration procedure by Čuta and Kučera (136) for the determination of unsaturation of a number of high molecular weight fatty acids (e. g., erucic acid). Substances with multiple double bonds, such as methylfuran, rapeseed oil, and tobacco oil, gave low values by this method.

Mukherjee (448) employed aqueous hypochlorous acid for the determination of unsaturation in oxidized fatty acids. This reagent adds to the double bond as follows:

$$\ce{>C=C< + HOCl -> -\underset{HO}{\overset{}{C}}-\overset{Cl}{\underset{}{C}}-}$$

After a 15 minute reaction time at 37°C., the excess reagent was determined iodometrically. The author claimed complete absence of substitution; ketones, however, interfered. Hypochlorous acid was used earlier for determining unsaturation in fats and oils by Goswami and Basu (220). These procedures were applicable only to the aqueous solutions of sodium salts of fatty acids. By employing an acetic acid solution of the oil (or a suspension of the oil in acetic acid), Mukherjee (449) successfully extended the scope of the method to include glycerides as well. The results, which compare very favorably with those by the more complex standard methods, are but little affected by changes in reaction conditions (sample size, reagent excess, reaction time, temperature, etc.) and appear to be remarkably free from effects of secondary reactions.

Using aqueous hydrogen chloride at room temperature, Houtman (279) determined isobutylene selectively in the presence of propylene and C_4 olefins. Only isobutylene reacts, with the formation of *tert*-butyl chloride; however, other gases possess considerable solubilities in the reagent for which it is necessary to apply corrections. An accuracy of approximately 1% was reported for mixtures containing less than 85% isobutylene. Above this value it is advantageous to dilute the sample with a nonreactive gas.

2. Hydrogenation

Analytical hydrogenation in the presence of metallic catalysts as a means for determination of olefinic unsaturation has some advantages over other chemical methods. Errors due to substitution do not occur and, with proper choice of catalyst and solvent, interference due to hydrogenation of aromatic rings can be avoided.

Simple monoolefins do not react when treated with zinc and acid, sodium amalgam, or sodium and alcohol ("nascent" hydrogen). Only double bonds conjugated with an unsaturated group such as another ethylenic linkage, a carbonyl group, or an aromatic ring, are reduced by such reagents. For hydrogenation of ordinary olefins with hydrogen gas, the catalytic action of metals such as platinum, palladium, nickel, or copper is required:

$$\diagdown C{=}C\diagdown \ + \ H_2 \ \xrightarrow{\text{(Pt or Pd, etc.)}} \ -\overset{|}{\underset{H}{C}}-\overset{|}{\underset{H}{C}}-$$

At low temperatures, the catalytic addition of hydrogen is predominantly *cis*. A large amount of theoretical and experimental work has been done on the mechanism of hydrogenation, but no single theory has gained general acceptance. Various mechanisms involving ionic hydrogen, atomic hydrogen, metal hydrides, metal oxide hydrides, adsorbed complexes, etc., have been proposed. The chemistry of hydrogenation has been discussed in several reviews (5,101,169).

Because olefins usually can be completely hydrogenated under mild conditions, it is convenient to conduct the reaction near atmospheric pressure. The determination of unsaturation depends on measuring the quantity of hydrogen consumed by the sample when the reaction is complete. The measurement can be made manometrically or volumetrically. Many variations in apparatus design to provide intimate contact among the reactants, introduction of sample, equilibration, and ease of operation have been reported.

A. REAGENTS

(1) **Catalysts.** Various metals have been employed as hydrogenation catalysts, depending on the ease of hydrogenation of the sample, whether selectivity for differentiating types of double bonds is desired, etc. Since the reaction between hydrogen and the double bond occurs at or near the surface of the catalyst, it is desirable for the catalyst to possess a high surface area. Accordingly, the catalyst is usually employed as a finely divided or colloidal precipitate or is mounted on the surface of a carrier such as activated carbon or silica. The rate of hydrogenation depends on the amount of catalyst used. In order to attain a sufficiently high rate,

e. g., for difficultly hydrogenated polyenes such as the carotenoids, it is occasionally necessary to use a weight of catalyst equal to or even greater than the weight of sample taken.

The sample and solvent must be free from catalyst "poisons." Sulfur compounds in general and carbon monoxide tend to destroy catalyst activity, but appreciable amounts of certain types of sulfur compounds (e. g., thiophenes) may be tolerated in some cases (357). Organic nitrogen and chlorine compounds inhibit the activity of Raney nickel catalyst.

Platinum. Probably the first satisfactory catalyst for organic hydrogenations was platinum black, described by Loew (386). This material, still widely used, can be prepared by treating a dilute hydrochloric acid solution of platinum chloride (chloroplatinic acid, H_2PtCl_6) with formaldehyde and strong alkali. The precipitated platinum black is washed and stored under distilled water. Improved procedural details for this preparation have been given by Willstätter (667,668) and by Feulgen (187). The catalyst is fairly active, especially when fresh, catalyzing the hydrogenation of aromatics as well as olefins.

A catalyst prepared by suspending activated carbon in water, adding platinum chloride solution, and reducing with hydrazine in alkaline solution was described by Kaffer (314). A similar preparation, containing 8 to 10% platinum on activated carbon, was used by de Kok, Waterman, and van Westen (357) for determination of unsaturation in hydrocarbons, fatty acids and esters, and tung oil. Olefinic materials are hydrogenated at ordinary pressure and in most cases at room temperature quite rapidly. Aromatic compounds can be hydrogenated, but at a much lower rate, such that selective hydrogenation of olefins in the presence of aromatics, or of only the ethylenic side chain in styrene, is possible. Silica gel and other materials also have been used to support the platinum.

Platinum Oxide. A very active oxide of platinum prepared by the fusion of platinum chloride with sodium nitrate was discovered by Voorhees and Adams (630). The optimum fusion temperature for preparation of the catalyst was found to be at about 500°C. (2). After fusion, the mixture is cooled and the oxide is washed and dried. This catalyst, known as Adams platinum oxide and having the composition $PtO_2.H_2O$, was found to have far greater activity than other platinum oxides obtained by various methods (630). The catalyst has been used for preparative reductions of various oxygen-containing compounds such as phenols, pyridine derivatives, aldehydes, and ketones. It is reduced to platinum black by the action of hydrogen. For analytical hydrogenation of olefins it is usually used in the reduced form.

Palladium. Palladium black catalyst can be prepared by reduction of palladous chloride with formaldehyde and alkali. This material is a milder catalyst than platinum black prepared by a similar procedure.

A palladium-on-charcoal catalyst, prepared by reduction of palladous chloride with hydrazine, in a manner similar to the preparation of platinum on charcoal, was described by de Kok, Waterman, and van Westen (357). Another method for preparation, involving hydrogenation of a suspension of activated carbon in palladous chloride solution under 35 p. s. i. pressure, was used by Ogg and Cooper (470). This type of catalyst also can be obtained commercially with various palladium contents. Palladium on charcoal is one of the most widely used catalysts for analytical hydrogenations. Aromatic compounds are not hydrogenated at room temperature and atmospheric pressure, permitting selective hydrogenation of olefinic double bonds.

Nickel. Catalysts consisting of nickel deposited from nickel nitrate solution on clay chips, asbestos, kieselguhr, etc., and reduced with hydrogen at incandescence, have been rather extensively used for preparative hydrogenations. Most unsaturated materials, including aromatics, can be completely hydrogenated with such catalysts at 175–200°C. and 1000–2000 p. s. i. hydrogen pressure. Raney nickel, a nickel–aluminum alloy, is commercially available. Before use, the aluminum is dissolved out with alkali. The residual nickel should be stored under alcohol. With Raney nickel, selective hydrogenation of olefins in the presence of many aromatic compounds can be accomplished near room temperature and atmospheric pressure. At higher temperatures (e.g., 100–125°C.) and pressures, however, aromatics may be completely hydrogenated.

Copper Chromite and Other Catalysts. Although occasionally used preparatively for selective hydrogenation of olefins in the presence of aromatics and for hydrogenolysis of oxygenated compounds, copper chromite has seldom been used for analytical hydrogenations because it usually required high hydrogen pressures. Oxides of copper, chromium, zinc, and molybdenum have catalytic activity but require high temperatures and are rapidly deactivated. Cobalt, iron, and various other substances have catalytic activity but apparently have not been used in analytical procedures.

(2) Hydrogen. The hydrogen employed must be free from oxygen and hydrogen sulfide. Electrolytic hydrogen, from a compressed gas cylinder or from a Kipp generator, usually is satisfactory with little or no purification. For highest accuracy and with impure hydrogen, it is advisable to pass the hydrogen through a train of wash bottles containing sodium plumbite solution, potassium permanganate solution, and concentrated sulfuric acid, then through a drying tube, and/or to pass the hydrogen over heated copper wire or platinum (or palladium) on asbestos.

(3) **Solvents.** Many different solvents have been employed in hydrogenation methods. In some cases, no solvent is required, especially if the sample is a liquid of low viscosity and a fairly large quantity of sample can be employed. Glacial acetic acid is the most frequently used solvent, but ethers, dioxane, alcohols, esters, saturated cyclic hydrocarbons, chloroform, and other solvents also have been employed. The rate of hydrogenation may vary widely, depending on the solvent. Pesez and Poirier (482) reported the relative rates of hydrogenation of sorbic acid in the presence of platinum to be as follows:

Solvent	Relative rate	Solvent	Relative rate
Acetic acid	1.00	Chloroform	0.45
Methanol	0.65	Cyclohexane	0.40
Ethanol	0.65	Dioxane	0.20

These results show the rate-increasing effect of a proton-providing solvent such as acetic acid. Also, the addition of a very small quantity of hydrochloric acid has been found to increase the rate of hydrogenation in neutral solvents (85). Dioxane has been reported to inhibit the hydrogenation of aromatic rings (399). The low rate for hydrogenation of sorbic acid in dioxane (above) indicates that this effect is probably quite general; dioxane is a fairly good proton acceptor. However, because of its excellent solvent properties, dioxane is often an excellent choice as a solvent for hydrogenation of olefinic double bonds in many solid materials, including polymers.

B. APPARATUS

For accurate quantitative work, reliable apparatus is necessary. Several of the published apparatus descriptions have been collected by Roth (543). Simple Warburg manometers were used by some of the early investigators (163,633,666) to measure hydrogen consumption. In order to obtain better accuracy (± 0.5 to 2%), Hyde and Scherp (283) and Kuhn and Möller (366) used modified manometric apparatus with differential manometers and compensating flasks. One early apparatus (642), subsequently improved (357), involved pumping off the unconsumed hydrogen into a measuring buret, and was suitable for volatile samples.

One of the first volumetric micro hydrogenation apparatus was reported by Smith (589); a compensation flask and a differential manometer were employed. Later refinements (79,585) gave improved accuracy but resulted in rather complicated apparatus. Further improvements in this type of apparatus have been described (294,295,496,553).

Simplified apparatus without compensation flask or differential manometer were in early use (180,323,422,692) for semimicro quantities of sam-

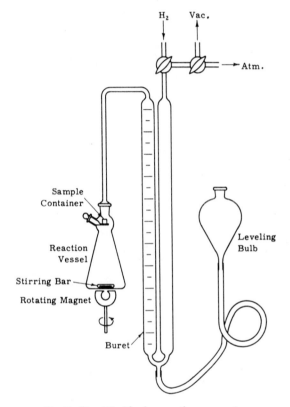

Fig. 2. Simplified hydrogenation apparatus.

ple (5 to 50 ml. of hydrogen absorbed). Significant improvements in micro scale hydrogenation apparatus (1 to 5 ml. of hydrogen absorbed) of this type have been contributed by Weygand and Werner (657) and Johns and Seiferle (307). Most modern micro- and semimicro apparatus are of this type, but vary considerably in details of construction. Depending on the scale of operations and the features preferred by the apparatus designer, various techniques have been devised to obtain agitation, provide for delayed introduction of sample (after saturating the catalyst and solvent with hydrogen), prevent leakage, maintain simplicity of operation, etc. The general appearance of the principal features adopted by several investigators is shown in Figure 2. The Weygand and Werner micro apparatus, with improvements by Ogg and Cooper (470) and Pesez and Poirier (482), and similar semimicro and macro apparatus, with 25 to 500 ml. gas burets, described by Noller and Barusch (459), Joshel (312), and Pack and Planck (474), are basically of this type, employing rotating magnetic stirrers. Other magnetically operated stirring devices have been described (193, 625,688). The Johns and Seiferle micro apparatus, with improvements by Colson (111), employs a similar gas-measuring arrangement, but provides for preflushing by passing hydrogen directly through the assembly and out a vent in the sample-holding arm of the reaction vessel, and requires shaking the entire apparatus, mounted on a board, to obtain agitation. Shaking to avoid possible dead spots also is preferred by Parrette (478), whose macro apparatus provides for connecting the reaction vessel to the gas-measuring system by means of a mercury-sealed flexible coupling. In order to minimize the number of connections at which leakage of hydrogen might occur, magnetically operated devices for delayed addition of sample have been employed (312,553). To avoid temperature changes, the entire apparatus may be enclosed in a cabinet maintained near room temperature by means of an electric heater, regulator, and fan (111). Constructional details of the above apparatus features are given in the original articles. The Ogg and Cooper micro apparatus (470), using a 7 ml. gas buret, is commercially available (29).

The apparatus referred to in the preceding paragraph are relatively simple to construct and operate. In most cases, the total hydrogen consumed can be determined with a precision of approximately 1 to 2%. For measurement of hydrogenation rates, Vandenheuvel (625) has described an apparatus employing an efficient plunger-stirrer rapidly oscillated by a magnet, and including a thermostatic water bath and an automatic leveling mechanism actuated by a differential manometer. With the steady agitation, and thermostatic and isobaric conditions provided by this apparatus, reliable hydrogenation rate data were obtained, and a precision of approximately ±0.3% for the hydrogenation value of fumaric acid was found.

For analytical hydrogenations at pressures up to 5 atmospheres, Gould and Drake (221) have described a macro apparatus wherein a metal syringe replaces the manometer.

C. PROCEDURE

With the type of apparatus shown in Figure 2, only a few simple operations are required to measure the quantity of hydrogen consumed by an unsaturated material.

The catalyst and solvent are introduced into the reaction vessel. A suitable portion of sample is weighed into the sample container, which is then placed in position isolated from the catalyst and solvent. Volatile samples should be sealed in a thin-walled tube, and provision made for breaking the container when desired. With the leveling liquid (usually mercury) lowered below the junction of the buret and leveling tube, the apparatus is filled with hydrogen by successively evacuating and admitting hydrogen five or six times. (In apparatus designed to permit direct flow-through of hydrogen, the apparatus is flushed with a stream of hydrogen for several minutes.) Before admission to the apparatus, the hydrogen should be bubbled through a scrubber containing the same solvent as used in the reaction flask in order to reduce the time necessary to saturate the atmosphere in the apparatus.

With the buret full of hydrogen, a small amount is carefully bled off to the vacuum, such that, when the leveling liquid is raised, the pressure in the reactor side of the apparatus will be equal to atmospheric pressure. (In apparatus designed for direct hydrogen flow-through, the pressure can be equalized after raising the leveling liquid by briefly opening the outlet in the arm of the reaction vessel.) Subsequent readings are made with the leveling leg of the buret open to the atmosphere.

The solvent and catalyst are stirred until saturated, as indicated by no further decrease in hydrogen volume. The stirrer is stopped and the system is allowed to come to thermal equilibrium. The buret reading, temperature, and atmospheric pressure are recorded.

The sample is then brought into contact with the solvent and catalyst, and the mixture is stirred until the consumption of hydrogen ceases. Buret reading, temperature, and atmospheric pressure are again recorded after thermal equilibrium is obtained.

In order to decrease the time necessary to complete the hydrogenation of slowly reacting samples, it may be desirable to increase the temperature of the reaction mixture. According to Smith, Alderman, and Nadig (588), the hydrogenation rate of phenylacetic acid is increased 5% per degree rise in temperature at 30°C.

The hydrogenation value is calculated from the volume of hydrogen consumed, corrected for the vapor pressure of the solvent at the temperature employed, and converted to standard temperature and pressure. Hydrogen deviates only slightly from the ideal gas law; 1 mole (2.016 grams) occupies 22.43 liters at 0°C. and 760 mm. of mercury. The result may be expressed in various ways, e. g., moles of hydrogen consumed per 100 grams of sample, grams of hydrogen consumed per 100 grams of sample, or grams of sample reacting with one mole of hydrogen ("hydrogen number"). The theoretical "hydrogen number" is equal to the molecular weight divided by the number of double bonds per molecule. For comparison with halogenation results, the hydrogenation value of animal and vegetable oils and various other materials occasionally is expressed as the equivalent halogenation number. The moles of hydrogen consumed per 100 grams of sample is multiplied by 160 to give the "hydrogen bromine number" or by 254 to give the "hydrogen iodine number."

D. APPLICATIONS

Hydrogenation rates vary considerably from one compound to another. It therefore becomes necessary to establish conditions under which the reaction can be made to go to completion within a reasonable length of time. In contrast to chemical reduction with sodium or zinc, which results in hydrogenation of conjugated systems only, catalytic hydrogenation often occurs more readily with simple monoolefins than with conjugated olefins or α,β-unsaturated carbonyl compounds. Aromatic double bonds are the most difficult to hydrogenate. In general, monosubstituted olefins are hydrogenated very rapidly, disubstituted olefins more slowly, and tri- and tetrasubstituted olefins still more slowly. The *cis* form of an olefinic compound usually is more readily hydrogenated than the *trans* form. The presence of aromatic or carboxyl groups in the molecule also tend to decrease the hydrogenation rate. These generalizations do not always hold, however, for several exceptions have been observed.

For selective hydrogenation, the type of catalyst, solvent, temperature, and pressure must be chosen so as to obtain the desired reaction without hydrogenation of other reducible groups. Palladium-on-charcoal appears to be the best catalyst for selective hydrogenation of ethylenic double bonds in the presence of aromatics. It may not always be possible to hydrogenate completely rather slowly reacting compounds such as polyenes without partially hydrogenating other materials that react at an even slower rate. However, the progress of a selective hydrogenation often can be followed by observation of changes in the rate at which hydrogen is consumed.

Some carbonyl and epoxy compounds may interfere, and certain methylol benzenes and benzyl amines may interfere by being reduced to the corresponding toluenes.

One advantage of hydrogenation as an analytical method is the possibility of recovering the hydrogenated sample for further investigation after separating the catalyst (345) and the solvent, if any, from the reaction mixture. This feature of the method has been used to aid in the characterization of various unsaturated hydrocarbons (638,639,644,645) and acids (637). A disadvantage of hydrogenation as a routine analytical method is the time required to make a determination. Rather long reaction times may be required and, in contrast to most other methods (e. g., halogenation), it is not practical to react several samples simultaneously unless a separate apparatus is provided for each sample. Consequently, the man-hours required per determination by hydrogenation is relatively high.

A large number of results on hydrogenations of olefinic materials have been described in the analytical literature. Various hydrogenation results on pure compounds are summarized in Table XVI. The results shown are typical but represent only a small portion of the materials for which analytical hydrogenation has been employed.

One important early analytical application was the complete hydrogenation of all eleven double bonds in carotene by Zechmeister, Cholnoky, and Vrabély (695). Others also employed hydrogenation to analyze carotenoid pigments (366,585,589), chlorophyll derivatives (283), enzymes (633), steroids (585), and other biological materials. The method has been found useful for the analysis of vegetable oils such as linseed, oiticica, and essang oils (323) and imported and domestic tung oils (475), and for the analysis of terpenes (313), petroleum products, and polymers.

Hydrogenation also has been used for determination of unsaturation in hydrocarbon gas mixtures (117,400,523,569a,572).

3. Oxidation

Although the ready oxidizability of the olefinic double bond was recognized early and reactions of this class have been used widely in preparative work, relatively few analytical methods based on the oxidation of the double bond have been developed. In the following discussion, these methods are grouped according to the oxidizing agent used under peracids, ozone, potassium permanganate, and osmium tetroxide. Of course, the wider reactivity of oxidizing agents than that of other reagents for the ethylenic linkage places an evident restriction on these methods. Therefore, most of these methods are quite specific in nature and are designed for the determination of the double bond in a characteristic position (e. g., propylidene group, external, or internal double bond only). Of the smaller number of methods intended for more general applicability, the rather recent titrimetric ozone procedure of Boer and Kooyman promises to be one of the most reliable methods for unsaturation analysis (61).

TABLE XVI

Hydrogenation Results on Various Olefinic Compounds

Unsaturated compound	Sample wt., mg.	Solvent	Catalyst	No. of double bonds		Ref.
				Present	Found[a]	
Hydrocarbons						
Pentene[b]	ca. 700	None	Pd on C	1	1.00, 1.02	(644)
n-1-Hexene	ca. 1 g.	None	Pd on C	1	1.01, 1.01	(638)
n-1-Heptene	ca. 1 g.	None	Pd on C	1	1.01, 0.99	(638)
n-1-Octene	ca. 1 g.	None	Pd on C	1	1.01, 1.00	(639)
n-Decene	ca. 1 g.	None	Pd on C	1	1.01–1.02(3)	(644)
n-Hexadecene	ca. 2 g.	None	Pd on C	1	0.99–1.01(3)	(644)
Cyclohexene	3–5	Methanol	Adams PtO_2	1	0.99–1.01(12)	(111)
α-Pinene	ca. 800	None	Pd on C	1	1.00, 1.01	(645)
	ca. 500	Acetic acid	Pd on ZrO_2	1	0.99	(313)
	ca. 500	Acetic acid	Adams PtO_2	1	1.03	(313)
β-Pinene	1.5 g.	None	Pd on C	1	1.00[c]	(644)
	ca. 500	Acetic acid	Pd on ZrO_2	1	1.00	(313)
	ca. 500	Acetic acid	Adams PtO_2	1	0.99	(313)
Isoprene	ca. 300	None	Pd on C	2	1.97, 2.02	(645)
2,4-Dimethyl-1,3-pentadiene	ca. 500	None	Pd on C	2	2.04, 2.02	(638)
2,6-Dimethylhepta-diene (nonconj.)	ca. 500	None	Pd on C	2	2.04, 2.00	(638)
Limonene	31, 39	Acetic acid	Pd	2	2.06, 2.02	(692)

Hydrocarbons (*continued*)

Unsaturated compound	Sample wt., mg.	Solvent	Catalyst	No. of double bonds		Ref.
				Present	Found[a]	
Dipentene.............	ca. 200	Acetic acid	Pd on ZrO_2	2	1.90	(313)
	ca. 200	Acetic acid	Adams PtO_2	2	1.99	(313)
Dihydromyrcene.......	ca. 200	Acetic acid	Pd on ZrO_2	2	1.96	(313)
	ca. 200	Acetic acid	Adams PtO_2	2	1.95	(313)
Myrcene..............	ca. 150	Acetic acid	Pd on ZrO_2	3	2.98	(313)
	ca. 150	Acetic acid	Adams PtO_2	3	2.93	(313)
Alloocimene..........	ca. 150	Acetic acid	Pd on ZrO_2	3	2.91	(313)
	ca. 150	Acetic acid	Adams PtO_2	3	2.90	(313)
β-Carotene...........	29	Acetic acid	Pd	11	10.95	(692)
	27, 39	Acetic acid	Pt on SiO_2	11	11.15, 11.13	(692)
Lycopene.............	30	Acetic acid	Pd	13	12.92	(692)
Styrene..............	ca. 1 g.	None	Pd on C	1	1.01	(639)
	ca. 1 g.	None	Pt on C	4[d]	3.98, 4.04[e]	(639)
trans-Stilbene........	31–35	No. 30 alcohol	Pd on C	1	1.01–1.03(5)	(553)
Stilbene.............	4	Acetic acid	Adams PtO_2	7[d]	7.08	(657)
Diphenylbutadiene.....	5	Acetic acid	Adams PtO_2	8[d]	8.00	(657)

Table continued

TABLE XVI (*continued*)

Unsaturated compound	Sample wt., mg.	Solvent	Catalyst	No. of double bonds		Ref.
				Present	Found^a	
Alcohols						
Terpineol............	ca. 500	Acetic acid	Pd on ZrO$_2$	1	1.01	(313)
	ca. 500	Acetic acid	Adams PtO$_2$	1	1.00	(313)
Pinocarveol...........	ca. 500	Acetic acid	Pd on ZrO$_2$	1	0.94	(313)
	ca. 500	Acetic acid	Adams PtO$_2$	1	0.99	(313)
Lutein..............	39, 43	Acetic acid	Pd	11	11.08, 11.07	(692)
Zeaxanthin..........	30, 40	Acetic acid	Pd	11	10.99, 10.93	(692)
Lycoxanthin..........	28	Acetic acid	Pd	13	12.89	(692)
Acids						
Crotonic............	4	Acetic acid	Adams PtO$_2$	1	1.00	(657)
Fumaric............	4	Acetic acid	Adams PtO$_2$	1	1.00	(657)
	5	Ethanol	Adams PtO$_2$	1	0.98	(314)
	74	Acetic acid	Pd	1	1.12	(692)
	74	Acetic acid	Pt on SiO$_2$	1	1.03	(692)
Maleic.............	5-260	95% ethanol	Adams PtO$_2$	1	0.996-1.005(30)	(625)
	7-13	Acetic acid	Adams PtO$_2$	1	0.98-1.00(3)	(496)
	ca. 20	Acetic acid	Pd on C	1	0.99-1.01(10)	(470)
	ca. 200	Acetic acid	Adams PtO$_2$	1	0.99	(475)
Citraconic...........	4	Acetic acid	Adams PtO$_2$	1	1.02	(657)
Oleic..............	58, 80	Acetic acid	Pd	1	0.98, 1.02	(692)
Elaidic.............	4	Acetic acid	Adams PtO$_2$	1	1.00	(657)
	40	Acetic acid	Pt or Pd	1	0.98, 0.98	(323)
	2 g.	None	Pd on C	1	0.99, 1.02	(637)

Acids (continued)

Unsaturated compound	Sample wt., mg.	Solvent	Catalyst	No. of double bonds Present	No. of double bonds Found[a]	Ref.
Erucic	4	Acetic acid	Adams PtO$_2$	1	0.99	(657)
Sorbic	3–4	Acetic acid	Adams PtO$_2$	2	1.93–2.00(3)	(111, 657)
	3–4	Methanol	Adams PtO$_2$	2	1.93–2.02(8)	(111)
Linoleic	ca. 35	Acetic acid	Pt or Pd	2	1.99, 2.01	(323)
9,11-Linoleic	ca. 25	Acetic acid	Pd on C	2	2.00, 2.01	(470)
9,12-Linoleic	1 g.	None	Pd on C	2	2.06, 2.03	(637)
10,12-Linoleic	ca. 25	Acetic acid	Pd on C	2	1.99, 2.00	(470)
Linolenic	ca. 20	Acetic acid	Pt or Pd	3	2.94, 2.95	(323)
β-Licanic	ca. 20	Acetic acid	Pt or Pd	3	2.99, 2.98	(323)
Cinnamic	7, 8	Methanol	Adams PtO$_2$	1	0.99, 1.01	(111)
	15–40	No. 30 alcohol	Raney Ni	1	0.99–1.01(4)	(553)
	18–20	No. 30 alcohol	Pd on C	1	0.99–1.02(4)	(553)
	0.5–1 g.	Ethanol	Raney Ni	1	1.00–1.02(3)	(221)
	1 g.	DMF[f]	Raney Ni	1	1.00	(221)
α-Eleostearic	5, 12	Acetic acid	Adams PtO$_2$	4[d]	4.00, 4.00	(496, 657)
β-Eleostearic	ca. 200	Acetic acid	Adams PtO$_2$	3	2.97	(475)
β-Eleostearic	ca. 200	Acetic acid	Adams PtO$_2$	3	2.97	(475)

Table continued

TABLE XVI (*continued*)

Unsaturated compound	Sample wt., mg.	Solvent	Catalyst	No. of double bonds		Ref.
				Present	Found[a]	
Esters						
Dimethyl fumarate......	ca. 200	Acetic acid	Adams PtO₂	1	1.00	(475)
Dimethyl maleate......	ca. 200	Acetic acid	Adams PtO₂	1	1.00	(475)
Diethyl maleate.......	28–35	No. 30 alcohol	Pd on C	1	1.00–1.01(5)	(553)
Methyl oleate.........	ca. 40	Acetic acid	Pd on C	1	1.00, 1.01	(470)
Ethyl oleate..........	ca. 2 g.	None	Pd on C	1	0.99	(357)
Methyl linoleate......	ca. 20	Acetic acid	Pd on C	2	1.98–2.01(3)	(470)
Same, alkali isomerized	ca. 20	Acetic acid	Pd on C	2	1.99–2.00(3)	(470)
Ethyl eleostearate.....	ca. 1 g.	None	Pd on C	3	2.99	(640)
Miscellaneous						
Hendecene-10-amide...	ca. 30	Acetic acid	Pd on C	1	1.00, 1.00	(470)
Deaminocolchicinic anhydride...........	7–62	Acetic acid	Pd on C	2	0.98–1.00(3)	(553)
Colchicine...........	21, 28	Acetic acid	Pd on C	3	2.12, 2.25	(553)
Colchiceine..........	26	Acetic acid	Pd on C	3	1.82[g]	(553)
Colchiceine amide......	8–29	Acetic acid	Adams PtO₂	3	3.41–3.65(4)	(553)
	17–31	Acetic acid	Adams PtO₂	3	3.02–3.42(3)	(553)
Bixin...............	3	Ethyl acetate	Adams PtO₂	9	9.02	(657)
	38, 52	Acetic acid	Pd	9	9.08, 9.00	(692)
Capsanthin..........	33	Acetic acid	Pt on SiO₂	10	10.08	(692)
	31	Acetic acid	Pt on SiO₂	11[h]	11.11	(692)

[a] Number in parentheses indicates the number of replicate determinations.
[b] Mainly 1-methyl-2-butene.
[c] Slow reaction near room temperature over several days.
[d] Including benzene ring(s).
[e] Slow reaction over several hours.
[f] Dimethyl formamide.
[g] Total, end of 12 days.
[h] Including the ketone group.

A. PERACIDS

The reaction of an organic peracid with an ethylenic compound yields an α-epoxide, which may be converted to a hydroxy ester or, in the presence of water, to the corresponding glycol:

$$-\overset{|}{C}=\overset{|}{C}- + RCO_3H \longrightarrow -\overset{|}{C}\underset{\diagdown O \diagup}{}\overset{|}{C}- + RCOOH \longrightarrow -\overset{|}{\underset{OH}{C}}-\overset{|}{\underset{OCOR}{C}}-$$

$$\Big\downarrow H_2O$$

$$-\overset{|}{\underset{OH}{C}}-\overset{|}{\underset{OH}{C}}-$$

The relative quantities of these products depend upon the peracid used and the conditions of the reaction.

The reaction has been studied extensively and numerous preparative uses have been reported (608). It proceeds smoothly and quantitatively with many unsaturated compounds. The ease of oxidation, however, is markedly dependent on the nature of substituents on the carbon atoms joined by the double bond. Oxidation of internal isolated double bonds, such as present in most fatty acids and oils, occurs easily in 2 to 4 hours, as compared with 2 to 3 days under the same conditions for terminally unsaturated compounds, such as 1-tetradecene, 1-octadecene, etc. Also, in compounds such as isoprene, the more substituted double bond is attacked first, in spite of the greater steric hindrance. Crotonic acid reacts slowly, while maleic and fumaric acids fail to react.

These rate differences are successfully explained by assuming that the active oxygen from the peracid molecule is cationoid and approaches the anionoid ethylenic bond very much in the same manner as the positively charged component of a halogen molecule (607). Thus alkyl or phenyl substitution increases the reactivity of a double bond, while electron-attracting carbonyl or carboxyl groups attached, or in close proximity, to the double bond decrease the rate of reaction.

Recognition of the favorable features of this reaction (500) prompted numerous analytical investigations. In general, these methods involved the addition of an excess of the reagent to the solution of the unsaturated material in an inert solvent (e. g., chloroform) at a low temperature and, after the reaction was completed, the iodometric back-titration of the unreacted portion of the peracid.

It is essential to the success of these methods that easily oxidizable configurations be absent from the olefinic sample. Benzene and some of its lower homologs are not attacked, but naphthalene, phenanthrene, and anthracene, as well as organic sulfides and mercaptans, are readily oxidized. Aldehydes, phenols, amines, and azo compounds also undergo oxidation (606). The extent of these interfering reactions, however, has not been studied systematically under the actual conditions of any of the analytical methods reported in the literature. Long reaction times, however, which may be necessary for a general method to yield quantitative conversion of all double bonds should be considered a definite disadvantage. Stability of the peracids used is another problem to consider. Short-chain aliphatic organic peracids (performic, peracetic, perpropionic acids), especially in solutions, possess satisfactory stability for safe handling in routine analytical manipulations.

(1) **Perbenzoic Acid.** Of the peracids used, perbenzoic acid gained the greatest popularity because of its relative stability in anhydrous solvents, and greater ease of handling. It was found to give quantitative results for a number of straight-chain, branched, and cyclic olefins (453) and terpenes (424,519,547). It was also used to measure the olefinic unsaturation in dearomatized cracked petroleum products (454) for which the determination of halogen values was stated to be unreliable.

The oxidation of rubber by perbenzoic acid was also studied and was found to be both rapid and quantitative with one perbenzoic acid molecule disappearing for each double bond (502).

The difference in reaction rates of internal and external double bonds is utilized in several perbenzoic acid methods designed to study the extent of 1,2- and 1,4-addition in synthetic rubber polymers. The method of the German rubber industry (652) employed calibration curves, constructed from the peracid values of low molecular weight compounds with known structures, and assumed equivalent addition rates for large polymer molecules.

Kolthoff and Lee (360) utilized this difference in reaction rates of internal and external double bonds to measure the number of vinyl groups in a variety of rubber polymers and copolymers. First the total concentration of double bonds is determined by using a modified version of the iodine monochloride method of Kemp and Peters (338); then, keeping the initial concentration of perbenzoic acid at a defined value, the external double bond content is estimated from a calibration curve. The calibration curve was obtained from determinations made on a series of oleic acid–undecylenic acid mixtures. The amount of peracid consumed is determined by back-titration of the excess after 4.5 and 7 hours for butadiene and poly-isoprene polymers, respectively. For samples of the first type, the reaction was carried out at 25°C.; the latter types with a markedly higher rate constant required a reaction temperature of 0°C.

Difficulties in the interpretation of results arose only in the case of sodium polyisoprene, which contains the grouping, $R(CH_3)C=CH_2$, characteristic of the less common 3,4-addition. This vinyl group adds perbenzoic acid approximately 30 times faster than the external double bond of the $R—CH-=CH_2$ type, resulting from 1,2-addition.

The method is also applicable to the determination of external double bonds in low molecular weight compounds or mixtures.

Saffer and Johnson (548) proposed an extrapolation procedure (to zero time) to determine the internal double bonds in polymers. Under the conditions of the reaction, the internal double bonds were expected to be saturated in about 10 hours; the addition rate curve beyond this time was accepted as a measure of the external double bond reaction. The extrapolation of the 17 to 24 hour portion of the curve, obtained by analyzing three or four aliquots of the reaction mixture, gives the internal double bond content. Using a low excess of perbenzoic acid in chloroform solution and carrying out the reaction at 6°C., about 1% accuracy was obtained on oleic acid–10-undecylenic acid mixtures containing 70% or more internal double bonds. Measurements on a variety of polymer samples were duplicated with a precision of 1%. However, the method is not applicable to systems containing less than 70% internal double bonds.

Directions given by Braun (76), as modified by Swern (608) and Kolthoff, Lee, and Mairs (361), are probably the most satisfactory for the preparation of stable solutions of perbenzoic acid. In brief this procedure consists of: (a) reacting benzoyl peroxide with sodium methoxide in a solvent mixture of chloroform and methanol, (b) contacting the sodium perbenzoate formed with water, and, after (c) acidifying with sulfuric acid, (d) extracting the perbenzoic acid with an organic solvent.

Pure chloroform has been used as a solvent for perbenzoic acid reactions in almost all of the work reported in the literature. However, the apparently good stability reported for chloroform solutions was established by iodometric titration, which does not distinguish between perbenzoic acid itself and oxidizing agents formed during storage; the latter are capable of not only balancing the decomposition of the acid but actually increasing the iodometric titer of the solution (361). Kolthoff, Lee, and Mairs found that benzene, when present to the extent of 10%, entirely prevents the formation of these oxidizing agents, and recommended benzene or chloroform–benzene mixtures as solvents for perbenzoic acid. For greater stability, benzene solutions should be stored in the dark at 5 to 10°C.; the reactivity under these conditions has been found to remain constant over a period of about a month. As a sample solvent or reagent diluent, purified benzene is preferable to other grades, but since the reaction with the impurity is rapid the use of other grades should not cause an error, provided neither the blank nor the sample is titrated sooner than two hours after the stock solution is added.

It is therefore a satisfactory analytical procedure to dissolve the unsaturated compound under investigation in purified chloroform (washed with concentrated sulfuric acid, neutralized, and dried) and add a portion (about 10% by volume) of the benzene stock solution of the reagent. The rate of reaction in the presence of 10% benzene is only somewhat slower than in chloroform alone.

For analytical purposes normalities of 0.5 to 1.0 (0.25 to 0.5 M) are recommended. In an actual determination of unsaturation, a measured volume of the standard solution is usually added to a solution of the sample so that the initial concentration of perbenzoic acid in the reaction mixture is 0.05 to 0.1 N.

Perbenzoic acid in an organic solvent can be determined iodometrically by shaking the solution with an aqueous solution of potassium iodide and titrating the liberated iodine with standard sodium thiosulfate solution to the starch end point. The end point is stable.

Analytical data shown in Table XVII were obtained by Boer and Kooyman (61). The agreement with the theoretical values seems only fair for the majority of the hydrocarbons tested. Their method does not seem to be applicable to nonhydrocarbons.

(2) **Other Peracids.** Performic, peracetic, perpropionic, percamphoric, and perfuroic acids have also been tested in the course of a search for a more stable and more rapidly acting oxidation reagent. However, none of these acids seems to have shown any definite advantage over perbenzoic acid, although their analytical application to various unsaturated compounds in many cases produced satisfactory results. Thus, Smit (587) obtained good agreement with Wijs values using peracetic acid on a number of unsaturated fatty acids and esters and on several vegetable oils. Herzenberg (257) determined unsaturation of several synthetic mixtures of hydrocarbons by means of perpropionic acid. His results were within 3% of the actual amount of unsaturates in the mixture. Percamphoric acid was prepared and tested by Milas and Cliff (437); these authors obtained 98 to 100% addition to a number of unsaturated compounds of wide variety. Milas

TABLE XVII

Analytical Data by Perbenzoic Acid Oxidation (61)

Compound[a]	Unsaturation, expressed in Br No.		
	Theor.	Found	% of theory
1-Hexene	190	181	95.3
2-Hexene	190	193	101.6
1-Heptene	163	153	93.9
3-Heptene	163	170	104.3
Cetene	71.5	64	89.5
2-Methyl-2-butene	228	253	111.0
3,3-Dimethyl-1-butene	190	227	119.5
2,2,4-Trimethyl-1-pentene	143	143	100.0
2,2,4-Trimethyl-2-pentene	143	143	100.0
Diisobutylene	143	146	102.1
2,2,5,5-Tetramethyl-3-hexene	114	118	103.5
2-Methyl-1-undecene	95.3	96	100.7
2,3-Dimethyl-1,3-butadiene	391	448	114.6
Cyclopentene	235	264	112.3
1-Propyl-1-cyclopentene	145	146.5	101.0
Dicyclopentadiene	242	235	97.1
Cyclohexene	195	202	103.6
Limonene	235	228	97.0
Allyl alcohol	276	183	66
Methallyl alcohol	222	224	101
Allyl chloride	209	10.5	5
Methallyl chloride	177	82.5	47
Allyl acetate	160	15	9
Diallyl ether	326	80	25

[a] Purity doubtful in some cases.

and McAlevy (438) also tried perfuroic acid, but the results were not quantitative in many cases. Böhme and Steinke (60) used monoperphthalic acid for the oxidation of oleic acid, elaidic acid, "triolein," and several vegetable oils. Quantitative or nearly quantitative results were obtained with the pure compounds containing isolated double bonds at 20°C. in 1 to 2 days reaction time, but with natural oils known to contain conjugated double bonds the results were low (compared to Kaufmann iodine values). A conjugated C_{18} acid reacted only to the extent of 50%.

Peroxytrifluoroacetic acid has recently been reported as a novel reagent for the oxidation of the olefinic double bond (176). Prepared from trifluoroacetic anhydride and 90% hydrogen peroxide in methylene chloride, peroxytrifluoroacetic acid reacted almost instantly even at ice temperature with a variety of olefins, including those with electronegative substituents.

The products obtained are hydroxytrifluoroacetates, which are readily converted to glycols by methanolysis. The formation of some high-boiling contaminants was prevented by adding triethylammonium trifluoroacetate to the solvent (177)

B. OZONE

Ethylenic bonds are readily attacked by ozone, with the result that the double bond is ruptured and the fragments of the original olefin appear as aldehydes, ketones, or acids in the reaction mixture. The following mechanism for this degradation process (ozonolysis) was suggested by Criegee (125):

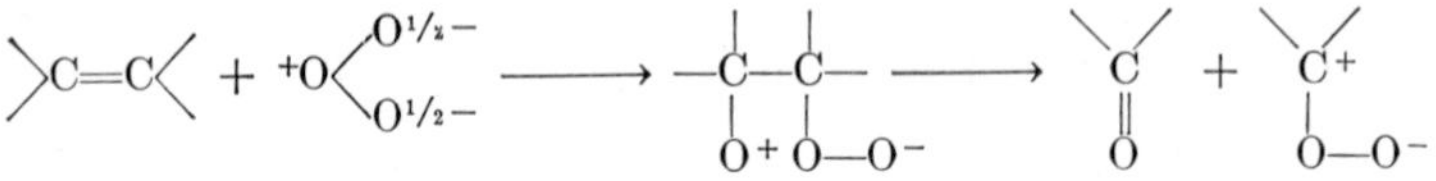

The "zwitterion" formed in the second step then undergoes a variety of reactions to yield an aldehyde, a ketone, or an acid. A cyclic ozonide structure:

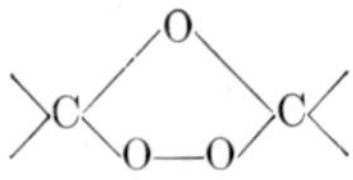

previously proposed as an intermediate, could form from the carbonylic fragment and the zwitterion only in nonaqueous systems and only when the double bond is part of a five-membered ring. These reactions seem to be perfectly general in nature and are fairly selective for olefins (126,389).

There are various configurations that have a marked effect on the course of the reaction. Ozone reacts most rapidly with isolated open-chain ethylenic linkages. It reacts quantitatively with conjugated systems, but one of the double bonds is oxidized rapidly, the others at a considerably slower rate. Allenic double bonds, which are not attacked by permanganate oxidation, can be ozonized and determined from the carbon dioxide formed as a cleavage product (64):

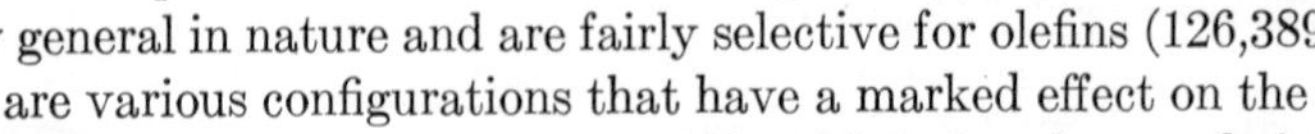

$$>C{=}C{=}C< \xrightarrow{2O_3\ +\ 2H_2O} >C{=}O + CO_2 + O{=}C< + 2H_2O_2$$

The rate of ozone addition is decreased when electronegative groups are adjacent, or attached, to the doubly bound carbon atoms (460).

Acetylenic and, at a markedly lower rate, aromatic bonds are also attacked by ozone, the products of ozonolysis being monobasic and dibasic acids, respectively (663). Organic acids and primary and secondary amines are not attacked, but alcohols, aldehydes, ketones, the C=N bond, and especially ethers are very reactive toward ozone.

Incorrect indications of the position of a double bond by means of ozonolysis seldom occur. However, the observations of Knights and Waight (353a) and others indicate that structures containing a hydroxyl, amino or alkoxyl group on the carbon atom adjacent to one of the olefinic carbon atoms follow an abnormal course of reaction. Thus, Knights and Waight found that compounds of the type $RR'C$=$CHCH_2OH$ (e. g., geraniol, 3-methyl-2-buten-1-ol) and, to a lesser extent, the type RCH=$CHCH_2OH$ (e. g., 2-buten-1-ol) produce formaldehyde even though there is no CH_2=$C\big\langle$ group present. Moreover, compounds of the type CH_2=$CHCH(OH)R$ (e. g., linalool, 1-penten-3-ol, 1-octen-3-ol) were found to give less than the theoretical proportion of formaldehyde (see also Table XVIII). These anomalous results were attributed to partial rearrangement of one or the other of the two zwitterions (see above) before further decomposition. The esters of allylic alcohols (e. g., geraniol acetate) do not undergo this abnormal reaction, however. Difficulties in the full interpretation of the reaction may also arise owing to interactions (e. g., polymerization), oxidation, or further decomposition of the primary decomposition products. Thus, unstable aldehydes may either polymerize or decompose at the temperatures necessary for ozonolysis.

Ozonization may be carried out with the pure (liquid-phase) olefins, but the use of dilute solutions to avoid overozonization is strongly recommended. The gas-phase reaction of ozone with olefins is markedly more complex and, at present, does not seem to be suited to analytical applications (99). Of considerable importance in the choice of solvent are relatively low vapor pressure and chemical inertness to ozone. Water, acetic acid, carbon tetrachloride, ethyl chloride, and ethyl acetate were found (190,661) to give the least reduction of ozone.

An obvious disadvantage of the reaction is the explosibility of certain ozonides. In almost every case, however, it is possible to avoid explosions either by exercising special precautions, such as working at low temperatures, or by carrying out the decomposition of the ozonide in solution.

Despite its limitations, the method has decided advantages. The reaction has been described as the most general and reliable procedure for oxidative cleavage and simultaneous location of the olefinic double bond. It permits the isolation of the primary cleavage products, for the excess oxidant, ozone, can be removed before the ozonide is cleaved, while in reactions with other oxidizing agents, such as $KMnO_4$ or Cr_2O_3, the cleavage products are exposed to the action of the oxidant.

Analytical methods based on ozonization are divided into two groups. In the first type of method, ozone addition is followed by decomposition of the ozonides formed and quantitative information as to the number of double bonds (as well as to their position) is gained from analytical methods applicable to these products of decomposition. The successful use of ozone as a titrimetric agent is relatively new. In this type of method the ozone consumed by the reaction mixture is the measure of the number of double bonds present.

(1) **Methods Based on the Analysis of Products of Ozonolysis.** Decomposition of ozonides may be effected by simple hydrolysis on either oxidative (e. g., alkaline permanganate, alkaline peroxide) or reductive (e. g., zinc and acetic acid, sodium bisulfite, catalytic hydrogenation) conditions to produce ketones and aldehydes or ketones and acids:

$$R_2C{=}CR_2 \xrightarrow[\text{reduction}]{\text{oxidation}} 2R_2CO$$

$$RCH{=}CHR{-}\begin{cases} \xrightarrow{\text{oxidation}} 2RCOOH \\ \\ \xrightarrow[\text{reduction}]{} 2RCHO \end{cases}$$

The number of double bonds in the sample may be calculated through conventional analytical methods to obtain a quantitative measure of the functional groups present. Specific methods are also available to determine individual ozonolysis products, permitting thereby a deeper insight into the structure of the parent olefin. This approach has been successfully applied to unsaturation and constitution studies of synthetic rubber polymers (512,686). The elaborate chromatographic method of Gordon, Wopat, Burnham, and Jones (218) summarizes the techniques for the separation and spectrometric determination of products of ozonolysis in the C_1 to C_4 range through their 2,4-dinitrophenylhydrazones.

Doeuvre (152) used ozone for the estimation of the terminal methylene group by measuring the formaldehyde formed in the decomposition colorimetrically using Déniges' reagent. Moderate concentrations of ozone (5% in oxygen) and, as reaction solvent, ethyl acetate–acetic acid (3:2) were employed. The method gave 90 to 95% reaction in the more favorable cases. Aromatic or internal olefinic bonds showed only small interference. Typical results are shown in Table XVIII.

TABLE XVIII

Analytical Data by the Doeuvre Method (152)

Form of methylene group	Compound	Reaction time	Per cent reaction (as double bond)
CH$_2$=C(CH$_3$)—......	2,6-Dimethyl-1,5-heptadiene	45 min.	95
	d-Limonene	1 hr.	86
	Isopulegone	3 min.	88
	Semicarbazone of isopulegone	3 min.	90
	Semicarbazone of d-carvone	3 min.	95
	2,4-Dinitrophenylhydrazone of d-carvone	1 hr., 30 min.	88
	2,4-Dinitrophenylhydrazone of d-carvone	3 hr.	95
CH$_2$=CH—CH$_2$—....	Methylallylisobutylcarbinol	3 min.	90
	Eugenol	5 min.	92
	Benzoyleugenol	2 hr.	84
	Benzoyleugenol	4 hr.	91
	Allylbenzene	3 min.	75
CH$_2$=CH—CHO.....	Acrolein	1 hr.	83
	Acrolein	2 hr.	88
CH$_2$=CH—C—OH...	Allyl alcohol	10 min.	71
	Allyl alcohol	2 hr.	74
	Methylvinylcarbinol	1 hr.	75
	Methylvinylcarbinol	6 hr.	80
CH$_2$=C—C=CH$_2$....	Isoprene	20 min.	104
No terminal double bonds............	Crotonaldehyde	20 min.	4
	Crotonic acid	6 hr.	1
	Cinnamic acid	15 min.	2
	Phenol	6 min.	2
	Naphthalene	1 hr.	2

A micro method, reported by Naves (455), corrected (in part) the shortcomings of the Doeuvre technique and yielded results between 94 and 102%.

A novel application of ozonization was reported by Bonner and Collins (67). An alcoholic solution of 2,4-dinitrophenylhydrazine sulfate was used as reaction solvent, permitting instantaneous hydrazone formation by the carbonylic products of ozonolysis. A 92 to 93% recrystallized yield of benzaldehyde hydrazone was obtained from stilbene.

A specific case of the application of ozone to structural studies is the determination of the isopropylidene group according to the method of Kuhn and Roth (367,542). The sample is ozonized in acetic acid solution. The ozonide formed is hydrolyzed into acetone and an aldehyde:

$$R—CH=C\diagup_{CH_3}^{CH_3} \xrightarrow{\text{O}_3,\ \text{H}_2\text{O}} RCHO + O=C\diagup_{CH_3}^{CH_3}$$

The aldehyde is oxidized to the corresponding acid with potassium permanganate. Acetone, not affected by the permanganate treatment, is then distilled and is converted to iodoform with excess alkaline iodine solution. The amount of iodine consumed, as determined by back-titration of the excess, is the measure of the isopropylidene group content.

$$3I_2 + 6KOH \longrightarrow 3KI + 3KOI + 3H_2O$$

$$CH_3—CO—CH_3 + 3KOI \longrightarrow CHI_3 + CH_3—COOK + 2KOH$$

In general, the method yields somewhat low results. On the other hand, since some higher methyl ketones behave like acetone toward permanganate and hypoiodite, in some cases high results could be encountered. Isopropyl groups present in certain configurations could also yield some acetone.

(2) **Titrimetric Methods.** The successful use of ozone as a titrimetric agent hinged on the development of a generator that is capable of providing a constant stream of concentrated ozone. The time elapsing between the beginning of ozone absorption and the appearance of unreacted ozone in the reaction mixture is a quantitative measure of the unsaturation, assuming the addition reaction to have proceeded to completion.

The method presented by Boer and Kooyman (61) uses a small amount of dye that rapidly decolorizes as soon as ozone addition is complete (indicator method). The gases escaping from the reaction vessel may also be checked by continuous iodometric titration, plotting the amount of escaping ozone against time for the calculation of the amount of ozone reacted (graphic method). The constant stream of ozone is prepared by electrolysis of dilute sulfuric acid.

Results on a wide variety of unsaturated compounds showed no major discrepancies from the theoretical values. Conjugated dienes reacted with both double bonds, and in mixed aromatic–olefinic systems (styrene, indene, etc.) the olefinic double bond reacted smoothly, the aromatic double bonds apparently being attacked only very slowly. The applicability of the method to nonhydrocarbon olefins was especially striking in comparison with standard halogenation methods. Very nearly theoretical results were also obtained on a number of petroleum distillate fractions. While it is preferable to remove aromatics (e. g., by adsorption on silica gel) prior to the analysis of such products, this may be absolutely necessary only in the presence of highly condensed aromatics. Substituted benzenes and naphthalenes gave rise to only minor deviations. Dialkyl sulfides were found to consume $1/4$ to $3/4$ of a molecule of ozone per atom of sulfur, dependent on the structure of the compound. Thiophene and dibenzothiophene did not interfere, whereas benzothiophene consumed exactly 1 mole of ozone. Typical results are shown in Table XIX.

TABLE XIX

Analytical Data by the Ozonization Method of Boer and Kooyman (61)

	Unsaturation, expressed in Br No.		
Olefin[a]	Theor.	Found (indicator method)	% of theor.
1-Hexene........................	190	192	101.1
1-Heptene........................	163	161	98.8
3-Heptene........................	163	162	99.4
1-Octene........................	143	143	100.0
Cetene........................	71.5	70.5	98.6
2,3-Dimethyl-2-butene.............	190	192	101.1
3,3-Dimethyl-1-butene.............	190	189.5	99.7
Diisobutylene.....................	143	150	104.9
Triisobutylene....................	95.3	95.5	100.2
2,2,5,5-Tetramethyl-3-hexene.........	114	119.5	104.8
1-Dodecene.......................	95.3	95.8	100.5
2,4-Hexadiene.....................	391	373	95.4
2,3-Dimethyl-1,3-butadiene...........	391	380	97.2
Cyclopentene.....................	235	230	97.9
1-Propyl-1-cyclopentene.............	145	144.5	99.7
Styrene..........................	154	156	101.3
Dimethallyl ether..................	254	250	98.4
1-Chloro-3-bromo-1-propene...........	103	107	103.9
Cinnamic acid.....................	108	114	105.6
Ethyl allyl phthalate...............	68.3	66.6	97.5
Oleic acid........................	56.7	51.5	90.8
Crotonaldehyde....................	228	226	99.1
Methacrolein......................	228	208	91.2
Methacrolein dimer.................	114	115	100.9

[a] Purity doubtful in some cases.

The applicability of this method to semiolefins (compounds having the double bond attached to a cyclane ring) was shown by van der Bij and Kooyman (53). These data, together with values by the McIlhiney and the DuBois-Skoog bromination methods, are given in Table XX. Results on some related compounds are also included. All McIlhiney values (corrected for substitution) are somewhat low; the DuBois-Skoog method, however, does not seem applicable to most of these samples.

TABLE XX

Analytical Data on Some Semiolefins (53)

| Compound | Extent of reaction, % of theoretical | | | |
| | Ozonization method | McIlhiney method | | DuBois-Skoog method |
		Addition	Substitution	
Methylenecyclopentane......	100.2	97.4	58	124.0
Methylenecyclohexane.......	100.2	97.8	43	124.8
Ethylidenecyclopentane......	102.0	91.2	61	126.6
Ethylidenecyclohexane.......	101.9	96.2	65	114.8
Vinylcyclopentane...........	99.8	97.2	9	107.4
Vinylcyclohexane............	101.6	99.7	13	105.2
1-Ethylcyclopentene.........	98.7	91.8	67	124.8

The method of Roelen (527) is based on weighing the amount of ozone absorbed by a given olefin, using the blue coloration caused by free ozone as the end point. The method has not been published in full.

C. POTASSIUM PERMANGANATE

The use of potassium permanganate in the so-called Baeyer test is the basis of one of the earliest methods for the detection of ethylenic unsaturation (37). The substance to be tested is dissolved in aqueous sodium carbonate (or sodium bicarbonate) to which a few drops of dilute potassium permanganate solution is added. In the presence of olefinic double bonds, the purple color of the permanganate disappears instantly and brown manganese hydroxide precipitates.

This reaction is quite general in its applicability; however, potassium permanganate will rarely react with completely substituted ethylenic linkages. Substances insoluble in water, such as organic acids, may be dissolved in alkali or pyridine; acetone or benzene may also be used as solvents. It must be kept in mind, however, that certain atomic groupings (e. g., aldehydes) are not resistant to permanganate and will decolorize permanganate although the compound does not contain ethylenic bonds. Nitrogen bases show positive reaction in alkaline solution, but behave normally when neutralized before permanganate is added or when the reagent is a dilute sulfuric acid solution of permanganate. The primary product of the reaction in cold buffered dilute aqueous solutions is a glycol:

$$>C=C< \xrightarrow{\text{KMnO}_4} \underset{\overset{|}{\text{OH}}}{-C-} \underset{\overset{|}{\text{OH}}}{-C-}$$

Isolated double bonds in a molecule yield polyglycols. Under more drastic conditions, the molecule is cleaved at the double bond to furnish aldehydes, ketones, acids, etc. Conjugated double bonds usually react by cleaving.

Glycol formation with permanganate and subsequent cleavage of the glycol with periodic acid is the basis of a method by Bricker and Roberts (81) for the determination of end unsaturation in organic compounds. Periodic acid oxidation yields formaldehyde and a higher aldehyde:

$$3 \; \begin{array}{c} \text{CH}_2 \\ \| \\ \text{CH} \\ | \\ \text{CH}_2 \\ | \end{array} + 2\text{MnO}_4{}^- + 2\text{H}_3\text{O}^+ \longrightarrow 3 \; \begin{array}{c} \text{CH}_2\text{OH} \\ | \\ \text{CHOH} \\ | \\ \text{CH}_2 \\ | \end{array} + 2\text{MnO}_2$$

$$\begin{array}{c} \text{CH}_2\text{OH} \\ | \\ \text{CHOH} \\ | \\ \text{CH}_2 \\ | \end{array} + \text{H}_5\text{IO}_6 \longrightarrow \begin{array}{c} \text{CHO} \\ | \\ \text{CH}_2 \\ | \end{array} + \text{HCHO} + \text{HIO}_3 + 3\text{H}_2\text{O}$$

The formaldehyde formed is separated from the reaction mixture by steam distillation and a portion of the distillate is analyzed for formaldehyde by means of chromotropic acid. A calibration curve is used to correlate the amount of formaldehyde found with the vinyl group (terminal double bond) content of the sample.

The method has several limitations. Formaldehyde obtained from compounds containing end unsaturation is not stoichiometric; therefore, the amount of formaldehyde found cannot be used to calculate directly the percentage of vinyl groups. However, the percentage of formaldehyde produced by a certain end-unsaturated compound appears to be constant over a considerable concentration range but varies somewhat with each compound. Therefore, to apply this procedure quantitatively, it is necessary to prepare a calibration curve with a pure sample of the compound to be determined and then use this curve in subsequent determinations of this substance. This feature renders the usefulness of the method rather limited when mixtures of unknown composition and of complex nature are to be analyzed. It may be concluded that the interpretation of results from a petroleum distillate which contains a great variety of α-olefins would be complicated by the known variations in reactivity of different α-olefins (607). It may be deemed as unlikely that the same correction factor would be applicable to all end double bonds present. Also, formaldehyde is known to be formed from the chemical attack of permanganate and periodic acid on compounds that do not contain terminal olefinic groups (e. g., methyl alcohol or any 1,2-glycols that may be present in the original sample).

Bricker and Roberts' method was also tested for the determination of free methyl methacrylate in poly(methyl methacrylate) samples by Dal Nogare, Perkins, and Hale (138) and, although the formaldehyde values found could not be correlated with the known monomer concentrations, it was noted that the volume of permanganate solution required by the sample in the presence of periodic acid was proportional to the amount of sample present. The oxidative titration method that evolved from this observation involves the isolation of the methyl methacrylate monomer by distillation from an acetic acid–water solution of the polymer sample and titration of the monomer in the distillate with permanganate in the presence of sulfuric and periodic acids. Difficulties encountered in the observation of the correct end point, due to the formation of colored permanganate reduction products, were overcome by using transmitted light or observing the surface of the solution. The method has proved satisfactory for the analysis of a large variety of poly(methyl methacrylate) samples, giving a precision of 5% of the amount of monomer present. It was concluded that the method may be applicable to the problem of measuring unsaturation in a number of aliphatic compounds, providing a satisfactory water-soluble solvent can be found for both the reagent and sample. Of the compounds examined, styrene, methyl acrylate, and acrylonitrile were reproducibly determined by this procedure.

Lemieux and von Rudloff (378a) found that similar oxidative cleavage of olefinic double bonds occurs readily near room temperature in neutral or slightly alkaline periodate solutions containing only catalytic amounts of permanganate. The permanganate first oxidizes the double bond to form an α-glycol or an α-hydroxy carbonyl compound (in alkaline solution, the latter product is favored). These oxidation products are rapidly cleaved by the periodate to form aldehydes or ketones and carboxylic acids. Only aldehydes (except formaldehyde) are further oxidized to acids by the permanganate. The crucial feature of the reaction is that the permanganate is regenerated by the action of periodate on the manganate formed in the oxidations. Nearly quantitative yields of carboxylic acids (separated by liquid-liquid partition chromatography) were obtained with oleic, elaidic, eicosenoic, 10-undecenoic, linoleic, and erucic acids, and with methyl linoleate (544b). Semiquantitative determination of terminal unsaturation (comparing favorably with ozonolysis) by means of the formaldehyde produced from 18 α-olefinic compounds was found (378b). Quantitative yields of acetone from the isopropylidene group in mesityl oxide, 3-methyl-2-butenoic acid, etc., were obtained (544a). This method is therefore of interest for locating and determining double bonds in a variety of materials. Periodic acid, without any catalyst, has been found to give nearly stoichiometric yields of formaldehyde from vinyl compounds and benzaldehyde from styryl compounds (105a).

Hilditch and Lea (263) demonstrated that, from the fragments formed on oxidizing under drastic conditions, it is possible to determine the position of the double bond in an unsaturated ester or acid. In a typical procedure, methyl oleate, heated with solid potassium permanganate in refluxing acetone solution, yielded the methyl half ester of azaleic acid and pelargonic acid.

The disruptive oxidation of the doubly bound carbon atoms to carboxyl groups:

$$R—CH{=}CH—R' + 4O \longrightarrow R—COOH + R'—COOH$$

in acetic acid solution at room temperature in the presence of an emulsifier is the principle of a titrimetric procedure developed by Knowles, Lawson, and McQuillen (354). After 1 hour reaction time, the unused potassium permanganate is reacted with excess ferrous sulfate, which is back-titrated with standard permanganate. Although, the method gave less reliable values on edible oils than obtainable by Wijs method, the authors preferred it to iodine values for the drying (conjugated) oils, such as tung or oiticica. Typical results are shown in Table XXI.

TABLE XXI
Analytical Data for Disruptive Oxidation of Oils (354)

| | Iodine Number | |
Sample	Calc. from oxygen absorption	Wijs Method
Linseed oil	180	183
Tung oil	208	160
Oiticica oil	208	165
Japanese sardine oil	198	183
Oleic acid	93	91

A similar procedure was reported by Ioffe (293) for the oxidation of maleic acid.

D. OSMIUM TETROXIDE

Osmium tetroxide reacts readily with ethylenic double bonds. The reaction first reported by Neubauer (457) and characterized by immediate dark discoloration, due to oxidation products and precipitated metallic osmium, was widely used as a qualitative test for olefinic and acetylenic compounds.

If the reaction is carried out in the presence of pyridine, nicely crystalline addition compounds having cyclic structures of the type:

$$
\begin{array}{c}
\text{Py} \\
\text{R—CH—O} \diagdown \; \vdots \; \diagup \text{O} \\
| \qquad \text{Os} \\
\text{R—CH—O} \diagup \; \vdots \; \diagdown \text{O} \\
\text{Py}
\end{array}
$$

are usually obtained in theoretical yield in a few minutes (127). These complexes give diols on mild hydrolysis.

Osmium tetroxide-catalyzed oxidation of olefinic double bonds with periodate has recently been described (476a). The reaction is similar to the permanganate-catalyzed oxidation (378a) described above, except that the reaction does not proceed beyond the aldehydic oxidation state. Semiquantitative yields of undecanal, benzaldehyde, ad paldehyde, and glutaraldehyde (as their 2,4-dinitrophenylhydrazones) were obtained from 1-dodecene, *trans*-stilbene, cyclohexene, and cyclopentene, respectively.

The addition of osmium tetroxide to aromatic double bonds takes place very slowly. Benzene is not attacked under normal conditions, but polycyclic aromatics react at the positions that are also sensitive to ozone (115).

4. Nitration

The nitration of olefinic double bonds involves significant experimental difficulties that stem partly from the unstable and hazardous nature of most of the nitration reagents and partly from the instability of the reaction products. Despite these difficulties, the field seems to be explored to a sufficient extent that a few useful methods are available for specific applications. Both nitrogen tetroxide and nitrogen trioxide have been found practical to employ. Procedures involving the use of nitric acid, nitrosyl chloride, nitrosobenzene, and tetranitromethane are considered only briefly here.

A. NITROGEN TETROXIDE

Nitrogen tetroxide (sometimes termed dinitrogen tetroxide) is, near room temperature, a brown equilibrium mixture of nitrogen dioxide and the undissociated form:

$$N_2O_4 \rightleftharpoons 2NO_2$$
$$\text{ca. } 80\% \qquad \text{ca. } 20\%$$

Physical evidence (infrared, Raman, and x-ray analysis) indicate that the structure of nitrogen tetroxide is:

$$\underset{-O}{\overset{O}{>}}\overset{+}{N}-\overset{+}{N}\underset{O}{\overset{O^-}{<}}$$

This formula is in harmony with the mechanism of ionic addition of nitrogen tetroxide to the ethylenic double bond (287). Nitrogen tetroxide is commercially available in cylinders. The commercial material freezes at approximately $-13°C$. and boils at $21°C$.

Semenoff (563) over 90 years ago studied the reaction between nitrogen tetroxide and ethylene, and since that time there have been many attempts to elucidate the addition of this compound to olefins. The field was reviewed by Riebsomer (521) in 1945. Later, the addition of nitrogen tetroxide to several olefins was carefully examined in its qualitative aspects by Levy, Scaife, Wilder-Smith, and Baldock (38,380,381,556). These authors found that of the several possibilities (dinitro, dinitrite, nitrosonitrate, or nitronitrite derivatives), there are two simultaneously formed first products, namely, a dinitro compound and a nitronitrite. The latter may be oxidized to a nitronitrate or hydrolyzed to a nitroalcohol:

$$\underset{-CH=CH_2}{\overset{\delta^+ \quad \delta^-}{}} + N_2O_4 \longrightarrow$$

$$\begin{cases} \overset{NO_2}{\underset{NO_2}{|}} \\ -CH-CH_2 \\ \text{and} \\ \overset{ONO}{\underset{NO_2}{|}} \\ -CH-CH_2 \xrightarrow{\text{oxidation}} \overset{ONO_2}{\underset{NO_2}{|}} -CH-CH_2 \end{cases}$$

$$\downarrow \text{hydrolysis}$$

$$\overset{OH}{\underset{NO_-}{|}}$$
$$-CH-CH_2$$

Nitrogen tetroxide seems to follow the rules of ionic addition to the olefinic double bond, the attack on the olefin being led by the cationoid and highly reactive nitronium ion, NO_2^+. The nitrite ion fragment is attached where the halide would go in an addition of HX. The reactions of nitrogen tetroxide with olefins were also examined by Porter and Wood (491,492) and by Weghofer (651) with results that were in agreement with those of Levy *et al.*

The reaction with nitrogen tetroxide is best carried out in the liquid phase between -10 and $+25°C$. The products from these reactions are unstable solids or heavy oils, and generally are difficult to handle. For these reasons, analytical nitration of simple olefinic mixtures with nitrogen tetroxide offers no advantage over halogenation or other standard methods. With cracked gasoline, however, the reaction offers the advantage that the addition products are, in general, of low volatility, from which the unreacted components of the sample can be removed readily by simple steam distillation. The change in volume of the sample gives a direct measure of the olefin content.

An analytical procedure based on this principle was reported by Smirnov (586). Cracked gasoline was added to liquid (-15 to $-20°C$.) nitrogen tetroxide (generated from nitric acid with copper shavings) and the neutralized reaction mixture was distilled with steam. The distillate was dried and purified over silica gel, and its volume was compared with the original volume of the sample. A similar distillation procedure employing pure gaseous nitrogen tetroxide was published by Bond (65). In a variation of this procedure, Bond reacted the products of nitration ("nitrosates") with alcoholic potassium hydroxide and potassium sulfide to form products soluble in aqueous alcohol. The upper phase of this mixture contained the unreacted portion of the sample. Details of these two procedures follow.

Steam Distillation Procedure. The sample (50 ml.) is placed in a special reaction flask (Fig. 3) and chilled in an ice bath. Gaseous nitrogen tetroxide is introduced from a cylinder warmed to $30°C$., at a controlled rate to keep the temperature of the reaction mixture below $30°C$., until brown fumes appear in the spray trap for 5 minutes. Then some aqueous urea solution is added to the flask to decompose the excess nitrogen tetroxide, and the mixture is steam-distilled in an apparatus similar to the one shown in Figure 4. The hydrocarbon layer in the receiver is treated with methanolic potassium hydroxide solution and washed with water, and its volume is measured in a buret. The olefin content is obtained from the difference in volume of the unreacted hydrocarbons in the distillate and the volume of the original sample. A blank distillation test is made to determine and correct for handling losses.

Direct Volumetric Procedure. The chilled sample (10 ml.) in a graduated flask is reacted with nitrogen tetroxide gas as described above. Then the nitrosates formed are reacted with methanolic potassium hydroxide and potassium sulfide solution and the reaction mixture is diluted with water to bring the unreacted portion of the sample into the graduated portion of the

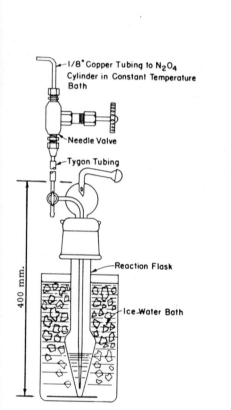

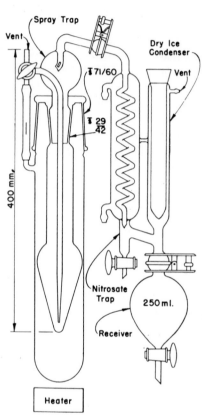

Fig. 3. Nitrogen tetroxide reaction apparatus (555).

Fig. 4. Steam distillation apparatus for nitrogen tetroxide method (555).

flask. After the flask is shaken and centrifuged, the volume of the hydrocarbon phase is measured.

The evaluation and standardization of these procedures were subsequently carried out by an A.S.T.M. group (555) on four synthetic blends of olefins. The average of results by the distillation method on three samples, containing no highly branched olefins, showed a deviation of less than 1% from the blended values.   The deviation was about 2% for the fourth sample, which contained diisobutylene and branched nonenes. Deviations for the direct volumetric procedure were somewhat higher.

These results indicate the distinct superiority of the nitrogen tetroxide method for the determination of total olefin content over the standard halogenation methods where an assumption for the molecular weight of the olefins must be made.   However, the applicability of these methods is limited to the gasoline range, because naphthalene and higher polyaromatics react with nitrogen tetroxide.   Application of the distillation method to aromatic-free materials in the higher boiling ranges is limited by the increasing proximity of the boiling points of the nitrosates and the non-olefinic portion, but such materials distilling up to approximately 250°C. may be successfully analyzed.   The direct volumetric procedure for this latter purpose is more successful and its scope might be extended to materials boiling up to 350°C.

Two possible hazards exist in the handling of nitrogen tetroxide in combination with olefins: the degree of stability of the reaction products and the toxicity of nitrogen tetroxide.   An investigation (555) of products from several thermal and catalytic gasolines showed them to be nonexplosive, even by use of detonators.   However, olefin-nitrogen tetroxide compounds are thermally unstable and subject to rapid decomposition if heated directly above 120 to 150°C.   Violent reactions have occurred where nitrogen tetroxide has been left in contact with hydrocarbons for long periods of time.   The presence of oil in pipes, valves, etc. used for nitrogen tetroxide should be avoided.   Since nitrogen tetroxide is highly toxic, reactions should be carried out in a hood.

Dinneen, Smith, and Ball (149) applied the Bond method to nine petroleum and ten shale-oil naphthas.   For twelve of these samples, the deviation from results by the "referee" silica gel adsorption method was only 1%.   For the other seven samples, the nitrogen tetroxide method gave higher values, the greatest variation being 6%.   These high values are partly due to the fact that aromatic olefins are determined by the nitrogen tetroxide method as olefins, whereas the silica gel method classifies them as aromatics.   These authors also showed that sulfur compounds, commonly present in gasolines, and in a higher concentration in shale-oil distillates, also react with nitrogen tetroxide, contributing to high values.   Pyrrolic-type nitrogen compounds should be expected to show similar reactivity.

B. NITROGEN TRIOXIDE

Nitrous fumes generated from nitric acid with arsenous oxide, or ob-

tained from the reaction of concentrated sulfuric acid and a nitrate, contain nitrogen trioxide, N_2O_3, as the main component but, depending on the
conditions of the reaction, varying amounts of tetroxide as well.   Therefore it must be assumed that, in most earlier researches where the components of the reagents suggest nitrogen trioxide as the active agent, the
reagent was actually a mixture of trioxide and tetroxide in an indefinite
ratio.   This fact contributes greatly to the difficulties encountered in
studying the course of nitrogen trioxide additions to olefinic systems.   The
expected product is the nitronitroso derivative but with some aliphatic
olefins this could be obtained only in negligible yield even under optimum
conditions (430,491).   The major portion of nitrated sample is a heavy
unstable oil.

In spite of these difficulties, the reagent has been successfully used in a
few specific applications.   An early analytical use of nitrous fumes (evolved
from dilute nitric acid and arsenous oxide) for the determination of rubber
hydrocarbons gave values that agreed well with theory.   The product of
nitration was extracted with ethyl acetate and the isoprene content was
calculated from the carbon dioxide found in the "wet" combustion (with
potassium dichromate–sulfuric acid) of the extract (655).

Bond (66) determined styrene in hydrocarbon solutions gravimetrically with nitrogen trioxide generated in the reaction mixture from
sodium nitrite and dilute sulfuric acid.   After purification by extraction
with cold alcohol, a white, or pale yellow, crystalline product, corresponding to the formula C_6H_5—$CH(NO)$—CH_2NO_2 was isolated in approximately
82% yield.   The constancy of this yield with styrene solutions of varying
concentration justified the inclusion of a correction factor in the calculation.
Several olefinic and aromatic compounds, likely to be present in styrene
mixtures, either did not react or gave products that dissolved readily during
extraction.   In difficult cases, however, a pretreatment of the sample
(e. g., with sulfur dioxide) might be advisable.

This method was adopted by Marquardt and Luce (416) for the determination of divinylbenzene, in dehydrogenated diethylbenzene.   The
accuracy of this method was found to be within ±0.5% of the absolute
value.   Ethylvinylbenzenes and styrene interfered only when divinylbenzene was present in low concentration.

A colorimetric nitration method for the determination of styrene in the
air was published by Poletaev (490).   A measured volume of air was
passed through the reagent (ammonium nitrate in sulfuric acid) and the
color stabilized with excess ammonia was compared with standards.

C. OTHER NITRATION REAGENTS

Nitric Acid. Fuming nitric acid (204), and nitric acid in the presence of sulfuric acid (166,258,409), have been used for the simultaneous removal of olefins and aromatics from cracked petroleum products. The determination of olefins requires an independent estimation of the aromatic content. The reliability of results is low because cyclic paraffins are also nitrated to varying extents.

A method utilizing a mixture of equal volumes of concentrated sulfuric acid and nitric acid as nitration reagent was published by Crippen and Bonilla (128) for the determination of styrene in hydrocarbon copolymers. The sample is depolymerized at 300 to 400°C. and the styrene is distilled out with steam. An aliquot of the carbon tetrachloride solution of the distillate is nitrated and the color produced measured in a spectrophotometer. By comparison with a calibration curve and by using an empirical calibration factor, the amount of styrene in the polymer is obtained. Results on sixteen samples, checked against carbon-hydrogen determinations, showed a mean deviation of 2.7%. Butadiene did not interfere, but the presence of substituted styrene or other aromatics would require separate standardizations.

Nitrosyl Chloride. Olefinic compounds add nitrosyl chloride to furnish derivatives that have been used in many instances (e. g., terpenes) for characterization purposes. Ingold (285) assumes that these additions are oriented like those of iodine monochloride or hydrogen halides:

$$\overset{\delta^-}{\underset{}{\diagup}}C{=}C\overset{\delta^+}{\underset{}{\diagdown}} + NOCl \longrightarrow \overset{|}{\underset{\underset{NO}{|}}{-C}}\overset{\overset{Cl}{|}}{\underset{|}{-C-}}$$

There are various products of this reaction (428,620). The $R_2C{=}CR_2$ olefinic type gives the true nitroso derivatives, which are blue to green heavy liquids or crystals with a disagreeable odor. Compounds with $R_2C{=}CHR$ grouping form derivatives that undergo a shift of the hydrogen atom to furnish crystalline colorless oximes. The olefinic types, $R_2C{=}CH_2$, $RCH{=}CHR$, and $RCH{=}CH_2$, react with difficulty and give no solid reaction products.

Free nitrosyl chloride is seldom used. More conveniently the hydrocarbon is dissolved in an alcoholic solution of hydrogen chloride and cooled; then a concentrated solution of sodium nitrite is added dropwise. On diluting with water, the reaction product precipitates.

Kaufmann and Röver (335) used nitrosyl chloride to obtain the "nitrosyl number" of several unsaturated oils and fatty acids. The same degree of unsaturation was found as with iodine. Nitrosyl bromide gave similar results.

Nitrosobenzene. Bruni and Geiger (89) found that nitrosobenzene reacts almost quantitatively with natural rubber to form nitrone. By employing proper experimental conditions, Pummerer and Gündel (501) showed that this reaction could be used for determining the unsaturated hydrocarbon content of rubber:

$$\left[\begin{array}{c} CH_3 \\ | \\ -CH_2-C=CH-CH_2- \end{array}\right] + 3C_6H_5NO \longrightarrow$$

$$\left[\begin{array}{c} CH_3 \\ | \\ -CH=C-C-CH_2- \\ \| \\ C_6H_5-NO \end{array}\right] \qquad \begin{array}{c} O \\ \| \\ + C_6H_5-N=N-C_6H_5 + H_2O \end{array}$$

or

$$\left[\begin{array}{c} CH_2 \\ \| \\ -CH_2-C-C-CH_2- \\ \| \\ C_6H_5-NO \end{array}\right]$$

Rehner (512) applied this reaction to polyisobutylene and butyl rubber samples and analyzed the purified precipitate for nitrogen. Inconveniently long reaction times were needed to reach constant values, which were high compared to results by the more reliable ozonization method (see Section II.3.B(1)).

More recently, the reaction of nitrosobenzene with conjugated dienes was studied by Arbuzov (28).

Tetranitromethane. Tetranitromethane produces yellow to reddish-brown colorations in carbon tetrachloride or chloroform solutions of ethylenic compounds. The reaction is sensitive but not specific for olefins. Some other types of compounds (aromatics, sulfides, thiols, dioxane, thiourea, cyclopropane) also show positive reaction. Moreover, unsaturated alcohols and ketones give only weak coloration and α,β-unsaturated aldehydes and acids do not react (332). The nature of the color is different from compound to compound (584); therefore the reaction can be applied quantitatively only to individual olefinic compounds. When used in this manner by Kaufmann, Kirsch, King, and Huang (333), halogen values calculated from spectrophotometric measurements on several unsaturated fats and fatty acid samples checked with iodine numbers within $\pm 5\%$.

5. Sulfuric Acid Absorption

Olefins react with sulfuric acid in various ways, depending on the nature of the olefin and the acid concentration. In strong sulfuric acid, many simple olefins react as follows:

$$\text{>C=C<} + \text{H—OSO}_2\text{OH} \longrightarrow \text{H—C—C—OSO}_2\text{OH}$$

In fuming sulfuric acid, they react with pyrosulfuric acid:

$$\text{>C=C<} + \text{HOO}_2\text{S—OSO}_2\text{OH} \longrightarrow \text{HOO}_2\text{S—C—C—OSO}_2\text{OH}$$

Esters, polymers, and oxidation products also may be produced by reaction with sulfuric acid, and tertiary olefins yield tertiary alcohols.

Numerous applications in determination of unsaturated hydrocarbon gases and liquids by means of extraction with various strengths of sulfuric acid or solutions of metal salts in sulfuric acid have been reported. Because of the complexity of the reactions and the large excesses of acid required, it is not practical to base the analysis on determination of reaction products or on the amount of acid consumed. Therefore, these methods nearly always depend on measuring the volume (or weight) of sample before and after extraction with the acid reagent.

A. GASES

Convenient apparatus and procedures for analysis of fixed and hydrocarbon gases have been described by Brooks, Lykken, Milligan, Nebeker, and Zahn (84) and the field of gas analysis has recently been reviewed by Mullen (450). A number of reagents have been employed for the complete absorption of olefins from gas mixtures. Fuming sulfuric acid is sometimes used, but it also absorbs saturated hydrocarbons to some extent (681) and requires the subsequent use of alkali to remove sulfur trioxide vapors from the unabsorbed portion of the sample. Concentrated sulfuric acid containing silver salts (215) absorbs gaseous olefins rapidly and completely but reacts also with carbon monoxide and catalyzes the formation of interfering polymers from propylene and butylenes.

The best general reagent for total removal of olefins from gases is a solution of mercuric sulfate in sulfuric acid. This reagent absorbs rapidly and completely and has a high absorption capacity. To suppress the slow reaction of the reagent with carbon monoxide to form carbon dioxide, the solution should be saturated with magnesium sulfate. A preparation consisting of 164 grams of mercuric oxide dissolved in 715 ml. of 20% sulfuric acid and then mixed with 480 grams of magnesium sulfate heptahydrate until saturated is recommended (84).

An activated acid reagent, Lusorbent (Burrell Corp.), absorbs olefinic and aromatic hydrocarbons and does not absorb paraffins in significant amount if the total hydrocarbon content of the gas sample does not exceed 25%. Some carbon monoxide is absorbed when present in excess of 6%.

For selective absorption of particular olefinic hydrocarbons from unsaturated gas mixtures, sulfuric acid in varied concentrations appears to be the only convenient method. Isobutylene can be preferentially absorbed from other butylenes by means of 65% sulfuric acid; tertiary amylene can be selectively removed from C_5 fractions by means of 70% sulfuric acid; and propylene and all butylenes can be absorbed away from ethylene, except when the ethylene content exceeds 20 or 25%, by means of 87% sulfuric acid. Because these reagents are not completely selective, corrections for small coabsorptions are sometimes necessary.

B. LIQUIDS

Although largely superseded by better methods, absorption in sulfuric acid has been widely used for the determination of olefins and aromatics in petroleum and coal tar oil distillates. Because aromatic hydrocarbons react fairly readily with concentrated sulfuric acid to form hydrocarbon-insoluble sulfonic acids, numerous attempts have been made to extract only the olefins from hydrocarbon mixtures by means of lower concentrations of sulfuric acid. Some of the reagents suggested for selective extraction of olefins include 80% sulfuric acid (340), 91% sulfuric acid followed by distillation to remove olefin polymers from the raffinate (445), and 93% sulfuric acid cooled to 35°F. (618). Fisher and Eisner (191) showed that these methods are not very satisfactory for coal tar and petroleum oils in general, especially when large amounts of aromatics are present, and described a graphic method based on successive extraction with sulfuric acid in increasing concentrations between 75 and 98%, following the stepwise removal of olefins and aromatics by measurement of physical properties such as specific dispersion and refractivity intercept. The same workers (192) investigated optimum conditions for extraction of olefins and found that 80 to 84% sulfuric acid may be employed to extract reactive olefins with only negligible sulfonation of aromatics, but that less reactive olefins such as diisobutylene, diamylene, and cetene are only partially extracted. Addition of silver sulfate or boric acid to the sulfuric acid is known to increase the extraction of olefins but also promotes interference by aromatics.

A number of such studies on effects of acid concentration and other experimental conditions have rather conclusively shown that there very probably is no single set of conditions under which sulfuric acid will extract all olefins without removing any aromatics. Consequently, selective olefin absorption methods are useful only for particular samples of known behavior or for empirical comparisons among similar samples.

The determination of total olefins plus aromatics by extraction with strong sulfuric acid reagents, however, can be made with reasonably good reliability for many hydrocarbon mixtures. With fuming sulfuric acid, complete extraction of olefins and aromatics usually is obtained, but some saturated hydrocarbons also are absorbed. Allen and Duckwall (11) used 101% sulfuric acid (4.4% sulfur trioxide in anhydrous sulfuric acid) at 0°C., with acid to sample ratios of 4 to 1, 3 to 1, and 2 to 1, and then extrapolated the volume per cent absorbed and the physical properties of the raffinate to a hypothetical 0 to 1 acid to sample ratio in order to correct for absorption of saturated hydrocarbons. With less concentrated acid, e. g., 98% sulfuric acid, the absorption of saturated hydrocarbons is decreased, but some olefins are not completely absorbed due to formation of hydrocarbon-soluble polymers or alkylates and some aromatics are not completely sulfonated under these conditions.

Berg and Parker (50) found that, by adding 25 ml. of fuming sulfuric acid (15% sulfur trioxide) to a solution of 10 ml. of sample in 15 ml. of acetic acid at 0°C., essentially complete extraction of olefins plus aromatics from gasoline and almost negligible extraction of saturated hydrocarbons are obtained. Modified sulfuric acid reagents containing silver sulfate (409) as a catalyst have been used to obtain complete extraction of aromatics. A reagent containing 14% by weight phosphorus pentoxide in concentrated sulfuric acid was proposed by Kattwinkel (317). A modified Kattwinkel reagent, containing 30% by weight of phosphorus pentoxide and 70%w of 95 to 96% sulfuric acid, is probably the most satisfactory reagent for extraction of total olefins plus aromatics. This method has been evaluated by Mills, Kurtz, Heyn, and Lipkin (440) and adopted by the American Society for Testing Materials (19a) and the Institute of Petroleum (290a). To reduce absorption of saturated hydrocarbons, the extraction is conducted near 0°C. Various techniques for shaking by hand or by machine in a vertical or in a 45 degree position have been studied. Approved procedures for each shaking method are described in A.S.T.M. D 1019; an arrangement for shaking individual flasks at a 45 degree angle in an ice-water bath is shown in Figure 5. Since significant departures from correct values may arise from variations in procedure, particularly in regard to the reaction temperature and manner of shaking, the procedure should be tested with pure materials. To ascertain that saturated hydrocarbons are not absorbed, a test is made with methylcyclohexane, which reacts more readily with the reagent above 0°C. than do paraffins

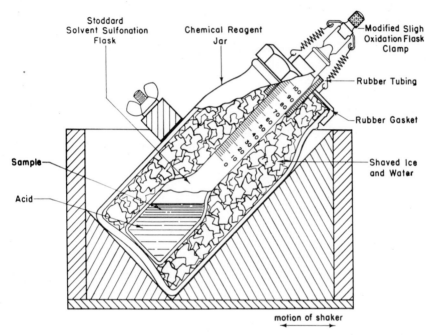

Fig. 5. Ice-water bath and carriage for shaking sulfonation flask. (Reproduced from ASTM Method D 1019–55T by permission of the American Society for Testing Materials.)

or other naphthenes. Not more than 1% of the methylcyclohexane should be absorbed if the correct procedure is followed. On actual samples, a correction of 0.7 to 1.4% is made to allow for the extraction of saturated hydrocarbons. To ascertain that aromatic hydrocarbons are completely absorbed, a test is made with a 40% by volume solution of benzene in a saturated hydrocarbon such as n-heptane or isooctane. Benzene is the most difficult of the lower aromatics to sulfonate. The observed absorption should be within 1% of the benzene content added and the raffinate should be essentially free of benzene. After dilution with additional acid and centrifuging, the volume of unabsorbed portion of sample is measured in the graduated neck of a flask of the type shown in Figure 5. With samples containing less than 50% olefins, a 10 ml. sample is employed. With samples containing more than 50% by volume olefins, better results can be obtained by using only 5 ml. of sample and adding the reagent slowly with cooling before mixing vigorously.

By means of the A.S.T.M. D 1019 acid absorption method, the total olefin plus aromatic content of petroleum distillates boiling below 600°F. usually can be determined with an accuracy of 1 or 2% of the sample. To obtain olefin content from this result, the aromatic content must be determined by an independent method, such as specific dispersion. However, for analysis of cracked gasolines, kerosines, and even many light gas oils, the chromatographic FIA method (see Section IV.1.A (2)) is preferable to acid adsorption since it provides a simultaneous determination of saturates, olefins, and aromatics, and is more reliable than acid absorption in combination with specific dispersion or bromination when appreciable amounts of olefins are present. Nevertheless, the acid absorption method is useful for checking the accuracy of the sum of olefin and aromatic contents found by chromatography or other methods.

6. Thiocyanation

The thiocyanation of ethylenic bonds as a means for determination of olefinic unsaturation was first proposed by Kaufmann and Liepe (319, 334). Although the use of "nascent" thiocyanogen generated in situ by oxidation of thiocyanate salts offers some definite advantages (90), commonly a solution of free thiocyanogen is employed:

$$\mathrm{>C{=}C<} + (SCN)_2 \longrightarrow -\overset{|}{\underset{|}{C}}\overset{SCN}{\underset{SCN}{-}}\overset{|}{\underset{|}{C}}-$$

The preparation of the reagent in this form demands carefully controlled experimental conditions.

Usually lead thiocyanate is the starting material, obtained in high purity and stability, and in nearly theoretical yield, from lead nitrate and ammonium thiocyanate (374). The thiocyanogen reagent is prepared from this salt by the slow addition of bromine in glacial acetic acid–carbon tetrachloride (1:1 by volume) to an acetic acid solution of lead thiocyanate:

$$\mathrm{Pb(SCN)_2 + Br_2 \longrightarrow (SCN)_2 + PbBr_2}$$

The precipitate of lead bromide is filtered off and the clear, straw-colored reagent is stored in a sealed bottle in the dark at 5°C. Although thiocyanogen in free form is extremely unstable, its solution in acetic acid–carbon tetrachloride deteriorates only slowly if reducing substances and moisture have been carefully eliminated from the solvents.

For the determination of thiocyanogen value, the sample is weighed into a dry, glass-stoppered erlenmeyer flask, a 200% excess of the 0.2 N reagent is added, and the mixture is allowed to stand in the dark at room temperature for 24 hours. Reagent blanks are treated in the same manner. The unused amount of thiocyanogen is determined by reaction with excess aqueous potassium iodide:

$$(SCN)_2 + 2KI \longrightarrow 2KSCN + I_2$$

and, after the addition of some water, titrating the liberated iodine with standard thiosulfate solution.

The analytical use of thiocyanogen has been largely restricted to the field of fatty acids and glycerides and is based on the unusual selectivity this reagent displays toward compounds possessing isolated double bonds. The original indications were that thiocyanogen adds to the double bond of oleic acid and its esters but to only one of the two double bonds in linoleic acid and to only two of the three double bonds in linolenic acid (321). Since iodine monochloride adds to all double bonds in these acids, a set of simultaneous equations incorporating the iodine value (as obtained by the Wijs method) and thiocyanogen value of a mixture permitted the calculation of the proportions of saturated and each of the unsaturated acids. However, subsequent investigations showed that the stoichiometric constants were incorrect, the thiocyanogen value of linoleic acid being higher, and that of linolenic acid lower, than theoretical. These considerations resulted in a set of empirical constants (425) based on the best average values (Table XXII) obtained by strict adherence to the standard procedure (32). Since these equations can only deal with three unknown quantities, if the oil contains stearic or other saturated acids as well as oleic, linoleic, and linolenic acids, it is necessary to ascertain the percentage of saturated acids by independent means (e. g., lead salt precipitation or low-temperature crystallization methods). Elaidic acid adds iodine and thiocyanogen in the same manner as oleic acid; hence, the method can be used in the presence of either or both acids but it cannot distinguish between them. A separate set of equations is available for triglyceride mixtures; standard iodine and thiocyanogen values used for calculating the constants in the formulas are also given in Table XXII. Similar equations may be set up for mixtures containing other than C_{18} unsaturated acids.

TABLE XXII

Standard Iodine and Thiocyanogen Values of Linolenic, Linoleic, and Oleic Acids and
Their Triglycerides (425)

Compound	Iodine Number	Thiocyanogen value[a]
Acid:		
Linolenic	273.7	167.1
Linoleic	181.1	96.7
Oleic	89.9	89.3
Triglyceride:		
Linolenin	261.8	159.8
Linolein	173.3	92.5
Olein	86.0	85.5

[a] Expressed as the equivalent Iodine Number.

This calculation method cannot be applied to glycerides and mixtures of fatty acids and esters containing conjugated double bonds since neither the addition of iodine nor that of thiocyanogen is quantitative in these cases.

Several attempts were made to apply thiocyanation to hydrocarbon olefins (318,363) including rubber hydrocarbons (503) and petroleum products (230). Quantitative addition occurred with several of the pure compounds but in other instances the results were low and depended greatly on reagent concentration and reaction time. Addition to styrene or stilbene could be effected only when the reaction mixture was exposed to light. Even light does not promote addition to crotonic, fumaric, maleic, or cinnamic acids.

A recent investigation by Bugorkova, Petrova, and Rodinov (92) showed that the reactivity of an olefinic hydrocarbon depends greatly on the position of the double bond in the molecule (Table XXIII). Primary olefins add thiocyanogen to an extent of only 50% of theoretical in 24 hours; within the same period, cyclohexene with a double bond between secondary carbon atoms thiocyanates completely; and terpene hydrocarbons with tertiary-secondary carbon atoms in the double bond which display excessive bromine absorption (see earlier) react quantitatively in 5 minutes. Compounds possessing oxygen-containing functional groups showed considerably lower reactivity, the reaction being quantitative only when the double bond was removed from the functional group. It was also observed that while a propenyl group in the side chain of a benzene derivative reacts incompletely in 24 hours, the addition is quantitative if the ring also carries a methoxy group (e. g., anethole). This effect was similar although less pronounced for the allyl group (e. g., safrole). How-

TABLE XXIII
Addition of Thiocyanogen to Olefinic Compounds (92)

Compound	Extent of reaction, % of theoretical		
	5 min.	1 hr.	24 hr.
α-Pinene	99.7	102.8	157.5
Δ³-Carene	97.9	124.8	135.7
Cyclohexene	12.9	40.0	96.9
1-Heptene	12.4	36.8	55.0
4,4-Dimethylpentene	4.1	23.9	49.4
Allyl alcohol	1.0	9.5	19.4
Methylallylcarbinol	1.4	10.5	60.2
Citronellol	93.2	99.6	100.1
Geraniol	46.3	50.8	51.7
Citronellal	85	100.0	100.2
Cinnamic aldehyde	0	0	0
Cinnamic acid	0	0	0
Citronellic acid	87.5	95.5	98.4
Mesityl oxide	2.2	3.2	14.2
Allylbenzene	—	2.4	58.3
Propenylbenzene	2.3	7.7	59.0
Safrole	1.5	14.6	82.6
Anethole	98.8	99.4	100.2

ever, compounds with two isolated double bonds (limonene, 1,5-hexadiene, geraniol, etc.) added thiocyanogen readily only to one of the ethylenic linkages (as observed earlier for linoleic acid), the other double bond reacting very slowly.

Characteristic behavior was observed for silicon-containing primary olefins (allylsilenes). The silicon-carbon bond is ruptured in these compounds on bromine addition and the reaction is accompanied by excessive bromine uptake (590). Only one mole of thiocyanogen was found to add to these compounds, and the reaction was quantitative in most cases within one hour. The reaction followed one of two courses:

$$R_3Si-CH_2-CH=CH_2 + (SCN)_2 \Big\langle \begin{array}{l} R_3Si-CH_2-CH(SCN)-CH_2(SCN) \\ R_3Si-SCN + CH_2(SCN)-CH=CH_2 \end{array}$$

7. Addition of Metal Salts

Olefins form addition compounds with many metal salts. More or less stable molecular complexes between olefins and salts of platinum, palladium, and copper have been reported. These compounds are regarded as

covalent coordination complexes. Silver and mercury salts also form
addition compounds with olefins; however, these compounds probably
involve ionic addition to the double bond. With the mercuric salts of
organic acids, or with basic or alkoxy mercuric salts, true addition compounds are formed by saturation of the double bond. Thus, olefins react
with mercuric acetate in acetic acid as follows:

$$>C=C< \; + \; Hg(O-\overset{\overset{O}{\|}}{C}-CH_3)_2 \; \longrightarrow \; \begin{array}{c} HgO-\overset{\overset{O}{\|}}{C}-CH_3 \\ | \\ -\overset{|}{C}-\overset{|}{C}- \\ | \\ CH_3-\overset{}{C}-O \\ \| \\ O \end{array}$$

In aqueous or alcoholic solution, the solvent participates in the reaction:

"Hydroxymercuration":

$$>C=O< \; + \; Hg(O-\overset{\overset{O}{\|}}{C}-CH_3)_2 \; + \; H_2O \; \longrightarrow \; \begin{array}{c} HgO-\overset{\overset{O}{\|}}{C}-CH_3 \\ | \\ -\overset{|}{C}-\overset{|}{C}- \\ | \\ OH \end{array} \; + \; CH_3COOH$$

"Alkoxymercuration":

$$>C=C< \; + \; Hg(O-\overset{\overset{O}{\|}}{C}-CH_3)_2 \; + \; ROH \; \longrightarrow \; \begin{array}{c} HgO-\overset{\overset{O}{\|}}{C}-CH_3 \\ | \\ -\overset{|}{C}-\overset{|}{C}- \\ | \\ OR \end{array} \; + \; CH_3COOH$$

Various reactions other than the simple addition may occur, depending
on the type of olefin and the reaction conditions. Thus, coordination
complexes, substitution products, oxidation products such as glycols and
carbonyl compounds, and polymeric materials may be formed under certain conditions.

Simple mercuric halides and mixed salts such as mercuric iodoacetate do
not add to olefins to any appreciable extent. The addition products formed
by mercuric salts such as the acetate can be decomposed to the free olefin
by treatment with hydrochloric acid.

The mechanism of the addition reaction is as yet uncertain. This subject and the chemistry of the mercury addition compounds have been reviewed in detail by Chatt (105). Two mechanisms, both having points in
their favor but neither completely satisfactory, are current. There are a

number of reasons in favor of an ionic mechanism analogous to the halogenation of olefins:

$$HgX_2 \rightleftharpoons (HgX)^+ + X^-$$

$$\underset{\overset{|}{C}}{\overset{\overset{|}{C}}{\|}} + (HgX)^+ \rightleftharpoons \left[\underset{\overset{|}{C}}{\overset{\overset{|}{C}}{\|}} \rightarrow HgX \right]^+$$

$$\left[\underset{\overset{|}{C}}{\overset{\overset{|}{C}}{\|}} \rightarrow HgX \right]^+ + ROH \rightleftharpoons \underset{-C-HgX}{\overset{RO-\overset{|}{C}-}{\underset{\overset{|}{H}}{|}}} \rightleftharpoons \underset{-C-HgX}{\overset{RO-\overset{|}{C}-}{|}} + H^+$$

This mechanism accounts for the observations that: (*1*) the addition gives solely the *trans* product, (*2*) the olefin is liberated predominantly in the original isomeric form by decomposition with hydrochloric acid, (*3*) the reaction is most rapid with the most ionic mercury salts, such as when $X^- = CH_3COO^-$ or NO_3^-, but is very slow when $X^- = Cl^-$, and does not occur at all when $X^- = CN^-$ or CNS^-, and (*4*) the solvent appears in the product. Certain other features of the reaction also favor an ionic mechanism.

A different mechanism, involving the formation of an alkoxy (or hydroxy) mercuric salt and coordination between the methoxyl oxygen atom and one carbon atom of the double bond, has been proposed by Wright (683):

$$HgX_2 + ROH \rightleftharpoons \overset{\overset{OR}{|}}{HgX} + HX$$

$$\underset{\overset{|}{C}}{\overset{\overset{|}{C}}{\|}} + \overset{OR}{\underset{HgX}{|}} \rightleftharpoons \underset{:\overset{}{C}}{\overset{-C\leftarrow OR}{\underset{HgX}{|}}} \rightleftharpoons \underset{XHg-\overset{|}{C}-}{\overset{-\overset{|}{C}-OR}{|}}$$

Several observations favoring such a nonionic mechanism have been reported (82,83).

Solutions of various mercury salts, such as mercuric nitrate (133) and mercuric sulfate (196), have been used for determination of gaseous olefins by absorption. The best reagent for complete absorption of olefins from gas mixtures appears to be a solution of mercuric sulfate in dilute sulfuric acid saturated with magnesium sulfate (84), described earlier (Section II.5.A). A method has been described for determination of low concentrations of ethylene in air by absorption in butanol and reaction with mercuric perchlorate. The ethylene–mercury complex is subsequently decomposed with hydrochloric acid to liberate ethylene, which is measured in a micromanometer (687). Isobutylene has been determined by passing the gas into mercuric nitrate solution (458) or mercuric sulfate solution (421) to form an insoluble complex, which is then isolated, dissolved in nitric acid, and titrated with potassium thiocyanate to establish the mercuric ion content.

Tausz (612) investigated the addition of mercuric acetate to various substituted olefins and employed the reaction for determination of olefinic unsaturation in petroleum oils (611) and turpentine (610). Since *cis*-olefins usually react more rapidly than their *trans*-isomers, the reaction rate has been used to determine the configuration of the *cis*- and *trans*-isomers of butene (614) and styryl cyanide (87) and for determination of isomer distribution in mixtures of *cis*- and *trans*-stilbene (154) and ethyl oleate and ethyl elaidate (112). Also, the reaction rate decreases with increasing substitution on the olefinic carbon atoms. Thus, reaction with mercuric acetate has been used to determine rapidly reacting 2,4,4-trimethyl-1-pentene in the presence of slowly reacting 2,4,4-trimethyl-2-pentene (597).

More recently, analytical procedures for determination of various olefinic materials have been described by Marquardt and Luce (414,415), Martin (420), and Das (140). In the first procedure reported by Marquardt and Luce (414), the sample is hydroxymercurated with mercuric acetate in 40% aqueous dioxane solution. Sodium hydroxide is added to convert the unconsumed mercuric acetate to mercuric oxide, which is then reduced to metallic mercury by boiling with hydrogen peroxide. The solution is acidified with nitric acid and titrated with ammonium thiocyanate, which reacts with the addition product to form mercuric thiocyanate with liberation of the original olefin. The method was found applicable to styrene, ethylvinylbenzene, divinylbenzene, and certain other styrene derivatives such as α-methylstyrene and vinyltoluene.

Because this method gave low results with dichlorostyrene, Marquardt and Luce subsequently employed a somewhat different procedure (415), in which the sample is reacted with excess mercuric acetate in methanol solution:

$$RCH{=}CH_2 + Hg(OOCCH_3)_2 + CH_3OH \longrightarrow$$

$$RCH(OCH_3){-}CH_2HgO{-}CO{-}CH_3 + CH_3COOH$$

The unconsumed mercuric acetate is treated with acetone and a measured excess of standard sodium hydroxide solution to form a soluble complex, trimercuric diacetone hydrate:

$$3Hg(OOCCH_3)_2 + 2CH_3COCH_3 + 6NaOH \longrightarrow$$

$$+ 6CH_3COONa + 3H_2O$$

After addition of potassium iodide to convert the mercuric acetate–methoxy addition product to the corresponding mercuric iodide–methoxy compound:

$$RCH(OCH_3)-CH_2HgO-CO-CH_3 + KI \longrightarrow$$

$$RCH(OCH_3)-CH_2HgI + CH_3COOK$$

and to regenerate the hydroxide consumed in formation of the trimercuric diacetone hydrate:

$$+ 12KI + 3H_2O \longrightarrow$$

$$6KOH + 3K_2HgI_4 + 2CH_3COCH_3$$

the excess hydroxide is determined by partially neutralizing with a standard amount of dilute acetic acid solution and titrating with hydrochloric acid to the disappearance of the pink phenolphthalein color. The difference between this titration and a blank determination provides a measure of the acetic acid formed in the methoxymercuration and is therefore a measure of the olefinic double bond content.

Reagent. The mercuric acetate reagent is prepared by dissolving 38.0 grams of analytical-reagent grade mercuric acetate in approximately 900 ml. of methanol and 2.0 ml. of glacial acetic acid. The solution is diluted to 1 liter with methanol and filtered. This reagent is approximately 0.24 N.

Procedure. A weighed amount of sample containing approximately 4 millimoles of olefinic material is added to precisely 50 ml. of mercuric acetate reagent and mixed. The mixture is allowed to stand for 5 minutes at room temperature. (A longer time or higher temperature may be necessary. For dichlorostyrene, the mixture is heated to 50°C. for 1 hour in a tightly sealed bottle.) 10 ml. of acetone is then added, 20 ml. of 1 N sodium hydroxide is pipetted into the flask, and the mixture is swirled occasionally until all the mercuric oxide is dissolved. Then 25 ml. of 30% aqueous potassium iodide solution (neutral to phenol-

TABLE XXIV. Analytical Results on Olefinic Compounds by Methoxymercuration Methods
(Results obtained by original authors, except where noted)

Compound	Method of Marquardt and Luce (415)		Method of Martin (420)		Method of Das (140)	
	Reaction conditions	Per cent found[a]	Reaction conditions	Per cent found[a]	Reaction conditions	Per cent found[a]
Styrene	5 min., 25°C.; 5–10 min., 30°C.	99.4–99.7(5); 99.4, 99.7[b]	10–15 min., 25°C.	99.7–99.9(4)	5–10 min., 30°C.	99.2, 99.6
α-Methylstyrene	—	Low[c]				Low[c]
Ethoxystyrene	5 min., 25°C.	ca. 100[e]				
Ethylvinylbenzene	"	98.7–98.8(3) }	10–15 min., 25°C.	100.1, 100.5[d]		
Divinylbenzene	"	98.8–99.0(3) }				
Vinyltoluene	"	ca. 100[e]				
Vinylxylene	"	ca. 100[e]				
Monochlorostyrene	15 min., 25°C.	ca. 100[e]				
Vinylchlorostyrene	"	ca. 100[e]				
2,5-Dichlorostyrene	"	99.8–100.1(5)				
Cyclohexene	1 hr., 50°C.	96.7, 96.3[b]	10–15 min., 25°C.	96.8	10–15 min., 30°C.	96.6, 96.9
Divinyl ether	10–15 min., 30°C.		"	99.9		
Diallyl ether	—		"	99.5, 98.7		
Allyl alcohol	30 min., 30°C.	97.7[b]	"	101.5	30 min., 30°C.	98.2, 98.2
Crotyl alcohol	—		"	15		
β-Chloroallyl alcohol	—		"	201		
Vinyl acetate	30 min., 30°C.	88, 76[b]	10–15 min., 25°C.	187	30 min., 30°C.	97.4, 96.8
Allyl acetate	"	33, 28[b]	"	94.5	"	96.9–97.5(3)
Vinyl benzoate	—		"	44		
Diallyl phthalate	—		"	1.3		
Methyl acrylate	—	Low[b,c]	"	4.0		Low[c]
Methyl methacrylate	—	Low[b,c]	"	Trace		Low[c]
Diethyl maleate	—		"	3.4		
Diethyl itaconate	—		"	40		
Acrylonitrile	—		"	99.4, 99.7		
2-Vinylpyridine	—		"			
N-Vinylcarbazole	—		"			
Rotenone	—		25 min., 25°C.	100.0[e]		

[a] Number in parentheses indicates the number of replicate determinations.   [b] Results obtained by Das (140).   [c] Numerical data not given in the original publication.   [d] Results on a mixture, compared with the method of Marquardt and Luce (415).   [e] Results obtained by Hornstein (278).

phthalein) is added. Most of the excess alkali is neutralized by pipetting 20 ml. of 0.65 N acetic acid into the flask while swirling to prevent any part of the solution from becoming acidic. Phenolphthalein (20 to 30 drops of 1% indicator solution) is added and the titration is completed with standard 0.1 N hydrochloric acid, swirling constantly, to the disappearance of the pink color.

A blank determination is made in the same manner, omitting the sample. For convenience, the concentration of the acetic acid solution should be adjusted such that the blank titration is approximately 49 ml. of 0.1 N hydrochloric acid.

Calculation. The number of milliequivalents of acid required to titrate the blank minus the number of milliequivalents required to titrate the sample represents the number of millimoles of monoolefin in the sample.

This procedure was successfully used for the determination of styrene, ethylvinylbenzene, divinylbenzene, vinyltoluene, vinylxylene, and ethoxystyrene (reaction time 5 minutes at room temperature (415)), cyclohexene (140), monochlorostyrene and vinylchlorotoluene (15 minutes at room temperature (415)), allyl alcohol (30 minutes at room temperature (140)), and 2,5-dichlorostyrene (1 hour at 50°C (415)). Low results were obtained with α-methylstyrene (415), and with vinyl and allyl acetate (140). Typical results on various substances are included in Table XXIV. Compounds not containing terminal double bonds, such as propenylbenzene, react slowly and not quantitatively; under favorable conditions, terminal unsaturation may be determined in the presence of other unsaturated compounds.

Martin (420) has described a somewhat similar procedure based on measuring the acetic acid formed by methoxymercuration. Martin's procedure differs from the acidimetric method of Marquardt and Luce in that the reaction is conducted in a mixture of carbon tetrachloride and methanol, and sodium chloride is added to convert the excess mercuric acetate to mercuric chloride in order to permit direct titration with standard alkali of the acetic acid formed in the analytical reaction. Sodium nitrate may be added to accelerate the methoxymercuration reaction.

Reagent. Mercuric acetate, analytical-reagent grade (low in free acetic acid content), thoroughly blended before use.

Procedure. A weighed portion of sample containing approximately 4 millimoles of olefinic material is introduced into 20 to 25 ml. of carbon tetrachloride. Then 4.00 g. of mercuric acetate and 30 ml. of methanol (acid- and aldehyde-free) are added. If the sample reacts slowly, the use of 30 ml. of a saturated solution of sodium nitrate in methanol in place of pure methanol will increase the reaction rate. The flask is stoppered, swirled, and warmed slightly, if necessary, to dissolve the mercuric acetate. The mixture is allowed to stand for 10 to 15 minutes at room temperature. At the end of the reaction period, 75 ml. of neutral saturated sodium chloride solution and 50 to 100 ml. of water are added. Phenolphthalein solution (20 drops) is added and the mixture is titrated with standard 0.1 N sodium hydroxide to a light pink color while shaking vigorously to extract the acetic acid from the carbon tetrachloride layer.

A blank determination is made immediately after mixing the reagents, omitting the sample. The blank has a tendency to increase slowly if allowed to stand.

Calculation. The number of milliequivalents of alkali required to titrate the sample, after correction for the blank, represents the number of millimoles of monoolefin in the sample.

This procedure was found to give satisfactory results with styrene, ethylvinylbenzene, divinylbenzene, allyl alcohol, crotyl alcohol, divinyl ether, diallyl ether, certain allyl esters, and N-vinylcarbazole. Low results were obtained with acrylate, methacrylate, itaconate, and maleate esters and with β-chloroallyl alcohol, acrylonitrile, and 2-vinylpyridine. High values (approximately twice theory) were obtained with vinyl esters, probably because of hydrolysis. Typical results on various materials are shown in Table XXIV.

Hornstein (278) used a procedure similar to that of Martin for determination of rotenone; ethylene dichloride was used in place of carbon tetrachloride and a reaction time of 25 minutes at room temperature was adopted (see Table XXIV).

Das (140) has reported a procedure based on the measuring of unconsumed mercuric acetate, rather than the acetic acid liberated. The excess mercuric acetate in the reaction mixture is titrated with hydrochloric acid in a medium of propylene glycol and chloroform, using thymol blue as indicator:

$$Hg(OOCCH_3)_2 + 2HCl \longrightarrow HgCl_2 + 2CH_3COOH$$

The methoxymercuration product also reacts, but consumes only one equivalent of hydrochloric acid:

$$\underset{\substack{| \\ OCH_3 \;\; HgO-C-CH_3 \\ \;\;\;\;\;\; \| \\ \;\;\;\;\;\; O}}{-C\!-\!-\!-\!C-} + HCl \longrightarrow \underset{\substack{| \\ OCH_3 \;\; HgCl}}{-C\!-\!-\!-\!C-} + CH_3COOH$$

The color change at the end point (yellow to pink) is very sharp. Mercuric chloride may be precipitated during the titration but does not interfere with the detection of the end point.

Reagents. The mercuric acetate reagent is prepared by dissolving 20 g. of analytical-reagent grade mercuric acetate in 500 ml. of methanol and 1 ml. of glacial acetic acid. The reagent is standardized by titration in propylene glycol–chloroform (1:1) solvent medium with standard $0.1N$ hydrochloric acid in the same solvent medium, using thymol blue as indicator.

The standard hydrochloric acid solution is prepared by adding 8 to 9 ml. of concentrated hydrochloric acid to 1 liter of propylene glycol–chloroform mixture (1:1). It is standardized against a weighed amount (ca. 0.2 g.) of analytical-reagent grade mercuric oxide dissolved in 5 ml. of acetic acid, evaporated nearly to dryness, and redissolved in 25 ml. of propylene glycol–chloroform; thymol blue is used as indicator.

Procedure. A weighed portion of sample containing approximately 2 millimoles of olefinic material is introduced into a measured volume (20 to 25 ml.) of standardized mercuric acetate reagent. The mixture is allowed to stand at room temperature for 10 to 30 minutes. The reaction mixture is diluted with about 25 ml. of propylene glycol–chloroform (1:1, neutral to thymol blue) and then titrated with standard 0.1 N hydrochloric acid in propylene glycol–chloroform to the thymol blue end point.

Calculation. The number of milliequivalents of hydrochloric acid corresponding to the quantity of mercuric acetate reagent added minus the number of milliequivalents of acid used in titrating the sample represents the number of millimoles of monoolefin in the sample.

This procedure is particularly useful for determination of unsaturated esters such as vinyl acetate and allyl acetate, for which the procedures of Marquardt and Luce and Martin do not give quantitative results because of hydrolysis. The determination of excess mercuric acetate by the Das procedure was found to give satisfactory results for these unsaturated esters, as well as for allyl alcohol, styrene, and cyclohexene (140). All mercury addition compounds of olefinic substances are unstable toward halogen acids. With the above unsaturated compounds, the decomposition is very slow, such that the end point is stable for several minutes. However, in some cases, such as with α-methylstyrene, cinnamic acid, and diisobutylene, the addition products decompose so rapidly that the titration with hydrochloric acid is not possible under the conditions of the method. Typical results by the Das procedure on various substances are included in Table XXIV.

These mercuration methods are most suitable for determination of unsaturated compounds containing a terminal double bond or an internal double bond with a *cis*-configuration (e. g., cyclohexene). α,β-Unsaturated nitriles (e. g., acrylonitrile) and esters (e. g., acrylates, methacrylates, and maleates) do not react quantitatively under the conditions employed.

It is to be expected that α,β-unsaturated aldehydes and ketones also would not be determined by these methods.

8. Addition of Maleic Anhydride

The addition of maleic anhydride to a diene is the most important of the limited number of chemical methods available for the determination of conjugated ethylenic systems. The reaction, first studied in detail by Diels, Alder, and their co-workers (147), involves the condensation of a conjugated diene, through its 1,4-carbon atoms, with a dienophile to form a six-membered hydroaromatic ring:

A great variety of compounds containing an ethylenic or acetylenic linkage, usually activated by additional unsaturation or by one or more electron-supplying groups, may serve as dienophiles and have been utilized in synthetic work (98,276,350,464). Of these, maleic anhydride is possibly the most important and has been used almost exclusively in analytical work.

Several mechanisms (polar, radical, biradical molecular rearrangement) have been proposed for this reaction and are discussed in detail by Ingold (286).

The ease of reaction is governed by the character of the double bonds forming the diene. With acyclic dienes, stereoisomeric differences affect the rate of reaction to a marked extent. The *trans-trans* diolefins react with great facility at room temperature when the components are mixed in equivalent proportions. The *cis-trans* isomer requires more drastic conditions and, due to steric hindrance, the *cis-cis* compound is usually completely unreactive. These effects were demonstrated by von Mikusch (431) with *cis-trans* linoleates, and by Alder and Vogt (9) with *cis-2-trans-*4- and all-*trans* hexadiene and other dienes. Excessive alkyl substitution at the ends of the diene system reduces reactivity, and halogen atoms on the doubly bound carbon atoms may render the system completely inert toward the reagent. Polyenic systems react in such a manner that the double bonds are saturated in pairs. Allenes and higher cumulenes, however, do not add maleic anhydride. Five- and six-membered alicyclic compounds that contain conjugated systems in the ring frequently react readily with maleic anhydride in the cold, but seven-membered rings may require heating. In the resulting bridged ring adduct, the carbonyl groups of the maleic anhydride component are oriented to the *endo* position. Substitution on the ring (alkyl, aryl, or alkoxy groups) influences but does not destroy the reactivity of the ring conjugated system. However, when the diene system is partially in the side chain, or when the conjugation extends over two rings of a polycyclic compound, reaction may not occur to any measurable extent. Polymerization of the dienes, or copolymerization with the reagent, sometimes takes place in strong competition with the Diels-Alder reaction; especially dienes with substitution on the terminal carbon atoms of the conjugated chain (such as 2-methyl-2,4-hexadiene or terpenes with conjugated systems within the ring) tend to produce polymers rather than normal adducts. In some cases (e. g., 1,1-diphenylethylene) the adduct contains two molecules of maleic anhydride.

These features of the Diels-Alder synthesis greatly hinder the quantitative analytical evaluation of the reaction. In addition, the reaction is not free of disturbing interferences encountered when complex products (especially petroleum distillates) are to be analyzed. Thus, an aromatic double bond in conjugation with an ethylenic linkage in the side chain may produce an active system to form adducts with maleic anhydride, as has been observed for 1-vinylnaphthalene, 9-propenylphenanthrene, and certain derivatives of styrene. The reaction of polycyclic hydrocarbons with maleic anhydride is reversible, and results in an equilibrium mixture that is shifted in favor of the adduct with lower temperature, and higher excess of maleic anhydride (35,351,352). The reaction time may have to be prolonged to reach this equilibrium. By using thirty moles of maleic anhydride to one of the hydrocarbon in boiling benzene, 80 to 99% yields of adduct were obtained from anthracene and several of its derivatives. The *endo* succinic anhydride component of the adduct bridges the 9,10-carbon atoms of the anthracene molecule. Lower equilibrium yields, 1 to 45%, were observed for a number of alkylnaphthalenes, and 90% for 1,2,3,4-tetramethylnaphthalene, under conditions similar to those employed for the anthracenes. Several heterocyclic compounds (furans, some substituted thiophenes, many nitrogen heterocycles) also react with maleic anhydride.

The reaction is usually carried out at room temperature or by warming the reactants either along or in an inert solvent. Catalytic agents are not required, although the reaction is susceptible to general acid catalysis;

hence, the use of basic solvents (e. g., dioxane) should be avoided. Results are expressed as "diene number" or "maleic anhydride value" and are often calculated in terms of the number of grams of iodine equivalent to the maleic anhydride used per 100 grams of sample.

The first analytical method based on the Diels-Alder addition of maleic anhydride to conjugated fats and oils was developed by Kaufmann and Baltes (324,325). Although the method was intended for fat analysis, it may be applied to other compounds with suitable modifications. It involves the heating of the sample with an acetone solution of excess maleic anhydride in a sealed tube at 100° C. for 20 hours. The cooled solution is poured into water and the hydrolyzed excess anhydride is determined by titration with standard alkali in the water solution after separating it from the oily layer by filtration. Alternatively, the excess acid is determined iodometrically. This procedure, modified in some details, was recommended by Priest and von Mikusch (499) for the analysis of dehydrated castor oil.

A similar method was announced a short time later by Ellis and Jones (171), who employed toluene as solvent and dispensed with the sealed tube in favor of refluxing under an efficient condenser in a nitrogen atmosphere for 3 hours. After hydrolyzing the excess anhydride, ether is added and the maleic acid washed out in a separating funnel for titration. In a variation of this method, a small amount of iodine, added to the reaction mixture as catalyst, enabled Ellis and Jones to reduce the reaction time to 1 hour. Although both Kaufmann and Baltes, and Ellis and Jones, showed that their methods gave theoretical, or nearly theoretical, results on a number of pure compounds, subsequent checks (398) gave low values on α-eleostearic acid by the Kaufmann method and several investigators (52,88,153,481) cast doubt on the reliability of both methods when applied to fatty materials. Dependence on reaction conditions (sample size in particular) and the reactivity of maleic anhydride with certain configurations in the sample (hydroxyl groups, peroxides, and other oxidation products) are the chief reasons why the diene value is considered only an approximate index of conjugated unsaturation in fats and oils. At present the Ellis and Jones modification is the more accepted procedure; it has been adopted by the A. S. T. M. and is being considered by the A. O. C. S. The following details are from A. S. T. M. Standard D 555–54 (17):

Procedure. The fatty sample (3 g.) is placed in an erlenmeyer flask and freshly filtered maleic anhydride reagent (25 ml., 6% in toluene) is added. Another flask is prepared with reagent alone as a blank. Both flasks are gently refluxed under air condensers on a hot plate for 3 hours. Freshly boiled and cooled distilled water (5 ml.) is added to both flasks and the refluxing is continued for 15 minutes. When cool, ether (5 ml.) and water (10 ml.) are added to both flasks through the condensers; then the contents are quantitatively transferred to separatory funnels using ether (45 ml.) and water (45 ml.) in several portions. After shaking, the lower phase is drawn off and the ether layer is further extracted with five portions (25, 10, 10, 10, 10 ml.) of water. The combined aqueous extracts are titrated with 1 N standard sodium hydroxide using phenolphthalein indicator.

Recent work by von Mikusch (431,434) showed that a great deal of the difficulties encountered in the analytical applications of the Diels-Alder synthesis may be explained by stereoisomeric differences in the configuration of the conjugated system. The *cis-trans* conjugated linoleates were shown to react very slowly, if at all, with maleic anhydride at temperatures of about 100°C. or lower, whereas the *trans-trans* isomers reacted readily under these conditions. These observations seem to indicate that a pair of conjugated acyclic double bonds must be *trans-trans* in order to react completely with maleic anhydride at 100°C. or lower, the temperature range of both common maleic anhydride methods.

Based on these assumptions, von Mikusch developed a method in which a small amount of iodine is used to catalyze the conversion of *cis* configurations (prominent in natural oils) to the reactive *trans* arrangement. The catalytic effect of iodine for such purposes has long been known and has been used extensively in the study of configurations of carotenoids which contain long polyenic chains (689). Although iodine catalysis always leads to an equilibrium of the possible stereoisomers, continual elimination of the reactive all-*trans* form should lead to quantitative addition. The name, "pandiene number," was proposed by von Mikusch for the results when iodine treatment was used. The method is essentially the Kaufmann-Baltes procedure with 1 ml. of a 0.1% solution of iodine in acetone added to the reaction mixture. Certain conjugated linoleic acid isomers that did not react appreciably with maleic anhydride gave quantitative results; for isomers that were proved to contain the *trans-trans* configuration (432,433), the theoretical diene value was obtained by both the Kaufmann-Baltes and the pandiene number method. As a further proof, good agreement was shown with conjugation calculated from ultraviolet absorption measurements on a number of natural samples. This latter technique has repeatedly shown higher values on such materials and, by revealing residual conjugated unsaturation in uncatalyzed maleic anhydride reaction mixtures, clearly pointed to incomplete addition.

Relatively few publications have appeared dealing with the determination of dienes in petroleum products by means of maleic anhydride. This is partly due to the development of spectrometric methods, especially for the analysis of C_4 and C_5 dienes. A gasometric method of analysis was developed by Tropsch and Mattox (619), who showed that 1,3-butadiene can be accurately determined in a special absorption pipet containing molten maleic anhydride (at 100°C.). For the successful application of this method to samples containing isobutylene in concentrations 10% or higher, Robey, Morrell, and Vanderbilt (524) found it necessary to use redistilled maleic anhydride and to add about 1% di-n-amylamine to the reagent. The difficulties were attributed to the polymerizing action on the tertiary olefin of small amounts of free maleic acid as a contaminant in the anhydride. Work by Brooks, Lykken, Milligan, Nebeker, and Zahn (84) showed that the maleic anhydride must contain about 7% diamylamine to inhibit the polymerization of isobutylene when a water-saturated sample is used. A scheme involving the removal of most of the isobutylene by first passing the sample through a 50% solution of sulfuric acid was proposed by Roman (528). The molten maleic anhydride technique is also applicable to the determination of isoprene and cyclopentadiene (526) but of the two stereoisomeric piperylenes only the *trans*-compound was found to react readily under the conditions of the method (525). Several publications (e. g., 84,174,227) deal with modifications of the original absorption apparatus. The method of the A. S. T. M. (19) employs a stream of carbon dioxide to sweep the unreactive portion of the sample through the molten reagent; the residual gas volume is measured over a solution of potassium hydroxide.

The application of the Diels-Alder synthesis, using maleic anhydride, to gasoline-range hydrocarbon samples met with somewhat less success. The gravimetric methods of Birch and Scott (55) and of Kurtz and Headington (369) were preparative in scale and cumbersome for analytical purposes. A titrimetric procedure developed by Grosse-Oetringhaus (231) consisted in heating the hydrocarbon mixture with an excess of a solution of maleic anhydride in xylene (0.2 M). In order to minimize polymerization and possible reactions between ethylenic hydrocarbons and the reagent, the temperature was not allowed to rise over 100°C. Results were not consistent, the diene number tending to increase with reaction time, which was varied from 5 to 30 hours. Results obtained in toluene medium were less reliable. A method that has been in use in the authors' laboratories (568) utilizes the short (iodine-catalyzed) procedure of Ellis and Jones, but the sample is reacted with the maleic anhydride–toluene solution (3%) in a pressure bottle in a steam bath. The method is precise and the over-all accuracy is assumed to be satisfactory for gasoline range samples where the diene concentrations encountered usually do not exceed a few per cent.

A method based on the addition of chloromaleic anhydride to conjugated dienes was published by Putnam, Moss, and Hall (504). The highly reactive tertiary chlorine atom in the adduct is determined by the Volhard method, after refluxing with aqueous silver nitrate. The vinyl chlorine of the reagent is completely unreactive under the same conditions. The use of an empirical correction factor was found necessary because even with extensive purification it was difficult to obtain chloromaleic anhydride that gave theoretical results. Results on standard samples containing isoprene, cyclopentadiene, and butadiene were accurate to about 0.5%.

9. Other Chemical Methods

A variety of chemical methods in addition to those described in the earlier sections of this chapter have been used to determine olefinic compounds. Most of these miscellaneous methods are limited in scope; that is, only certain types of olefinic substances are determinable by the particular method. However, such selectivity may be useful when analysis for one olefinic compound or type in the presence of other unsaturated materials is desired.

A. ADDITION OF MERCAPTANS

Reaction with a mercaptan, e. g., dodecanethiol (lauryl mercaptan), has been used for determination of acrylonitrile and α,β-unsaturated aldehydes and esters (45). In alkaline alcohol solution, the reaction with excess mercaptan goes to completion in 2 to 15 minutes at room temperature:

$$R-CH=CH-CN + R'SH \rightleftharpoons RCH(SR')-CH_2-CN$$
$$R-CH=CH-CHO + R'SH \rightleftharpoons RCH(SR')-CH_2-CHO$$
$$R-CH=CH-COOR + R'SH \rightleftharpoons RCH(SR')-CH_2-COOR$$

The unconsumed mercaptan can be determined either by titration with iodine to a visual end point or by electrometric titration with silver nitrate. Analytical results and mean deviations found (45) for various purified materials were: acrylonitrile $99.7 \pm 0.2\%$, crotonaldehyde $99.4 \pm 0.1\%$, cinnamaldehyde $99.4 \pm 0.2\%$, methyl acrylate $99.8 \pm 0.1\%$, ethyl acrylate $98.4 \pm 0.0\%$, methyl methacrylate $98.8 \pm 0.2\%$, allyl crotonate $98.7 \pm 0.3\%$, and diethyl maleate $99.3 \pm 0.1\%$. The reaction is apparently not quantitative with α,β-unsaturated ketones unless a very large excess of mercaptan is used.   Unsaturated acids and their salts do not react.   The method is essentially specific for α,β-unsaturated carbonyl compounds (including esters) and related nitriles.   Some other unsaturated compounds tested, including acetylene, allyl acetate, allyl alcohol, benzanilide, butadiene, myrcene, vinyl chloride, and 2-vinylpyridine, were found to give no reaction.   Vinyl acetate reacted partially, possibly by acetylation of the mercaptan.   Interferences from elemental sulfur, peroxides, hydroquinone, and quinone were reported (45).   Slow oxidation of the mercaptan by air can be minimized by using a short reaction time and a small reagent excess whenever possible and by making a proportional blank correction, or by blanketing the reaction mixture with nitrogen or carbon dioxide.

The mercaptan addition reaction has been used to determine acrylonitrile in air (247).   The air is bubbled through a cold solution of dodecanethiol in isopropyl alcohol.   Potassium hydroxide is then added to catalyze the reaction between the mercaptan and the acrylonitrile.   After acidification with acetic acid, an amount of iodine equivalent to the original mercaptan content is added.   The residual iodine, which is proportional to the amount of acrylonitrile, is then measured by light absorption.   The average recovery of added 20 to 100 mg. of acrylonitrile per cubic meter of air was found to be approximately 90%, which was satisfactory for the purpose of the method.   Other α,β-unsaturated nitriles, aldehydes, and esters would be determined by the method.

B. REACTION WITH THIOGLYCOLIC ACID

Many olefinic compounds react with thioglycolic acid (mercaptoacetic acid), $HS-CH_2-COOH$, to form compounds of the type $R_2CH-CR_2-S-CH_2COOH$.   The first unsaturated substances reported to react in this manner include rubber (274), fatty oils (34), and styrene (275).   Hoog and Eichwald (277) studied the reaction as a possible analytical method for removing olefins from hydrocarbon mixtures.   The addition of propionic acid to the two-phase system of hydrocarbon and thioglycolic acid was found to produce a homogeneous solution, resulting in rapid reaction at room temperature.   When treated for 1 hour at 20°C. with an excess of thioglycolic acid (3 moles/mole of olefin) and sufficient propionic acid to result in homogeneity, followed by neutralization with caustic, many olefins were found to be removed from n-heptane solution.   Of the C_5 to C_8 olefins studied, those of the types $RCH=CH_2$ and $RCH=CHR$ were found to be readily removed, except that the type $R_3C-CH=CHR$, e. g., 4,4-dimethyl-2-pentene, was not removed at all.   (Other studies show that the type R_2CH—CH=CHR, e. g., 4-methyl-2-pentene, also does not react.) Cyclohexene is removed almost completely. Partial to complete removal of the types R_2C=CH_2 and R_2C=CHR, and partial removal of the type R_2C=CR_2, can be obtained. More complete removal of these partially removed types can be realized by using a greater excess of thioglycolic acid and longer reaction time.

The scope of thioglycolic acid methods for quantitative determination of olefinic unsaturation is limited by the partial reaction or lack of reaction for certain types of olefins and by the fact that catalytic effects of air, peroxides, and light introduce complications (134,566). However, the reaction has been used to measure olefin content (from decrease in volume) and also to prepare an olefin-free portion for subsequent determination of aromatics, paraffins, and naphthenes in hydrocarbon mixtures (277). It is also possible to measure the unconsumed excess thioglycolic acid by titration with standard iodine solution. The reaction has also been employed by Holmberg (273) to determine the rubber content of kok-saghyz, obtained from a rubber-bearing dandelion, by comparison with the yield in the reaction of *Hevea* rubber with thioglycolic acid (95%). Balata and gutta-percha were reported to react similarly to rubber (273). Cunneen (134), however, was unable to obtain a reaction between thioglycolic acid and rubber or squalene, although cyclohexene, 1-methylcyclohexene, and dihydromyrcene reacted readily with thioglycolic acid in the presence of ascaridole or when ordinary laboratory specimens, presumably containing peroxides, were used. Reactions of thioglycolic acid and other mercaptans with cyclohexene, oleic acid, linoleic acid, 10-undecylenic acid, and various polymers have been described by Serniuk, Banes, and Swaney (566). Copolymers of butadiene and styrene or acrylonitrile were found to react readily under mild conditions to give double bond saturation values of 38 to 47%. Natural rubber, however, was found to react very slowly. The difference in reaction rates indicates different double bond structures in the polymers; the readily reacting double bonds in butadiene polymers seem to be predominantly those present as vinyl side groups.

C. ADDITION OF BISULFITE

Carbonyl compounds, especially aldehydes, react reversibly with bisulfite or sulfite to form addition compounds. Analytical procedures based on this reaction have been described in Volume I of *Organic Analysis* (442). α,β-Unsaturated aldehydes such as acrolein and crotonaldehyde consume two moles of bisulfite per mole:

$$\text{R—CH=CH—CHO} + 2\text{HSO}_3{}^- \longrightarrow \underset{\underset{\text{SO}_3{}^-}{|}}{\text{R—CH}}\text{—}\underset{}{\text{CH}_2}\text{—}\underset{\underset{\text{SO}_3{}^-}{|}}{\text{CHOH}}$$

The addition to the ethylenic double bond is irreversible. This fact has been employed in analytical methods for separation of saturated from α,β-unsaturated carbonyl compounds by distillation (579) or by means of anion exchange columns in the bisulfite form (580,581).

Certain unsaturated acids, esters, and nitriles also react with bisulfite to form addition compounds. Thus, bisulfite adds to the double bond of maleic acid when the reaction mixture is heated:

$$
\begin{array}{ccc}
\text{COOH} & & \text{COOH}\\
| & & |\\
\text{CH} & & \text{CH}_2\\
\| & + \text{HSO}_3{}^- \longrightarrow & |\\
\text{CH} & & \text{CHSO}_3{}^-\\
| & & |\\
\text{COOH} & & \text{COOH}
\end{array}
$$

This reaction was used by Rosenthaler (537) for determination of maleic acid; under the conditions adopted, fumaric acid could not be determined. The reaction conditions have been studied by Wurzschmitt (684). Conditions were found under which fumaric acid and its esters will not react; under other conditions, the fumaric acid is isomerized to maleic acid, which reacts more readily. By combination of different conditions, the determination of formaldehyde, crotonaldehyde, maleic acid, fumaric acid, and a saturated acid such as benzoic acid in the presence of each other is possible (684). The reaction was studied further by Critchfield and Johnson (130), who established conditions for quantitative determination of acrylic acid, methyl acrylate, ethyl acrylate, acrylonitrile, crotonic acid, maleic acid, diethyl maleate, and diethyl fumarate. The analytical procedure is based on the decrease in acidity, as determined by titration with sodium hydroxide to alizarin yellow R–xylene cyanole FF mixed indicator. Because of side reactions or slow reaction rates, amides and certain substituted acids, esters, and nitriles cannot be determined by this procedure.

D. REACTION WITH SULFUR DIOXIDE

Sulfur dioxide reacts with many unsaturated hydrocarbons, alcohols, aldehydes, and acids at moderate temperatures in the presence of light or a catalyst to form resinous polysulfones. This reaction has been discussed by Grummitt and Ardis (232); it does not appear to be useful for quantitative analysis.

A different reaction with sulfur dioxide may be obtained in the case of conjugated diolefins. In the presence of an antioxidant to avoid formation of polysulfones, sulfur dioxide reacts by 1,4-addition to the conjugated system to form an unsaturated cyclic sulfone in a manner similar to the Diels-Alder addition of maleic anhydride to conjugated diolefins:

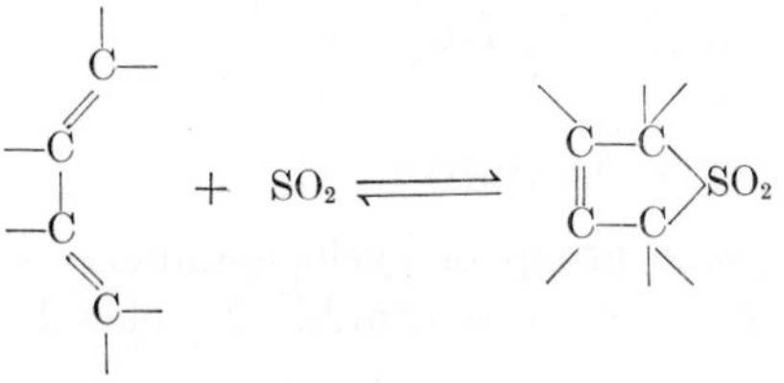

Since these cyclic sulfones are water-soluble and can be decomposed to regenerate the diolefin and sulfur dioxide, this reaction has been used to separate conjugated diolefins from other unsaturated hydrocarbons. Thus, butadiene can be separated from admixture with butanes and butylenes, and isoprene can be separated from C_5 hydrocarbons (232). This procedure provides a good means for purification of conjugated diolefins, but since reported recoveries are only semiquantitative (70 to 80%) the method is of limited value for analysis. Addition of maleic anhydride appears to be more general and quantitative.

E. REACTION WITH SULFUR MONOCHLORIDE

Olefinic hydrocarbons react readily with sulfur monochloride, S_2Cl_2, to form chlorinated mono- and disulfide compounds. The reaction is vigorous and nearly quantitative. The products are high-boiling, and unreacted hydrocarbons can be separated from them by distillation. Lorand (390) suggested this reaction as a means for determination of olefins in petroleum distillates. He found that saturated hydrocarbons react slowly to form chlorinated materials but that comparative values for olefins in petroleum fractions could be obtained. Faragher, Morrell, and Levine (184) employed reaction with sulfur monochloride, followed by distillation, to remove olefins before determination of aromatic hydrocarbons. These workers conducted the reaction under conditions such that essentially only the olefins are reacted but less than 1% olefins remain unreacted. The aromatic hydrocarbon content of the olefin-free distillate was subtracted from the sum of olefins and aromatics found by absorption in sulfuric acid to provide a measure of the olefin content. Satisfactory results were obtained for synthetic mixtures and cracked gasoline samples.

Harvey and Schuette (245) concluded that measurement of the heat of reaction of sulfur monochloride with unsaturated fatty oils is at best of only limited analytical value because of nonspecificity of reaction with double bonds and inconsistent results with oils of the same degree of unsaturation. However, certain organic compounds such as pyridine were found to catalyze the reaction such that increases in reaction velocity are characteristic of individual fatty oils.

F. REACTION WITH CARBONYL COMPOUNDS

The active methylene group of cyclopentadiene reacts with carbonyl compounds in alkaline solution to form highly colored fulvenes:

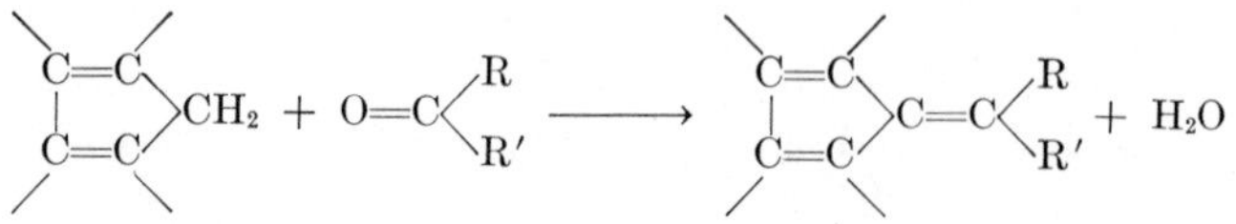

This reaction is the basis for a colorimetric method for determination of cyclopentadiene described by Uhrig, Lynch, and Becker (624). Benzaldehyde was found to be most satisfactory as the reagent; the color of the phenylfulvene formed (yellow to orange) was found to be stable for at least 2 hours. Dicyclopentadiene, formed by spontaneous dimerization, does not react, but it can be quantitatively depolymerized to the monomer and subsequently determined.

The reaction was extended to mixtures of cyclopentadiene and methylcyclopentadiene in hydrocarbon mixtures by Powell, Edson, and Fisher (493). From the absorption coefficients for the reaction product of each compound with benzaldehyde and also for the products with acetone, the individual concentrations of cyclopentadiene and methylcyclopentadiene can be calculated by means of simultaneous equations. Paraffinic, naphthenic, aromatic, and other olefinic hydrocarbons (except substituted cyclopentadienes) do not interfere.

The reaction with benzaldehyde can also be employed for the colorimetric determination of indene, which undergoes a reaction similar to cyclopentadiene, but at a considerably slower rate. Analytical procedures have been reported by Skoog and DuBois (583) and by Roman and Smith (529).

G. ADDITION OF FORMIC ACID

Formic acid, at its boiling point, readily adds to the double bond of many olefinic materials to form formate esters. The reaction has been studied by Knight, Koos, and Swern (353), who prepared such products from 1-hexene, cyclohexene, oleic acid, elaidic acid, undecylenic acid, methyl oleate, and oleyl alcohol.   The yields obtained were not sufficiently quantitative (55 to 80% addition) for analytical use.   However, Bergmann and Japhe (51) found that the reaction of dicyclopentadiene with formic acid goes to completion when the mixture is refluxed for five hours:

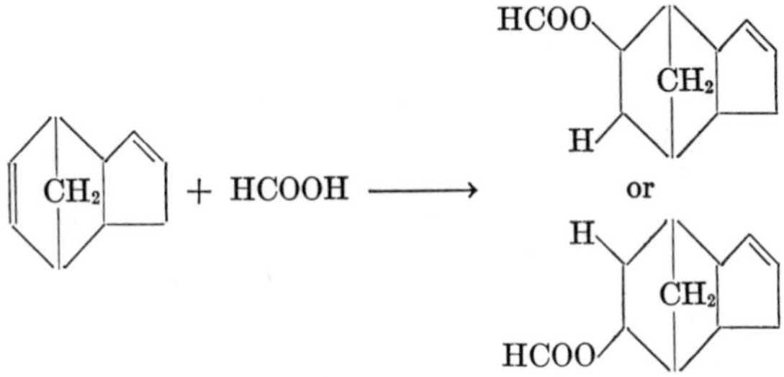

The formate ester produced by the reaction is separated from the unconsumed formic acid by extraction between benzene and water.   The ester in the benzene layer is then determined by saponification.   The results obtained indicate that the method is reliable to ±0.5% or better and that impurities in technical preparations of dicyclopentadiene do not interfere.   Since higher polymers of cyclopentadiene react in the same manner as the dimer, mixtures containing higher polymers must be fractionated by distillation prior to analysis.

H. ADDITION OF AMINES

Many α,β-unsaturated compounds react with primary and secondary amines to form addition compounds (secondary or tertiary amines). Critchfield, Funk, and Johnson (129) have described an analytical procedure based on the reaction of the unsaturated compound with morpholine, a secondary amine, in the presence of acetic acid catalyst:

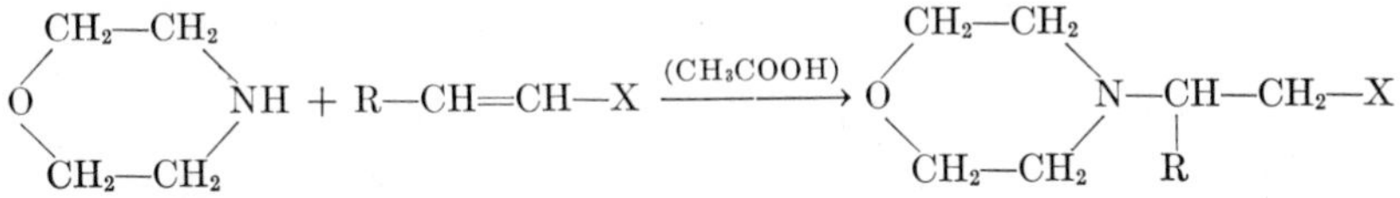

where X is a strong electron-attracting group such as carboxyl, carboxylate, amide, or nitrile.   After this reaction is complete, the excess morpholine is acetylated with acetic anhydride in acetonitrile solution.   The tertiary amine formed in the first reaction is titrated with alcoholic hydrochloric acid to the methyl orange–xylene cyanole FF mixed indicator end point. When the tertiary amine is too weak to titrate in this manner, a conductimetric titration can be used. Quantitative results were obtained on several unsaturated nitriles and on various acrylate, crotonate, maleate, and fumarate acids and esters. The reactivity of unsaturated compounds is influenced both by the nature of the electron-attracting group and by substitution on either the α- or β-carbon atom. Attempts to determine α,β-unsaturated carbonyl compounds and the sodium or potassium salts of α,β-unsaturated acids were unsuccessful and compounds substituted in both the α- and β-positions usually failed to react. Most compounds with unsaturation not conjugated to a strong electron-attracting group do not react; however, certain β,γ-unsaturated compounds such as allyl cyanide apparently are isomerized to the corresponding α,β-unsaturated compounds and can be determined. Most α-epoxides react quantitatively with morpholine to form tertiary amines which would be included in the titration. Organic halides and large amounts of aldehydes, ketones, or anhydrides interfere.

I. REACTION WITH AZO COMPOUNDS

Diazomethane reacts with compounds containing olefinic double bonds to form pyrazoline derivatives:

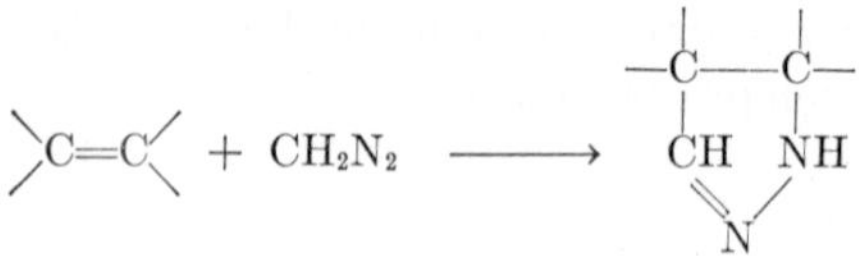

The chemistry of this reaction has been reviewed by Eistert (168). The pyrazolines are generally decomposed by heating, to evolve nitrogen and form cyclopropane derivatives. Although this reaction of olefins with diazomethane has been employed for preparative purposes, it apparently has not found analytical application, probably because diazomethane reacts too readily with various other types of organic compounds.

Conjugated dienes can be coupled with aromatic diazo compounds. From butadiene and 2,4-dinitrobenzenediazonium sulfate, Meyer (429) obtained a yellow compound, $CH_2=CH-CH=CH-N=N-C_6H_3(NO_2)_2$. Analogous p-nitrobenzeneazo and 2,4-dinitrobenzeneazo derivatives were obtained from 1,3-pentadiene (piperylene), isoprene, and 2,3-dimethyl-butadiene. This reaction might serve as the basis for a colorimetric method.

Phenyl azide reacts with many olefinic compounds to form phenyldi-hydrotriazoles:

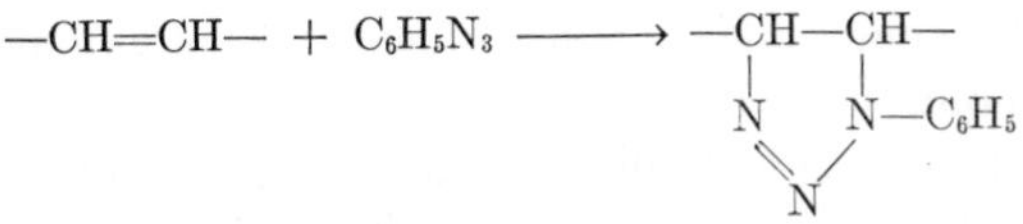

$$-CH=CH- + C_6H_5N_3 \longrightarrow -CH-CH-$$

$$\underset{\diagdown\ \diagup}{\underset{N}{\overset{|}{N}}\ \underset{N-C_6H_5}{\overset{|}{N}}}$$

This reaction was shown by Alder and Stein (8) to be much more rapid with olefinic bonds in bicycloheptene structures than with either aliphatic or simple cyclic olefins. The reaction was employed by Danish and Lidov (139) for colorimetric determination of small amounts of aldrin, a chlorinated insecticide with the structure:

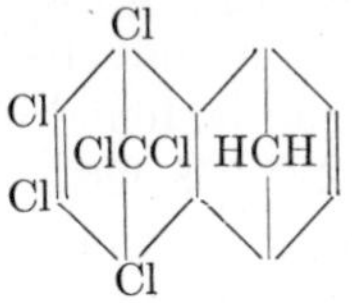

Cl
Cl
Cl
ClCCl HCH
Cl

The phenyldihydrotriazole formed by addition of phenyl azide to the unchlorinated bicycloheptene ring is treated with acid to form an aniline derivative by loss of nitrogen. The aniline derivative is then coupled with diazotized 2,4-dinitroaniline to give an azo compound that gives a strong red color on treatment with sulfuric acid. The procedure has been improved by O'Donnell, Neal, Weiss, Bann, DeCino, and Lau (469), who have shown that as little as 0.1 p. p. m. of aldrin residue in agricultural crop materials can be determined. These authors also found that certain other olefinic compounds, e. g., 1-dodecene, cyclohexene derivatives, and bicycloheptene compounds (tricyclopentadiene, endomethylenetetrahydrobenzoic acid, Octacide 264, etc.), produced colored products by the method, although most of these materials do not interfere in the aldrin method because they are removed by evaporation or chromatographic cleanup.

III. INSTRUMENTAL METHODS

Spectrometric analysis and certain other methods based on physical or physicochemical properties usually are classified as instrumental methods. Although polarography depends on chemical reactivity, it also is frequently considered to be an instrumental technique because of the nature of the apparatus employed. The segregation of instrumental from chemical methods is, in a sense, unrealistic. In fact, most chemical methods are amenable to instrumentation. The deadstop method for detection of bromination end points, described in an earlier section of this chapter, is an example.   Automatic titration instruments for potentiometric and other types of end point measurements have become commercially available. As a result of increasing specialization, analytical chemists sometimes do not give due consideration to the possibilities of instrumentation.   The advantages of convenience and time saving that may result from adopting instrumental techniques often offset the initial cost of apparatus.   More-over, physical methods frequently may provide information on chemical structure, etc., which cannot be readily obtained by conventional "wet chemical" methods.

It is beyond the scope of the present discussion to describe the theory of instrumental methods or to include technical details of instrument design and operation.   These can be found in standard works on spectros-copy (243,656), polarography (143,358,426), and various physical methods (653) and in the technical literature.   Collections of spectral data on pure compounds, such as the American Petroleum Institute (A. P. I.) catalogs of infrared, ultraviolet, Raman, and mass spectra (15) and the Institute of Petroleum (I. P.) infrared spectra (288) are useful for reference purposes. The sections that follow are intended to familiarize the analytical chemist who is not well versed in instrumental methods with general principles and certain applications in determination of olefinic unsaturation by these important methods.

Coggeshall, in Volume I of *Organic Analysis* (110), has described spectro-scopic functional group analysis in the petroleum industry, including de-termination of olefins by infrared absorption, Raman spectroscopy, and mass spectrometry.   The present discussion deals largely with applica-tions not covered in the earlier chapter and with more recent develop-ments in the determination of unsaturation.   For new analytical applica-tions, the reader should examine the annual reviews in *Analytical Chem-istry*, which include surveys on infrared (39,219), Raman (77,593), ultra-violet (530), mass spectrometry (145,146,264,569) and organic polaro-graphy (647), and reviews on new methods and techniques in specific in-dustrial fields.

1. Infrared Absorption

Absorption bands in the conventional infrared region result principally from stretching or deformation ("bending") vibrations of atoms within the molecule.   Each absorption frequency corresponds to the frequency of a particular vibration that causes a change in dipole moment.   Many of the absorption bands due to vibrations are found at wave lengths of 2 to 15 μ (wave numbers, or "frequencies" of 5000 to 667 cm.$^{-1}$), which is the most easily investigated region of the infrared spectrum. Since each molecular species gives a unique absorption spectrum, the identification of compounds that are available in the pure state for comparison is simple and positive. (In order to distinguish very similar materials, it is sometimes necessary to obtain more specific "fingerprints" by comparing the spectra in the far infrared region, 15 to 35 μ.) The A. P. I. (15) and I. P. (288) collections of infrared spectra of pure hydrocarbons, including many aliphatic, alicyclic, and aromatic olefins, and the many spectra of unsaturated compounds in the literature (41) are useful for identification purposes. Because absorption spectra of organic compounds are essentially additive (i. e., the spectra of mixtures do not usually differ appreciably from a superposition of the spectra of the individual components), the detection, identification and determination of individual compounds in simple mixtures is generally possible. Binary mixtures seldom present difficulties, and mixtures with as many as 6 or 8 components frequently can be analyzed for the individual compounds present with good accuracy by determining absorptions at carefully selected key wave lengths and solution of simultaneous equations based on the absorptivities of pure compounds at the particular wave lengths selected. Such multicomponent analyses of simple systems by infrared absorption are very useful in many instances. A good example is the analysis of 6-component C_4 hydrocarbon mixtures for individual butanes and butenes (74).

Although multicomponent analysis has many valuable applications, limitations due to spectral discrimination, instrument precision, availability of pure compounds, and deviations from additivity prevent the extension of multicomponent analysis to complex mixtures or samples containing substances not included in the system of equations. It therefore becomes important for the analytical or organic chemist to make use of absorption bands that are produced by particular atomic arrangements or functional groups and are characteristic of these groups in related compounds. The characteristic frequencies of olefinic and acetylenic hydrocarbons in infrared and Raman spectra have been discussed in an excellent review by Sheppard and Simpson (570) and in a book by Bellamy (47); correlations between infrared spectra and structure of hydrocarbons, including olefins, have been described by numerous investigators (26, 185,401,509,571).

A. C=C STRETCHING VIBRATION

The frequency most characteristic of olefins in general is due to the C=C stretching vibration, which occurs in the vicinity of 6.0 to 6.1 μ

(ca. 1650 cm.$^{-1}$) in the infrared and Raman spectra. However, since infrared absorption depends on changes in dipole moment, the C=C absorption band is strong only in the infrared spectra of highly unsymmetrical olefins, such as α-olefins, being very weak for compounds that have approximately centrosymmetric structures about the C=C bond and completely absent for symmetrical compounds such as ethylene, *trans*-2-butene, and tetramethylethylene. In Raman spectroscopy, however, the C=C stretching vibration is intense for all olefins because the Raman line arises from polarizability of the bond and is not materially affected by the symmetry of substituents on the ethylenic carbon atoms. With conjugated diolefins, the coupled C=C—C=C vibrations produce an infrared absorption band of enhanced intensity near 6.25 μ (due to unsymmetrical stretching), and a Raman line near 6.1 μ (due to symmetrical stretching), which appears in the infrared spectra of unsymmetrically substituted diolefins only. With allenes, the C=C=C vibrations show as a strong infrared absorption band near 5.1 μ (due to unsymmetrical stretching), and a Raman line near 9.4 μ (due to symmetrical stretching), which appears in the infrared only for unsymmetrical allenes.

In spite of the limitations of infrared measurement of C=C stretching, this absorption has been found to be useful for determination of particular olefins (40) and, in connection with other characteristic absorptions, to provide information regarding the residual unsaturation in olefin polymers such as natural and synthetic rubbers, polyvinyl compounds, polyacrylates, etc. (40,615).

B. =C—H VIBRATIONS

Because of the limited usefulness of the C=C absorption in the 6 μ region, it is usually advantageous to utilize other infrared absorption bands characteristic of olefins. For all olefins except the type RR'C=CR″R‴, where the four R groups are not hydrogen, the vibrations of the hydrogen atoms attached to ethylenic carbon atoms can be employed for analysis. The C—H stretching vibrations in the 3.2 to 3.5 μ region are intense and characteristic, but overlap in part the C—H stretching modes of saturated alkyl groups. This region, however, has been used by Saier and Coggeshall (549) for the analysis of simple mixtures of olefins and other materials with good accuracy. Some of the bands due to in-plane "bending" vibrations of C—H bond angles, which occur in the region of 7 to 12 μ, are fairly characteristic, but these absorptions are rather weak and lie in the range of C—C stretching vibration absorptions.

However, the out-of-plane "bending" vibrations of C—H bond angles, which give bands in the 10 to 15 μ region, are very intense and highly specific for some types of olefins, in spite of the fact that many C—C stretching and CH_3 rocking vibrations occur in this region. This region is therefore most frequently used for olefin-type determination by infrared absorption. The five classes of olefins other than totally substituted ethylenes are characterized by one or two such bands for hydrocarbons (R,R',R" = alkyl group). Anderson and Seyfried (26) report the characteristic bands for each class as follows:

Class	Wave length, μ
$RCH=CH_2$	10.05 and 10.98 $\pm$ 0.02
$RR'C=CH_2$	11.24 $\pm$ 0.02
trans-$RCH=CHR'$	10.36 $\pm$ 0.02
cis-$RCH=CHR'$	14.0 to 14.6 (variable)
$RR'C=CHR''$	11.9 to 12.7 (variable)

The first three classes give characteristic bands that are strong, sharp, and easily identified; the other two classes unfortunately give weaker and more variable bands. For determination of olefin types, Coggeshall and co-workers (110,550) employed characteristic wave lengths of 10.95, 11.24, 10.36, 14.44, and four dominant wave lengths between 12.0 and 12.5 μ for the above classes, with average molar absorptivities of 0.963, 1.17, 1.09, 0.338, and 0.172, respectively, for each class. These values, together with the small absorptivities of each class at the other key wave lengths, permit the solution of simultaneous equations for the amount of each of the five classes in unknown mixtures, with fairly satisfactory accuracy. Although tetrasubstituted olefins and cyclic olefins are not included, this method provides information that cannot be obtained in a practical manner by any other means.

All of these characteristic absorption bands are, for some groups, shifted to other wave lengths when one or more of the R groups is not an alkyl radical, or when conjugation exists. Leonard and Gash (379) have used the effect of conjugation on the C=C stretching absorption to distinguish α,β-unsaturated amines from other unsaturated amines. A similar shift in the C=C stretching band occurs with conjugated unsaturated carbonyl compounds. Kitson (348) has reported the effects of certain substituents on the positions of the C—H bending bands, based on the spectra of over 100 substituted olefins, principally halo and cyano derivatives, as well as on the positions of other bands that correlate with structure. Davison and Bates (141) have described the effects of polar substituents on the spectra of vinyl and isopropenyl compounds.

One difficulty encountered in olefin type analysis of complex mixtures is the nonconstancy of molar absorptivity within the classes. However, reasonable assumptions can be made, and average absorptivities for each class give fairly good accuracy for petroleum distillates (26,110,550). When the number of components present in a mixture is not large and the spectra of all components in pure form is available, better accuracy can of course be obtained by multicomponent analysis for the individual compounds present.

Another difficulty in analysis of complex mixtures results from interferences or "background" absorption. If the interferences are slight and the nature and amount of interfering substance is known, it is possible to apply corrections to the observed absorptions. Since the interferences of olefin classes on each other at their characteristic C—H bending wave lengths is small (less than one-tenth), appropriate corrections can readily be made. Also, corrections have been employed for hydrocarbon mixtures containing straight-chain paraffins and small amounts of aromatics (26). If the interferences are large, it is preferable to separate the interfering substances out of the sample before analysis. Chromatographic separation to remove saturated hydrocarbons and aromatics has been employed (110, 309,550). Removal of polar components is sometimes necessary to eliminate interferences.

The number of applications of infrared spectroscopy for determination of unsaturation have rapidly increased and it would be impractical to attempt a complete listing here. References of particular interest include studies on allenes (682), butenes and butadiene (73,74), chlorinated butadienes (609), complex materials (574), crude oil (236,505), esters of unsaturated fatty acids (203,296,395,479), Fischer-Tropsch products (26), gaseous hydrocarbons (441,472,596,617a), gasolines and other petroleum distillates (309,339,427,550), halogenated ethylenes (408), lubricating oil (197), pentenes (616), and polymers (40,54,132,240,518,545,551,615).

2. Raman Spectroscopy

In Raman spectroscopy the sample is irradiated with intense monochromatic ultraviolet or visible light and the light scattered at right angles is analyzed spectroscopically. In addition to the line corresponding to the frequency of the incident radiation (Rayleigh scattering), small amounts of light are found as lines slightly displaced from the original frequency. These displacements, usually expressed in cm.$^{-1}$, correspond to the vibration frequencies of the atoms constituting the molecules in the sample just as in infrared absorption.   The intensities of the displaced lines are proportional to concentrations of the vibrating molecules.   Since both Raman and infrared spectra result from the same vibrations, the spectra are similar in character.   However, the strength of a fundamental frequency usually is not equivalent in the two techniques because Raman lines arise principally from changes in polarizability resulting from the vibrations, whereas infrared absorptions depend on changes in dipole moment resulting from the vibrations.   Accordingly, a vibration that gives only a weak absorption band in the infrared often gives a strong Raman line;   the Raman technique may have analytical advantages in such cases.

The principles of Raman spectroscopy and numerous applications to various materials, including substituted ethylenes, cycloolefins, and acetylenes have been described by Hibben (262).   Collections of Raman spectra are being assembled (15,78) and the possibilities of the technique have been described in the analytical literature (97,253,594).

Whereas the intensities of infrared absorption bands due to $C{=}C$ stretching depend strongly upon the arrangement and nature of the substituents on the ethylenic carbon atoms, being very weak or absent in olefins that are symmetrical or nearly so, the intensities of Raman lines due to $C{=}C$ stretching are more independent of the effects of substituents because the polarizability of the $C{=}C$ bond is relatively constant in all olefins.   Heigl, Black, and Dudenbostel (253) made use of Raman frequency shifts in the 1640 to 1680 cm.$^{-1}$ region produced by $C{=}C$ stretching for the determination of total olefin content.   They found the integrated intensity per mole of C_6 to C_{10} olefins to be sufficiently constant to give satisfactory accuracy in complex hydrocarbon mixtures.   Although no information regarding the distribution of olefin types is obtained by this procedure, the technique provides a direct measure of total olefins, including tetrasubstituted ethylenes that are not determined by infrared absorption.   The method is expected to find significant applications in the analysis of complex mixtures.

Frequency shifts in the 1650 cm.$^{-1}$ region have been used to investigate *cis-trans* isomerism about the double bonds in unsaturated fatty acid esters (395).

3. Ultraviolet Absorption

Whereas infrared and Raman spectra arise from vibrations of the atoms in the molecule, absorptions in the ultraviolet and visible light regions are due to excitation of electronic energy levels in particular atomic groupings. In groups possessing unsaturation, the valence electrons are relatively mobile; the greater the mobility, the greater the resonance and the lower the frequency of the radiation absorbed. Thus, compounds containing a single C=C group (or isolated C=C groups) absorb in the vicinity of 170 to 200 mμ (1700 to 2000 A.), conjugated dienes absorb strongly in the 210 to 240 mμ region, etc. A compound becomes visibly colored (yellow) with five conjugated double bonds. Additional double bonds shift the absorption farther into the visible region; thus (in carbon disulfide solution) α-carotene with 11 double bonds, 10 conjugated, has absorption maxima at 477 and 509 mμ; β-carotene with 11 double bonds, all conjugated, has maxima at 485 and 520 mμ; and lycopene with 13 double bonds, 11 conjugated, has maxima at 507 and 548 mμ. (The spectra of polyenes are also affected by *cis-trans* isomerism.) Conjugation with aromatic rings also shifts the absorption toward longer wave length; styrene has an intense absorption maximum near 244 mμ due to conjugation. The principles and applications of ultraviolet and visible spectroscopy of unsaturated compounds and other organic materials has recently been reviewed by Gillam and Stern (212).

A. MONOOLEFINS

Analytical applications for polyolefins from their absorption in the near ultraviolet (210 to 400 mμ) and visible (400 to 700 mμ) regions are very numerous, largely because these regions are readily accessible for accurate measurements with relatively inexpensive commercial spectrometers. The far ultraviolet region below 210 mμ, frequently known as the vacuum ultraviolet because high absorption by oxygen and certain other gases in this region require the use of instruments that have been evacuated or filled with a transparent gas such as hydrogen or helium, has been much less used for analysis. Because the principal electronic absorption bands of simple unsaturated compounds lie in the far ultraviolet, this area is of interest to the analyst. Jones and Taylor (310) have recently described the analytical potentialities of this region for unsaturated hydrocarbons. These workers, using a recording vacuum spectrometer with a photoelectric detector, have measured the 170 to 230 mμ spectra of 69 pure hydrocarbons, including all of the aliphatic monoolefins through C_6, as well as cyclopentene, cyclohexene, and several diolefins, allenes, and acetylenes, mainly in the vapor phase. Except for ethylene, the monoolefins were found to have remarkably similar spectra, particularly within groups arranged according to the number of alkyl groups attached to the doubly bound carbon atoms. as shown in Table XXV.

TABLE XXV

Average Position and Peak Intensity of Absorption Bands in the Vapor Spectra of the Alkenes (310)

(Smoothed spectral curves)

Olefin type	Av. position of absorption max., mμ	Molar absorptivity, liters/mole cm.
1-Alkenes	175.0 ± 2.5	$11,800 \pm 1200$
cis-2-Alkenes	176.5 ± 1.5	$12,300 \pm 200$
trans-2-Alkenes	179.0 ± 1.0	$11,700 \pm 800$
2-Alkyl-1-alkenes	187.5 ± 1.5	$8,900 \pm 1200$

Three of the four trialkylethylenes studied also showed a strong family resemblance. In going from vapor-phase spectra to spectra in heptane solution, the absorption maxima for hexenes were found to shift about 4 mμ toward longer wave lengths, with a slight decrease in peak intensity and a compensating increase in band width.

Because of the strong similarities of the monoolefin spectra in the far ultraviolet, a total olefin determination may be possible even in complex mixtures, although classification according to olefin types does not appear practical. Thus, in the vapor state, the average molar absorptivity at 179.5 mμ for all the olefins studied by Jones and Taylor (310) was 9800, with a standard deviation of 2680. Solution spectra appear more favorable. In n-heptane solution, the average molar absorptivity of six hexenes at 186.0 mμ was 9200, with a standard deviation of 930, or 10.1%. The limited data on cyclopentene and cyclohexene suggest that cyclic olefins would be included in the total olefin determination. Diolefins with double bonds isolated by two or more methylene groups give spectra resembling the monoolefins except for a two-fold gain in intensity. A single methylene group between the double bonds only partially shields the groups from interaction. Allenes also were found to have a strong absorption band near 180 mμ.

A method for distinguishing and determining olefin types by means of the ultraviolet absorption spectra of complexes reversibly formed with iodine has been reported by Long and Neuzil (388). The method is of particular interest because tetrasubstituted olefins (which have no ethylenic hydrogens and therefore are not determinable by means of C—H bonds in the infrared), and trisubstituted olefins (which give variable infrared bands) give characteristic strong ultraviolet absorption bands when complexed with iodine. The positions and relative intensities of the bands are given in Table XXVI.

TABLE XXVI

Average Position and Peak Intensity of Absorption Bands of Olefin-Iodine Complexes
(388)

Olefin type	Av. position of absorption max., mμ	Apparent absorptivity[a]
RCH=CH$_2$	275	12
RR'C=CH$_2$	290–295	25
cis-RCH=CHR'	295–300	19
trans-RCH=CHR'	295–300	11
RR'C=CHR''	317	27
RR'C=CR''R'''	337	33

[a] Liters per mole of olefin, per gram of iodine per liter, for a 1 cm. light path.

Only a small proportion of the olefin and the iodine is in the complexed state under the conditions of the method. However, molar absorptivities of the complexes are high (10,000 to 25,000 liters per mole-cm.). Thus, the apparent absorbance values are appreciable, even though only small fractions of the olefin present are complexed. The absorbance is proportional to the product of the olefin and iodine concentrations. To avoid the undesirable addition of iodine to form diiodo compounds, the spectra are measured within a short time after mixing the components. Alternatively, the solutions can be kept in the dark until measured. Saturated hydrocarbons do not interfere, but aromatic hydrocarbons interfere because the spectra of their iodine complexes overlap those of the olefin–iodine complexes, and diolefins interfere by reacting with iodine. The method was employed for quantitative determination of individual olefins of various types in simple mixtures. In combination with infrared analysis for RCH=CH$_2$, RR'C=CH$_2$, and trans-RCH=CHR', the method was also used for determination of olefin types in a propylene polymer, which was found to contain large amounts of RR'C=CHR'' and RR'C= CR''R'''.

B. DIOLEFINS

Although 1,3-butadiene absorbs most strongly in the 210 to 220 mμ region, analytical applications have frequently made use of slightly longer wave lengths, at which the absorptions are still quite high. Thus the A. S. T. M. method (20) for 1,3-butadiene in C$_4$ and lighter hydrocarbon gas samples uses a selected wave length in the 226 to 241 mμ region, comparing the absorptivity of the sample to that of pure 1,3-butadiene. However, measuring at 216 mμ (using 1 mm. or 0.1 mm. absorption cells with pressures between 50 and 500 mm.) decreases the interference from vinyl-acetylene and the slight interference from 1,2-butadiene. If the concentrations of these two components are determined by an independent method, such as infrared absorption, corrections can be subtracted from the apparent 1,3-butadiene content found. For 1% of vinyl acetylene, the corrections are 1.8% at 235 mμ, 2.2% at 226 mμ, and 0.4% at 216 mμ; for 1% of 1,2-butadiene, they are 0.25% at 235 mμ, 0.08% at 226 mμ, and 0.008% at 216 mμ. C_4 and lighter paraffins and olefins, alkyl acetylenes, hydrogen, carbon monoxide, carbon dioxide, air, and water do not interfere.

Individual conjugated dienes in C_5 hydrocarbon fractions in the vapor state can be determined by taking advantage of the differences in their ultraviolet absorption spectra. Cyclopentadiene has a broad absorption band near 240 mμ. The noncyclic C_5 dienes, *cis*-1,3-pentadiene, *trans*-1,3-pentadiene, and isoprene, have similar spectra with maxima in the 210 to 230 mμ region; however, these spectra differ sufficiently to permit selection of key wave lengths for analysis. Dudenbostel and Priestley (157) recommend analytical wave lengths as follows:

Compound	Wave length, mμ
trans-1,3-Pentadiene	220
Isoprene	225
cis-1,3-Pentadiene	230
Cyclopentadiene	244

By solving four simultaneous equations containing the known absorptivity of each component at each wave length, the concentration of each conjugated C_5 diene can be obtained. Dudenbostel and Priestley indicate that, with precise measurement, the accuracy of the procedure is ±2% for cyclopentadiene and *cis*-1,3-pentadiene and ±5% for *trans*-1,3-pentadiene and isoprene, except in the 0–10% range, where the accuracy is within ±0.2% of the total sample.

The selective absorptions of various substituted dienes have been reviewed by Booker, Evans, and Gillam (68).

C. POLYOLEFINS

Analytical applications of ultraviolet absorption for higher polyolefins, generally in liquid solution, are similar in principle to the diolefin applications described above. It is usually only necessary to obtain the absorption curves of the compounds of interest in a suitable solvent and to select key wave lengths for analysis, allowing for the absorptions due to other components in the sample.

Diphenylpolyenes containing up to seven conjugated ethylenic double bonds have been studied (248). In addition to simple determination of concentration of known compounds in solution, considerable information on the stereochemistry of polyenes can be obtained with the aid of ultraviolet and visible absorption spectra. An example is the effects of *cis-trans* isomerism in carotenes and other polyenes (689).

D. NONHYDROCARBONS

The presence of olefinic unsaturation may markedly affect the ultraviolet absorption spectra of compounds containing other functional groups, especially if conjugation exists. Thus, saturated carbonyl compounds have a strong absorption band in the 180 to 200 mμ region and a low-intensity band in the vicinity of 270 to 290 mμ. In α,β-unsaturated carbonyl compounds these bands are shifted to the 210 to 240 mμ and 300 to 330 mμ regions. The α,β-unsaturated nitro compounds and other conjugated systems show similar behavior. The usefulness of such effects for analytical determination of unsaturated materials is obvious. The influence of solvents on the ultraviolet spectra is often very pronounced and should always be considered in analytical work. For example, the two bands of α,β-unsaturated carbonyl compounds are considerably closer to each other in a polar solvent such as water than in a nonpolar solvent such as hexane.

Conjugated polyene systems have been studied rather extensively for series of aliphatic aldehydes and carboxylic acids (250) and 2-furyl polyunsaturated aldehydes and acids (57,249–251) as model compounds for carotenoid pigments.

A good example of an analytical application is the A. O. C. S. method for polyunsaturated fatty acids in animal and vegetable fats and oils (14). This method was preceded by a large number of studies on the use of ultraviolet spectra of unsaturated fatty acids; the early literature has been reviewed by Markley (412). In the A. O. C. S. method, conjugated diene, triene, and tetraene acids are calculated from measurements in the vicinity of their strong absorptions at 233, 268, and 315 mμ, respectively. The nonconjugated polyunsaturated acids, linoleic, linolenic, and arachidonic, are partially converted to conjugated diene, triene, and tetraene materials, respectively, by heating in potassium hydroxide–glycol solution. The conjugated substances formed are measured at the above wave lengths. More accurate spectroscopic constants for nonconjugated polyunsaturated acids were obtained by Brice, Swain, Herb, Nichols, and Riemenschneider

(80) by standardization with natural methyl esters of linoleic, linolenic, and arachidonic acids purified by crystallization and chromatography. Herb and Riemenschneider (255), studying the effects of alkali concentration and other factors, found that heating in 21% potassium hydroxide in glycol for 15 minutes at 180°C. is optimum for methyl arachidonate. With these conditions, the sensitivity of the method for several other polyunsaturated esters also is improved. These workers also give constants for two pentaene acids, which can be measured at 346 mμ.

O'Connor, Stansbury, Damaré, and Stark (468) have described a simplified method for calculating linoleic acid in vegetable oils by the A. O. C. S. method. The accuracy of the nonconjugated polyunsaturated acid determination is seriously affected by the presence of conjugated polyunsaturated materials; however, O'Connor, Heinzelman, Pack, and Planck (467) have extended the method to linoleic acid and conjugated dienoic acids in the presence of conjugated trienoic acids (eleostearic acid) by equations that correct for background absorption.

The far ultraviolet absorption spectra (down to 173 mμ) of a variety of fatty acids and esters were measured by Rusoff, Platt, Klevens, and Burr (546). Saturated acids were found to have a broad, low intensity band in the 190 to 210 mμ region and a strong band centered somewhere below 173 mμ. Nonconjugated mono- and polyunsaturated acids, however, were found to exhibit intense absorption in the 170 to 200 mμ region. In comparison, α,β-unsaturated acids (crotonic, 2-heptadecenoic) and conjugated diene acids (9,11- and 10,12-linoleic) gave absorption bands centered near 210 and 230 mμ, respectively. In the 170 to 200 mμ region, conjugated diene and triene acids absorb only about 10% as strongly as nonconjugated polyunsaturated acids. The absorption band of nonconjugated acids shifts slightly toward longer wave length with increasing number of double bonds. Thus, for one double bond (oleic and elaidic acids) the absorption maximum is near 185 mμ, for two double bonds (linoleic acid) it is near 190 mμ, and for three double bonds (linolenic and elaidolinolenic acids) it is near 195 mμ. Rusoff, Platt, Klevens, and Burr (546) suggest that nonconjugated polyunsaturated acids in oils could be determined, without the use of alkali to produce conjugation, by means of measurements at 210 mμ or shorter wave lengths (on the long wave length side of the bands); accurately determined absorption coefficients would be required.

4. Mass Spectrometry

Mass-spectrometric analysis is described by Dibeler in this volume;

applications to hydrocarbon mixtures were discussed by Coggeshall in Volume I of this series (110). A major application of mass spectrometry for determination of unsaturated hydrocarbons is included in the hydro-carbon-type analysis of gasoline described by Brown (86). The method is based on the observation that each class of hydrocarbons, C_nH_{2n+2}, C_nH_{2n}, C_nH_{2n-2}, etc., when bombarded with electrons gives patterns of ionized fragments that are characteristic of each class. Moreover, the sum of ion intensities for certain selected ions is an almost constant fraction of the total ion intensity; hence, the total amount of each class can be measured by means of intensity factors averaged over a large number of hydrocarbons of each class. For monoolefins, the characteristic ions belong to the series, $(C_nH_{2n-1})^+$, formed by loss of a hydrogen atom and successive methylene groups. However, this series of ions is also charac-teristic of cycloparaffins. The method therefore does not distinguish be-tween monoolefins and cycloparaffins. Similarly, cycloolefins, diolefins, acetylenes, and bicycloparaffins are all characterized by ions of the types $(C_nH_{2n-2})^+$ and $(C_nH_{2n-3})^+$. Despite this limitation, the mass-spectrometric method is a useful adjunct to infrared and ultraviolet ab-sorption analysis, particularly for wide-boiling range fractions for which deviations of components do not seriously affect the averaged intensities.

The application of mass spectrometry, in combination with infrared, ultraviolet, fractional distillation, adsorption, and hydrogenation, is demonstrated by a detailed analysis of a catalytically cracked naphtha re-ported by Melpolder, Brown, Young, and Headington (427). By the combination of these methods, 152 individual hydrocarbons and groups of hydrocarbons were determined in the 34–218°C. naphtha product studied.

Mass spectrometry is, of course, a very general method of analysis, applicable to virtually any type of material that can be vaporized con-veniently, and is eminently suitable for multicomponent analysis of rela-tively simple mixtures of compounds for which the mass spectra have been determined. However, applications to complex mixtures are in-creasing, and compound-type analyses such as the method of Brown are particularly promising for such samples.

5. Polarography

Unsaturated compounds containing only isolated ethylenic double bonds are not polarographically reducible, although such materials can be determined indirectly by titration with bromine and following changes in the polarographic wave of bromine (56). However, when an ethylenic or acetylenic bond is conjugated or twinned with another double or triple bond, a benzene ring, or another unsaturated group such as carbonyl, polarographic reduction waves can be obtained. Polynuclear aromatic hydrocarbons also are reducible. Polarography of unsaturated hydrocarbons, carbonyl compounds, acids, and other organic materials has been discussed in detail by Kolthoff and Lingane (362) and reviewed by Page (476) and by Elving in Volume II of this series (172a). The possibility of polarographic oxidation of olefinic materials apparently has been given very little study.

A. UNSATURATED HYDROCARBONS

Both allenes and conjugated diolefins are reducible at the dropping mercury electrode. Using 0.05 M tetraethylammonium bromide in 75% dioxane, von Stackelberg and Stracke (592) obtained half-wave potentials of -2.29 and -2.59 v. (vs. a saturated calomel electrode) for allene and 1,3-butadiene, respectively. Waves also have been obtained for cyclic conjugated olefins such as dimethylfulvene (649), and although benzene is not reducible cyclooctatetraene has been determined from its reduction wave at -1.51 v. in alcoholic tetramethylammonium hydroxide solution (172). Carotene also has been determined polarographically (234,261).

Aromatic olefins in which the double bond is conjugated with a benzene ring (styrene derivatives) give well-defined waves in the -2.0 to -2.5 v. region (vs. a saturated calomel electrode) in 75% dioxane containing a tetraalkylammonium iodide. Laitinen and Wawzonek (372) investigated a number of phenyl-substituted olefins. The half-wave potentials were found to be independent of pH. These workers concluded that the reduction mechanism is as follows:

$$R + e^- \rightleftharpoons R^-$$

$$R^- + e^- \longrightarrow R^{--}$$

$$R^{--} + 2H_2O \longrightarrow RH_2 + 2OH^-$$

and that only the first stage is reversible and is the potential-determining step. Goulden and Warren (222) studied the effects of substituents on the position and height of reduction waves of stilbenes (diphenylethylenes). The course of polarographic reduction of conjugated diphenylpolyenes (1,4-diphenylbutadiene, 1,6-diphenylhexatriene, etc.) has been examined by Hoijtink and van Schooten (269), and was found to be in agreement with the mechanism proposed by Laitinen and Wawzonek. Styrene in a crude styrene fraction (494) and in the presence of its homologs (604) and styrene and indene in coal tar fractions (495), have been determined polarographically.

In addition to the analytical applications mentioned above, polarography has been found useful for qualitative analysis, for example, locating the position of the double bond in phenyl-substituted cyclic olefins (648).

B. UNSATURATED CARBONYL COMPOUNDS

Saturated carbonyl compounds are polarographically reducible; aldehydes are reduced at a lower potential than most ketones. Unsaturated carbonyl compounds in which the carbonyl group is conjugated with a double bond give two polarographic waves. The first wave, which is believed to be due to reduction of the double bond via 1,4-reaction, occurs at a lower potential (usually between −1.0 and −1.5 v., depending on the electrolyte used) than the wave due to reduction of the carbonyl group of the unsaturated carbonyl compound or of the corresponding saturated carbonyl compound (usually between −1.5 and −2.0 v.). The positions and heights of both the double bond wave and the carbonyl wave are affected by pH. It is therefore possible to determine α,β-unsaturated carbonyl compounds in the presence of saturated carbonyl compounds from the height of the first wave in a suitable buffer solution.

For determination of acrolein, a pH 7.5 lithium phosphate buffer containing 0.01 M lithium chloride has been recommended by Moshier (447), but acidic and weakly alkaline solutions also have been suggested (209, 210,347). The two waves of crotonaldehyde in various electrolytes have been described (3). Fields and Blout (188) studied the polarographic reduction of crotonaldehyde and polyene aldehydes of the type $CH_3(CH=CH)_nCHO$ in 50% dioxane solution buffered at various pH values between 1 and 11. The half-wave potential of the first (double bond) wave was found to become more negative approximately linearly with increasing pH and to become less negative with increasing number of double bonds conjugated with the carbonyl group. Other unsaturated aldehydes investigated include 2,4-hexadieneal (646), furfural (397,406), and various terpene aldehydes (210,561).

The polarographic behavior of unsaturated ketones is similar to that of unsaturated aldehydes. Whereas saturated ketones are reduced only at high potentials (−2.0 to −2.5 v.), the ethylene group of α,β-unsaturated ketones is easily reduced (usually between −1.2 and −1.7 v.). As in the case of aldehydes, the half-wave potential and wave height are influenced by pH. Polarography has been used to determine methyl vinyl ketone

(199), unsaturated monocyclic and bicyclic terpene ketones (559,560), substituted ionones (210), and 1,2- or 4,5-unsaturated 3-ketosteroids such as testosterone, progesterone, corticosterone, and desoxycorticosterone (167,497), cortisone (497), isomeric cholestenones (4,497), methyltestosterone, and pregnenin-17-ol-3-one (552). When condensed with hydrazine, phenylhydrazine, or Girard T reagent (trimethylammonium acetohydrazine hydrochloride), both saturated and unsaturated ketones are reducible at lower potentials than are the free ketones; analytical methods frequently make use of these derivatives.

C. UNSATURATED ACIDS AND ESTERS

Acids and esters containing a double bond conjugated with the carboxyl group are polarographically reducible. The half-wave potentials are influenced by pH and by *cis-trans* isomerism. Thus, maleic and fumaric acids give sufficiently distinct waves to allow quantitative analysis for each acid in mixtures of the two (173,175,635). Other analytical applications include determination of maleic acid in succinic acid (577), maleic anhydride (after hydrolysis) in polymers (662), fumaric acid in the presence of aconitic and citraconic acids (508,564), aspartic acid by conversion into a mixture of maleic and fumaric acids (636), *cis-* and *trans*-aconitic acids (565), etc.

Polarography has been used to determine α,β-unsaturated esters in the presence of their β,γ-unsaturated isomers (116), maleate unsaturation in polyesters (266), and the polymerization of methyl methacrylate in the presence of peroxides (456).

6. Other Physical Methods

Physical properties are sometimes useful in identification and determination of unsaturated compounds. In particular, optical properties such as refractive index and dispersion have been found particularly useful in characterizing and analyzing hydrocarbons. Wendland (654) has described a system for characterization of hydrocarbons based largely on refractometric analysis. The specific dispersion:

$$S = \frac{n_F - n_C}{d} \times 10^4$$

where n_F and n_C are the refractive indices for the F or H_β (4861 A.) and C or H_α (6563 A.) lines of the hydrogen spectrum and d is the density of the sample, is especially characteristic of the degree of unsaturation and the presence of conjugation. The refractivity intercept of Kurtz and Ward

(371), defined as $n - 0.5d$, is another property that is fairly characteristic of hydrocarbon types. The approximate values of these properties for various hydrocarbons, based on the tabulations of Ward and Kurtz (634) and other sources, are shown in Table XXVII.

TABLE XXVII

Approximate Values of Specific Dispersion and Refractivity Intercept for Various Hydrocarbon Types

Hydrocarbon type	$\dfrac{n_{\mathrm{F}}^{20} - n_{\mathrm{C}}^{20}}{d_{20}} \times 10^4$			$n_{\mathrm{D}}^{20} - 0.5d_{20}$		
	Boiling range, °C.					
	30–100	100–150	150–200	30–100	100–150	150–200
Alkanes (paraffins)..........	99	99	99	1.045	1.046	1.047
Cyclanes (naphthenes).......	99	99	99	1.038	1.039	1.040
Alkenes...................	130	125	120	1.051	1.052	1.053
Cyclenes..................	118	118	118	1.038	1.044	1.047
Alkadienes, nonconj.........	145	140	135	1.062	1.063	1.058
Alkadienes, conj............	220	210	200	1.083	1.080	1.075
Cyclodienes, conj...........	170	185	180	1.05	1.060	1.062
Alkyl benzenes.............	190	180	170	1.062	1.063	1.063
Alkenyl benzenes, nonconj....	—	—	175	—	—	1.064
Alkenyl benzenes, conj......	—	260	250	—	1.092	1.090

In addition to being useful for characterization, refractometric properties frequently may be used for quantitative determination of hydrocarbons in simple mixtures, such as conjugated and nonconjugated olefins, or as part of an analytical scheme for complex mixtures such as light petroleum fractions containing several types of hydrocarbons (369). Refractive index also has been correlated with unsaturation in soybean, linseed, and other vegetable oils (404), and has been used in connection with a distillation method for polymeric fat acids in drying oils (119) and for determination of styrene in synthetic rubber (680).

Among the newer physical tools, nuclear magnetic resonance deserves mention as an analytical method. Groups containing atoms with magnetic nuclei (e. g., hydrogen, fluorine) can be characterized by high resolution nuclear magnetic resonance spectrometry (573). Nuclei of hydrogen atoms resonate at characteristic frequencies in a constant magnetic field (or, alternatively at characteristic field strengths for a constant applied frequency), depending on the type of atom to which the hydrogen atoms are attached and the type of atom or functional group bonded to the adjacent atom. Thus, hydrogen atoms attached to olefinic carbon atoms should be distinguishable from hydrogen atoms in other atomic groupings, and even the characterization of olefin types appears possible. Quantitative applications of nuclear magnetic resonance can be expected for a wide variety of chemical compounds, including unsaturated substances.

IV. CHROMATOGRAPHIC METHODS

Chromatography is primarily a preparative procedure. It fractionates mixtures into individual components, or groups of components, according to characteristic qualities as recognized by the fractionating principle utilized. Recognition of the extent of this fractionation and detection, identification, and measurement of the separated substances requires the use of additional analytical techniques. These techniques are largely those discussed in the previous sections; their applicability, however, will be greatly enhanced by the fact that the products examined are fractions of greatly simplified composition. If the chromatographic separation yields the individual components of the sample, qualitative identification and a simple weight or volume measurement concludes the analysis.

The principles and techniques of chromatography have been treated in several excellent monographs and reviews (103,120,376,600–603,691,693). Therefore, these points will be discussed only to an extent necessary for presenting an understandable picture of their application to the analysis of olefinic materials.

Chromatographic separations result from the differential migration of solutes in a predetermined direction through a polyphase system in which the driving force (generally a solvent flow) is opposed by a resistive force of the sorbent medium, or fixed phase. According to the resistive force, it is customary to distinguish between three main types of chromatography: *adsorption chromatography*, which depends on physical adsorption on solid surfaces; *partition chromatography*, which involves distribution between two immiscible fluid phases; and *ion exchange chromatography*, which utilizes chemical as well as physical binding. All these systems are characterized by a reversible distribution of the solutes between the fixed non-mobile phase and the mobile solvent, liquid or gas.

The three general procedures for developing a chromatogram are commonly denoted as: (*a*) *frontal analysis*, in which the sample solution is percolated continuously through the separating medium; (*b*) *displacement analysis*, in which a small volume of sample is followed by a more strongly retained substance (or some other desorbing force such as high temperature) that displaces the sample completely; and (c) *development* (*Tswett-type*) *analysis*, in which a small volume of sample is followed by a substance that is retained to a smaller degree than the sample and transports the components of the sample at different rates. When the fractionation of the sample by this process is complete, the stationary phase, or its carrier (adsorbent column or paper), may be sectioned for recovery of the separated components. If the development is continued until the components leave the system, the procedure is commonly referred to as *elution analysis*.

Both adsorption and partition chromatography have received consider-able use in the analysis of olefinic materials. Of the three developing techniques, displacement and development analysis have furnished the most informative results. Frontal analysis is useful only for simple mix-tures because its applicability to complex samples is hindered by involved calculations.

1. Adsorption Chromatography

The resistive force in adsorption chromatography is commonly that of an active solid (adsorbent) and the driving force is a flowing liquid or gas (solvent). The adsorption of an organic compound in this system is a function of its shape and chemical structure, the nature of the adsorbent, and that of the solvent.

Adsorbents most commonly used are activated carbon, alumina, and silica gel. On nonpolar adsorbents such as carbon, adsorption in a homolo-gous series increases with increasing molecular weight; the sequence of emergence of hydrocarbon gases from a carbon column is: methane, acety-lene, ethylene, ethane, etc. Adsorption on polar adsorbents (alumina, silica gel) occurs through certain anchoring groups (690). The ethylenic linkage is such an anchoring group and places olefinic hydrocarbons in the adsorbability sequence between the very weakly adsorbed saturated hy-drocarbons and the more strongly adsorbed aromatic hydrocarbons. Open-chain olefins (alkenes) are generally somewhat less strongly adsorbed than cyclic olefins (cyclenes). Additional ethylenic bonds in the molecule, especially when they are part of a conjugated system, increase the ad-sorption affinity of a molecule, and a compound with a sufficiently long conjugated double bond chain (e. g., β-carotene) is more strongly adsorbed on a polar adsorbent than benzenoid aromatics. These rules are generally valid for liquid and solid hydrocarbons. For hydrocarbon gases, the size of the molecule partially retains its governing effect; the sequence of emergence from a polar adsorbent column is: methane, ethane, ethylene, acetylene, propane, etc. The presence of an additional functional group in an olefinic compound, such as the carboxyl group in unsaturated acids or the carbonyl group in unsaturated aldehydes and ketones, increases adsorption affinity to a marked extent.

A. DISPLACEMENT DEVELOPMENT

A small amount of sample is placed on the top of the column (or introduced at the bottom if upward flow is used), and the displacing agent is added. For polar adsorbents, the displacing material is chosen to be a highly polar compound, usually an alcohol or a ketone. On the nonpolar carbon, a high molecular weight substance may serve as an effective desorbent. Heating has been used primarily to displace adsorbed gases and vapors. With this latter technique, the whole adsorbent column may be heated in steps; alternatively an oven, kept at a temperature several degrees above the boiling point of the highest boiling component of the sample and enclosing the adsorbent column, may be moved in the direction of desorption. Components of the sample move ahead of these forces and become arranged according to increasing adsorbability. The development is continued until the whole sample is forced off the column.

The emerging fractions are commonly characterized by means of refractive index, density (liquids and gases), or thermal conductivity (gases). Various other physical and chemical methods may be applied, depending on the amount of material available. The applicability of some novel and promising techniques to gases and vapors (flow impedence, specific heat, heat of adsorption, surface potential measurements) has been studied by Griffiths, James, and Phillips (228). Usually a typical curve is produced by plotting the weight or volume of the displaced fractions against such a physical or chemical property. The height of each step characterizes the component and the length is proportional to its amount. Special markers may be used to identify the boundaries of components that cannot otherwise be easily located in the plot.

The main advantage of the displacement method is that desorption is generally complete and that the back edges of the zones remain sharp, being continuously displaced by the following zone. A disadvantage is that the zones leave the column immediately behind one another and overlap to some extent even in optimum cases. The composition of these intermediate zones can be calculated from the properties of the component substances. However, an arbitrary division of the intermediate portions furnishes results of sufficient accuracy in many instances. A strongly adsorbed displacing agent leaves the column incapable of taking up a new sample. Therefore it is usually necessary to employ new adsorbent charge for each experiment.

(1) **Gases and Vapors.** A number of methods in this group involve adsorption of the gaseous sample at a low temperature, followed by fractional desorption in partial vacuum at different fixed temperatures and

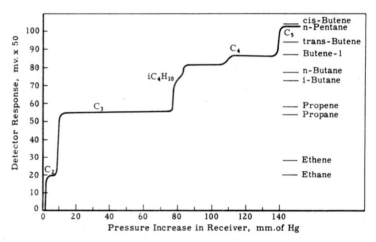

Fig. 6. Separation of a shale-gas fraction by displacement chromatography (239). Adsorbent, active carbon. Development by traveling heater. Detector, thermal conductivity cell.

pressures. This technique was used for the separation of C_1 to C_3 paraffinic and olefinic hydrocarbons (164,165,186,484,676–678), and was also extended to the determination of hydrocarbons boiling up to 145°C. (244). However, these methods are slow, inconvenient in operation, and not particularly selective. Moreover, the complete desorption of the sample is rather difficult to achieve.

Displacement by heating the adsorbent so that the hot zone moves slowly along the column has proved more successful. After considerable earlier development (182,254,365,557), Hammar (239) applied this technique to blends of C_2 to C_4 paraffins and olefins and to several shale-gas fractions (adsorbent, carbon; detection, thermal conductivity). The time required by this technique is usually less than one hour for a complete analysis, but the separation is sharp only for hydrocarbons of different carbon number (Fig. 6). Olefins are incompletely (or not at all) separated from paraffins of the same carbon number (ethane/ethylene, propane/propylene, n-butane/1-butene). When separation could be achieved, the accuracy was about 0.7% absolute, and the results compared very favorably with those obtained by low temperature distillation analysis using a Podbielniak column. A shortcoming of the thermal conductivity measurement was evident with some hydrocarbon pairs. Insufficient step height differences made it difficult to recognize some separations that might have been achieved by the column.

Strongly adsorbed displacing agents have also been applied with considerable success. As an extension of this technique, the column is operated at temperatures well above room temperature, which makes possible the analysis of a variety of liquid samples. In such procedures, the sample is vaporized on to the adsorbent and then displaced by a more strongly adsorbed vapor carried in a stream of nitrogen. It is desirable that such a displacing agent possess relatively high vapor pressure to ensure sufficiently high concentration in the desorbing stream. Claesson (106) built an entirely automatic apparatus and used the simple esters of acetic acid for the analysis of C_5 to C_8 hydrocarbons with excellent results (adsorbent, active carbon). A noteworthy feature of the method is that the accuracy with which the amount of one component is determined seems to be independent of the amounts of the other constituents present. The method is therefore suitable for the estimation of a small percentage of one component in a relatively large amount of the mixture.

Using Claesson's technique, simple mixtures containing ethylene were separated by Phillips (486). In a continuation of this work, James and Phillips (303) used bromobenzene as displacer and separated materials boiling as high as 150°C. on active carbon columns operated at 100°C. Turner (621,622) employed mercury vapors in combination with a traveling heater for stripping.

(2) **Liquids.** The chromatographic separation of liquids by the displacement technique is best carried out on highly adsorptive materials. Silica gel has been favored by most investigators, especially for the separation of hydrocarbons; active carbon and alumina have been employed to a lesser extent.

Displacement development has been applied to liquid olefinic hydrocarbon samples with reliable accuracy only when synthetic blends containing one saturated, one aromatic and one or two olefinic compounds (402) were to be separated. The resulting step heights (refractive indices) in such cases are sufficiently distinct to define the boundaries of the olefinic components (Fig. 7). For greater accuracy, the composition of the inter-

mediate portions may be calculated from the refractive indices of the overlapping components. However, with complex olefinic petroleum distillates,
a separation only according to types can be expected. The separation of
the olefinic aggregate of a quite narrow boiling range cracked gasoline
fraction may be accomplished with acceptable accuracy (108), especially

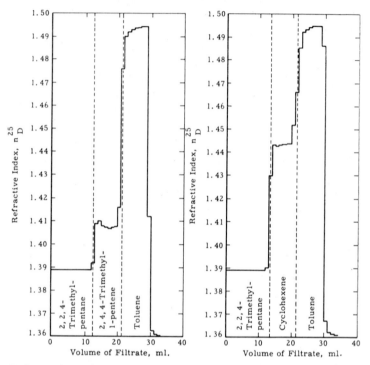

Fig. 7. Separations of simple mixtures of paraffinic, olefinic, and aromatic hydrocarbons by displacement chromatography (402). Adsorbent, silica gel. Displacing
agent, ethanol.

when the increased separating power of long narrow columns is utilized
(189). With wide distillation fractions, the boundaries are generally diffuse
and the information available is not sufficient for accurate evaluation.
These points are illustrated by the adsorptogram of a full range cracked
gasoline in Figure 8. The boundaries of the olefinic aggregate in this plot
are indistinct; a minor overlap with the saturates (on the left) and a more
pronounced mixed zone with the aromatics (on the right) is indicated by
bromine absorption values. There is no olefinic plateau (cf. Fig. 7) and the

selection of representative refractive indices for calculating the composition of the intermediate portion is not evident. Nevertheless, displacement development has been applied to cracked gasolines (213), shale oils (148, 150), synthol (466), and jet fuels (591) by the incorporation of special

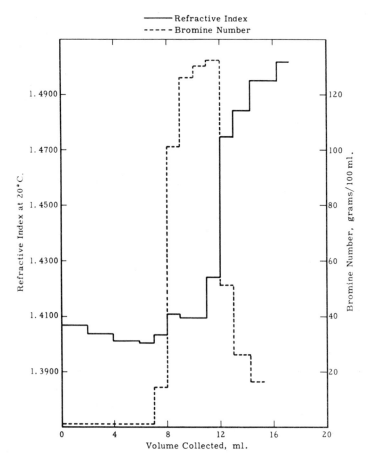

Fig. 8. Separation of a catalytically cracked gasoline by displacement chromatography (189). Adsorbent, silica gel. Displacing agent, ethanol.

techniques, but the precision obtained was only moderate or the procedures were generally too involved and time-consuming. Evaluation of the adsorptogram is particularly difficult when the olefin content is low (less than 5%).

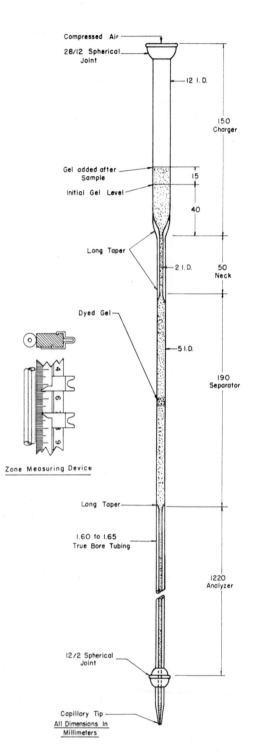

Fig. 9. Column for fluorescent indicator adsorption (FIA) method (23). (Reproduced from ASTM Method D 1319-55T by permission of the American Society for Testing Materials.)

A novel approach to these problems has been reported by Conrad (113), who employed a fluorescent dye to indicate the position of aromatics when the gasoline sample was displaced on a silica gel column with alcohol. The ratio of the length of the aromatic zone to that of the whole sample was taken as the volume fraction of the aromatic compounds in the sample. Several refinements enabled Criddle and LeTourneau (124) to extend the applicability of this technique to olefin-containing materials. An improved fluorescent dye mixture makes it possible to observe both the saturates/olefins and the olefins/aromatics boundaries. A modified column with a long, narrow final section, in which the lengths of zones are measured, improves the separation and increases the accuracy in reading zone lengths.

Details given below are essentially identical with those adopted by the A. S. T. M. (23).

Indicator. A mixture consisting of Sudan III together with selected fluorescent fractions of coal tar origin dissolved in xylene. (This dye mixture is available from Patent Chemicals Inc., Paterson, New Jersey.) To facilitate adding the proper amount of dye, it is convenient to use a previously prepared dyed gel.

Procedure. The glass adsorption column shown in Figure 9 is packed with Davison grade 923 (100 to 200 mesh) silica gel, to which a very small amount of dyed gel is added in the separator section of the column. (Uniform packing may be achieved by applying a rubber-padded vibrator to the column.) Approximately 0.75 ml. of sample is introduced and additional gel is added to absorb the sample. Then isopropyl alcohol is added and forced down the column by air pressure (approximately 5 p. s. i.). The hydrocarbons are separated into saturates, olefins, and aromatics (including aromatics with olefinic side chain, plus any sulfur-, nitrogen-, and oxygen-containing compounds), followed by the alcohol. The indicator dyes are also selectively separated; Sudan III appears at the aromatics/alcohol boundary and the fluorescent dyes mark the other two boundaries. The lengths of the three zones, as indicated by these dyes in ultraviolet light (Plate I, opposite p. 350) are measured after the sample passes into the long, narrow extension (analyzer section) of the column. The type composition of the sample, in volume per cent, is calculated from the ratios of the lengths of the respective fractions to the total length of the sample.

The scope of the fluorescent indicator adsorption (FIA) method depends, in the first place, on adsorption differences exhibited by the components of the sample. In the gasoline and kerosine boiling ranges, these differences on silica gel columns are sufficiently large to give segregation of the three hydrocarbon types, aromatics, olefins, and saturates, in a highly efficient column by the displacement technique. The full utilization of this separation has been hampered rather by the lack of convenient methods of detection of the interface between types. The ability of the dye mixture to indicate these boundaries has been established by cooperators of the A. S. T. M. for the gasoline, kerosine, and jet fuel (up to 315°C.) boiling ranges. The accuracy of the method is approximately 2% and frequently better. Difficulties have been experienced only with heavily cracked samples that tend to yield indistinct olefinic boundaries. The time required to complete an analysis is approximately two hours; the actual operations, however, require less than one-half hour of the analyst's time.

A similar indicator method, published recently by Harvey and Pearson (246) suggests the use of bisdiphenylene-ethylene or, for samples containing C_9 and higher hydrocarbons, carotene as a visual marker for the olefins/aromatics boundary. The authors also used fluorescent markers that were prepared from an asphalt fraction.

Displacement analysis on silica gel has been investigated by Glasser, Harris, Christensen, and Bope (214) as a method for separating terpene hydrocarbons.

The separability of saturated acids from unsaturated acids by displacement development on silica gel was demonstrated by Claesson (107). A more detailed study with saturated and unsaturated acids varying from 4 to 22 carbon atoms in chain length, and with their glycerides, was undertaken by Holman, Williams, Abu-Nasr, and Hamilton (1,238,272). Active carbon was used as adsorbent and the separations were carried out in a modified Tiselius-Claesson interferometric apparatus (271). Samples were dissolved in benzene or in an alcohol, and a high molecular weight acid or glyceride dissolved in the same solvent was employed as displacer. It was found that, within a family of acids of equal chain length, increasing unsaturation decreases adsorbability if the unsaturation is nonconjugated (e. g., stearic, oleic, linoleic acids); on the other hand, if the double bonds are conjugated either with the carboxyl group or with themselves, the adsorbability is increased. Two of the systems studied included (in order of decreasing adsorbability) α-, and β-eleostearic, stearic, oleic, and linoleic acids, and α,β-unsaturated caproic, caproic, and β,γ-unsaturated caproic acids. Adsorbabilities within a homologous series increased with increasing molecular weight. In addition to these rules, the separability of the glycerides was also influenced by the solvent chosen. In the polar solvent, ethanol, the least polar glyceride (triglyceride) was adsorbed most strongly; in the nonpolar benzene, the most polar glyceride (monoglyceride) was

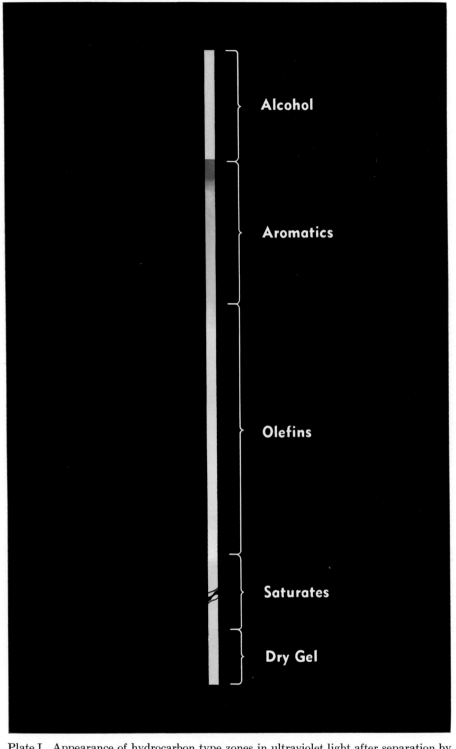

Plate I. Appearance of hydrocarbon type zones in ultraviolet light after separation by the fluorescent indicator adsorption (FIA) method.

adsorbed most strongly. The separations were very satisfactory in most cases. The detection and separation of minor components was further improved by the use of "carrier" displacers (270).

The separation of dibasic acids with isolated and conjugated double bonds on active carbon was studied by English (179).

B. DEVELOPMENT (ELUTION) ANALYSIS

The sample is introduced at the top of the column and, after it has entirely entered the adsorbent, the developing solvent is added. For the separation of gases and vapors, this solvent is an inert gas (nitrogen, hydrogen, or carbon dioxide). Solid samples, and usually liquid samples, are dissolved in a solvent that has lower adsorption affinity toward the adsorbent than any component of the sample. Development is continued by adding subsequent portions of this solvent. During this process of development a continuous adsorption and desorption of the sample components takes place, different substances being retained in the adsorbed phase for different lengths of time. As a result of these different adsorption affinities toward the adsorbent, components of a mixture travel down the column at different rates and arrange into more or less distinct zones. If the position of these zones can be detected on the column, they may be isolated by simply pushing the column of adsorbent out of the chromatographic tube and sectioning it with a knife. The material adsorbed in each segment is then eluted with an appropriate solvent. Recovery of the material from the eluate may be accomplished by evaporation of the solvent, or simple water washing if the eluent is water soluble (e. g., alcohol) but the sample is not.

With colorless samples, it is customary to continue the development until components of the sample appear in the effluent (elution analysis). Since this can become a rather lengthy process if the mixture to be separated contains several components of widely different adsorption affinities, it is common practice to complete the desorption with successively stronger developers (513). Alternately, gradually increasing concentrations of a powerful developer in the solution of the initial weak solvent may be used (12). Changing the developing solvent serves another purpose. Most compounds possess curved isotherms on adsorbents commonly used in adsorption chromatography, the result of which is that the rate of movement of the zones depends on the concentration and the zone traveling down the column develops a diffuse, "tailing," back edge. This phenomenon is particularly noticeable when colored materials are separated or when the elution curve is continuously recorded (as, for example, in gas chromatography). "Tailing" is greatly suppressed when developers of gradually increasing desorptive strength are used.

Active carbon and silica gel have been used almost exclusively in the elution chromatography of gases. For liquid and solid samples, a large variety of adsorbents is available. Of these, the use of a moderately retentive material, on which a wider choice of developers is applicable, should be preferred.

When colored materials are separated, the process can be followed visually. Various chemical and physical methods have been employed, in addition to those discussed in the previous section, for the detection of colorless materials.

(1) **Gases and Vapors.** Schuftan (557) was the first to publish a method that incorporated the use of a developing gas. After the nonhydrocarbon components of a cracked gas (hydrogen, nitrogen, oxygen, and carbon dioxide) passed through the cooled (-100 to $-120°$C.) active carbon column, methane and ethylene were fractionally desorbed with a stream of carbon dioxide. The desorption of the higher boiling components of the sample was further aided by removing the column from the cooling bath and slowly heating it to 200°C. The appearance of each component in the effluent gas was recognized with a gas interferometer. Quantitative recoveries were obtained in several experiments.

Development with carbon dioxide was also used by Hesse, Eilbracht, and Reicheneder (259) to fractionate a high-boiling organic acid fraction on a silica gel column. The saturated components of the sample were removed at 120 to 140°C. column temperature. Raising the temperature to 200 to 240°C. yielded the unsaturated components. However, only partial fractionation was achieved when this technique was applied to a cyclohexene–benzene mixture (260).

By suitable choice of column length, temperatures, and gas velocity, Cremer, Müller, and Prior (121–123) reported quantitative separation of binary and ternary mixtures of carbon dioxide, nitrogen, acetylene, ethylene, propylene, and vinyl chloride on active carbon and silica gel columns using hydrogen as developing gas. Characteristic emergence times were observed. Recoveries of better than 99% were calculated from the half-intensity width of the curves obtained by thermal conductivity measurements for sample sizes between 1 and 10 mg.

With the combination of a stream of air and a traveling furnace as developing and desorbing agents, Zhukhovitskiĭ, Zolotareva, Sokolov, and Turkel'taub (698) separated methane, ethane, ethylene, propane, propylene, butylene, and isobutylene into seven distinct peaks on a column of silica gel using a gas interferometer for detection. This so-named "chromathermographic" method permitted variation of several factors including the velocity of the air stream and the temperature and velocity of the furnace. This method was successfully used also by Aivazov and Vyakhirev (6).

Janák and Rusek (304) separated C_2 and C_3 hydrocarbons on carbon and silica gel using carbon dioxide as developer. From a carbon column, the C_2 hydrocarbons emerged in the order of acetylene, ethylene, and ethane; this order was reversed on silica gel. When the desorption was accomplished with the addition of a traveling heater, a seven-component mixture was separated with ±1.5% accuracy. Less accurate results were obtained

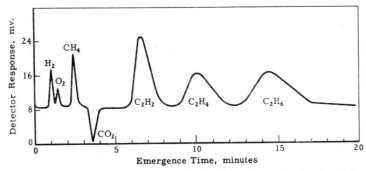

Fig. 10. Separation of a gas mixture by elution chromatography (480). Column, active carbon. Developer, nitrogen. Detector, thermal conductivity cell.

with some saturated and unsaturated halogenated hydrocarbons because of the partial hydrolysis of these materials by the potassium hydroxide solution used for the absorption of the developing gas (305).

Ray (511) separated mixtures of hydrogen, carbon monoxide, carbon dioxide, methane, ethane, ethylene, and acetylene (in this order of desorption) on a column of activated charcoal (20 to 40°C.) using nitrogen as developing gas. Patton, Lewis, and Kaye (480) obtained satisfactory separations of ethylene, propylene, *trans*-2-butene, and *cis*-2-butene from admixture with hydrogen, oxygen, air, carbon dioxide, and saturated hydrocarbons of the C_2–C_4 range (Fig. 10). Active carbon, silica gel, and alumina columns were used, and hydrogen, nitrogen, or carbon dioxide were employed as eluents. Quantitative results, calculated from the plot of the thermal conductivity measurements using the product of the peak height and its half-width, were accurate to ±1 to 2% of the amount found.

Martin and Smart (418) used an active carbon column with nitrogen as the developing gas, and converted all components to carbon dioxide and water by passing the separated components over copper oxide heated to approximately 600°C. This technique has several advantages, of which the uniform response of all hydrocarbons in the thermal conductivity cell and the increased sensitivity are the most significant.

(2) Liquids and Solids. Silica gel is used almost exclusively for the fractionation of petroleum distillates by the elution analysis technique. Saturates, the least strongly adsorbed component, are commonly developed and carried into the filtrate with pentane. The completion of the removal of the saturated zone is indicated by the return of the refractive index of the effluent to that of the developing pentane. Continued use of pentane will result in the slow appearance of olefins in the effluent. However, when the developer plateau is reached, it is advantageous to change to a stronger developer such as pentene (490a). A new refractive index peak, corresponding to the olefins zone, appears; then the readings return to that of this new developer. A strongly polar compound such as ether, acetone, or an alcohol is used at this point to elute the aromatics and completely clear the column. The fractionation of individual components within these three hydrocarbon types is negligible. For ease of recovery of the sample, the developers should boil outside the range of the sample; the polar eluent is generally soluble in water and can be readily washed out. Pentane is the most widely used developer for the saturates in all boiling ranges; a saturates aggregate boiling in the kerosine range has also been employed for the development of cracked gasoline saturates (507). Pentene is a very suitable substance to produce a "wedge" between the olefins and the aromatics of kerosines and depentanized gasolines. However, pentene is not effective in the higher boiling ranges, and no other developer has been found as yet to accomplish the quantitative separation of olefins from aromatics in cracked gas oils and olefin-containing lubricating oils.

Adsorbent-coated glass strips ("chromatostrips") were employed by Kirchner, Miller, and Keller (346) for the separation of limonene, α-pinene, pulegone, and other terpene-type compounds. The location of the developed spots was revealed by spraying with suitable reagents.

Elution chromatography has been used with some success for the resolution of various saturated and unsaturated acids (160,256,320,336) and esters (161,522) and glycerides of linseed oil (631,632) and of soybean oil (516) on active carbon, alumina, and silicic acid. In most cases, hexane was used as developer and diethyl ether as eluent. Pure fractions were produced in several instances, but the separation of the components was not quantitative. It was shown later by Kurtz (368) that the separation of C_{18} acids and esters can be made more effective by the use of solutes of intermediate adsorptivity ("amplified chromatographic separation").

A magnesium oxide column impregnated with phenol red was used by Graff and Skau (226) to separate stearic and oleic acids. Phenol red changes its color when in contact with the acids; thus, the development of the chromatogram can be followed visually. After development with petroleum ether, the column was extruded and sectioned. The stearic and oleic acids were recovered with very good yields.

2,4-Dinitrobenzenesulfenyl chloride was reported by Kharasch and Buess (344) to add to olefinic bonds in the manner:

$$
\begin{array}{c} \diagdown C \diagup \\ \| \\ C \\ \diagup \diagdown \end{array} \quad + \quad \text{ArS—Cl} \quad \longrightarrow \quad \begin{array}{c} | \\ \text{—C—SAr} \\ | \\ \text{—C—Cl} \\ | \end{array}
$$

This reaction was used by Simmons and Quackenbush (578) in the chromatographic separation of oleic, linoleic, and linolenic acids. The derivatives of these acids were separated into well-defined bands on a column of anhydrous magnesium sulfate (developer, 5% ethyl ether in benzene). The individual derivatives were recovered in the eluate with yields above 95%. Results obtained on several common vegetable oils compared favorably with those by the ultraviolet method of Brice, Swain, Herb, Nichols, and Riemenschneider (80)(see Section III.3.D). The chromatographic separation of adducts of olefinic hydrocarbons with the Kharasch reagent on specially prepared silicic acid columns was recently reported by Malmberg (405).

In addition to petroleum olefins and unsaturated fatty materials, a large variety of compounds containing olefinic linkages have been separated by development chromatography. The spectacular growth of the field of carotenoids during the past two decades is the direct result of the use of chromatographic techniques. Primarily analysis by development chromatography is responsible for the great progress made in the study of other naturally occurring pigments, such as flavins, anthocyanins, chlorophylls, porphyrins, and related products. Elution analysis has been found useful also in the investigation of colorless compounds with olefinic bonds as shown by the numerous applications of this procedure in the field of terpenes, sterols, bile acids, vitamins, hormones, enzymes, etc. Several special techniques have been worked out to aid in the detection of the extent of separation. Coffmann (109) chromatographed colored esters of sterols prepared with p-phenylazobenzoyl chloride. The chromatography of the

2,4-dinitrophenylhydrazones of aldehydes and ketones, recommended by Strain (601), has been used by many workers for the separation of saturated and unsaturated carbonylic compounds (442a). A method, proposed by Zechmeister, consists in applying a thin streak of a convenient reagent, with a brush, down the length of the column after it has been extruded from the chromatographic tube. The position of a vitamin A zone was determined by this technique, using antimony trichloride in chloroform solution (694), producing the deep blue color of the Carr-Price reaction. Dilute permanganate solution was used to detect the *cis*- and *trans*-forms of stilbene; permanganate rapidly turns brown where it crosses a zone containing olefinic unsaturation, while the empty sections remain purple for several minutes (696).

2. Partition Chromatography

The basis of separation in partition chromatography is the differential distribution of the components of a mixture between two immiscible or semimiscible solvents. One fluid phase is held stationary on the surface of an inert solid carrier while the solutes to be separated, dissolved in the second fluid phase (mobile phase) pass by. The chromatogram is formed by the selective retention of the components of the sample by the stationary phase (419). The solid carrier is usually a polar material that holds the stationary liquid phase by adsorptive forces. A variety of solids has been used as supports; diatomaceous earth (kieselguhr) has been found especially suitable. As efficient fractionation demands the rapid attainment of equilibrium, supports with many fine capillaries should be avoided. Paper as the carrier of the stationary phase is one of the most useful developments of partition chromatography (114). Amplified separations may be achieved in this medium if, after development in one direction is completed, the sheet is turned 90 degrees and development is continued with a different mobile phase. The resulting chromatogram is a set of spots, usually detected by spraying the paper with suitable reagents.

Partition chromatography possesses several advantages over adsorption chromatography. The choice of the partition system can be based on rational considerations, as the partition of various types of substances between many solvent pairs is well known. By varying the chemical nature of the stationary phase, the order of emergence can be altered, hence rechromatography in a new system can yield quantitative separation of difficult mixtures. A basic advantage of the partition method over physical adsorption lies in the different type of distribution isotherm involved. While in adsorption chromatography, the isotherms are usually curved, in partition chromatography linear or nearly linear isotherms have been observed in most cases. The result is symmetrical elution peaks with no significant "tailing."

Partition chromatography separation in columns are usually run as elution processes. When the developing mobile phase is a liquid, the technique is called liquid–liquid partition chromatography, as distinguished from gas–liquid partition chromatography introduced recently for the separation of gaseous and vaporized samples.

A. LIQUID–LIQUID PARTITION CHROMATOGRAPHY

Both column and paper partition chromatography have received numerous applications to the separation of substances containing olefinic linkages in various fields of organic chemistry (376,691). The behavior on paper of higher saturated and unsaturated fatty acids, including oleic, 9,11-linoleic, 9,12-linoleic, linolenic, β-eleostearic, and erucic acids, was studied by Kaufmann, Budwig, and Schmidt (326,327). Binary mixtures were separated using aqueous methyl alcohol of varying concentrations as the mobile phase. Characteristic color reactions, particularly in ultraviolet light, with dyes such as rhodamine B and Nile blue served to locate the separated components. A wide variety of other color-forming reagents also proved useful. Kaufmann, Budwig, and Schmidt (327) showed later that the Diels-Alder reaction can be carried out on paper using only minute quantities of reactants; upon development with petroleum ether, the conjugated acids are clearly distinguished.

Boldingh (62) achieved good separation of the ethyl esters of oleic and erucic acids from C_{12} to C_{18} saturated acids on paper impregnated with rubber latex using a methanol–acetone mixture as the developing solvent. A similar columnar "reversed phase" partition system, consisting of powdered rubber saturated with benzene and, as mobile phase, aqueous ethanol, was also found successful for the separation of oleic, linoleic, and linolenic acids. However, the operating variables seemed critical. Separations of unsaturated hydroxy and keto acids by partition chromatography on paper have also been reported (104,392,473).

Liquid–liquid partition chromatography for the separation of olefinic hydrocarbons apparently has not as yet been studied.

B. GAS–LIQUID PARTITION CHROMATOGRAPHY

The use of a gas as the mobile phase in partition chromatography was introduced by James and Martin (297,299,300,302) for the separation of volatile acids and bases. A silicone oil–stearic acid mixture, glycerol, undecanol, and undecanol–liquid paraffin mixtures on diatomaceous earth were used as stationary phases. With nitrogen as the mobile phase, and column temperatures of 79 to 137°C., the separation and recovery of components boiling as high as 225°C. were accomplished.

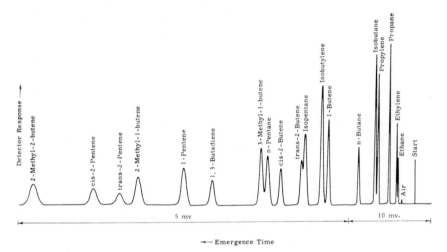

Fig. 11. Separation of C_2–C_5 hydrocarbons by gas–liquid partition chromatography (198). Column, dimethylsulfolane on firebrick. Developer, helium. Detector, thermal conductivity cell.

The great interest in this extremely promising technique was demonstrated by the appearance, in rapid succession, of a number of publications reporting the separations of aromatic hydrocarbons (71,301,303,341,384, 510,511), aliphatic halides (301,303,341), aliphatic alcohols (301,511), higher fatty acids (131), esters (301,511), ketones and aldehydes (301,511), and ethers (511). The separation of olefinic hydrocarbons has been reported by Ray (511), Bradford, Harvey, and Chalkley (71), Lichtenfels, Fleck, and Burow (384), Keulemans and Kwantes (341), and Fredericks and Brooks (198) (see Fig. 11). Keulemans and Kwantes also obtained separations with unsaturated chlorine compounds.

The experimental arrangement of gas–liquid partition chromatography is simple. The nonvolatile solvent, supported on a finely divided inert solid, is packed into a long, narrow (e. g., $^1/_4$ inch by several feet) glass or metal tube. This column is enclosed (folded or coiled when too long) in a jacket kept at the required temperature. A small amount of sample is introduced at the head of the column and transported through it by the controlled flow of an inert gas. The separated components are detected by a suitable device in the gas flow emerging from the column.

A wide variety of materials has been used as the stationary phase, of which dinonyl phthalate (341,511), acetonyl acetone (71), dioctyl phthalate (384), "Octoil-S" (384), diisodecyl phthalate (198), and dimethylsulfolane (198) have been found especially suitable for the separation of olefin-containing samples. The support most commonly employed has been diatomaceous earth (e. g., Celite 545, Johns-Manville), but carbon, silica gel, and alumina (452) and ground firebrick (198,341) also have been used. Gas–liquid partition columns can be reused many times without noticeable loss of efficiency.

As carrier gas, nitrogen has been found satisfactory in most applications, but the use of hydrogen (384), helium (198,384), and carbon dioxide (341) has been reported. The rate at which a component of the sample mixture moves through the column is determined by its vapor pressure over the stationary liquid phase at the temperature of the system, and by the flow rate of the carrier gas. In general, components of mixtures will have different vapor pressures; consequently, they will travel through the column at different rates and will emerge separately in the carrier gas. The process of separation is clearly analogous to extractive distillation, and in fact the efficiency of a column may be expressed in terms of theoretical plates. On this basis, efficiencies as high as 1000 plates in a 4 foot column are possible (300). Components of a homologous series are separated according to their relative solubilities in the liquid phase; usually, this is in the order of their boiling points or molecular weights. For difficultly separable pairs, solubility differences may be increased by an appropriate choice of the stationary phase. The order of emergence from a column may be changed by employing a polar liquid phase in which hydrogen bonding comes into play in addition to the ordinary van der Waals solution forces. Bradford, Harvey, and Chalkley (71) demonstrated these effects for unsaturated hydrocarbons. It was also shown that special separations can be achieved by loose complex formation between olefins and metal ions contained in the stationary phase. A saturated solution of silver nitrate in glycol was used with some success. A discussion of the role of the stationary liquid in gas–liquid partition chromatography has been prepared by Keulemans, Kwantes, and Zaal (342).

Separations are usually detected by means of a thermal conductivity cell inserted in the effluent gas stream. (Satisfactory equipment employing a thermal conductivity cell is illustrated in the chapter on "Determination of Organic Acids" in this volume.) This method has high sensitivity, is rapid in response, and can be conveniently coupled to an electrical recorder. This arrangement produces peaks representing sample components, separated by valleys representing the carrier gas. Because of their separation, neighboring sample components with similar thermal conductivity can be clearly differentiated. Several other physical methods for detection have been suggested (228,298,341). Chemical methods can be used for compounds with functional groups. James and Martin used titration by an automatic recording buret to detect acids and bases.

The emerging components of a mixture may be identified by measuring their retention volume, i. e., the volume of carrier gas passed through the column before the peak occurs. Martin and James (300) showed that this value is characteristic for a given compound emerging from a column at a definite temperature, and that for a homologous series the plot of logarithms of these values against the number of carbon atoms approximates a straight line. An unknown component may be identified by interpolation. If the flow of the carrier gas is kept constant, usually the retention time (emergence time) is measured.

Quantitative measurements are based either on the area under the peak of the recorded plot or on the peak height. The column can be calibrated with measured amounts of pure substances. Alternatively, a known percentage of a compound (internal standard), similar in nature to the sample components, can be added and its peak area used for calculation of the sample components (510). Recoveries of $\pm 3\%$ and better (198,384, 510) have been reported. When the sample size is large enough, the emerging pure components may be collected in a trap and examined by a chemical or spectrometric method. When carbon dioxide is used as a carrier, gaseous samples can be obtained undiluted by collecting fractions over a solution of base (341).

V. RECOMMENDATIONS

There appear to be few analytical techniques applicable to all types of olefinic compounds. For many simple mixtures, however, there are several methods that yield about equally reliable results. For complex mixtures, many analytical procedures have been described; some of these cannot be evaluated very well. Hydrogenation probably is the most general chemical method for determination of unsaturation, but for many types of samples other methods are more convenient and at least as reliable. The selectivity

TABLE XXVIII
Applicability of Methods to Various Types of Samples

Type of olefinic compound determined	Recommended methods	Comments	See page
	I. One C=C Bond (or Isolated C=C bonds)		
	A. Hydrocarbons		
1. General	Hydrogenation	Most general chem. method. Reactivity varies with type of sample and catalyst. Time requirement per analysis rather high.	256, 266
	Halogenation	Several rapid methods suitable for individual hydrocarbons (except highly branched) and simple mixtures (see below). No halogenation method is completely reliable for petroleum distillates.	210
	Ozonization method of Boer and Kooyman	Titrimetric procedure. Highly condensed aromatics and some sulfur compds. also react. Apparatus required.	280
	Infrared	Individual compds. in simple mixts. Good type analysis for $RCH=CH_2$, $RR'C=CH_2$, and *trans*-$RCH=CHR'$.	324, 327
	I_2 complexes by ultraviolet	Analysis for 6 types, including $RR'C=CR''R'''$, $RR'C=CHR''$, and *cis*-$RCH=CHR'$.	331
2. Structural types: terminal			
$\diagup\!\!\!\diagdown C=CH_2$	Perbenzoic acid method of Kolthoff and Lee	Designed primarily for rubber, polymers and copolymers.	272
	Ozonolysis	Measure formaldehyde produced.	278
	Infrared	10.05 and 10.96 μ for $RCH=CH_2$, 11.24 μ for $RR'C=CH_2$.	327
internal			
$\diagup\!\!\!\diagdown C=C\diagup\!\!\!\diagdown$	Perbenzoic acid method of Saffer and Johnson	Not applicable to mixts. containing less than 70% internal double bonds.	273
	Infrared	10.36 for *trans*-$RCH=CHR'$; other internal types variable.	327
	I_2 complexes by ultraviolet	295–300 mμ for *cis*-$RCH=CHR'$, 317 mμ for $RR'C=CHR''$, 337 mμ for $RR'C=CR''R'''$.	331
$RCH=C(CH_3)_2$ ..	Ozonolysis	Measure acetone produced.	279

Table continued

TABLE XXVIII (*continued*)

Type of olefinic compound determined	Recommended methods	Comments	See page
highly branched..	Ozonization method of Boer and Kooyman	Titrimetric procedure. Highly condensed aromatics and some sulfur compds. also react.	280
	Iodine monochloride method of Lee, Kolthoff, and Johnson	Rather lengthy procedure, principally for research work.	224
	KBr₃ in methanol, modification of Wilson	Probably the best bromination method for branched olefins.	240
semiolefins....... e. g. ⬡〉C=C⟨	Ozonization method of Boer and Kooyman	Titrimetric procedure. Highly condensed aromatics and some sulfur compds. also react.	281
styrenes.........	Mercuration	Three procedures, all applicable to styrene, divinylbenzene, and several derivs.; applicability to other unsatd. compds. varies.	301
	Nitrogen trioxide	Gravimetric method. No interference from several olefins and aromatics.	291
	Nitrogen trioxide	Colorimetric method for styrene in air.	291
	Polarography	Some specificity possible.	336
divinylbenzenes..	Nitrogen trioxide	Gravimetric method. No interference from α-methylstyrene or moderate amounts of styrene and ethylvinylbenzenes.	291
indene..........	Condensation with benzaldehyde	Colorimetric method. Cyclopentadienes interfere.	320
bicycloheptenes..	Phenyl azide	Colorimetric method. Other types of olefins less reactive.	322
dicyclopentadiene	Formic acid	Determine ester formed. Higher polymers of cyclopentadiene also react.	320
	Depolymerization, then condensation with benzaldehyde	Colorimetric method for cyclopentadiene monomer.	320
3. Gases...........	Bromine in acetic acid	Direct titration of C₃ and C₄ olefins; ethylene not determined unless excess reagent is added.	233
	Acid absorption	Mercuric sulfate in H₂SO₄ for total olefins; 65 to 87% H₂SO₄ solns. for olefin type selectivity.	294
	Infrared	Individual compds., C₂–C₅.	324
	Gas chromatography	Individual compds., C₂–C₄, some C₅.	352, 358

TABLE XXVIII (*continued*)

Type of olefinic compound determined	Recommended methods	Comments	See page
4. Gasoline range....	Bromine in CCl₄	Shell extrapolation method. Good results on most olefins, but conjugated diolefins react only about 50%.	237
	Bromide–bromate	A. S. T. M. versions recommended. The electrometric procedure is more rapid than the color indicator procedure. High results on branched olefins; conjugated diolefins react only about 50%.	248, 249
	Sulfuric acid absorption	Reliable for total vol. of olefins plus aromatics.	296
	Nitrogen tetroxide	Volumetric measure of total olefins (including aromatic olefins). Polyaromatics interfere.	287
	Infrared plus mass spectrometry	Type analysis.	324, 335
	Refractometry	Characterization and type analysis.	339
	Displacement chromatography on silica gel (FIA method)	Volumetric measure of total olefins (excluding aromatic olefins) plus volumetric measures of total saturates and total aromatics.	349
	Development chromatography on silica gel	Isolates the olefinic aggregate (excluding aromatic olefins), as well as the saturates and aromatics aggregates.	354
5. Kerosine range...	Bromine in CCl₄	Shell extrapolation method.	237
	Sulfuric acid absorption	Reliable for total vol. of olefins plus aromatics.	296
	Displacement chromatography on silica gel (FIA method)	Volumetric measure of total olefins (excluding aromatic olefins) plus volumetric measures of total saturates and total aromatics.	349
	Development chromatography on silica gel	Isolates the olefinic aggregate (excluding aromatic olefins), as well as the saturates and aromatics aggregates.	354
6. Gas oil and lubricating oil range...	Hydrogen perbromide complex	Possibly the halogenation method least affected by interfering side reactions.	243
	Development chromatography on silica gel	Isolates the olefinic aggregate (excluding aromatic olefins). Separation from the aromatics aggregate is not complete.	354

Table continued

TABLE XXVIII (*continued*)

Type of olefinic compound determined	Recommended methods	Comments	See page
7. Polymers........	Iodine monochloride method of Lee, Kolthoff, and Johnson	For butyl rubbers, etc. Lengthy procedure, principally for research work.	224
	Iodine in presence of mercuric acetate	For isoprene-isobutylene polymers. Rapid semiempirical procedure, suitable for routine work.	221
	Bromination, gravimetric procedure	For crude rubber and latex.	254
	Perbenzoic acid	For rubber polymers, etc. Reactivity varies with structure of olefin.	272

B. Nonhydrocarbons

1. General..........	Hydrogenation	Most general chem. method. Reactivity varies; some interferences.	256, 268
	KBr$_3$ in water	Good results on many unsatd. alcs., acids, esters, ethers, carbonyl compds., and chlorinated hydrocarbons. Most satd. oxygen-containing compds. do not interfere.	240
	Bromine in acetic acid (trace method)	For dilute solns. of allyl alcohol, crotonaldehyde, etc.	233
	Ozonization method of Boer and Kooyman	Titrimetric procedure. Good results on several unsatd. aldehydes, ethers, acids, and esters.	280
	Mercuration methods of Marquardt and Luce and Martin	Reactivity varies widely. Good results on several vinyl and allyl ethers, alcohols, etc., poor results on most esters.	304, 307
	Mercuration method of Das	Good results on allyl alcohol, allyl and vinyl acetates; low results on esters of unsatd. acids.	308
2. Fatty acids and esters...........	Iodine monochloride, standard Wijs method	Most reliable and widely used method for nonconjugated fats and oils.	222
	Iodine monochloride, deadstop procedure	Micro method; primarily for oils.	224
	Iodine monochloride, in presence of mercuric acetate	More rapid than standard Wijs method, but less reliable; not applicable in presence of hydroxyl groups (e. g., castor oil).	224
	Thiocyanation	Selective for isolated double bonds. In conjunction with the standard Wijs method, oleic, linoleic, and linolenic acids or their glycerides can be determined in mixts.	298

TABLE XXVIII (*continued*)

Type of olefinic compound determined	Recommended methods	Comments	See page
	Hypochlorous acid	Rapid method for fats and oils.	256
	KOH–ultraviolet	Isomerization to form conjugated diene, triene, and tetraene compds. measured at 233, 268, and 315 mμ.	334
3. Essential oils.....	Pyridine methylbromide dibromide	Pretreatment steps prevent interference from aldehydes, peroxides, amines, phenols, etc.	254
4. Vinyl ethers......	Iodine in methanol	Acetaldehyde and acetals do not interfere.	228
	Mercuration method of Martin	Other mercuration methods probably also applicable.	307
5. α,β-Unsaturated compounds			
aldehydes and ketones	KBr₃ in water	Satd. carbonyl compds. do not interfere.	240
	KBr₃ in methanol	Back-titration of excess reagent can be made using anethole.	239
	Bisulfite	Aldehyde group also determined.	317
	Mercaptan	Not quantitative with α,β-unsatd. ketones; sulfur and peroxides interfere.	315
	Polarography	Satd. carbonyl compds. reduce at higher potentials.	338
acids...........	Same methods as for α,β-unsatd. carbonyl compds. (except mercaptan method) plus morpholine method	Reactivity varies depending on structure in vicinity of the double bond. Epoxides also determined; org. halides and large amts. of carbonyl compds. interfere.	321
esters, amides, and nitriles..........	Same methods as for α,β-unsatd. acids, plus mercaptan method	Reactivity varies, depending on structure in vicinity of the double bond.	
6. Halogen-containing compounds.......	KBr₃ in water	Two procedures; some compds. require the more drastic reaction conditions.	240
chlorostyrenes....	Mercuration method of Marquardt and Luce	Dichlorostyrenes require warming and increased reaction time.	304
pesticides with bicycloheptene rings	Phenyl azide	Colorimetric method of high sensitivity.	322
7. Allylsilenes......	Thiocyanation	Bromination methods not applicable.	301
8. Polymers........	Bromide–bromate	Applicable to polymerized acrylic and allyl esters.	253

Table continued

TABLE XXVIII (*continued*)

Type of olefinic compound determined	Recommended methods	Comments	See page
	II. Two or More Conjugated C=C Bonds		
	A. Hydrocarbons		
1. General..........	Hydrogenation	Reactivity varies.	256
	Infrared	6.25μ band is characteristic.	326
	Polarography	Allenes and styrenes also are reducible.	337
2. Butadiene........	Ultraviolet	216 mμ recommended.	332
3. Pentadienes......	Ultraviolet	Vapor spectra at 220 to 230 mμ for individual C$_5$ dienes.	333
4. Cyclopentadienes..	Ultraviolet	244 mμ in vapor spectrum for cyclopentadiene in admixture with noncyclic C$_5$ dienes.	333
	Condensation with carbonyl compds.	Colorimetric methods for cyclopentadiene and methylcyclopentadiene by reaction with benzaldehyde and also with acetone.	320
5. Dienes in petroleum distillates....	Maleic anhydride	Modified Ellis and Jones method applicable to gasolines, etc.	314
6. Carotenes........	Ultraviolet and visible absorption	Some selectivity.	332
	Development chromatography	Individual stereoisomers can be isolated.	355
	B. Nonhydrocarbons		
1. General..........	Hydrogenation	Reactivity varies.	256
2. Fatty acids and esters............	Maleic anhydride	Pandiene number method. Isolated double bonds are not determined.	313
	Pyridinium sulfate dibromide in presence of mercuric acetate (Planck, Pack, and Goldblatt procedure)	Total unsatn. (conjugated plus isolated double bonds) is determined.	245
	Iodine monobromide (Woburn method)	Total unsatn. (conjugated plus isolated double bonds) is determined.	226
	Ultraviolet	Conjugated diene, triene, and tetraene acids measured at 233, 268 and 315 mμ.	334
3. Carotenoids......	Ultraviolet and visible absorption	Some selectivity.	334
	Development chromatography	Individual compds. (including some stereoisomers) can be separated.	355
	III. Coupled C=C=C Bonds		
	Ozonolysis	Measure CO$_2$ formed.	276
	Infrared	5.1 μ band is characteristic.	326
	Polarography	Conjugated diolefins and styrenes also are reducible.	337

of some methods in regard to type of unsaturated compound determined is frequently a useful feature. All methods are subject to interferences and other limitations. Many methods have been tested only for a few types of olefinic compounds and a few types of possible interferences. In some instances further evaluation may be warranted before the most useful procedure for a given type of sample is selected.

In the earlier sections of this chapter, an effort was made to arrange the subject matter according to type of analytical method (depending on the nature of the chemical reagent, separation technique, or principle of measurement). As a guide to these methods, Table XXVIII is arranged according to type of sample. The methods recommended for each type of sample are those which, in the opinion of the authors, appear to be most useful in regard to some feature such as scope, accuracy, selectivity, sensitivity, or extent of interferences. These features are discussed in the earlier sections; for further details, the reader should consult the original literature referred to in the text.

Before using a method on a system other than those described, the analyst should establish the applicability of the procedure to the sample in question. If the composition of the sample is so complex or unknown that the preparation of synthetic mixtures on which to test the method is not feasible, the results of two or more independent methods should be compared. In some instances, a quantitative separation technique (e. g., elution development chromatography of cracked petroleum distillates in the gasoline and kerosine ranges) serves as a "referee" method to establish more rapid methods for use on the same type of sample.

The authors wish to express their appreciation to several of their fellow analytical chemists at Shell Development Company, particularly to Fred T. Weiss for the assistance he provided on organic chemistry and his advice in revising the original manuscript, to Edward D. Peters for his interest and constant encouragement, and to Sigurd Groennings for review and helpful suggestions.

References

1. Abu-Nasr, A. M., and R. T. Holman, *J. Am. Oil Chemists' Soc.*, *31*, 41 (1954).
2. Adams, R., and R. L. Shriner, *J. Am. Chem. Soc.*, *45*, 2171 (1923).
3. Adkins, H., and F. W. Cox, *ibid.*, *60*, 1151 (1938).
4. Adkins, H., R. M. Elofson, A. G. Rossow, and C. C. Robinson, *ibid.*, *71*, 3622 (1949).
5. Adkins, H., and R. L. Shriner, in H. Gilman, ed., *Organic Chemistry*. 2nd ed., Vol. I, Wiley, New York, 1943, pp. 779–834.
6. Aivazov, B. V., and D. A. Vyakhirev, *Zhur. Priklad. Khim.*, *26*, 505 (1953); *Chem. Abstracts*, *48*, 6372 (1954); *J. Appl. Chem. U. S. S. R.*, *26*, 467 (1953).

7. Albertson, C. E., and I. R. MacGregor, *Anal. Chem., 22,* 806 (1950).
8. Alder, K., and G. Stein, *Ann., 485,* 211 (1931); *501,* 1 (1933).
9. Alder, K., and W. Vogt, *ibid., 571,* 137 (1951).
10. Allen, A. H., *Analyst, 6,* 177, 215 (1881).
11. Allen, C. C., and H. W. Duckwall, *Ind. Eng. Chem., Anal. Ed., 16,* 558 (1944).
12. Alm, R. S., R. J. P. Williams, and A. Tiselius, *Acta Chem. Scand., 6,* 826 (1952).
13. American Oil Chemists' Society, *Official and Tentative Methods.* V. C. Mehlenbacher, ed., revised to 1952, Method Number Cd 1-25.
14. *Ibid.,* Method Number Cd 7-48.
15. American Petroleum Institute, Research Project 44, National Bureau of Standards, *Catalogue of Infrared, Ultraviolet, Raman, and Mass Spectral Data.*
16. American Society for Testing Materials, *Standards.* Designation: D 460-54.
17. *Ibid.,* Designation: D 555-54.
18. *Ibid.,* Designation: D 875-53T.
19. *Ibid.,* Designation: D 973-50.
19a. *Ibid.,* Designation: D 1019-55T.
20. *Ibid.,* Designation: D 1096-54.
21. *Ibid.,* Designation: D 1158-55T.
22. *Ibid.,* Designation: D 1159-55T.
23. *Ibid.,* Designation: D 1319-55T.
24. American Society for Testing Materials, *1952 Book of ASTM Standards.* Part 5. Am. Soc. Testing Materials, Philadelphia, 1953, p. 576.
25. Anantakrishnan, S. V., and C. K. Ingold, *J. Chem. Soc., 1935,* 1396.
26. Anderson, J. A., Jr., and W. D. Seyfried, *Anal. Chem., 20,* 998 (1948).
27. Angell, F. G., *Analyst, 72,* 178 (1947).
28. Arbuzov, Yu. A., *Izvest. Akad. Nauk S. S. S. R., Otdel. Khim. Nauk, 1952,* 344, 547, 658, 665; *Chem. Abstracts, 47,* 3317, 4874, 10493 (1953).
29. Arthur H. Thomas Co., Philadelphia, Pa.
30. Association of Official Agricultural Chemists, *Official Methods of Analysis.* 8th ed., Washington, 1955, pp. 464–465.
31. *Ibid.,* p. 465.
32. *Ibid.,* pp. 465–466.
33. Atmore, M., and F. Hawke, *J. S. African Chem. Inst., 3,* 23 (1951).
34. Axberg, G., and B. Holmberg, *Ber., 66,* 1193 (1933).
35. Bachmann, W. E., and M. C. Kloetzel, *J. Am. Chem. Soc., 60,* 481 (1938).
36. Bacon, F. S., *Ind. Eng. Chem., 20,* 970 (1928).
37. Baeyer, A., *Ann., 245,* 146 (1888).
38. Baldock, H., N. Levy, and C. W. Scaife, *J. Chem. Soc., 1949,* 2627.
39. Barnes, R. B., and R. C. Gore, *Anal. Chem., 21,* 7 (1949).
40. Barnes, R. B., U. Liddel and V. Z. Williams, *Ind. Eng. Chem., Anal. Ed., 15,* 83 (1943).
41. Barnes, R. B., U. Liddel, and V. Z. Williams, *ibid., 15,* 659 (1943).
42. Bartlett, P. D., G. L. Fraser, and R. B. Woodward, *J. Am. Chem. Soc., 63,* 495 (1941).
43. Bartlett, P. D., and D. S. Tarbell, *ibid., 58,* 466 (1936).
44. Becker, P., *Z. angew. Chem., 36,* 539 (1923).
45. Beesing, D. W., W. P. Tyler, D. M. Kurtz, and S. A. Harrison, *Anal. Chem., 21,* 1073 (1949).

46. Belcher, R., and C. L. Wilson, *New Methods in Analytical Chemistry*. Reinhold, New York, 1955, pp. 156–157.
47. Bellamy, L. J., *The Infra-red Spectra of Complex Molecules*. Wiley, New York, 1954, pp. 31–53.
48. Benham, G. H., and L. Klee, *J. Am. Oil Chemists' Soc.*, *27*, 127 (1950).
49. Benson, S. W., *Ind. Eng. Chem., Anal. Ed.*, *14*, 189 (1942).
50. Berg, C., and F. D. Parker, *Anal. Chem.*, *20*, 456 (1948).
51. Bergmann, F., and H. Japhe, *ibid.*, *20*, 146 (1948).
52. Bickford, W. G., F. G. Dollear, and K. S. Markley, *J. Am. Chem. Soc.*, *59*, 2744 (1937).
53. Bij, J. R. van der, and E. C. Kooyman, *Rec. trav. chim.*, *71*, 837 (1952).
54. Binder, J. L., *Anal. Chem.*, *26*, 1877 (1954).
55. Birch, S. F., and W. D. Scott, *Ind. Eng. Chem.*, *24*, 49 (1932).
56. Blažek, A., *Sborník Mezinárod. Polarog. Sjezdu Praze, 1st Congr., 1951*, Pt. III, Proc., 563 (in English); *Chem. Abstracts*, *47*, 11078 (1953).
57. Blout, E. R., and M. Fields, *J. Am. Chem. Soc.*, *70*, 189 (1948).
58. Böeseken, J., and E. T. Gelber, *Rec. trav. chim.*, *46*, 158 (1927).
59. Böeseken, J., and P. Pols, *ibid.*, *54*, 162 (1935).
60. Böhme, H., and G. Steinke, *Ber.*, *70*, 1709 (1937).
61. Boer, H., and E. C. Kooyman, *Anal. Chim. Acta*, *5*, 550 (1951).
62. Boldingh, J., *Rec. trav. chim.*, *69*, 247 (1950).
63. Bolton, E. R., and K. A. Williams, *Analyst*, *55*, 5 (1930).
64. Bon, M. D., *Ann. Leningrad State Univ., Chem. Ser.*, *3*, 3 (1938); *Chem. Zentr.*, *1939, II*, 366.
65. Bond, G. R., Jr., *Ind. Eng. Chem., Anal. Ed.*, *18*, 692 (1946).
66. Bond, G. R., Jr., *Anal. Chem.*, *19*, 390 (1947).
67. Bonner, W. A., and C. J. Collins, *J. Am. Chem. Soc.*, *75*, 3693 (1953).
68. Booker, H., L. K. Evans, and A. E. Gillam, *J. Chem. Soc.*, *1940*, 1453.
69. Boyd, H. M., and J. R. Roach, *Anal. Chem.*, *19*, 158 (1947).
70. Braae, B., *ibid.*, *21*, 1461 (1949).
71. Bradford, B. W., D. Harvey, and D. E. Chalkley, *J. Inst. Petroleum*, *41*, 80 (1955).
72. Bradley, T. F., and E. L. Kropa, in J. J. Matiello, ed., *Protective and Decorative Coatings*. Vol. V, Wiley, New York, 1946, pp. 175–246.
73. Brady, L. J., *Ind. Eng. Chem., Anal. Ed.*, *16*, 422 (1944).
74. Brattain, R. R., R. S. Rasmussen, and A. M. Cravath, *J. Appl. Phys.*, *14*, 418 (1943).
75. Bratzler, K., and H. Kleemann, *Erdöl u. Kohle*, *7*, 559 (1954).
76. Braun, G., in H. Gilman and A. H. Blatt, ed., *Organic Syntheses*. Coll. Vol. I, 2nd ed., Wiley, New York, 1941, pp. 431–434.
77. Braun, W. G., and M. R. Fenske, *Anal. Chem.*, *21*, 12 (1949); *22*, 11 (1950).
78. Braun, W. G., D. F. Spooner, and M. R. Fenske, *ibid.*, *22*, 1074 (1950).
79. Bretschneider, H., and G. Burger, *Chem. Fabrik*, *10*, 124 (1937).
80. Brice, B. A., M. L. Swain, S. F. Herb, P. L. Nichols, Jr., and R. W. Riemenschneider, *J. Am. Oil Chemists' Soc.*, *29*, 279 (1952).
81. Bricker, C. E., and K. H. Roberts, *Anal. Chem.*, *21*, 1331 (1949).
82. Brook, A. G., A. Rodgman, G. F Wright, *J. Org. Chem.*, *17*, 988 (1952).
83. Brook, A. G., and G. F Wright, *Can. J. Research*, *B28*, 623 (1950); *Can. J. Chem.*, *29*, 308 (1951).

84. Brooks, F. R., L. Lykken, W. B. Milligan, H. R. Nebeker, and V. Zahn, *Anal. Chem., 21*, 1105 (1949).
85. Brown, J. H., H. W. Durand, and C. S. Marvel, *J. Am. Chem. Soc., 58*, 1594 (1936).
86. Brown, R. A., *Anal. Chem., 23*, 430 (1951).
87. Brown, W. H., and G. F Wright, *J. Am. Chem. Soc., 62*, 1991 (1940).
88. Bruce, R. J., and P. G. Denley, *Chemistry & Industry, 15*, 937 (1937).
89. Bruni, G., and E. Geiger, *Atti accad. nazl. Lincei, Mem. Classe sci. fis. mat. e nat.*, [5] II, 823 (1927); *Rubber Chem. and Technol., 1*, 177 (1928).
90. Bruson, H. A., and W. A. Calvert, *J. Am. Chem. Soc., 50*, 1735 (1928).
91. Buckwalter, H. M., and E. C. Wagner, *ibid., 52*, 5241 (1930).
92. Bugorkova, A. A., L. N. Petrova, V. M. Rodinov, *Zhur. Obshcheĭ Khim., 23*, 1808, 1813, 1822 (1953); *J. Gen. Chem., U. S. S. R., 23*, 1909, 1915, 1923 (1953).
93. Burden, E. H. W. J., and D. N. Grindley, *Analyst, 78*, 619 (1953).
94. Burgin, J., W. Engs, H. P. A. Groll, and G. Hearne, *Ind. Eng. Chem., 31*, 1413 (1939).
95. Burke, O. W., Jr., C. E. Starr, Jr., and F. D. Tuemmler, *Light Hydrocarbon Analysis.* Reinhold, New York, 1951, p. 197.
97. Busing, W. R., *J. Opt. Soc. Amer., 42*, 774 (1952).
98. Butz, L. W., and A. W. Rytina, in R. Adams, ed., *Organic Reactions.* Vol. V, Wiley, New York, 1949, pp. 136–192.
99. Cadle, R. D., and C. Schadt, *J. Am. Chem. Soc., 74*, 6002 (1952).
100. Campbell, J. R., and W. Gibb, *Methods of Analysis of Fuels and Oils.* Constable, London, 1951, p. 115.
101. Campbell, K. N., and B. K. Campbell, *Chem. Revs., 31*, 77–175 (1942).
102. Casimir, E., and M. Dimitriu, *Petroleum Z., 31*, No. 33, 1 (1935).
103. Cassidy, H. G., *Adsorption and Chromatography.* Interscience, New York-London, 1951.
104. Cavallini, D., N. Frontali, and G. Toschi, *Nature, 163*, 568 (1949).
105. Chatt, J., *Chem. Revs., 48*, 7–43 (1951).
105a. Chatterjee, A., and S. G. Majumdar, *Anal. Chem., 28*, 878 (1956).
106. Claesson, S., *Arkiv Kemi, Mineral. Geol., 23A*, No. 1 (1946).
107. Claesson, S., *Rec. trav. chim., 65*, 571 (1946).
108. Clark, A., A. Andrews, and H. W. Fleming, *Ind. Eng. Chem., 41*, 1527 (1949).
109. Coffmann, J. R., *J. Biol. Chem., 140*, XXVIII (1941).
110. Coggeshall, N. D., in *Organic Analysis.* Vol. I, Interscience, New York-London, 1953, pp. 403–450.
111. Colson, A. F., *Analyst, 79*, 298 (1954).
112. Connor, T., and G. F Wright, *J. Am. Chem. Soc., 68*, 256 (1946).
113. Conrad, A. L., *Anal. Chem., 20*, 725 (1948).
114. Consden, R., A. H. Gordon, and A. J. P. Martin, *Biochem. J. (London), 38*, 224 (1944).
115. Cook, J. W., and R. Schoental, *J. Chem. Soc., 1948*, 170.
116. Cope, A. C., and E. M. Hardy, *J. Am. Chem. Soc., 62*, 3319 (1940).
117. Corner, E. S., and R. N. Pease, *Ind. Eng. Chem., Anal. Ed., 17*, 564 (1945).
118. Cortese, F., *Rec. trav. chim., 48*, 564 (1929).
119. Cowan, J. C., L. B. Falkenburg, and H. M. Teeter, *Ind. Eng. Chem., Anal. Ed., 16*, 90 (1944).
120. Cramer, F., *Papierchromatographie.* 2nd ed., Verlag Chemie, Weinheim, 1953.

121. Cremer, E., and R. Müller, *Mikrochemie ver. Mikrochim. Acta, 36/37*, 553 (1951).
122. Cremer, E., and R. Müller, *Z. Elektrochem., 55*, 217 (1951).
123. Cremer, E., and F. Prior, *ibid., 55*, 66 (1951).
124. Criddle, D. W., and R. L. LeTourneau, *Anal. Chem., 23*, 1620 (1951).
125. Criegee, R., paper presented at Am. Chem. Soc. meeting, New York, September, 1951.
126. Criegee, R., in Houben-Weyl, *Methoden der organischen Chemie*. Vol. VIII, 4th ed., Thieme, Stuttgart, 1952, pp. 1–74.
127. Criegee, R., B. Marchand, and H. Wannowius, *Ann., 550*, 99 (1942).
128. Crippen, R. C., and C. F. Bonilla, *Anal. Chem., 21*, 927 (1949).
129. Critchfield, F. E., G. L. Funk, and J. B. Johnson, *ibid., 28*, 76 (1956).
130. Critchfield, F. E., and J. B. Johnson, *ibid., 28*, 73 (1956).
131. Cropper, F. R., and A. Heywood, *Nature, 172*, 1101 (1953).
132. Cross, L. H., R. B. Richards, and H. A. Willis, *Discussions Faraday Soc., No. 9*, 235 (1950).
133. Cuneo, J. F., and R. L. Switzer, *Ind. Eng. Chem., Anal. Ed., 15*, 508 (1943).
134. Cunneen, J. I., *J. Chem. Soc., 1947*, 36.
135. Currie, L. L., *Anal. Chem., 24*, 1327 (1952).
136. Čuta, F., and Z. Kučera, *Chem. Listy, 47*, 1166 (1953); *Chem. Abstracts, 48*, 3850 (1954).
137. Dal Nogare, S., in *Organic Analysis*. Vol. I, Interscience, New York-London, 1953, pp. 329–402.
138. Dal Nogare, S., L. R. Perkins, and A. H. Hale, *Anal. Chem., 24*, 512 (1952).
139. Danish, A. A., and R. E. Lidov, *ibid., 22*, 702 (1950).
140. Das, M. N., *ibid., 26*, 1086 (1954).
141. Davison, W. H. T., and G. R. Bates, *J. Chem. Soc., 1953*, 2607.
142. DeGrotte, M., B. Keiser, A. F. Wirtel, and L. T. Monson, *Ind. Eng. Chem., Anal. Ed., 3*, 243 (1931).
143. Delahay, P., *New Instrumental Methods in Electrochemistry*. Interscience, New York-London, 1954.
144. Dewar, M. J. S., *The Electronic Theory of Organic Chemistry*. Calderon, Oxford, 1949.
145. Dibeler, V. H., *Anal. Chem., 26*, 58 (1954); *28*, 610 (1956).
146. Dibeler, V. H., and J. A. Hipple, *ibid., 24*, 27 (1952).
147. Diels, O., and K. Alder, *Ann., 460*, 98 (1928), *et seq.*
148. Dinneen, G. U., C. W. Bailey, J. R. Smith, and J. S. Ball, *Anal. Chem., 19*, 992 (1947).
149. Dinneen, G. U., J. R. Smith, and J. S. Ball, *Petroleum Refiner, 29*, No. 5, 129 (1950).
150. Dinneen, G. U., C. J. Thompson, J. R. Smith, and J. S. Ball, *Anal. Chem., 22*, 871 (1950).
151. Divine, R. E., J. E. Doherty, C. P. Long, E. B. Millard, M. L. Sheely, H. P. Trevithick, and F. W. Smither, *Ind. Eng. Chem., Anal. Ed., 14*, 558 (1942).
152. Doeuvre, J., *Bull. soc. chim. France, 3*, 612 (1936).
153. Dollear, F. S., and K. S. Markley, *Oil & Soap, 15*, 256 (1938).
154. Downing, D. C., and G. F Wright, *J. Am. Chem. Soc., 68*, 141 (1946).
155. DuBois, H. D., and D. A. Skoog, *Anal. Chem., 20*, 624 (1948).
156. Dubovitz, H., *Chem.-Ztg., 38*, 1111 (1914).

157. Dudenbostel, B. F., and W. Priestley, Jr., in B. T. Brooks, S. S. Kurtz, Jr., C. E. Boord, and L. Schmerling, ed., *The Chemistry of Petroleum Hydrocarbons.* Vol. I, Reinhold, New York, 1954, pp. 337–349.
158. Duin, C. F. van, *Rec. trav. chim., 45,* 345 (1926).
159. Duke, J. A., and J. A. Maselli, *J. Am. Oil Chemists' Soc., 29,* 126 (1952).
160. Dutton, H. J., *J. Phys. Chem., 48,* 179 (1944).
161. Dutton, H. J., and C. L. Reinbold, *J. Am. Oil. Chemists' Soc., 25,* 120 (1948).
162. Earle, F. R., and R. T. Milner, *Oil & Soap, 16,* 69 (1939).
163. Ebel, F., R. Brunner, and P. Mangelli, *Helv. Chim. Acta, 12,* 19 (1929).
164. Edse, R., and P. Harteck, *Angew. Chem., 52,* 32 (1939).
165. Edse, R., and P. Harteck, *ibid., 53,* 210 (1940).
166. Egloff, G., and J. C. Morrell, *Ind. Eng. Chem., 18,* 354 (1926).
167. Eisenbrand, J., and H. Picher, *Z. physiol. Chem., 260,* 83 (1939); *Chem. Abstracts, 33,* 8228 (1939).
168. Eistert, B., in *Newer Methods of Preparative Organic Chemistry.* Interscience, New York-London, 1948, pp. 513–570.
169. Eley, D. D., *Quart. Revs. (London), 3,* 209–225 (1949).
170. El Khishen, S. A., *Anal. Chem., 20,* 1078 (1948).
171. Ellis, B. A., and R. A. Jones, *Analyst, 61,* 812 (1936).
172. Elofson, R. M., *Anal. Chem., 21,* 917 (1949).
172a. Elving, P. J., in *Organic Analysis.* Vol. II, Interscience, New York-London, 1954, pp. 195–236.
173. Elving, P. J., and I. Rosenthal, *ibid., 26,* 1454 (1954).
174. Elving, P. J., and T. L. Stein, *Ind. Eng. Chem., Anal. Ed., 17,* 722 (1945).
175. Elving, P. J., and C. Teitelbaum, *J. Am. Chem. Soc., 71,* 3916 (1949).
176. Emmons, W. D., and A. F. Ferris, *ibid., 75,* 4623 (1953).
177. Emmons, W. D., A. S. Pagano, and J. P. Freeman, *ibid., 76,* 3472 (1954).
178. Englert, S. M. E., and S. M. McElvain, *ibid., 51,* 863 (1929).
179. English, J., Jr., *ibid., 63,* 941 (1941).
180. Erdös, J., *Mikrochemie, 18,* 305 (1935).
181. Eschinazi, H. E., and E. D. Bergmann, *J. Am. Chem. Soc., 72,* 5651 (1950).
182. Eucken, A., and H. Knick, *Brennstoff-Chem., 17,* 241 (1936).
183. Faragher, W. F., W. A. Gruse, and F. H. Garner, *J. Ind. Eng. Chem., 13,* 1044 (1921).
184. Faragher, W. F., J. C. Morrell, and I. M. Levine, *Ind. Eng. Chem., Anal. Ed., 2,* 18, 199 (1930).
185. Fellgett, P. B., G. P. Harris, D. N. Simpson, G. B. B. M. Sutherland, H. W. Thompson, D. H. Whiffen, and H. A. Willis, Institute of Petroleum, Hydrocarbon Research Group Report XI (1946).
186. Ferber, E., and H. Luther, *Angew. Chem., 53,* 31 (1940).
187. Feulgen, R., *Ber., 54,* 360 (1921).
188. Fields, M., and E. R. Blout, *J. Am. Chem. Soc., 70,* 930 (1948).
189. Fink, D. F., R. W. Lewis, and F. T. Weiss, *Anal. Chem., 22,* 858 (1950).
190. Fischer, F. G., H. Düll, and L. Ertel, *Ber., 65,* 1467 (1932).
191. Fisher, C. H., and A. Eisner, *Ind. Eng. Chem., Anal. Ed., 9,* 366 (1937).
192. Fisher, C. H., and A. Eisner, *U. S. Bur. Mines, Rept. Invest., 3356* (1937).
193. Foresti, B., *Ann. chim. appl., 26,* 207 (1936).
194. Foulk, C. W., and A. T. Bawden, *J. Am. Chem. Soc., 48,* 2045 (1926).
195. Francis, A. W., *Ind. Eng. Chem., 18,* 821, 1095 (1926).

196. Francis, A. W., and S. J. Lukasiewicz, *Ind. Eng. Chem., Anal. Ed.*, *17*, 703 (1945).
197. Fred, M., and R. Putscher, *Anal. Chem.*, *21*, 900 (1949).
198. Fredericks, E. M., and F. R. Brooks, *ibid.*, *28*, 297 (1956).
199. Fulmer, E. I., J. J. Kolfenbach, and L. A. Underkofler, *Ind. Eng. Chem., Anal. Ed.*, *16*, 469 (1944).
200. Galle, E., *Z. angew. Chem.*, *44*, 474 (1931).
201. Gallo, S. G., H. K. Wiese, and J. F. Nelson, *Ind. Eng. Chem.*, *40*, 1277 (1948).
202. Gal'pern, G. D., and J. V. Vinogradova, *Neftyanoe Khoz.*, *1*, 59 (1936).
203. Gamble, D. L., and C. E. Barnett, *Ind. Eng. Chem.*, *32*, 375 (1940).
204. Garner, F. H., *J. Inst. Petroleum Technol.*, *14*, 695 (1928).
205. Garre, B., and H. Grosse-Oetringhaus, *Oel u. Kohle ver. Erdoel u. Teer*, *14*, 94 (1938).
206. Gelber, E. T., and J. Böeseken, *Rec. trav. chim.*, *48*, 377 (1929).
207. George, J., H. Mark, and H. Wechsler, *J. Am. Chem. Soc.*, *72*, 3896 (1950).
208. George, J., H. Wechsler, and H. Mark, *ibid.*, *72*, 3891 (1950).
209. Gerber, M. I., A. A. Dobrinskaya, and M. B. Neĭman, *Trudy Vsesoyuz. Konferents. Anal. Khim.*, *2*, 585 (1943); *Chem. Abstracts*, *39*, 3760 (1945).
210. Gerber, M. I., Z. B. Kuznetsova, and M. B. Neĭman, *Zhur. Anal. Khim.*, *4*, 103 (1949); *Chem. Abstracts*, *44*, 2416 (1950).
211. Gero, A., J. J. Kershner, and R. E. Perry, *J. Am. Chem. Soc.*, *75*, 5119 (1953).
212. Gillam, A. E., and E. S. Stern, *Electronic Absorption Spectroscopy*. Arnold, London, 1954.
213. Glasgow, A. R., Jr., C. B. Willingham, and F. D. Rossini, *Ind. Eng. Chem.*, *41*, 2292 (1949).
214. Glasser, A. C., L. E. Harris, B. V. Christensen, and F. W. Bope, *J. Am. Pharm. Assoc., Sci. Ed.*, *43*, 294 (1954).
215. Gluud, W., and G. Schneider, *Ber.*, *57*, 254 (1924).
216. Goldenson, J., and S. Sass, *Anal. Chem.*, *20*, 1118 (1948).
217. Goldstein, R. F., *The Petroleum Chemicals Industry*. Wiley, New York, 1950, pp. 153–174.
218. Gordon, B. E., F. Wopat, Jr., H. D. Burnham, and L. C. Jones, Jr., *Anal. Chem.*, *23*, 1754 (1951).
219. Gore, R. C., *ibid.*, *22*, 7 (1950); *23*, 7 (1951); *24*, 8 (1952); *26*, 11 (1954); *28*, 577 (1956).
220. Goswami, M., and K. L. Basu, *Analyst*, *59*, 533 (1934).
221. Gould, C. W., and H. J. Drake, *Anal. Chem.*, *23*, 1157 (1951).
222. Goulden, F., and F. L. Warren, *Biochem. J.* (*London*), *42*, 420 (1948).
223. Gowans, W. J., and F. E. Clark, *Anal. Chem.*, *24*, 529 (1952).
224. Graefe, E., *Petroleum Z.*, *1*, 631 (1906).
225. Graefe, E., *Z. angew. Chem.*, *18*, 1580 (1905).
226. Graff, M. M., and E. L. Skau, *Ind. Eng. Chem., Anal. Ed.*, *15*, 340 (1943).
227. Gregg, C. L., *ibid.*, *17*, 728 (1945).
228. Griffiths, J., D. James, and C. Phillips, *Analyst*, *77*, 897 (1952).
229. Grosse-Oetringhaus, H., *Brennstoff-Chem.*, *19*, 417 (1938).
230. Grosse-Oetringhaus, H., *Petroleum Z.*, *35*, 75, 112 (1939).
231. Grosse-Oetringhaus, H., *ibid.*, *35*, 567 (1939).
232. Grummitt, O., and A. Ardis, *J. Chem. Educ.*, *23*, 73 (1946).

233. Grunbaum, B. W., and P. L. Kirk, *Mikrochemie ver. Mikrochim. Acta, 39,* 268 (1952).
234. Günther, E., *Pharmazie, 6,* 577 (1951); *Chem. Abstracts, 46,* 5657 (1952).
235. Gurvits, S. S., and P. A. Mel'nikova, *Zavodskaya Lab., 15,* 672 (1949); *Chem. Abstracts, 44,* 485 (1950).
236. Haak, F. A., and K. van Nes, *J. Inst. Petroleum, 37,* 245 (1951).
237. Hablitzel, C. P., and J. L. Jezl, *Anal. Chem., 21,* 1049 (1949).
238. Hamilton, J. G., and R. T. Holman, *J. Am. Chem. Soc., 76,* 4107 (1954).
239. Hammar, C. G. B.,. *Svensk Kem. Tidskr., 63,* 125 (1951).
240. Hampton, R. R., *Anal. Chem., 21,* 923 (1949).
241. Hanson, N. W., and D. M. Williams, *J. Chem. Soc., 1930,* 1059.
242. Hanus, J., *Z. Untersuch. Nahr.- u. Genussm., 4,* 913 (1901).
243. Harrison, G. R., R. C. Lord, and J. R. Loofbourow, *Practical Spectroscopy.* Prentice-Hall, New York, 1948.
244. Harteck, P., and K. A. Suhr, *Die Chemie, 56,* 120 (1943).
245. Harvey, E. H., and H. A. Schuette, *Ind. Eng. Chem., Anal. Ed., 2,* 42 (1930).
246. Harvey, P. G., and R. M. Pearson, *Analyst, 79,* 158 (1954).
247. Haslam, J., and G. Newlands, *ibid., 80,* 50 (1955).
248. Hausser, K. W., R. Kuhn, and A. Smakula, *Z. physik. Chem., B29,* 384 (1935).
249. Hausser, K. W., R. Kuhn, A. Smakula, and A. Deutsch, *ibid., B29,* 378 (1935).
250. Hausser, K. W., R. Kuhn, A. Smakula, and M. Hoffer, *ibid., B29,* 371 (1935).
251. Hausser, K. W., and A. Smakula, *Angew. Chem., 47,* 657 (1934); *48,* 152 (1935).
252. Hehner, O., *Analyst, 20,* 49 (1895).
253. Heigl, J. J., J. F. Black, and B. F. Dudenbostel, Jr., *Anal. Chem., 21,* 554 (1949).
254. Henjes, R., *Oel u. Kohle ver. Erdoel u. Teer, 14,* 1079 (1938).
255. Herb, S. F., and R. W. Riemenschneider, *J. Am. Oil Chemists' Soc., 29,* 456 (1952).
256. Herb, S. F., L. P. Witnauer, and R. W. Riemenschneider, *ibid., 28,* 505 (1951).
257. Herzenberg, J., *World Petroleum Congr., Proc. Vol. II, 1933,* p. 30.
258. Hess, W., *Z. angew. Chem., 33,* 147, 176 (1920).
259. Hesse, G., H. Eilbracht, and F. Reicheneder, *Ann., 546,* 251 (1941).
260. Hesse, G., and B. Tschachotin, *Naturwissenschaften, 30,* 387 (1942).
261. Heyrovský, J., and H. Hasselbach, *Z. Pflanzenzücht, 25,* 443 (1943); *Chem. Abstracts, 43,* 6692 (1949).
262. Hibben, J. H., *The Raman Effect and Its Chemical Applications.* Reinhold, New York, 1939, pp. 161–177, 200–208, 213–221.
263. Hilditch, T. P., and C. H. Lea, *J. Chem. Soc., 1927,* 3106.
264. Hipple, J. A., and M. Shepherd, *Anal. Chem., 21, 32* (1949).
265. Hiscox, D. J., *ibid., 20,* 679 (1948).
266. Hobart, E. W., *ibid., 26,* 1291 (1954).
267. Hoffman, H. D., and C. E. Green, *Oil & Soap, 16,* 236 (1939).
268. Hofmann, H.-J., *Angew. Chem., 52,* 99 (1939).
269. Hoijtink, G. J., and J. van Schooten, *Rec. trav. chim., 72,* 691 (1953).
270. Holman, R. T., *J. Am. Chem. Soc., 73,* 5289 (1951).
271. Holman, R. T., and L. Hagdahl, *Anal. Chem., 23,* 794 (1951).
272. Holman, R. T., and W. T. Williams, *J. Am. Chem. Soc., 73,* 5285 (1951).
273. Holmberg, B., *Arkiv Kemi, Mineral. Geol., B23,* No. 6 (1946); *Rubber Chem. and Technol., 20,* 978 (1947).
274. Holmberg, B., *Ber., 65,* 1349 (1932).

275. Holmberg, B., *J. prakt. Chem.*, *141*, 93 (1934).
276. Holmes, H. L., in R. Adams, ed., *Organic Reactions.* Vol. IV, Wiley, New York, 1948, pp. 60–173.
277. Hoog, H., and E. Eichwald, *Rec. trav. chim.*, *58*, 481 (1939).
278. Hornstein, I., *Anal. Chem.*, *23*, 1329 (1951).
279. Houtman, J. P. W., *J. Inst. Petroleum*, *34*, 255 (1948).
280. Hübl, B., *Dinglers Polytech. J.*, *253*, 281 (1884).
281. Hübl, B., *J. Soc. Chem. Ind. (London)*, *3*, 641 (1884).
282. Hunt, F. W., *ibid.*, *21*, 454 (1902).
283. Hyde, J. F., and H. W. Scherp, *J. Am. Chem. Soc.*, *52*, 3359 (1930).
284. Ingold, C. K., *Structure and Mechanism in Organic Chemistry.* Cornell University Press, Ithaca, 1953.
285. Ingold, C. K., *ibid.*, pp. 669–670.
286. Ingold, C. K., *ibid.*, pp. 716–719.
287. Ingold, C. K., and E. H. Ingold, *Nature*, *159*, 743 (1947).
288. Institute of Petroleum, Hydrocarbon Research Group Reports I to XI (1941 to 1946).
289. Institute of Petroleum, *Standard Methods for Testing Petroleum and Its Products.* 10th ed., London, 1949. Designation: 9/42.
290. *Ibid.*, 14th ed., London, 1955. Designation: 84/53T.
290a. *Ibid.*, Designation: 128/53.
291. *Ibid.*, Designation: 129/53T.
292. *Ibid.*, Designation: 130/53.
293. Ioffe, I. I., *Zavodskaya Lab.*, *16*, 1252 (1950); *Chem. Zentr.*, *1951*, I, 2781.
294. Jackson, H., *J. Soc. Chem. Ind. (London)*, *57*, 96T (1938); *Chemistry & Industry*, *16*, 1076 (1938).
295. Jackson, H., and R. N. Jones, *J. Chem. Soc.*, *1936*, 895.
296. Jackson, J. E., R. F. Paschke, W. Tolberg, H. M. Boyd, and D. H. Wheeler, *J. Am. Oil Chemists' Soc.*, *29*, 229 (1952).
297. James, A. T., *Biochem. J. (London)*, *52*, 242 (1952).
298. James, A. T., *Mfg. Chemist*, *26*, 5 (1955).
299. James, A. T., and A. J. P. Martin, *Analyst*, *77*, 915 (1952).
300. James, A. T., and A. J. P. Martin, *Biochem. J. (London)*, *50*, 679 (1952).
301. James, A. T., and A. J. P. Martin, *Brit. Med. Bull.*, *10*, 170 (1954).
302. James, A. T., A. J. P. Martin, and G. H. Smith, *Biochem. J. (London)*, *52*, 238 (1952).
303. James, D. H., and C. S. G. Phillips, *J. Chem. Soc.*, *1953*, 1600.
304. Janák, J., and M. Rusek, *Chem. Listy*, *47*, 1190 (1953); *Chem. Abstracts*, *48*, 3853 (1954).
305. Janák, J., and M. Rusek, *Chem. Listy*, *48*, 207 (1954); *Chem. Abstracts*, *48*, 6321 (1954).
306. Jasperson, H., *J. Soc. Chem. Ind. (London)*, *61*, 115 (1942).
306a. Johansen, E. M., *Ind. Eng. Chem.*, *14*, 288 (1922).
307. Johns, I. B., and E. J. Seiferle, *Ind. Eng. Chem., Anal. Ed.*, *13*, 841 (1941).
308. Johnson, H. L., and R. A. Clark, *Anal. Chem.*, *19*, 869 (1947); *20*, 490 (1948).
309. Johnston, R. W. B., W. G. Appleby, and M. O. Baker, *ibid.*, *20*, 805 (1948).
310. Jones, L. C., Jr., and L. W. Taylor, *ibid.*, *27*, 228, 2015 (1955).
311. Jordan, C. W., *J. Am. Chem. Soc.*, *63*, 2687 (1941).

312. Joshel, L. M., *Ind. Eng. Chem., Anal. Ed.*, *15*, 590 (1943).
313. Joshel, L. M., S. A. Hall, and S. Palkin, *ibid.*, *13*, 447 (1941).
314. Kaffer, H., *Ber.*, *57*, 1261 (1924).
315. Kaller, A., *Angew. Chem.*, *A60*, 334 (1948).
316. Kass, J. P., W. R. Roy, and G. O. Burr, *Anal. Chem.*, *19*, 21 (1947).
317. Kattwinkel, R., *Brennstoff-Chem.*, *8*, 353 (1927).
318. Kaufmann, H. P., *Arch. Pharm.*, *267*, 1 (1929).
319. Kaufmann, H. P., *Ber. deut. pharm. Ges.*, *33*, 139 (1923); *Chem. Abstracts*, *17*, 3480 (1923).
320. Kaufmann, H. P., *Fette u. Seifen*, *46*, 268 (1939).
321. Kaufmann, H. P., *Studien auf dem Fettgebiet*. Verlag Chemie, Berlin, 1935.
322. Kaufmann, H. P., *Z. Untersuch. Lebensm.*, *51*, 3 (1926); *Chem. Abstracts*, *20*, 2256 (1926).
323. Kaufmann, H. P., and J. Baltes, *Ber.*, *70*, 2537 (1937).
324. Kaufmann, H. P., and J. Baltes, *Fette u. Seifen*, *43*, 93 (1936).
325. Kaufmann, H. P., J. Baltes, and H. Büter, *Ber.*, *70*, 903 (1937).
326. Kaufmann, H. P., and J. Budwig, *Fette u. Seifen*, *53*, 390 (1951); *54*, 7 (1952).
327. Kaufmann, H. P., J. Budwig, and C. W. Schmidt, *ibid.*, *54*, 10 (1952).
328. Kaufmann, H. P., and H. Grosse-Oetringhaus, *Ber.*, *69*, 2670 (1936).
329. Kaufmann, H. P., and H. Grosse-Oetringhaus, *ibid.*, *70*, 911 (1937).
330. Kaufmann, H. P., and H. Grosse-Oetringhaus, *Oel u. Kohle ver. Erdoel u. Teer*, *14*, 199 (1938).
331. Kaufmann, H. P., and L. Hartweg, *Ber.*, *70*, 2554 (1937).
332. Kaufmann, H. P., and P. Kirsch, *Fette u. Seifen*, *50*, 314 (1943).
333. Kaufmann, H. P., P. Kirsch, B. W. King, and L.-S. Huang, *Ber.*, *75*, 1201 (1942).
334. Kaufmann, H. P., and J. Liepe, *ibid.*, *56*, 2514 (1923).
335. Kaufmann, H. P., and P. Röver, *Fette u. Seifen*, *47*, 103 (1940).
336. Kaufmann, H. P., and W. Wolf, *ibid.*, *50*, 519 (1943).
337. Kemp, A. R., and G. S. Mueller, *Ind. Eng. Chem., Anal. Ed.*, *6*, 52 (1934).
338. Kemp, A. R., and H. Peters, *ibid.*, *15*, 453 (1943).
339. Kent, J. W., and J. Y. Beach, *Anal. Chem.*, *19*, 290 (1947).
340. Kester, E. B., and W. D. Pohle, *Ind. Eng. Chem., Anal. Ed.*, *3*, 294 (1931).
341. Keulemans, A. I. M., and A. Kwantes, paper presented at the 4th World Petroleum Congress, Rome, 1955.
342. Keulemans, A. I. M., A. Kwantes, and P. Zaal, *Anal. Chim. Acta*, *13*, 357 (1955).
343. Kharasch, M. S., E. V. Jensen, and W. H. Urry, *J. Am. Chem. Soc.*, *69*, 1100 (1947).
344. Kharasch, N., and C. M. Buess, *ibid.*, *71*, 2724 (1949).
345. Kipnis, F., *Ind. Eng. Chem., Anal. Ed.*, *16*, 637 (1944).
346. Kirchner, J. G., J. M. Miller, and G. J. Keller, *Anal. Chem.*, *23*, 420 (1951).
347. Kirillova, S., and I. A. Korshunov, *Zhur. Anal. Khim.*, *6*, 257 (1951); *Chem. Abstracts*, *45*, 10140 (1951).
348. Kitson, R. E., *Anal. Chem.*, *25*, 1470 (1953).
349. Klee, L., and G. H. Benham, *J. Am. Oil Chemists' Soc.*, *27*, 130 (1950).
350. Kloetzel, M. C., in R. Adams, *Organic Reactions*. Vol. IV, Wiley, New York, 1948, pp. 1–59.
351. Kloetzel, M. C., R. P. Dayton, and H. L. Herzog, *J. Am. Chem. Soc.*, *72*, 273 (1950).
352. Kloetzel, M. C., and H. L. Herzog, *ibid.*, *72*, 1991 (1950).

353. Knight, H. B., R. E. Koos, and D. Swern, *ibid.*, *75*, 6212 (1953).
353a. Knights, J., and E. S. Waight, *J. Chem. Soc.*, *1955*, 2830.
354. Knowles, G., J. C. Lawson, and T. McQuillen, *J. Oil & Colour Chemists' Assoc.*, *23*, 4 (1940).
355. Knowles, G., and G. F. Lowden, *Analyst*, *78*, 159 (1953).
356. Koch, H., and F. Hilberath, *Brennstoff-Chem.*, *21*, 185 (1940).
357. Kok, W. J. C. de, H. I. Waterman, and H. A. van Westen, *J. Soc. Chem. Ind.* (*London*), *55*, 225T (1936).
358. Kolthoff, I. M., *Polarography.* Vol. I, 2nd ed., Interscience, New York-London, 1952.
359. Kolthoff, I. M., and F. A. Bovey, *Anal. Chem.*, *19*, 498 (1947).
360. Kolthoff, I. M., and T. S. Lee, *J. Polymer Sci.*, *2*, 206 (1947).
361. Kolthoff, I. M., T. S. Lee, and M. A. Mairs, *ibid.*, *2*, 199 (1947).
362. Kolthoff, I. M., and J. J. Lingane, *Polarography.* Vol. II, 2nd ed., Interscience, New York-London, 1952.
363. Krassilchik, A., *Ann. office natl. combustibles liquides*, *10*, 923 (1935); *Chem. Abstracts*, *30*, 1023 (1936).
364. Kraus, G., and W. B. Reynolds, *J. Am. Chem. Soc.*, *72*, 5621 (1950).
365. Küchler, L., and O. G. Weller, *Mikrochemie ver. Mikrochim. Acta*, *26*, 44 (1939).
366. Kuhn, R., and E. F. Möller, *Angew. Chem.*, *47*, 145 (1934).
367. Kuhn, R., and H. Roth, *Ber.*, *65*, 1285 (1932).
368. Kurtz, F. E., *J. Am. Chem. Soc.*, *74*, 1902 (1952).
369. Kurtz, S. S., Jr., and C. E. Headington, *Ind. Eng. Chem.*, *Anal. Ed.*, *9*, 21 (1937).
370. Kurtz, S. S., Jr., I. W. Mills, C. C. Martin, W. T. Harvey, and M. R. Lipkin, *Anal. Chem.*, *19*, 175, 696 (1947).
371. Kurtz, S. S., Jr., and A. L. Ward, *J. Franklin Inst.*, *222*, 563 (1936); *224*, 583, 697 (1937).
372. Laitinen, H. A., and S. Wawzonek, *J. Am. Chem. Soc.*, *64*, 1765 (1942).
373. Lambert, J. L., *Anal. Chem.*, *25*, 984 (1953).
374. Lambou, M. G., and F. G. Dollear, *Oil & Soap*, *23*, 97 (1946).
375. Lane, J. F., and L. Spialter, *J. Am. Chem. Soc.*, *73*, 4408 (1951).
376. Lederer, E., and M. Lederer, *Chromatography.* Elsevier, Houston, 1953.
377. Lee, T. S., I. M. Kolthoff, and E. Johnson, *Anal. Chem.*, *22*, 995 (1950).
378. Lee, T. S., I. M. Kolthoff, and M. A. Mairs, *J. Polymer Sci.*, *3*, 66 (1948).
378a. Lemieux, R. U., and E. von Rudloff, *Can. J. Chem.*, *33*, 1701 (1955).
378b. Lemieux, R. U., and E. von Rudloff, *ibid.*, *33*, 1710 (1955).
379. Leonard, N. J., and V. W. Gash, *J. Am. Chem. Soc.*, *76*, 2781 (1954).
380. Levy, N., and C. W. Scaife, *J. Chem. Soc.*, *1946*, 1093, 1100.
381. Levy, N., C. W. Scaife, and A. E. Wilder-Smith, *ibid.*, *1946*, 1096; *1948*, 52.
382. Lewis, J. B., and R. B. Bradstreet, *Ind. Eng. Chem.*, *Anal. Ed.*, *12*, 387 (1940).
383. Lewis, J. B., and R. B. Bradstreet, *ibid.*, *16*, 617 (1944).
384. Lichtenfels, D. H., S. A. Fleck, and F. H. Burow, *Anal. Chem.*, *27*, 1510 (1955).
385. Lips, H. J., *J. Am. Oil Chemists' Soc.*, *30*, 399 (1953).
386. Loew, O., *Ber.*, *23*, 289 (1890).
387. Lombard, R., and G. Heywang, *Bull. soc. chim. France*, *1952*, 331.
388. Long, D. R., and R. W. Neuzil, *Anal. Chem.*, *27*, 1110 (1955).
389. Long, L., Jr., *Chem. Revs.*, *27*, 437–493 (1940).
390. Lorand, E., *Ind. Eng. Chem.*, *19*, 733 (1927).

391. Lucas, H. J., and D. Pressman, *Ind. Eng. Chem., Anal. Ed., 10*, 140 (1938).
392. Lugg, J. W. H., and B. T. Overell, *Australian J. Sci. Research, A1*, 98 (1948).
393. McCullough, R. L., and K. G. Stone, *Anal. Chem., 24*, 1206 (1952).
394. McCutcheon, J. W., *Ind. Eng. Chem., Anal. Ed., 12*, 465 (1940).
395. McCutcheon, J. W., M. F. Crawford, and H. L. Welsh, *Oil & Soap, 18*, 9 (1941).
396. McIlhiney, P. C., *J. Am. Chem. Soc., 21*, 1084 (1899).
397. MacKinney, G., and O. Temmer, *ibid., 70*, 3586 (1948).
398. McKinney, R. S., and G. S. Jamieson, *Oil & Soap, 15*, 30 (1938).
399. McLaughlin, R. L., and R. W. Schiessler, in B. T. Brooks, C. E. Boord, S. S. Kurtz, Jr., and L. Schmerling, ed., *The Chemistry of Petroleum Hydrocarbons.* Vol. I, Reinhold, New York, 1954, p. 616.
400. McMillan, W. A., H. A. Cole, and A. V. Ritchie, *Ind. Eng. Chem., Anal. Ed., 8*, 105 (1936).
401. McMurry, H. L., and V. Thornton, *Anal. Chem., 24*, 318 (1952).
402. Mair, B. J., *J. Research Natl. Bur. Standards, 34*, 435 (1945).
403. Mair, B. J., C. B. Willingham, and A. J. Streiff, *Ind. Eng. Chem., 30*, 1256 (1938).
404. Majors, K. R., and R. T. Milner, *Oil & Soap, 16*, 228 (1938).
405. Malmberg, E., paper presented at Am. Chem. Soc. meeting, Minneapolis, September, 1955.
406. Malyugina, N. I., and I. A. Korshunov, *Zhur. Anal. Khim., 2*, 341 (1947); *Chem. Abstracts, 43*, 7377 (1949).
407. Manchot, W., and F. Oberhauser, *Z. Untersuch. Nahr.- u. Genussm., 47*, 261 (1924).
408. Mann, D. E., N. Acquista, and E. K. Plyler, *J. Chem. Phys., 21*, 1949 (1953); *22*, 1199 (1954).
409. Manning, A. B., *J. Chem. Soc., 1929*, 1014.
410. Margosches, B. M., W. Hinner, and L. Friedmann, *Z. angew. Chem., 37*, 334 (1924).
411. Margosches, B. M., B. Krakowetz, and F. Schnabel, *Petroleum Z., 9*, 691 (1914).
412. Markley, K. S., *Fatty Acids.* Interscience, New York-London, 1947.
413. Markownikoff, *Compt. rend., 81*, 670 (1875).
414. Marquardt, R. P., and E. N. Luce, *Anal. Chem., 20*, 751 (1948).
415. Marquardt, R. P., and E. N. Luce, *ibid., 21*, 1194 (1949); *22*, 363 (1950).
416. Marquardt, R. P., and E. N. Luce, *ibid., 23*, 629 (1951).
417. Marshall, A., *J. Soc. Chem. Ind. (London), 19*, 213 (1900).
418. Martin, A. E., and J. Smart, *Nature, 175*, 422 (1955).
419. Martin, A. J. P., and R. L. M. Synge, *Biochem. J. (London), 35*, 1358 (1941).
420. Martin, R. W., *Anal. Chem., 21*, 921 (1949).
421. Marushkin, M. N., and A. P. Belen'kaya, *Zhur. Anal. Khim., 5*, 358 (1950); *Chem. Abstracts, 45*, 983 (1951).
422. Mayeda, *J. Pharm. Soc. Japan, 56*, 511 (1936).
423. Mayo, F. R., and C. Walling, *Chem. Revs., 27*, 351–412 (1940).
424. Meerwein, H., A. Ogait, W. Prang, and A. Serini, *J. prakt. Chem., 113*, 9 (1926).
425. Mehlenbacher, V. C., *Chem. Eng. News, 22*, 606 (1944).
426. Meites, L., *Polarographic Techniques.* Interscience, New York-London, 1955.
427. Melpolder, F. W., R. A. Brown, W. S. Young, and C. E. Headington, *Ind. Eng. Chem., 44*, 1142 (1952).
428. Meyer, H., *Analyse und Konstitutionsermittlung organischer Verbindungen.* Springer, Vienna, 1938, p. 770.

429. Meyer, K. H., *Ber.*, *52*, 1468 (1919).
430. Michael, A., and G. H. Carlson, *J. Am. Chem. Soc.*, *57*, 1268 (1935).
431. Mikusch, J. D. von, *Angew. Chem.*, *62*, 475 (1950).
432. Mikusch, J. D. von, *J. Am. Oil Chemists' Soc.*, *28*, 133 (1951).
433. Mikusch, J. D. von, *ibid.*, *29*, 114 (1952).
434. Mikusch, J. D. von, *Z. anal. Chem.*, *130*, 412 (1950).
435. Mikusch, J. D. von, and C. Frazier, *Ind. Eng. Chem., Anal. Ed.*, *13*, 782 (1941).
436. Mikusch, J. D. von, and C. Frazier, *ibid.*, *15*, 109 (1943).
437. Milas, N. A., and I. S. Cliff, *J. Am. Chem. Soc.*, *55*, 352 (1933).
438. Milas, N. A., and A. McAlevy, *ibid.*, *56*, 1219 (1934).
439. Miller, S. A., and F. H. Pearman, *Analyst*, *75*, 492 (1950).
440. Mills, I. W., S. S. Kurtz, Jr., A. H. A. Heyn, and M. R. Lipkin, *Anal. Chem.*, *20*, 333 (1948).
441. Milsom, D., W. R. Jacoby, and A. R. Rescorla, *ibid.*, *21*, 547 (1949).
442. Mitchell, J., Jr., in *Organic Analysis*. Vol. I, Interscience, New York-London, 1953, pp. 260–263.
442a. Mitchell, J., Jr., *ibid.*, pp. 296–297.
443. Morrell, J. C., and G. Egloff, *Ind. Eng. Chem.*, *17*, 1259 (1925).
444. Morrell, J. C., and I. M. Levine, *Ind. Eng. Chem., Anal. Ed.*, *4*, 319 (1932).
445. Morrell, J. C., and I. M. Levine, *ibid.*, *4*, 321 (1932).
446. Morton, I. D., and P. W. Robertson, *J. Chem. Soc.*, *1945*, 129.
447. Moshier, R. W., *Ind. Eng. Chem., Anal. Ed.*, *15*, 107 (1943).
448. Mukherjee, S., *J. Am. Oil Chemists' Soc.*, *29*, 97 (1952).
449. Mukherjee, S., *ibid.*, *32*, 351 (1955).
450. Mullen, P. W., *Modern Gas Analysis*. Interscience, New York-London, 1955.
451. Mulliken, S. P., and R. L. Wakeman, *Ind. Eng. Chem., Anal. Ed.*, *7*, 59 (1935).
452. Munch, R. H., paper presented at Am. Chem. Soc. meeting, Cincinnati, March-April, 1955.
453. Nametkin, S., and L. Brüssoff, *J. prakt. Chem.*, *112*, 169 (1926).
454. Nametkin, S., and E. A. Robinzon, *Neftyanoe Khoz.*, *24*, 184, 230 (1933); *Chem. Abstracts*, *28*, 301 (1934).
455. Naves, Y.-R., *Helv. Chim. Acta*, *32*, 1151 (1949).
456. Neĭman, M. B., and M. A. Shubenko, *Zavodskaya Lab.*, *14*, 394 (1948); *Chem. Abstracts*, *43*, 1289 (1949).
457. Neubauer, O., *Z. angew. Chem.*, *15*, 1036 (1902).
458. Newton, A., and E. J. Buckler, *Ind. Eng. Chem., Anal. Ed.*, *12*, 251 (1940).
459. Noller, C. R., and M. R. Barusch, *ibid.*, *14*, 907 (1942).
460. Noller, C. R., J. F. Carson, H. Martin, and K. S. Hawkins, *J. Am. Chem. Soc.*, *58*, 24 (1936).
461. Nordling, W. D., *Chemist Analyst*, *42*, 70 (1953).
462. Norris, F. A., and R. J. Buswell, *Ind. Eng. Chem., Anal. Ed.*, *15*, 258 (1943).
463. Norris, F. A., and R. J. Buswell, *ibid.*, *16*, 417 (1944).
464. Norton, J. A., *Chem. Revs.*, *31*, 319–523 (1942).
465. Nozaki, K., and R. A. Ogg, Jr., *J. Am. Chem. Soc.*, *64*, 697, 704, 709 (1942).
466. O'Connor, B., *Ind. Eng. Chem.*, *40*, 2102 (1948).
467. O'Connor, R. T., D. C. Heinzelman, F. C. Pack, and R. W. Planck, *J. Am. Oil Chemists' Soc.*, *30*, 182 (1953).

468. O'Connor, R. T., A. F. Stansbury, H. G. Damaré, and S. M. Stark, Jr., *ibid.*, *29*, 461 (1952).
469. O'Donnell, A. E., M. M. Neal, F. T. Weiss, J. M. Bann, T. J. DeCino, and S. C. Lau, *J. Agr. Food Chem.*, *2*, 573 (1954).
470. Ogg, C. L., and F. J. Cooper, *Anal. Chem.*, *21*, 1400 (1949).
471. Ogg, R. A., Jr., *J. Am. Chem. Soc.*, *57*, 2727 (1935).
472. O'Neal, M. J., Jr., *Anal. Chem.*, *22*, 991 (1950).
473. Opienska-Blauth, J., O. Saklawska-Szymonowa, and M. Kanski, *Nature*, *168*, 511 (1951).
474. Pack, F. C., and R. W. Planck, *J. Am. Oil Chemists' Soc.*, *30*, 461 (1953).
475. Pack, F. C., R. W. Planck, and F. G. Dollear, *ibid.*, *29*, 227 (1952).
476. Page, J. E., *Quart. Revs. (London)*, *6*, 262–301 (1952).
476a. Pappo, R., D. S. Allen, Jr., R. U. Lemieux, and W. S. Johnson, *J. Org. Chem.*, *21*, 478 (1956).
477. Pardun, H., *Fette u. Seifen*, *56*, 283 (1954).
478. Parrette, R. L., *Anal. Chem.*, *26*, 237 (1954).
479. Paschke, R. F., W. Tolberg, and D. H. Wheeler, *J. Am. Oil Chemists' Soc.*, *30*, 97 (1953).
480. Patton, H. W., J. S. Lewis, and W. I. Kaye, *Anal. Chem.*, *27*, 170 (1955).
481. Pelikan, K. A., and J. D. von Mikusch, *Oil & Soap*, *14*, 209 (1937).
482. Pesez, M., and P. Poirier, *Methodes et reactions de l'analyse organique*. Vol. I, Masson, Paris, 1953, pp. 147–154.
483. Peters, E. D., private communication.
484. Peters, K., and W. Lohmar, *Angew. Chem.*, *50*, 40 (1937).
485. Petrova, L. N., *Zhur. Priklad. Khim.*, *22*, 122 (1949); *Chem. Abstracts*, *43*, 6540 (1949).
486. Phillips, C. S. G., *Discussions Faraday Soc.*, *No. 7*, 241 (1949).
487. Phillips, W. M., and W. C. Wake, *Analyst*, *74*, 306 (1949).
488. Planck, R. W., F. C. Pack, and L. O. Goldblatt, *J. Am. Oil Chemists' Soc.*, *30*, 417 (1953).
489. Pöll, H., *Petroleum Z.*, *27*, 817 (1931).
490. Poletaev, M. I., *Gigiena i Sanit.*, *1952*, No. 3, 46; *Chem. Abstracts*, *46*, 7000 (1952).
490a. Polgár, A., R. E. Murdock, G. C. Rounds, and S. Groennings, to be submitted for publication in *Anal. Chem.*
491. Porter, C. R., and B. Wood, *J. Inst. Petroleum*, *37*, 388 (1951).
492. Porter, C. R., and B. Wood, *ibid.*, *38*, 877 (1952).
493. Powell, J. S., K. C. Edson, and E. L. Fisher, *Anal. Chem.*, *20*, 213 (1948).
494. Pozdeeva, A. G., and A. G. Stromberg, *Zhur. Anal. Khim.*, *5*, 101 (1950); *Chem. Abstracts*, *44*, 4828 (1950).
495. Pozdeeva, A. G., and A. G. Volkov, *Zhur. Priklad. Khim.*, *26*, 1067 (1953); *Chem. Abstracts*, *48*, 14162 (1954).
496. Prater, A. N., and A. J. Haagen-Smit, *Ind. Eng. Chem., Anal. Ed.*, *12*, 705 (1940).
497. Prelog, V., and U. Häfliger, *Helv. Chim. Acta*, *32*, 2088 (1949).
498. Price, C. C., *Mechanism of Reactions at Carbon-Carbon Double Bonds*. Interscience, New York-London, 1946.
499. Priest, G. W., and J. D. von Mikusch, *Ind. Eng. Chem.*, *32*, 1314 (1940).
500. Prileschajew, N., *Ber.*, *42*, 4811 (1909).
501. Pummerer, R., and W. Gündel, *ibid.*, *61*, 1591 (1928).

502. Pummerer, R., and F. J. Mann, *ibid.*, *62*, 2636 (1929).
503. Pummerer, R., and H. Stärk, *ibid.*, *64*, 825 (1931).
504. Putnam, S. T., M. L. Moss, and R. T. Hall, *Ind. Eng. Chem.*, *Anal. Ed.*, *18*, 628 (1946).
505. Putscher, R. E., *Anal. Chem.*, *24*, 1551 (1952).
506. Ralls, J. O., *J. Am. Chem. Soc.*, *55*, 2083 (1933); *56*, 121 (1934).
507. Rampton, H. C., *J. Inst. Petroleum*, *39*, 305 (1953).
508. Rao, I. D. S., *J. Univ. Bombay*, *10*, Pt. 3, 56 (1941); *Chem. Abstracts*, *36*, 3786 (1942).
509. Rasmussen, R. S., and R. R. Brattain, *J. Chem. Phys.*, *15*, 120, 131, 135 (1947).
510. Ray, N. H., *J. Appl. Chem. (London)*, *4*, 21 (1954).
511. Ray, N. H., *ibid.*, *4*, 82 (1954).
512. Rehner, J., *Ind. Eng. Chem.*, *36*, 118 (1944).
513. Reichstein, T., and J. v. Euw, *Helv. Chim. Acta*, *21*, 1197 (1938).
514. Reid, V. W., and J. D. Beddard, *Analyst*, *79*, 456 (1954).
515. Reilley, C. N., W. D. Cooke, and N. H. Furman, *Anal. Chem.*, *23*, 1223 (1951).
516. Reinbold, C. L., and H. J. Dutton, *J. Am. Oil Chemists' Soc.*, *25*, 117 (1948).
517. Remick, A. E., *Electronic Interpretations of Organic Chemistry.* 2nd ed., Wiley, New York, 1949.
518. Richardson, W. S., and A. Sacher, *J. Polymer Sci.*, *10*, 353 (1953).
519. Richter, F., and W. Wolff, *Ber.*, *63*, 1714 (1930).
520. Richter, M., *Oel und Kohle ver. Erdoel u. Teer*, *15*, 69 (1939).
521. Riebsomer, J. L., *Chem. Revs.*, *36*, 157–233 (1945).
522. Riemenschneider, R. W., S. F. Herb, and P. L. Nichols, Jr., *J. Am. Oil Chemists' Soc.*, *26*, 371 (1949).
523. Robey, R. F., and C. E. Morrell, *Ind. Eng. Chem.*, *Anal. Ed.*, *14*, 880 (1942).
524. Robey, R. F., C. E. Morrell, and B. M. Vanderbilt, *Oil Gas J.*, *40*, No. 37, 41 (1942).
525. Robey, R. F., C. E. Morrell, and H. K. Wiese, *J. Am. Chem. Soc.*, *63*, 627 (1941).
526. Robey, R. F., and H. K. Wiese, *Anal. Chem.*, *20*, 926 (1948).
527. Roelen, O., paper presented at Tagung der Deutschen Gesellschaft für Mineralöl-wissenschaft u. Kohlenchemie, Hamburg, September, 1950.
528. Roman, W., *Anal. Chim. Acta*, *2*, 552 (1948).
529. Roman, W., and M. Smith, *Analyst*, *78*, 679 (1953).
530. Rosenbaum, E. J., *Anal. Chem.*, *21*, 16 (1949); *22*, 14 (1950); *23*, 12 (1951); *24*, 14 (1952); *26*, 20 (1954).
531. Rosenmund, K. W., *Z. angew. Chem.*, *37*, 58 (1924).
532. Rosenmund, K. W., and H. H. Grandjean, *Arch. Pharm.*, *286*, 531 (1953).
533. Rosenmund, K. W., and H. H. Grandjean, *Erdöl u. Kohle*, *5*, 348 (1952).
534. Rosenmund, K. W., and W. Kuhnhenn, *Ber.*, *56*, 1262 (1923).
535. Rosenmund, K. W., and W. Kuhnhenn, *Pharm. Zentralhalle*, *66*, 81 (1925).
536. Rosenmund, K. W., W. Kuhnhenn, D. Rosenberg-Gruszynski, and H. Rosetti, *Z. Untersuch. Nahr.- u. Genussm.*, *46*, 154 (1923).
537. Rosenthaler, L., *Pharm. Acta Helv.*, *17*, 196 (1942).
538. Ross, S. D., M. Markarian, H. H. Young, Jr., and M. Nazzewski, *J. Am. Chem. Soc.*, *72*, 1133 (1950).
539. Rossmann, E., *Angew. Chem.*, *48*, 223 (1935).
540. Rossmann, E., *ibid.*, *50*, 187 (1937).

541. Rossmann, E., *Ber.*, *65*, 1847 (1932).
542. Roth, H., in Houben-Weyl, *Methoden der organischen Chemie*. Vol. II, 4th ed., Thieme, Stuttgart, 1953, pp. 276–281.
543. Roth, H., *ibid.*, pp. 288–304.
544. Rowe, G., C. C. Furnas, and H. Bliss, *Ind. Eng. Chem.*, *Anal. Ed.*, *16*, 371 (1944).
544a. Rudloff, E. von, *Can. J. Chem.*, *33*, 1714 (1955).
544b. Rudloff, E. von, *J. Am. Oil Chemists' Soc.*, *33*, 126 (1956).
545. Rugg, F. M., J. J. Smith, and L. H. Wartman, *J. Polymer Sci.*, *11*, 1 (1953).
546. Rusoff, I. I., J. R. Platt, H. B. Klevens, and G. O. Burr, *J. Am. Chem. Soc.*, *67*, 673 (1945).
547. Ruzicka, L., H. Silbermann, and M. Furter, *Helv. Chim. Acta*, *15*, 482 (1932).
548. Saffer, A., and B. L. Johnson, *Ind. Eng. Chem.*, *40*, 538 (1948).
549. Saier, E. L., and N. D. Coggeshall, *Anal. Chem.*, *20*, 812 (1948).
550. Saier, E. L., A. Pozefsky, and N. D. Coggeshall, *ibid.*, *26*, 1258 (1954).
551. Salomon, G., A. C. van der Schee, J. A. A. Ketelaar, and B. J. van Eyk, *Discussions Faraday Soc.*, No. 9, 291 (1950).
552. Sartori, G., and E. Bianchi, *Gazz. chim. ital.*, *74*, 8 (1940).
553. Savacool, R. V., and G. E. Ullyot, *Anal. Chem.*, *24*, 714 (1952).
554. Savary, P., *Bull. soc. chim. France*, *1949*, 635; *1950*, 624.
555. Scafe, E. T., J. Herman, G. R. Bond, Jr., and cooperators, *Anal. Chem.*, *19*, 971 (1947).
556. Scaife, C. W., *Chemistry & Industry*, *66*, 340 (1947).
557. Schuftan, P., *Gasanalyse in der Technik*. Hirzel, Leipzig, 1931.
558. Schulek, E., and I. Boyer, *Acta Pharm. Intern.*, *1*, 177 (1950).
559. Schwabe, K., and H. Berg, *Z. Elektrochem.*, *56*, 961 (1952).
560. Schwabe, K., G. Ohloff, and H. Berg, *ibid.*, *57*, 34 (1953).
561. Schwabe, K., G. Ohloff, and H. Berg, *ibid.*, *57*, 293 (1953).
562. Scotti, G., *Olii minerali, grassi e saponi, colori e vernici*, *18*, 96 (1938); *Chem. Abstracts*, *34*, 4291 (1940).
563. Semenoff, A., *Z. chem. Pharm.*, 129 (1864); *Jahresber. Pharm.*, 480 (1864).
564. Semerano, G., *Mikrochemie*, *24*, 10 (1938).
565. Semerano, G., and L. Sartori, *ibid.*, *24*, 130 (1938).
566. Serniuk, G. E., F. W. Banes, and M. W. Swaney, *J. Am. Chem. Soc.*, *70*, 1804 (1948).
567. Shell Method Series. Designation: 221/50.
568. *Ibid.*, Designation: 247/54.
569. Shepherd, M., and J. A. Hipple, *Anal. Chem.*, *22*, 23 (1950).
569a. Shepp, A., and K. O. Kutscke, *Can. J. Chem.*, *32*, 1112 (1954).
570. Sheppard, N., and D. M. Simpson, *Quart. Revs. (London)*, *6*, 1–33 (1952).
571. Sheppard, N., and G. B. B. M. Sutherland, *Proc. Roy. Soc. (London)*, *A196*, 195 (1949).
572. Shively, J. H., F. Philgreen, and H. Levin, *Anal. Chem.*, *21*, 1566 (1949).
573. Shoolery, J. N., *ibid.*, *26*, 1400 (1954).
574. Shreve, O. D., *ibid.*, *24*, 1692 (1952).
575. Siggia, S., and R. L. Edsberg, *Anal. Chem.*, *20*, 762 (1948).
576. Siggia, S., and R. L. Edsberg, *ibid.*, *20*, 938 (1948).
577. Silverman, L., *Chemist Analyst*, *36*, 57 (1947).
578. Simmons, R. O., and F. W. Quackenbush, *J. Am. Oil Chemists' Soc.*, *30*, 614 (1953).

579. Sjöström, E., *Acta Chem. Scand.*, *7*, 1392 (1953).
580. Sjöström, E., *Svensk Kem. Tidskr.*, *64*, 301 (1952).
581. Sjöström, E., *Trans. Chalmers Univ. Technol.*, *Gothenburg*, No. 136 (1953).
582. Skell, P. S., and S. B. Radlove, *Ind. Eng. Chem.*, *Anal. Ed.*, *18*, 67 (1946).
583. Skoog, D. A., and H. D. DuBois, *Anal. Chem.*, *21*, 1528 (1949).
584. Slobodin, Ya. M., *Zhur. Obshcheĭ Khim.*, *16*, 1698 (1946); *Chem. Abstracts*, *41*, 5851 (1947).
585. Slotta, K. H., and E. Blanke, *J. prakt. Chem.*, *143*, 3 (1935).
586. Smirnov, P. S., *Neftyanoe Khoz.*, *15*, 217 (1928); *Chem. Abstracts*, *23*, 965 (1929).
587. Smit, W. C., *Rec. trav. chim.*, *49*, 691 (1930).
588. Smith, H. A., D. M. Alderman, and F. W. Nadig, *J. Am. Chem. Soc.*, *67*, 272 (1945).
589. Smith, J. H. C., *J. Biol. Chem.*, *96*, 35 (1932).
590. Sommer, L. H., L. J. Tyler, and F. C. Whitmore, *J. Am. Chem. Soc.*, *70*, 2872 (1948).
591. Spakowski, A. E., A. Evans, and R. R. Hibbard, *Anal. Chem.*, *22*, 1419 (1950).
592. Stackelberg, M. von, and W. Stracke, *Z. Electrochem.*, *53*, 118 (1949).
593. Stamm, R. F., *Anal. Chem.*, *26*, 49 (1954).
594. Stamm, R. F., *Ind. Eng. Chem.*, *Anal. Ed.*, *17*, 318 (1945).
595. Stanerson, B. R., and H. Levin, *ibid.*, *14*, 782 (1942).
596. Starr, C. E., Jr., and T. Lane, *Anal. Chem.*, *21*, 572 (1949).
597. Stern, G., *Reichsamt Wirtschaftsausbau*, *Prüf-Nr. 43* (PB52003), 15 (1940); *Chem. Abstracts*, *41*, 6490 (1947).
598. Steur, J. P. K. van der, *Rec. trav. chim.*, *46*, 278, 409, 414 (1927).
599. Stieglitz, E., K. Andress, and T. Demediuk, *Brennstoff-Chem.*, *30*, 356 (1949).
600. Strain, H. H., *Anal. Chem.*, *21*, 75 (1949); *22*, 41 (1950); *23*, 25 (1951).
601. Strain, H. H., *Chromatographic Adsorption Analysis*. Interscience, New York-London, 1942.
602. Strain, H. H., and G. W. Murphy, *Anal. Chem.*, *24*, 50 (1952).
603. Strain, H. H., T. R. Sato, and J. Engelke, *ibid.*, *26*, 90 (1954).
604. Stromberg, A. G., and A. G. Pozdeeva, *Zhur. Obshchei Khim.*, *20*, 54 (1950); *Chem. Abstracts*, *44*, 8267 (1950); *J. Gen. Chem.*, *U. S. S. R.*, *20*, 57 (1950).
605. Sweetser, P. B., and C. E. Bricker, *Anal. Chem.*, *24*, 1107 (1952).
606. Swern, D., *Chem. Revs.*, *45*, 1–68 (1949).
607. Swern, D., *J. Am. Chem. Soc.*, *69*, 1692 (1947).
608. Swern, D., in R. Adams, ed., *Organic Reactions*. Vol. VII, Wiley, New York, 1953, pp. 378–433.
609. Szasz, G. J., and N. Sheppard, *Trans. Faraday Soc.*, *49*, 358 (1953).
610. Tausz, J., *Chem.-Ztg.*, *42*, 349 (1918).
611. Tausz, J., *Petroleum Z.*, *13*, 649 (1918).
612. Tausz, J., *Z. angew. Chem.*, *32*, I, 233 (1919).
613. Thomas, C. L., H. S. Bloch, and J. Hoekstra, *Ind. Eng. Chem.*, *Anal. Ed.*, *10*, 153 (1938).
614. Thomas, M. H., and F. E. W. Wetmore, *J. Am. Chem. Soc.*, *63*, 136 (1941).
615. Thompson, H. W., and P. Torkington, *Trans. Faraday Soc.*, *41*, 246 (1945); *Proc. Roy. Soc. (London)*, *A184*, 3, 21 (1945).
616. Thornton, V., and A. E. Herald, *Anal. Chem.*, *20*, 9 (1948).
617. Toms, H., *Analyst*, *53*, 69 (1928).
617a. Towler, J. H., and B. H. Holland, *J. Appl. Chem. (London)*, *4*, 517 (1954).

618. Towne, C. C., *J. Inst. Petroleum Technol.*, *17*, 134 (1931).
619. Tropsch, H., and W. J. Mattox, *Ind. Eng. Chem.*, *Anal. Ed.*, *6*, 104 (1934).
620. Tuot, M., *Compt. rend.*, *204*, 697 (1937).
621. Turner, N. C., *Oil Gas J.*, *41*, No. 51, 48 (1943).
622. Turner, N. C., *Petroleum Refiner*, *22*, 140 (1943).
623. Uhrig, K., and H. Levin, *Ind. Eng. Chem.*, *Anal. Ed.*, *13*, 90, 194 (1941).
624. Uhrig, K., E. Lynch, and H. C. Becker, *ibid.*, *18*, 550 (1946).
625. Vandenheuvel, F. A., *Anal. Chem.*, *24*, 847 (1952).
626. Vaubel, W., *Z. angew. Chem.*, *23*, 2078 (1910).
627. Veksler, R. I., *Trudy Komissii Anal. Khim. Akad. Nauk S. S. S. R.*, *3*, 369 (1951); *Chem. Abstracts*, *47*, 2645 (1953).
628. Volmar, Y., and B. Samdahl, *J. pharm. chim.*, *7*, 106 (1928).
629. Volmar, Y., and Wagner, *Bull. soc. chim. France*, *2*, 826 (1935).
630. Voorhees, V., and R. Adams, *J. Am. Chem. Soc.*, *44*, 1397 (1922).
631. Walker, F. T., *J. Oil & Colour Chemists' Assoc.*, *28*, 119 (1945).
632. Walker, F. T., and M. R. Mills, *J. Soc. Chem. Ind. (London)*, *61*, 125 (1942); *62*, 106 (1943).
633. Warburg, O., and W. Christian, *Biochem. Z.*, *258*, 496 (1933); *266*, 387 (1933).
634. Ward, A. L., and S. S. Kurtz, Jr., *Ind. Eng. Chem.*, *Anal. Ed.*, *10*, 559 (1938).
635. Warshowsky, B., P. J. Elving, and J. Mandel, *Anal. Chem.*, *19*, 161 (1947).
636. Warshowsky, B., and M. W. Rice, *ibid.*, *20*, 341 (1948).
637. Waterman, H. I., S. H. Bertram, and H. A. van Westen, *J. Soc. Chem. Ind. (London)*, *48*, 50T (1929).
638. Waterman, H. I., and W. J. C. de Kok, *Rec. trav. chim.*, *52*, 234, 251, 298, 1007 (1933).
639. Waterman, H. I., and W. J. C. de Kok, *ibid.*, *53*, 725, 1133 (1934).
640. Waterman, H. I., W. J. C. de Kok, and C. van Vlodrop, *Chimie & industrie*, *31*, Special No., 899S (1934).
641. Waterman, H. I., and J. N. J. Perquin, *Rec. trav. chim.*, *40*, 677 (1921).
642. Waterman, H. I., J. N. J. Perquin, and H. A. van Westen, *J. Soc. Chem. Ind. (London)*, *47*, 363T (1928).
643. Waterman, H. I., P. van't Spijker, and H. A. van Westen, *Rec. trav. chim.*, *48*, 612 (1929).
644. Waterman, H. I., P. van't Spijker, and H. A. van Westen, *ibid.*, *48*, 612, 1097, 1103, 1191 (1929).
645. Waterman, H. I., and H. A. van Westen, *ibid.*, *48*, 637, 1084 (1929).
646. Wawzonek, S., *Anal. Chem.*, *21*, 61 (1949).
647. Wawzonek, S., *ibid.*, *21*, 61 (1949); *22*, 30 (1950); *24*, 32 (1952); *26*, 65 (1954); *28*, 638 (1956).
648. Wawzonek, S., *J. Am. Chem. Soc.*, *65*, 839 (1943).
649. Wawzonek, S., and J. W. Fan, *ibid.*, *68*, 2541 (1946).
650. Weger, M., *Chemische Industrie*, *28*, 24 (1905).
651. Weghofer, H., *Erdöl u. Kohle*, *4*, 1 (1951).
652. Weidlein, E. R., Jr., *Chem. Eng. News*, *24*, 771 (1946).
653. Weissberger, A., ed., *Physical Methods of Organic Chemistry*. Vol. I, Part II, 2nd ed., Interscience, New York-London, 1949.
654. Wendland, R. T., *J. Chem. Educ.*, *23*, 3 (1946).
655. Wesson, L. G., and E. S. Knorr, *Ind. Eng. Chem.*, *9*, 139 (1917).

656. West, W., ed., *Chemical Applications of Spectroscopy*. Interscience, New York-London, 1956.
657. Weygand, C., and A. Werner, *J. prakt. Chem.*, *149*, 330 (1937).
658. Whalley, C., and M. Ellison, *J. Oil & Colour Chemists' Assoc.*, *35*, 596 (1952).
659. White, E. P., and P. W. Robertson, *J. Chem. Soc.*, *1939*, 1509.
660. White, M. F., and J. B. Brown, *J. Am. Oil Chemists' Soc.*, *29*, 292 (1952).
661. Whitmore, F. C., and J. M. Church, *J. Am. Chem. Soc.*, *54*, 3710 (1932).
662. Whitnack, G. C., *Anal. Chem.*, *20*, 658 (1948).
663. Wibaut, J. P., F. L. J. Sixma, L. W. F. Kampschmidt, and H. Boer, *Rec. trav. chim.*, *69*, 1355 (1950).
664. Williams, G., *Trans. Faraday Soc.*, *37*, 749 (1941).
665. Willits, C. O., M. L. Swain, and C. L. Ogg, *Ind. Eng. Chem.*, *Anal. Ed.*, *18*, 439 (1946).
666. Willstaedt, H., *Ber.*, *68*, 333 (1935).
667. Willstätter, R., and D. Hatt, *ibid.*, *45*, 1471 (1912).
668. Willstätter, R., and E. Waldschmidt-Leitz, *ibid.*, *54*, 113 (1921).
669. Wilson, G. E., *J. Inst. Petroleum*, *36*, 25 (1950).
670. Wilson, G. E., and H. B. Nisbet, *Analyst*, *71*, 183 (1946).
671. Winkler, L. W., *Arch. Pharm.*, *265*, 554 (1927); *Chem. Abstracts*, *21*, 4080 (1927).
672. Winkler, L. W., in *Pharmacopea Hungarica*, 3rd ed., Budapest, 1909, p. XI; *Z. Untersuch. Nahr.- u. Genussm.*, *32*, 358 (1916).
673. Winkler, L. W., *Z. Untersuch. Nahr.- u. Genussm.*, *43*, 201 (1922).
674. Winkler, L. W., *ibid.*, *49*, 277 (1925); *Z. anal. Chem.*, *93*, 172 (1933).
675. Winward, A., and F. H. Garner, *J. Soc. Chem. Ind. (London)*, *69*, 147 (1950).
676. Wirth, H., *Mikrochemie ver. Mikrochim. Acta*, *40*, 15 (1952).
677. Wirth, H., *Monatsh.*, *84*, 156 (1953).
678. Wirth, H., *ibid.*, *84*, 741 (1953).
679. Witter, R. F., E. H. Newcomb, and E. Stotz, *J. Biol. Chem.*, *185*, 537 (1950).
680. Wood, L. A., *Natl. Bur. Standards, Misc. Publ.*, M 185 (1947).
681. Worstall, R. A., *J. Am. Chem. Soc.*, *21*, 245 (1899).
682. Wotiz, J. H., and W. D. Celmer, *ibid.*, *74*, 1860 (1952).
683. Wright, G. F, *Chemistry in Can.*, *2*, No. 9, 29 (1955).
684. Wurzschmitt, B., *Z. anal. Chem.*, *128*, 549 (1948).
685. Wys, J. J. A., *Ber.*, *31*, 750 (1898).
686. Yakubchik, A. I., A. A. Vasilev, and V. M. Zhabina, *Zhur. Priklad. Khim.*, *17*, 107 (1944); *Rubber Chem. and Techol.*, *18*, 780 (1945).
687. Young, R. E., H. K. Pratt, and J. B. Biale, *Anal. Chem.*, *24*, 551 (1952).
688. Zaugg, H. E., and W. M. Lauer, *ibid.*, *20*, 1022 (1948).
689. Zechmeister, L., *Chem. Revs.*, *34*, 267–344 (1944).
690. Zechmeister, L., *Discussions Faraday Soc.*, No. 7, 54 (1949).
691. Zechmeister, L., *Progress in Chromatography*, *1938–1947*. Chapman & Hall, London, 1950.
692. Zechmeister, L., and L. Cholnoky, *Chem.-Ztg.*, *60*, 665 (1936).
693. Zechmeister, L., and L. Cholnoky, *Principles and Practice of Chromatography*. Chapman & Hall, London, 1943.
694. Zechmeister, L., L. v. Cholnoky, and E. Ujhelyi, *Bull. soc. chim. biol.*, *18*, 1885 (1936).

695. Zechmeister, L., L. v. Cholnoky, and V. Vrabély, *Ber.*, *61*, 566 (1928); *66*, 123 (1933).
696. Zechmeister, L., and W. H. McNeely, *J. Am. Chem. Soc.*, *64*, 1919 (1942).
697. Zerbe, C., *Mineralöle und verwandte Produkte*. Springer, Berlin, 1952, p. 1280.
698. Zhukhovitskiĭ, A. A., O. V. Zolotareva, V. A. Sokolov, and N. M. Turkel'taub, *Doklady Akad. Nauk S. S. S. R.*, *77*, 435 (1951); *Chem. Abstracts*, *46*, 11011 (1952).

ANALYTICAL MASS SPECTROMETRY

VERNON H. DIBELER, *National Bureau of Standards, Washington, D. C.*

I. INTRODUCTION

The principles of the art of mass spectrometry were founded in the first quarter of this century in the works of J. J. Thomson (120), F. W. Aston (4), and A. J. Dempster (28). Aston, extending the work of Thomson, developed a new type of positive-ray apparatus that separated a positive ion beam into its component parts, each differing in mass-to-charge ratio, and recorded the "spectrum" on a photographic plate. The analogy of a light beam analyzed by an optical spectrograph caused the new apparatus to be called a mass spectrograph. Aston's apparatus was primarily suited for the proof of existence and the identification of the isotopes of the various elements and for measurements of their packing fractions. Dempster's apparatus, developed at about the same time, utilized electrical recording of the spectral lines and was primarily useful for the measurement of relative abundances of the isotopes. This apparatus was the forerunner of one type of present-day gas-analysis mass spectrometer.

Although important technical developments in apparatus and techniques by Bleakney (12), Tate (115), and Nier (82) and their students resulted in more versatile and reliable instruments, these were still utilized primarily for physics research. It was not until 1940 (53) that the principle of the mass spectrometer was applied to the analysis of complex gas mixtures and chemists first realized the potential usefulness of this very important research and analytical tool to science and industry.

Physicists and chemists actively engaged in various aspects of mass spectrometry are necessarily acquainted with major developments in their fields during the last decade. However, much of this work detailing the versatility of modern research and analytical instruments, the reliability of experimental results, and the striking contributions to the advancement of nearly every branch of the physical sciences appears in a few recently published books and reports and in various journals read only infrequently by chemists in general and by organic chemists in particular. Thus the purpose of this chapter is to assemble in a volume on organic analysis a brief description of fundamental principles and operational techniques together with recent advances in mass spectrometry particularly appropriate to organic analysis and of interest to organic chemists.

1. General Theory

For detailed discussions on the focusing properties of magnetic fields and experimental and theoretical developments in ion physics as applied to mass spectrometry, the reader is referred to some of the publications listed in a following section. However, for a better understanding of the applications, advantages, and limitations of the mass spectrometer, it is of interest to consider briefly the simple physical laws governing the fundamental principle of the mass spectrometer employing a magnetic analyzer.

Figure 1 is a schematic diagram of a Dempster-type mass spectrometer utilizing a homogeneous magnetic field, a monoenergetic source, and 180° deflection of the ion beam. If a singly charged particle of mass m and charge e is formed virtually at rest at point P and is accelerated by an

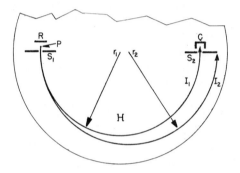

Fig. 1. Schematic diagram of a 180° direction-focusing mass analyzer using a single homogeneous magnetic field and a monoenergetic ion source.

electrostatic potential V impressed between the plate R and the slit S_1, the particle will acquire a kinetic energy equal to the electrostatic field potential times the electronic charge:

$$mv^2/2 = eV \tag{1}$$

Furthermore, as it is accelerated in a homogeneous magnetic field, H, the particle traveling in a circular path will undergo a centrifugal force equal to mv^2/r, which, under equilibrium conditions, is exactly balanced by the magnetic field force, Hev. Thus:

$$mv^2/r = Hev \tag{2}$$

If equations (1) and (2) are combined by eliminating the velocity term, proper arrangement will result in:

$$m/e = H^2r^2/2Vc^2 \tag{3}$$

Equation (3) is usually referred to as the mass spectrometer equation and when all terms are expressed in practical units, may be written as:

$$m/e = 4.8 \times 10^{-5} \, r^2 H^2 / V \tag{4}$$

where m is in atomic mass units, e is the number of single electronic charges per particle, H is in gauss, and V is in volts.

As illustrated in Figure 1, equation (3) requires that, for a particular geometry and values of the magnetic field and ion-accelerating voltage, an ion I_1 with a path of radius r_1 will pass through slit S_2 and register at the collector C, whereas an ion I_2 of larger m/e and radius r_2 will strike the wall. However, as m/e is directly proportional to the square of the magnetic field strength, and inversely proportional to the electrostatic accelerating field, variation in either one will cause different ion beams to pass in succession through S_2 and register at the collector.

The applications to which a mass spectrometer is suited depend in part on the minimum mass difference required of two ions in order to be separately collected. Thus an instrument with a mass resolving power of 120 (unit mass resolution at mass 120) is suitable for analysis of mixtures containing hydrocarbons up to octanes, whereas analyses of heavier compounds may require a resolving power of 400 or 600. The requirements of design, engineering, and construction rise very rapidly with the demand for increased resolving power in the conventional mass spectrometer. It is interesting to note, however, that instruments built for precise mass measurement in physics research do attain resolving powers of about 100,000.

2. Dissociation by Electron Impact

Complicated molecules when subjected to electron impact under conditions commonly existing in the ion source of a mass spectrometer generally ionize and dissociate to give reproducible patterns or spectra that are characteristic of the molecule. This fact was known for at least ten years before the mass spectrometer was considered seriously as a tool for chemical analysis.

The interaction between electrons and molecules is not a simple one. Starting with neutral molecules in the ground state, this interaction may result in neutral molecules in an excited state, ionized molecules, neutral fragments, positive fragment ions, and negative fragment ions. Any of these may be formed with excess kinetic or excitational energies. The mass spectrometer, however, can record only the presence of ions. Of these, the discussion in this chapter will be limited to positive ion spectra.

In all but the simplest cases, no theoretical predictions of mass spectral data from molecular structure are yet possible. In the case of the hydrogen molecule only, the application of quantum mechanics (112) permits the calculation of the relative probability of obtaining H^+ and H_2^+ ions. However, an ever-increasing amount of mass spectral data is being accumulated and published by laboratories in universities, government, and industry. Attempts are being made to formulate on the basis of this and related data general rules for the quantitative prediction of mass spectra. In the case of the propane molecule, Eyring and some of his students (99,125) have progressed remarkably by considering mass spectra in terms of a series of quasiequilibrium unimolecular decompositions.

TABLE I

Mass Spectra of Paraffinic Hydrocarbons for 70 v. Electrons (3)

m/e	Methane	Ethane	Propane
1	3.36	2.58	1.98
2	0.21	0.30	0.14
12	2.80	0.54	0.37
13	8.09	1.16	0.71
14	16.1	3.35	2.08
15	85.9	4.57	6.19
16	100.0	0.08	0.15
17	1.11	—	—
24	—	0.74	0.12
25	—	4.15	0.79
26	—	23.0	8.59
27	—	33.3	39.4
28	—	100.0	59.1
29	—	21.7	100.0
30	—	26.2	2.20
31	—	0.55	—
36	—	—	0.52
37	—	—	3.38
38	—	—	5.29
39	—	—	17.0
40	—	—	2.52
41	—	—	12.7
42	—	—	5.82
43	—	—	22.8
44	—	—	29.0
45	—	—	0.88
Sensitivity of most abundant ion in arbitrary units			
26.7	39.2	33.5

Thomson first demonstrated that the element neon consisted of two types of atoms, some of relative weight 20 and others of weight 22. A third species of weight 21 is now known to exist. In later investigations, Aston showed that many elements have two or more isotopes and that the

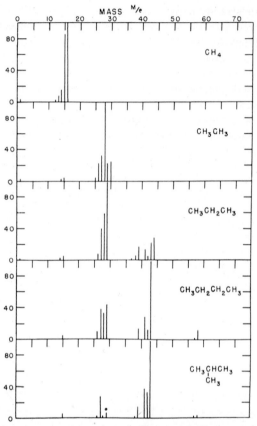

Fig. 2. Simplified presentation of the principal features of the mass spectra of methane, ethane, propane, and the butane isomers (77). The mass-to-charge ratio is plotted on as the abscissa; the ordinate is percentage abundance.

isotopic weights were very nearly integral values. Moreover, since most ions in molecular mass spectra are singly charged it has become conventional to express the mass of a polyatomic ion as an integral mass number equal to the sum of the mass numbers of the isotopic species comprising the ion. For example, the mass number of the $C_2^{12}H_5$ ion is 29; $C^{13}O^{16}O^{16}$

is 45; CCl_3^{35} is 117; and so forth.   Obviously some ions have the same mass numbers and many molecules have overlapping mass spectra, as shown in the following section.

Although dissociative ionization occurs when hydrocarbons are bombarded by electrons with energies of 10–15 v., greater sensitivity and more reproducible spectra result if data are obtained with 50–100 v. electrons. Much of the recently published spectra have been obtained with 70 v. electrons as illustrated by the spectra of several simple paraffinic hydrocarbons given in Table I.

Column 1 gives the mass-to-charge ratio of the ions.   Columns 2, 3, and 4 give the relative abundances of the principal ions in the spectra of methane, ethane, and propane.   Following the usual convention, the most abundant ion in each spectrum is assigned the value 100.   The abundances of the other ions are tabulated relative to the most abundant ion.   The observed ion current (measured in arbitrary units) per unit of pressure in the mass spectrometer is called the sensitivity and is given for the most abundant ion at the bottom of each column.   This is generally the same within a factor of two or three for all hydrocarbons so far studied.   Interesting features such as doubly charged ions are omitted from the table for the sake of brevity.   Following the mass spectrometer equation, these ions appear at a position on the mass scale of exactly one-half of the mass number of the ion.   Thus for an odd mass number the doubly charged ion will appear at a half-mass position. Triply and more highly charged ions are very rare in molecular mass spectra.

A very convenient way to show the principal characteristics of hydrocarbon spectra is that of Figure 2 (77), in which the mass-to-charge ratio of ions with relative abundances greater than 2% is plotted as the abscissa and the relative abundances are plotted as the ordinate for the principal ions of normal and isobutane as well as the compounds of Table I.

Qualitatively, the dissociation patterns of most hydrocarbons are generally as expected from their respective structures.   All possible fragments formed by the rupture of carbon-hydrogen and carbon-carbon bonds are observed.   In the case of propane, for example, these include $C_3H_8^+$. . . C_3^+, $C_2H_5^+$. . .C_2^+, and CH_3^+. . .C^+.   In methane, ionization is the most probable process with removal of a hydrogen atom only slightly less probable.   In ethane the loss of two hydrogen atoms is the most probable process, whereas the loss of a methyl group is the most probable process in propane and the two butane isomers.   Although the latter compounds produce ions with identical mass-to-charge ratios, they are characterized by very different dissociation probabilities and quantitative analyses of mixtures are possible over a wide concentration range.   The spectra of *cis* and *trans* isomers are generally very similar. Notable exceptions to this are the *cis* and *trans* isomers of decahydronaphthalene (79).

At the very low operating pressures of the mass spectrometer ($\sim 10^{-4}$ mm.), the probability of interaction between molecules, radicals, and ions is negligibly small. Thus no ions heavier than the molecule ion are observed excepting those resulting from the presence of C^{13} and D atoms in normal abundance. However, ions requiring an intramolecular rearrangement during the ionization-dissociation process, e. g., the $m/e = 29$ peak in isobutane, are quite common and often relatively abundant especially in the more complicated molecules.

An interesting characteristic of some mass spectra are the ions with broad peak contour and relatively low abundance appearing at nonintegral positions on the mass scale. Hipple (50) has shown that these ions are the result of a delay of the order of microseconds in a dissociation process, i. e., metastable transitions. Because of the delay the ions dissociate after being accelerated by the electrostatic field and appear at a position on the mass scale given by the relation:

$$m_a = m_f^2/m_i \tag{5}$$

where m_i and m_f are the masses of the ion before and after the delayed dissociation. Unfortunately the relative abundance of these ions is too small to make them generally useful for identification purposes. Furthermore their wide contour complicates the base line of the spectrum. Therefore some recent gas analysis mass spectrometers are provided with a suppressor electrode that prevents ions formed by metastable transition from reaching the collector. This results in a more easily read spectrum.

In addition to molecular structure, electron energy, and metastable transitions, mass spectra are dependent on several instrumental factors one of the most important of which is temperature of the ion source. The variation of mass spectra with temperature has been the subject of a number of papers (10,39,93,113) and it has been shown conclusively that rigid temperature control of the ion source is necessary for reproducible and accurate analysis. Modern commercial mass spectrometers designed for gas analysis are provided with means to control the temperature of the ion source.

3. Literature Survey

Although specific literature references are provided at the end of the chapter, the purpose of this section is to direct attention to general reference and background material of importance in the consideration of the theory, design, and application of mass spectrometry.

In addition to the classic works of Thomson (120) and Aston (4), an early review of the theory and practice of ionization and dissociation by low-speed electrons was published by Smyth (109) in 1931. A still broader and modern review of this field has appeared in the recent book by Massey and Burhop (71).

Probably the first important survey of advances in mass spectrometry up to 1942 appeared in a series of papers published in *The Journal of Applied Physics* in 1942 (49). Since that time a number of reviews of the entire field of mass spectrometry have appeared in *Analytical Chemistry* (29,31,105). Furthermore, a number of volumes on instrumental analyses, analytical methods, and advances in physical sciences have included chapters by Washburn (126), Wiley and Berry (128), Hipple (51), Stewart (114), and Inghram (54). Inghram and Hayden (55) have recently published a handbook on mass spectroscopy that is an excellent source of information on basic principles and procedures up to mid-1952.

Detailed descriptions of every important aspect of mass spectrometry are also available in two recent books by Ewald and Hintenberger (36) and by Barnard (6).

II. INSTRUMENTATION AND TECHNIQUES

1. Analytical Mass Spectrometers

The basic components of all conventional mass spectrometers designed for chemical analysis are similar. They consist of: (*1*) a chamber wherein gas molecules at low pressure are ionized and dissociated by electron impact (ion source); (*2*) an analyzer tube wherein the ions are deflected by an homogeneous magnetic field; and (*3*) an ion collector with suitable electrometer circuitry for measuring the currents of the separated and successively collected ion beams. In addition, certain apparatus such as a sample introduction system and an automatic recording system are important associated equipment.

Figure 3 is a photograph of one of the commercially available mass spectrometers designed for broad application to chemical analysis. The sample introduction system is contained in the cabinet on the left of the figure. To the left of center is the electromagnet with the 180° analyzer tube just visible between the horizontal pole faces. The control cabinet on the right contains power supplies and recording equipment.

Fig. 3. A commercial-mass spectrometer using a 180° analyzer tube. The sample handling cabinet appears at the far left. The electromagnet is left of center with the analyzer tube horizontally placed between the pole pieces. The main cabinet at the right contains power supplies, controls, and recording equipment. (Courtesy Consolidated Electrodynamics Corp., Pasadena, Cal.)

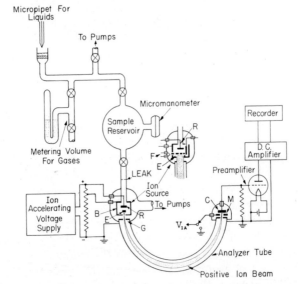

Fig. 4. Schematic diagram of a 180° mass spectrometer and associated apparatus including the sample handling apparatus, ion source, analyzer tube, and recording system.

Figure 4 is a simplified drawing indicating the relationships of these components for an instrument employing 180° deflection of the ions. The arrangement and use applies equally well to instruments designed for 60 or 90° deflection of the ions.

In recent years, several new types of mass spectrometers have been built. Especially notable among these is the ion resonance instrument described by Sommer, Thomas, and Hipple (111) that uses the cyclotron principle for separation of ions with various mass-to-charge ratios, and the cycloidal-path instrument using crossed electric and magnetic fields (96). "Time of flight" instruments have been described in which pulses of ions directed along a drift tube (94) or deflected into circular paths (108) arrived at a collector at short measured time intervals depending on their mass-to-charge ratios. In another type of instrument, velocity selection of the ions is made by radio frequency fields (8). Most of these instruments have been built primarily for physics research and will not be described in detail. The ion resonance, and the cycloidal mass spectrometers have proved particularly applicable as process control instruments.

A. SAMPLE INTRODUCTION SYSTEMS

The general procedure for introducing gaseous and liquid samples into an analytical mass spectrometer is illustrated in Figure 4. A gas or vapor is admitted to the metering volume of a few milliliters at pressures of the order of a few centimeters of mercury and expanded approximately one thousand fold into the reservoir bottle. Liquid samples in comparable quantity are introduced by touching the tip of a micropipet containing the sample to the surface of a porous disc covered with mercury (118) or liquid gallium, or through a mercury orifice (24).

The pressure of the expanded gas or vapor sample can be calculated from the manometer reading in the metering volume and the precise expansion ratio or from the known amount of liquid introduced from calibrated pipets. However, a much better way is direct measurement of the pressure of the expanded sample by means of a micromanometer. Several of these instruments have been described (23,30) that are independent of sample composition.

Measurement of relative pressure by means of internal standards has also been described (119) for use when micromanometers are not available or are inapplicable.

The expanded sample is admitted to the ion source through a leak consisting of one or more small holes in a very thin diaphragm. With proper choice of sample pressure, dimensions of reservoir, and leak orifice, gas flow into the ion source will be molecular (effusive), i. e., dependent only on the square root of the molecular weight of the gas. This is a desirable situation, as gas flow out of the ion source through the pumping system is necessarily molecular flow. Thus the composition of the gas in the ion source is proportional to the partial pressures of the components in the reservoir and is independent of the total pressure. This type of gas flow, usually preferred for analytical mass spectrometers, has been described in detail by Honig (52) and by Zemany (131).

Mass spectrometers designed primarily for measurements of isotope ratios almost invariably use viscous flow systems (45). However, the application to special gas analysis problems has also been discussed (72).

The materials of which the inlet system are constructed depend upon the type of samples to be analyzed. Although all-glass systems have a number of advantages, the virtual necessity of lubricated stopcocks is a serious disadvantage if hydrocarbons and other compounds that react with or are absorbed by lubricant are to be analyzed. All-glass systems with mercury or gallium cutoffs have been used particularly in heated inlet systems designed for the analysis of compounds of high molecular weight. Unfortunately these metals react with some types of compounds particularly at elevated temperatures. Stainless-steel systems using packless valves and valve closures of an inert polymer have a number of obvious advantages and are currently used successfully in many laboratories performing varied types of analyses.

B. ION SOURCE AND ANALYZER

After passing through the leak (see Fig. 4) the gas molecules enter the ion source, where they encounter the electron beam E originating from the filament F. Positive ions formed in the region of the electron beam are drawn from the ionization chamber by a small potential between B and R and are then accelerated by high voltage impressed between B and G. The ion beam then enters the magnetic analyzer which, as illustrated in Figure 3, is a direction-focusing analyzer. This is also true of the sector-field analyzers utilizing symmetrical 60 and 90° deflection of the ions.

As described above, the components of the ion beam are separated according to their mass to charge ratio and are caused to register separately at the collector C by varying the magnetic field or the potential between B and G. Which of these two methods is used is not of very great consequence in chemical analysis but may be of considerable importance in isotope abundance measurements.

The electrode, M, placed just before the collector may be connected to the ion-accelerating voltage divider or may be grounded. In the former case, ions that have lost energy in traversing the analyzer (e. g., ions resulting from metastable transitions) are turned back by the potential gradient and prevented from reaching the collector.

Single-ion collectors are most useful for general analytical application although multiple collectors have been used for special purposes, e. g., the dual collector system devised by Nier, Ney, and Inghram (83) for direct comparison of isotopic compositions. In such a system two or more ion currents can be compared directly by proper arrangement of collector slits and magnetic and electric fields. The principal advantage is independence of variation in ion currents during the period of measurement.

C. DETECTION AND RECORDING SYSTEMS

As ion currents encountered in the mass spectrometer are very small (usually in the range of 10^{-8} to 10^{-15} amp.), electrometer circuits must be used for detection. The output of the preamplifier is fed to a d. c. amplifier, where the signal is amplified sufficiently to drive sensitive galvanometers or specially designed slide-wire recorders. In special cases in which extreme sensitivity is desired for detection of trace elements or impurities, the collector has been replaced by the first plate of an electron multiplier (84). However, this device is not readily applied to a 180° instrument because of the necessity of operating in a strong magnetic field. Furthermore, operating characteristics of the multiplier are such that applications to general analytical problems are unlikely in the immediate future.

A vibrating-reed electrometer and a. c. amplifier (89) have been used in place of electrometer tubes for certain applications. Although this device has a very low noise level and only negligible zero drift, it is not without its own problems. Furthermore, the property of high zero stability is fully matched by recent developments in preamplifier circuitry, in which a pair of electrometer tubes are arranged so that drift due to the effects of variation in operating voltages is largely canceled.

One of the principal requirements of an analytical spectrometer is that of rapid and accurate recording of mass spectra. This requirement has been met in several ways. In one, the amplifier output is fed to a bank of five galvanometers appropriately shunted for relative sensitivities of 1, $\frac{1}{3}$, $\frac{1}{10}$, $\frac{1}{30}$, and $\frac{1}{100}$. By means of mirrored suspensions, a plot of ion current versus mass is traced on photographic paper. Figure 5 shows a spectrum of n-butane recorded in this manner. When deflection of the

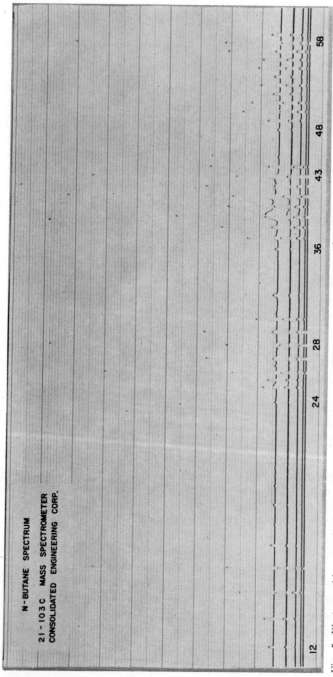

Fig. 5. Photographic record of the mass spectrum of *n*-butane obtained with a five-galvanometer recorder permitting the accurate measurement of peaks differing in intensity by a factor of 10,000. (Courtesy Consolidated Electrodynamics Corp., Pasadena, Cal.)

more sensitive galvanometers (upper traces) is off the paper, one of the less sensitive galvanometers is in proper range to record the peak. The horizontal grid lines are traced simultaneously to obviate possible effects of variation in paper width as a result of processing.

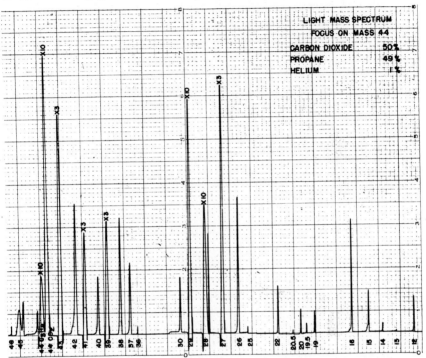

Fig. 6. Partial spectrum of a simple gas mixture obtained with a rapid pen recorder. The proper scale factor required by the different peak intensities is automatically selected by a "precollector" electrode. The resolution of the instrument is indicated by the separation of 0.16 mass unit for the molecule ions of propane and carbon dioxide at $m/e = 44$. (Courtesy General Electric Co., Schenectady, N. Y.)

Slide-wire recorders using a single pen trace are also in common use. However, these require shunt-selecting devices in order to record the necessary range of ion intensities (usually 1 to 10,000) with accuracies of 0.5% or better. One method of accomplishing this is first to scan the peak on a nonlinear scale to select the proper shunt and then rescan the peak on a linear scale (44). A second method makes use of an auxiliary collector that gages the ion beam intensity and selects the proper sensitivity range of the recorder just before the ion beam is swept over the main collector. The spectrum of a simple gas mixture recorded in this manner is shown in Figure 6. In all of these systems efforts are made to record spectra as accurately and rapidly as possible. However the limits to the speed and accuracy are not, in general, set by limitations of the recorder, but by a number of instrumental conditions including the collector slit width, amplifier noise level, sensitivity, and so forth. Under favorable conditions, however, spectra such as illustrated in Figure 5 can be recorded in three minutes or less.

Means by which a limited region of a mass spectrum can be repeatedly scanned very rapidly and displayed on a cathode ray tube have been described by a number of investigators (37,107,122). This technique is particularly useful for observing intermediate products or rapid changes in composition such as occur in combustion processes. The accuracy is not comparable with that of the more conventional recording systems.

2. General Principles of Analysis

A. SAMPLE HANDLING

One of the important aspects of the mass spectrometer is the small size of the sample required for an analysis, e. g., of the order of 0.2 cc. atmosphere of gas at room temperature. This is at once a great advantage and a source of possible difficulties. The problem of obtaining a truly representative sample is more critical for small samples. Furthermore, changes in composition are more readily effected in small samples by sorption and desorption on the interior walls of the sample-handling system.

The problem of representative sampling may be subdivided according to whether the components of a mixture are: (1) completely gaseous, (2) liquids boiling above room temperature at atmospheric pressure, (3) liquids boiling below room temperature at atmospheric pressure, or (4) solids.

The first case is a relatively straightforward one that includes samples commonly expanded from a storage bulb, a reaction vessel, a compressed gas cylinder, or a gas pipe line attached directly to the evacuated sample introduction system or to an evacuated sample bulb for subsequent attachment to the mass spectrometer. The sample transfer is usually accomplished under conditions of viscous flow and no mass fractionation occurs in the process. However, the nature of the mixture to be analyzed often requires careful consideration of the design of a sample container.

Probably the most commonly used sample holder for gases near atmospheric pressure is a glass bulb with a lubricated stopcock and standard taper or other device for connection to the mass spectrometer. Unfortunately, gas mixtures frequently include compounds that react with or are dissolved in most organic and semiorganic lubricants, resulting in a change in composition. Storage bulbs closed by means of porous discs covered with mercury (35) avoid this difficulty but introduce the problem of possible fractionation (118). Furthermore the mercury (or gallium) is by no means inert toward many gases.

Another useful method is that of torch-sealing gases at slightly less than atmospheric pressure into lengths of thin-walled glass capillary tubing. The gases are subsequently introduced into the mass spectrometer by breaking them inside an evacuated chamber. Several simple devices for accomplishing this have been described (48,85).

Recently, stainless-steel sample containers and connectors have become quite common. These together with associated valve closures and packings made from polymers of tetrafluoroethylene and chlorotrifluoroethylene have been applied successfully to a number of specialized analytical problems.

There are two methods in general use at present for introducing samples that are liquids under normal conditions of temperature and pressure. In one of these, a Corning Type F sintered-glass disc is attached to the sample inlet manifold and covered with a pool of mercury or gallium, thus excluding the atmosphere when the manifold is evacuated. When the tip of a micropipet suitable for delivering 0.001-ml. quantities of liquid is touched to the disc surface below the mercury, the liquid is drawn through the porous disc and into the manifold (40,118). Purdy and Harris (91) improved this technique by using a capillary dipper that is a constant-volume pipet small enough to be submerged below the mercury surface. Thus mercury replaces the sample in the dipper as the sample is drawn through the disc and precisely equal samples are introduced each time.

The second method (24,116) utilizes a vertical, 100 cm. length of glass tubing closed at the bottom with a pool of mercury and fitted with a re-entrant tube at the top drawn down to a small orifice. Connection to the sample inlet manifold is made by means of a side arm just below the orifice tip. The orifice is partly closed with a suitable plug and sealed from above by a pool of mercury. A sample is introduced by removing the plug and quickly substituting a filled capillary dipper. The sample is drawn into the orifice and vaporizes into the inlet manifold while any droplets of mercury fall into a reservoir at the bottom of the tube. One of the advantages of this method is that most liquids completely vaporize in a matter of seconds whereas the porous-disc method sometimes requires many minutes for complete vaporization.

The method of introducing a liquid mixture sample from a break-seal ampule is not considered good practice. It is a well-known fact that the composition of the vapor above the liquid is not representative of the sample. Furthermore, if the size of the liquid sample were limited to that which would completely vaporize upon expansion, adequate mixing of the vapor throughout the inlet system would remain an uncertainty. Careful consideration is required even in the case of "pure" samples used for calibration purposes. Traces of more volatile impurities may be relatively abundant in the vapor phase and the apparent percentage impurity greatly magnified in the mass spectrum.

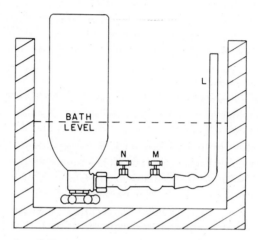

Fig. 7. Sample cylinder and isolator assembly for sampling liquefied gases that boil below room temperature at atmospheric pressure.

The problem of withdrawing a representative sample from a cylinder or pipe line containing liquids boiling below room temperature at atmospheric pressure is a difficult one. Shepherd (102,104) has pointed out the factors that influence the composition of a sample obtained by flashing the sample from a valve located below the liquid level. He also proposed a procedure for obtaining a small representative sample without fractionation as follows: (1) make the liquid phase homogeneous; (2) isolate an appropriate portion of the liquid without change in composition (i. e., without boiling); (3) completely vaporize the isolated sample; and (4) make the vapor phase homogeneous.

Dibeler and Mohler (32) studied methods of sampling for mass spectrometric analysis of a liquefied sample of C_3–C_5 paraffin–olefin synthetic mixture. Whereas sampling through a needle valve at low flow rate gave large systematic errors, excellent agreement between the observed and the known composition was obtained when the mixture was sampled in the manner illustrated in Figure 7. The cylinder valve and isolator were cooled to below the boiling point of the most volatile component. The cylinder was thoroughly shaken and the isolator filled with liquid. The isolater was then removed from the cylinder and the contents were completely expanded into an evacuated bulb sufficiently large for complete vaporization. After mixing, the vapor was analyzed. Several other methods for obtaining representative samples by employing the principles outlined by Shepherd have been described by Schuhmann (100).

The analysis of solid organic materials requiring heated inlet systems or furnace sources poses a number of special problems essentially unique for each subject. Several of these will be discussed in following sections.

The preferential adsorption of components in a mixture onto the interior walls of the mass spectrometer as well as the desorption from walls into the vapor are often a source of considerable error in mass-spectrometric analysis. Such effects are generally negligible for hydrocarbons of four carbon atoms or less whether in glass or metal systems. It is important to note, however, that lubricated stopcocks are usually associated with glass systems and sorption and solution effects will be observed in the greases particularly in regions exposed to samples at relatively high pressures, e. g., of the order of centimeters.

Compounds such as water, ammonia, amines, alcohols, and carboxylic acids are so strongly sorbed on walls that analysis is virtually impossible without unusual consideration and special techniques. These commonly include heated sample inlet lines and analyzer tubes, placement of the leak in close proximity to the ion source, elution, and repetitive sample flushing (42,57,62). By these means satisfactory analyses have been made on samples containing up to 99% water including analysis for the water content.

The importance of sorption effects is clearly demonstrated by the introduction of compounds containing exchangeable deuterium atoms into a conventional metal or glass inlet system. The mass spectrum of the first sample admitted usually shows only a small fraction of the original isotopic abundance and for a single analysis the amount of sample flushing required to condition the system completely is usually prohibitive. However, by minimizing sorption effects and other instrumental difficulties, Washburn, Berry, and Hall (127) report the successful isotopic analysis of water vapor on a routine basis.

The extension of mass-spectrometric analysis to include compounds exhibiting appreciable sorption characteristics makes it imperative that a means be provided to measure directly the true sample pressure in the reservoir volume. Diaphragm-type micromanometers have been described that are capable of measuring pressures in the range of 1 to 200 microns quite independently of the nature of the sample.

One design (23) is an absolute manometer in which a stretched diaphragm is used as one of the plates of a pressure-sensitive condenser. A

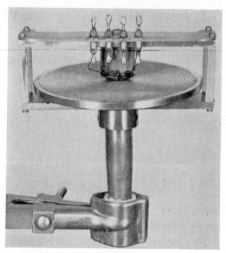

Fig. 8. Pressure-sensitive element of a diaphragm-type micro-manometer utilizing the change in mutual inductance of probe coils to measure pressure differentials (30).

pressure-induced deformation of the diaphragm is balanced to a null by an electrical restoring force. This force is converted to units of pressure.

A photograph of the pressure-sensitive element of another type of micromanometer (30) is shown in Figure 8. The displacement of the thin corrugated metal diaphragm of the capsule is measured by a change in the mutual inductance of two probe coils wound on the insulating form supported close above the diaphragm surface. When an r. f. current is applied to the primary winding, a voltage is obtained at the terminals of the secondary that is a linear function of the proximity of the diaphragm. Unlike the null instrument, the mutual inductance micromanometer achieves maximum precision only at full-scale readings of the pressure. However, a direct-reading instrument is a distinct advantage as it automatically indicates changes in sample pressure during the course of a run that may indicate undesirable effects in the inlet system.

B. COMPUTATION OF ANALYSES

There are three fundamental requirements that must be met for successful analysis by mass spectrometry. These are: (1) reproducibility of mass spectra, (2) reasonable constancy of sensitivity (ion current per unit of pressure) of a compound, and (3) linear additivity of the contributions to each mass from every component in the mixture. To illustrate the latter requirement, consider the mass spectrum of a multicomponent mixture obtained at some arbitrary pressure. The ion current obtained at each mass must be related to the ion currents for each component (calibration spectra) measured at the same pressure in the following way:

$$p_1 I_{11} + p_2 I_{12} + p_3 I_{13} + \ldots + p_n I_{1n} = M_1$$
$$p_1 I_{21} + p_2 I_{22} + p_3 I_{23} + \ldots + p_n I_{2n} = M_2$$

$$\cdot \quad \cdot \quad \cdot \quad \cdot \quad \cdot$$
$$\cdot \quad \cdot \quad \cdot \quad \cdot \quad \cdot$$

$$p_1 I_{n1} + p_2 I_{n2} + p_3 I_{n3} + \ldots + p_n I_{mn} = M_m \tag{6}$$

where p_n is the partial pressure of component n, I_{mn} is the ion current at mass m due to component n, and M_m is the current at mass m in the mixture spectrum.

The analytical procedure makes use of these relations and for a mixture of N components, the solution of a maximum of N linear simultaneous equations is sufficient to provide the N quantities, p_n. However, if mixture and calibration materials are not introduced by means of constant-volume gas or liquid pipets, it is not convenient to make all measurements at precisely the same pressure. Furthermore, ion currents are usually measured in arbitrary units such as recorder chart divisions. Therefore peak height or pattern coefficients (e. g., Table I) are commonly substituted for the I terms and mixture peak heights in chart divisions are substituted for the M terms. Solving the equations results in the computation of components in units of chart divisions and must be converted to partial pressure by dividing by the sensitivity (divisions per unit pressure). An alternative method is to use peak heights per unit pressure in the equations. The composition is then obtained directly in units of pressure.

Obviously, the task of computing the analysis of an 18- or 20-component mixture would be an arduous one if it were necessary to solve 18 or 20 simultaneous equations. Fortunately many simplifications are possible, principally due to the fact that not all components contribute to all peaks in the mixture spectrum. Mixture spectra often have unicomponent peaks that serve to identify and to establish the abundance of particular components. For example a ternary mixture containing only methane, ethane, and propane does not require the solution of simultaneous equations, whereas the addition of n-butane and isobutane requires the solution of one set of two equations.

As an illustration of one method of calculation, Table II summarizes the data for the computation of an hypothetical mixture such as might be encountered in the synthetic rubber industry. The problem and the table are purposely simplified in order to be as brief as possible.

TABLE II

Summary of Calibration Spectra and Mixture Data for a Hypothetical C_4 Mixture

	Calibration spectra					Mixture (chart divisions)	Resid- uals
m/e	n-C_4H_{10}	iso- C_4H_{10}	n-C_4H_8	1,3- C_4H_6	1,2- C_4H_6		
26	6.17	2.36	11.4	25.7	18.6	701.2	−0.1
27	37.1	27.8	31.7	67.9	53.1	1923.7	−0.8
28	32.6	2.62	30.6	45.6	33.8	1306.3	−1.0
29	44.2	6.16	14.3	0.97	0.77	130.9	+0.8
30	0.98	0.13	0.63	—	—	3.3	−0.1
37	1.01	1.41	2.93	6.22	6.75	182.7	0.0
38	1.89	2.77	4.49	7.53	8.44	227.3	−0.3
39	12.5	16.5	35.2	100.0	43.6	2533.6	−3.5
40	1.63	2.37	6.49	3.42	1.54	107.7	+0.1
41	27.8	38.1	100.0	0.10	0.04	401.9	+0.1
42	12.2	33.5	3.41	—	—	57.0	−0.1
43	100.0	100.0	0.07	—	—	211.7	+0.3
44	3.33	3.33	—	—	—	7.0	0.0
49	0.40	0.27	1.79	8.17	8.77	229.7	−0.4
50	1.29	0.89	5.79	24.5	26.1	690.2	−0.2
51	1.05	0.74	4.84	21.7	22.8	608.9	+0.3
52	0.26	0.15	1.46	10.6	11.8	297.7	+0.4
53	0.74	0.50	2.28	59.3	44.5	1525.5	−1.6
54	0.19	0.07	3.12	85.9	100.0	2398.7	−3.0
55	0.93	0.42	19.9	3.76	4.38	172.3	+0.2
56	0.72	0.34	42.5	0.09	0.08	144.6	+0.5
57	2.42	3.00	1.86	—	—	11.9	+0.1
58	12.3	2.73	0.03	—	—	17.1	0.0
59	0.54	0.11	—	—	—	0.7	0.0

	Sensitivity in chart divisions per micron						
	39.6	46.4	33.1	19.4	32.9		

Column 1 lists the masses of selected ions. In the illustration, the components are known and columns 2 to 6 give the calibration spectra obtained from the pure gases. The spectrum in column 4 is the average of the spectra of the individual *n*-butenes. Column 7 gives the mixture spectrum in units of chart divisions. Thus, a set of five simultaneous equations that define the solution can be written immediately from Table II such as:

$$m/e = 39,\ 0.125\ n\text{-B} + 0.165\ \text{iso-B} + 0.352\ \text{Bu} + 1.00\ 1,3\text{-Bd} + \\ 0.436\ 1,2\text{-Bd} = 2533.6 \quad (7)$$

However, several simplifications suggest themselves. Except for the very small contributions of the *n*-butenes to $m/e = 43$ and 58, the *n*- and isobutane composition could be determined directly from a set of two simultaneous equations. From Table II, column 4, it is apparent that the maximum possible contributions of butenes to the 43 and 58 peaks are equal to 0.07% of the 41 and 56 peaks, respectively. As this is very nearly a trivial correction in this case it can be made without further consideration. Thus the butane equations become:

$$m/e = 43,\qquad 1.00\ n\text{-B} + 1.00\ \text{iso-B} = 211.4 \quad (8)$$

and:
$$m/e = 58,\qquad 0.123\ n\text{-B} + 0.0273\ \text{iso-B} = 17.0 \quad (9)$$

from which the calculated number of divisions of *n*-butane and isobutane on the 43 peak are 117.4 and 94.0, respectively. The partial pressures are obtained by dividing these values by the respective sensitivities, i. e., 117.4/39.6 = 3.0 microns, and 94.0/46.4 = 2.0 microns.

The contributions of *n*- and isobutane to the 41 peak are calculated from the base peaks and the butane pattern coefficients as:

$$n\text{-B}_{41} = 117.4 \times 0.278 = 32.6\ \text{divisions} \quad (10)$$

$$\text{iso-B}_{41} = 94.0 \times 0.381 = 35.8\ \text{divisions} \quad (11)$$

and subtracted from the 41 peak in the mixture. From columns 5 and 6, Table II, it is apparent that the butadiene contribution to the 41 peak is 0.1% of the butadiene 39 peak. As the mixture 39 peak is principally butadiene, the calculated contribution of 2.5 divisions is also subtracted from the mixture 41 peak. The remainder, 331.0 divisions, is attributed to *n*-butenes and the calculated partial pressure is 331.0/33.1 = 10 microns.

The contributions of the butanes and the *n*-butenes are similarly subtracted from the 39 and the 54 peaks by means of the appropriate pattern coefficients and the base peaks. The 39 and 54 peaks are then used to separate the butadienes, as for example:

$$m/e = 39,\qquad 1.00\ 1,3\text{-Bd} + 0.436\ 1,2\text{-Bd} = 2386 \quad (12)$$

and:
$$m/e = 54,\qquad 0.859\ 1,3\text{-Bd} + 1.00\ 1,2\text{-Bd} = 2388 \quad (13)$$

The solution of these equations indicates the number of chart divisions on the 39 peak due to 1,3-butadiene to be 2155 divisions, whereas the 1,2-butadiene contribution to the 54 peak is 540.0 divisions. The partial pressures are, respectively, 2155/19.4 = 111 microns and 540/32.9 = 16.4 microns. Expressing each partial pressure as the percentage of the total pressure gives the mole percentage:

$$
\begin{array}{lcr}
\text{1,3-Butadiene} & = & 78.2 \\
\text{1,2-Butadiene} & = & 11.3 \\
\text{Total } n\text{-butenes} & = & 7.0 \\
n\text{-Butane} & = & 2.1 \\
\text{Isobutane} & = & 1.4 \\
\textit{Total} \ldots\ldots\ldots\ldots\ldots & & \textit{100.0}
\end{array}
$$

To check the internal consistency and completeness of the calculation, the contribution of each component to the mixture spectrum is computed by multiplying each base peak by the calibration spectrum. The contributions of all components to each mass are added and the sum is subtracted from the corresponding mixture peak. The positive or negative "residuals" appear in column 8 of Table II. Those indicated are generally smaller than usually encountered in actual analysis. Residuals of 1% or less of the mixture peak are generally ignored. Larger ones may indicate arithmetical errors or components improperly identified or overlooked.

The sum of the computed partial pressures should agree with the measured mixture pressure. Although there are a number of reasons why the agreement may not be exact, including sorption effects, variation in the sensitivity of the component, and so forth, disagreements of more than a few per cent may indicate the presence of components with spectra not included in the mass range selected for the mixture analysis. In the above illustration these might include hydrogen, helium, water vapor, or heavier compounds with no ion contributions in the mass range of 24 to 60.

A variety of computational methods are in use most of which have been developed for particular analytical problems. Some of these employ procedures applicable to commercially available (11) automatic computers capable of solving directly 12 linear simultaneous equations or to desk calculators (27). More elaborate methods using punched-card techniques and standard high-speed data-handling systems (58) are now in use in a few laboratories for routine analysis of mixtures. Completely automatic methods using electronic digital computers (33a) are currently under development. The analyst concerned with detailed methods and the choice between manual or machine computation should consult the literature and determine the method most applicable to his problem.

C. ACCURACY OF RESULTS

Probably the most satisfactory means of determining the accuracy of an analytical method is by comparison of analyses with the known composi-

TABLE III

Average Error in the Determination of Each Component in 93
Analyses of a Synthetic C_1–C_4 Paraffin–Olefin Mixture (126)

Component	Composition (mole per cent)	Average error (mole per cent)
Methane	15	±0.14
Ethane	20	±0.22
Propene	10	±0.17
Propane	20	±0.21
n-Butane	8	±0.18
Isobutane	10	±0.19
1-Butene	5	±0.83
2-Butene	5	±0.77
Isobutene	7	±0.33
Total butenes	*17*	*±0.27*

tion of a synthetic blend. This has been done in a number of instances
but mostly for relatively simple mixtures. Washburn (126) has tabulated
the results of running a synthetic mixture on 24 instruments. The mixture
was independently synthesized for each instrument and run three or more
times for a total of 92 analyses. Table III gives the average error in the
determination of each component. For all components except the butenes,
90% of the errors were ±0.5 mole per cent or less. In 1-butene, 2-butene,
and isobutene, 90% of the errors were less than ±1.4, ±1.2, and ±0.8
mole per cent, respectively. Total butenes were determined with greater
accuracy.

Barnard (6) quotes data communicated by Blears on a very similar

TABLE IV

Errors in Analyses of a Synthetic Blend (6)

Components	Composition (mole per cent)	Actual errors (mole per cent)			
		Run 1	Run 2	Run 3	Run 4
Methane	15.1	+0.61	+0.39	+0.17	+0.09
Ethane	19.9	+0.27	+0.23	+0.07	−0.09
Propene	9.9	+0.39	+0.44	+0.42	+0.34
Propane	20.1	−0.25	+0.02	+0.06	0.00
n-Butane	8.1	−0.51	−0.47	−0.45	−0.33
Isobutane	9.9	−0.23	−0.16	−0.21	−0.03
1-Butene	5.0	−0.60	−1.12	−0.84	−0.57
2-Butene	5.0	−0.54	+0.67	+0.24	−0.05
Isobutene	7.0	+0.85	+0.01	+0.44	+0.64
Total butenes	*17.0*	*−0.29*	*−0.44*	*−0.16*	*+0.02*

mixture analyzed with a British-made mass spectrometer. A brief summary is given in Table IV.

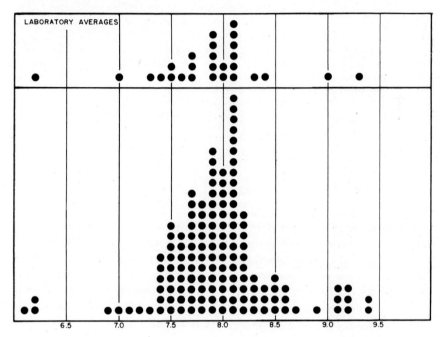

PER CENT METHANE

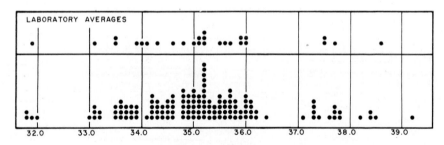

PER CENT HYDROGEN

Fig. 9. Frequency distribution plots for the reported composition of methane and of hydrogen in a standard sample of a carburetted water-gas.

The importance of conditioning the mass spectrometer to attain accurate analyses is unusually well illustrated by the data of Table IV. In general the deviation between calculated and known compositions decreases markedly with successive samples of the blend run through the mass spectrometer. This is illustrative of the generally accepted fact that instruments

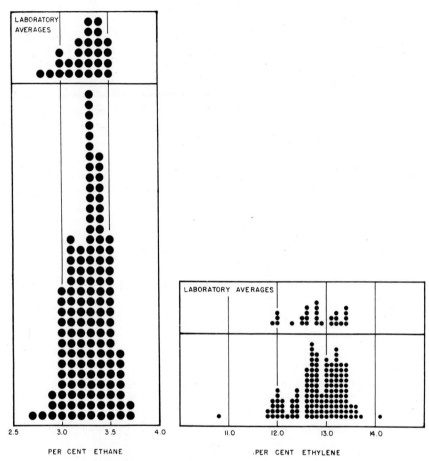

LABORATORY AVERAGES

2.5   3.0   3.5   4.0

PER CENT ETHANE

LABORATORY AVERAGES

11.0   12.0   13.0   14.0

.PER CENT ETHYLENE

Fig. 10. Frequency distribution plots for the reported composition of ethane and of ethylene in a standard sample of a carburetted water-gas.

continually analyzing hydrocarbon mixtures usually attain a greater degree of reproducibility and accuracy than those operating intermittently or analyzing various types of compounds.

Interesting indications of the recent state of the mass-spectrometric method of analysis of light gases and a comparison with volumetric chemical methods were obtained by Shepherd in a series of cooperative analyses of standard samples of a natural gas (101) and of a carburetted water-gas (103). In one of the latter studies, 27 mass spectrometer laboratories cooperated representing chemical industry and government. In addition to tabulating the analytical data reported by the various laboratories, Shepherd constructed a set of frequency-distribution plots in which filled circles represented a single determination of the component plotted. The number of circles placed equidistant along the ordinate indicated the number of times a particular mole percentage plotted as the abscissa was reported. The plots also included average values for each laboratory.

Plots of the results for methane and for hydrogen are given in Figure 9. For methane a Gaussian distribution is evident and the mean (three low values omitted) is 8.0 ± 0.4 mole per cent. The composition previously determined by volumetric chemical means is 8.4 ± 0.3 per cent (103). Rather wide variation is observed in reported values for hydrogen. Nevertheless, the mean value computed from values between 33 and 37.8 is 35.1 ± 0.8 mole per cent, in good agreement with the chemical determination of 35.0 mole per cent.

The frequency distribution plots for ethane and ethylene are given in Figure 10. Again the saturated hydrocarbon is determined with a relatively narrow spread of values. The mean value is 3.3 ± 0.15 mole per cent, whereas the chemically determined composition is 2.9 ± 0.2 mole per cent ethane. The ethylene analysis is less decisive with a mean value of 12.9 ± 0.4 mole per cent but is identical with the chemical value of 12.9 ± 0.4 per cent.

Carbon dioxide was analyzed with good reproducibility (mean 4.49 ± 0.14) and good agreement with the chemical value of 4.44 ± 0.04 mole per cent. However, wide distributions were observed for carbon monoxide and nitrogen resulting in part from the mutual interference of these two compounds and ethylene on their most sensitive peak ($m/e = 28$). In spite of the wide distribution of values in some cases, mean values were always obtained that were very close to the actual or most probable composition.

3. Operation Requirements

Modern commercial mass spectrometers are very nearly automatic in operation. Instrumental variations that commonly affect the accuracy of the analysis, such as the temperature of the ion source, electron energy and emission, ion draw-out, and other electrode voltages are generally removed from manual control. Furthermore, design factors usually limit possible variation in pumping speeds, pressure in the ion source, scanning rate, amplifier sensitivity, and recording speed.

At the present time the petroleum and related industries are the principal industrial users of mass spectrometers. The instruments are employed widely for the routine analysis of plant samples. For such applications the selection of suitable sample-handling procedures, appropriate calibration data, adequate coverage of mass range, and proper time schedules for precise comparison of calibration and mixture data need be determined only once for a particular type of sample. The established program is easily followed by personnel with a minimum of technical training. However, many analytical applications are of a research nature necessitating developmental work and perhaps modification of the mass spectrometer. This often requires considerable experience, judgment, and skill in chemistry, physics, and electronics.

Young (129) has summarized the cost, in terms of man-hours per sample analyzed, of operating a commercial mass spectrometer for routine analyses of refinery samples. Including the time of operating, computing, supervisory, maintenance, and supply personnel, the cost over a four-week period of analyzing 860 samples containing 3 to 4 components each was 1.31 man-hours per sample. The cost of 720 analyses containing 10 to 20 components each was 1.90 man-hours per sample. These data were based on instrumental efficiency and techniques of eight years ago. These have greatly improved since then.

Barnard (6) gives a brief description of the space, maintenance, sample preparation, and personnel requirements for mass spectrometer laboratories operating at several levels of activity. Specific information on power and refrigerant requirements, record processing, etc. varies with the instrument and application and is readily obtained by contacting manufacturers of commercial instruments.

III. APPLICATION TO QUALITATIVE ANALYSIS

One of the important features of a mass spectrometer is that specific tests are not required in order to detect mixture components. Provided that a sufficient mass range has been scanned, all of the data characterizing each component are automatically included in the spectrum. This is particularly advantageous for a qualitative survey of a completely unknown mixture. However, the successful interpretation of this information frequently depends on a broad knowledge of the characteristics of mass spectra, i. e., the specific mass numbers included or omitted from the spectrum of a given compound, the approximate relative abundances of the principal ions, the normal isotopic abundances of elements encountered in the mixture, the recognition of metastable and multiply charged ions, rearrangement peaks and ions characteristic of particular functional groups, and so forth. The application of some of these characteristics is discussed briefly in the following sections.

1. Identification by Mass Number

Unless a mixture is a very complex one in which all major peaks contain contributions from a number of compounds, the positions and relative abundances of mass numbers are often sufficient to establish the identity of several or all components. The lack of mixture peaks in particular mass ranges is also important information and, as in the case of optical spectrometry, is frequently used to establish the absence of or upper limit to the presence of possible components. An indispensable aid in these identifications is a cumulative library of mass spectral data in the form either of tables (3) or of punch cards. Sets of the latter, commercially available, include spectra of over 700 compounds and can be sorted on the basis of physical and chemical properties, as well as mass number and ion abundance. In addition, a very useful summary of the spectra of 279 compounds including many nonhydrocarbons has been published (98) in which peaks are roughly classified according to magnitude and are charted against mass.

Reference sources of mass spectral data serve not only by providing specific information on particular compounds but also as a basis for generalizations regarding the spectra of various classes of compounds, including members for which calibration spectra may not be available. Consideration of some of these mentioned above for hydrocarbons and of others for oxygenated compounds (98) indicate the feasibility of detecting the presence of light paraffins in mixtures of heavier hydrocarbons, the qualitative differentiation between straight and highly branched-chain hydrocarbons, the detection of alcohols, ethers, and esters in hydrocarbon mixtures, and the identification of aromatic types. Illustrations of some of these are given by Rock (98) in a detailed discussion of the use of the mass spectrometer in qualitative analysis.

Other correlations between mass spectra and structure have been made for a number of types of compounds (13,18,78,80). By means of correla-

tions between mass spectral data and the structure of benzene and thiophene homologs and by the use of mercuric acetate derivative and hydrogenation data, Kinney and Cook (59) have reported the feasibility of identifying any thiophene homolog through C_9 and certain higher homologs.
They also reported the possibility of identifying any mono- or disubstituted
benzene homolog through C_{11} and certain higher homologs. Although
trialkyl and higher substituted benzene homologs and homologs of benzenes

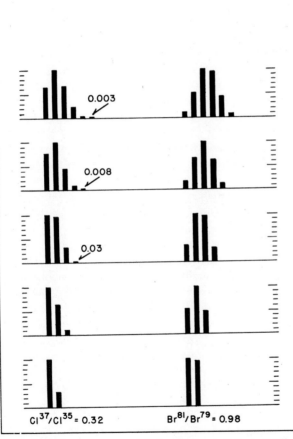

Fig. 11. Distinctive patterns associated with the statistical distribution of isotopic
species in ions containing one to five chlorine or bromine atoms.   The number of atoms
increases in ascending order.

and thiophenes with molecular weight greater than 154 were not identifiable, correlations were used to eliminate some possible structures from consideration. Undoubtedly this technique can be extended to other types of compounds.

2. Use of Isotope Abundance Ratios

Normal isotope abundance ratios for carbon and hydrogen are used extensively in qualitative (98) and quantitative (126) analyses. However, isotopes are particularly useful for the identification of components of semiorganic and nonhydrocarbon mixtures. For example, an ion containing one Cl^{35} atom appearing at mass, $(m/e)_x$ will be accompanied by an ion approximately one-third the abundance containing a Cl^{37} atom appearing at $(m/e)_{x+2}$. Similarly an ion containing two chlorine atoms appearing at $(m/e)_y$ will be accompanied by two other ions in the ratios of $1:0.6:0.1$ appearing at $(m/e)_{y+2}$ and $(m/e)_{y+4}$. Ions containing bromine atoms are characterized in a similar fashion.

TABLE V

Statistical Distribution of Isotopes in Ions
Containing One to Five Boron Atoms (33)

No. of boron atoms	Isotopic species	Relative abundance
1	B^{10}	0.250
	B^{11}	1.000
2	B_2^{10}	0.0625
	$B^{10}B^{11}$	0.500
	B_2^{11}	1.000
3	B_3^{10}	0.0156
	$B_2^{10}B^{11}$	0.1875
	$B^{10}B_2^{11}$	0.750
	B_3^{11}	1.000
4	B_4^{10}	0.0039
	$B_3^{10}B^{11}$	0.0625
	$B_2^{10}B_2^{11}$	0.3750
	$B^{10}B_3^{11}$	1.000
	B_4^{11}	1.000
5	B_5^{10}	0.00078
	$B_4^{10}B^{11}$	0.0156
	$B_3^{10}B_2^{11}$	0.125
	$B_2^{10}B_3^{11}$	0.500
	$B^{10}B_4^{11}$	1.000
	B_5^{11}	0.800

Figure 11 illustrates the statistical distribution of the halogen isotopes ($Cl^{37}/Cl^{35} = 0.32$, and $Br^{81}/Br^{79} = 0.98$) in ions containing one to five chlorine or bromine atoms. Each peak is separated by two mass units and the abundances are relative to the most abundant species in each group. A similar chart can be constructed for ions containing both bromine and chlorine atoms. The addition of fluorine or iodine does not change the distribution, as these halogens are monoisotopic. By the use of such charts or of tabulated abundances such as that published for chlorine (9), molecule or fragment ions containing these atoms are often readily identified.

Table V gives similar data for the statistical distribution of the isotopes of boron ($B^{10}/B^{11} = 0.250$) in ions containing one to five boron atoms (33). Mass spectra of hydroborons are obviously complicated by the presence of two isotopes with abundances of the same order of magnitude. Furthermore, similarity in mass numbers makes difficult the analysis of certain mixtures of hydrocarbons and hydroborons and identification of the components is frequently dependent entirely on the determination of isotope abundance ratios.

3. Determination of Functional Groups and Isomers

The absence of a theoretical basis for mass spectra comparable to that available for optical spectra requires that functional group determination and group type analysis be based on empirically established principles some of which have been discussed previously. However, a surprising amount of information is often obvious and immediately available from mass spectra. A simple illustration of this is the spectrum of a hydrocarbon in which ion peaks separated by unit mass, due to the dissociation of hydrogen atoms, are collected into groups the first members of which are twelve mass units apart. Frequently the most abundant ions in each of several groups are separated by 15 mass units, indicating the successive dissociation of methyl radicals. Other useful mass intervals are: 16, 17, 19, 29, 32, 35, 41, 43, 79, and 127 corresponding to the dissociations of O or NH_2, OH, F, C_2H_5, S, Cl, C_3H_5, C_3H_7, Br, and I, respectively.

Mass spectral data are often combined with data from infrared, ultraviolet, and Raman spectroscopy in order to obtain information that would not be available from one of these alone. A well-illustrated and detailed discussion of the manner in which these techniques contribute to information on functional groups and compound types was presented by Coggeshall in Volume I of this series (26).   Further discussion of type analysis will be found in a later section.

O'Neal (86) gives a specific illustration of the combined use of mass and infrared spectrometry in analyses of light paraffin and monoolefin hydrocarbons.   Data for total pressure computations and for the determination of most of the components was supplied by mass spectrometer, whereas the analysis of the *cis*- and *trans*-2-butene content was accomplished by infrared spectrometry.

4. Microeffusiometry

As previously noted, analytical mass spectrometers usually employ molecular flow of the sample into the ionization region in order to maintain linear additivity of ion currents in mixture spectra.   Under such conditions, the rate of effusion of each component through the leak is inversely proportional to the square root of the molecular weight of the component. As the gas is withdrawn from the reservoir into the ion source the partial pressure of a component A decreases according to the equation:

$$dp_A/dt = -c_A p_A \qquad (14)$$

where c_A is the diffusion constant for component A.   As peak heights are directly proportional to the partial pressure of each component, diffusion constants are conveniently measured in the mass spectrometer by the use of a reservoir volume properly sized to give a convenient rate of pressure decrease.   As all fragment ions of a particular component decrease in intensity at the same rate, any convenient peak can be selected.   Selected peaks in a mixture spectrum including a known component are repeatedly scanned on a precise time schedule.   The effusion constant and molecular weight of the known component are then related to those of the unknown components by Graham's law:

$$c_A(M_A)^{1/2} = c_B(M_B)^{1/2} = c_i(M_i)^{1/2} \qquad (15)$$

Eden, Burr, and Pratt (34) have determined molecular weights of mixture components by this means and Zemany (131) reports the successful application of this method in a number of instances including the identification of unusual compounds such as CH_2ClCOF.   The technique is also useful in distinguishing between unicomponent peaks and those representing superpositions of two or more ion currents, thus aiding in establishing the presence or absence of components with overlapping spectra.

IV. APPLICATION TO QUANTITATIVE ANALYSIS

1. Hydrocarbon Mixtures

A. GASES AND LIGHT LIQUIDS

The mass spectrometer has been applied rather extensively to the field of gas and light liquid analysis. Examples of several of these have already been discussed. In general, analysis of these mixtures yields satisfactory results without fractionation because of the relatively small number of isomers present. In fact one of the outstanding advantages of the mass spectrometer as applied to this type of sample is the large number of components that can be analyzed in a single mixture without supplementary distillation or fractionation procedures. Reported experience in refinery control laboratories indicates that mixtures containing C_1 through C_5 paraffins and olefins, hydrogen, nitrogen, oxygen, and hydrogen sulfide can be analyzed directly for most of the components. Usually the C_5 and C_4 olefin isomers are determined as total pentenes and total butenes. An analysis of separate butenes is possible but accuracy depends on a low C_5 olefin content. Frequently a low-temperature fractionation or infrared analysis is combined with mass spectrometer data for accurate olefin split.

With regard to refinery fractionating tower samples, Washburn (126) concludes that tower overheads including depropanizers, debutanizers, and

TABLE VI

Analysis of a Synthetic Mixture Approximating the
Composition of a Catalytic Cracking Overhead (126)

Component	Synthesized	Analyzed
H_2	3.0	3.2
CH_4	10.8	10.3
C_2H_4	6.0	5.9
C_2H_6	6.0	5.8
C_3H_6	11.1	11.1
C_3H_8	19.2	19.5
n-C_4H_8	2.9	4.1
(1-C_4H_8)	(1.5)	(2.4)
(2-C_4H_8)	(1.4)	(1.7)
Iso-C_4H_8	2.8	1.6
n-C_4H_{10}	5.0	5.2
Iso-C_4H_{10}	20.1	20.0
C_5H_{10} (total)	3.0	3.1
Iso-C_5H_{12}	10.1	10.2

depentanizers can be analyzed directly and completely by mass spectrometer. The analysis of a synthetic mixture similar to that encountered in catalytic cracking overheads (126) is given in Table VI. The accurate separation of the butenes is hindered by the high concentration of pentenes. The value for the total butenes is, however, satisfactory.

Fractionating tower feeds and bottoms usually require a rough stripping in a low-temperature distillation column. The light fraction is then analyzed by mass spectrometer and the results combined with data on C_6 and heavier fractions obtained from distillation column procedures.

B. LIQUID PETROLEUM DISTILLATES

The analysis of liquid petroleum products in the C_5 to C_8 mass range generally requires the determination of the composition of a series of close-boiling fractions (21) usually obtained by somewhat elaborate techniques (20). In some cases, however, the analytical problem is simplified if only particular components need be determined. An example of such a procedure has been reported by Meyerson (75) for the analysis of benzene and benzene-forming naphthenes (cyclohexane and methylcyclopentane) in naphthas. The necessary conditions for accurate analysis of these components has been established and Table VII gives comparative results for three samples analyzed by mass spectrometer and by ultraviolet absorption and three samples analyzed by mass spectrometer and by refractive index measurements. The mass-spectrometric method offers the important advantage of a rapid determination compared with the other two methods.

TABLE VII

Comparative Results for the Analysis of Benzene, Cyclohexane, and Methylcyclopentane by Various Methods (75)

| Component | Method | Sample | | | | | |
		1	2	3	4	5	6
Benzene	MS	29.5	27.7	8.0	1.8	26.0	1.3
	UV	29.7	27.1	7.9	—	—	—
	RI	—	—	—	1.8	25.2	1.6
Cyclohexane.	MS	11.0	11.6	1.0	10.0	7.1	8.0
	RI	—	—	—	10.1	7.7	8.6
Methylcyclopentane. . .	MS	14.3	14.1	17.2	36.2	24.5	28.9
	RI	—	—	—	36.1	24.4	28.1

Mass-spectrometric analysis of multicomponent liquid hydrocarbons such as light naphthas in which all components of a mixture of wide boiling range are calculable from a single mixture spectrum cannot be realized. Sobcov (110) has reported a study aimed at determining the smallest number of distillation cuts necessary to obtain sufficiently accurate analyses of olefin-free mixtures found in the boiling range from isopentane to toluene. By careful selection of matrices and IBM programming, a minimum number of four cuts was chosen and four overlapping matrices of order 9, 10, 12, and 10 were used to search for 28 compounds. Benzene and toluene were independently calculated because of the specific natures of their spectra. A check on the accuracy of the inverse of one of the chosen matrices was made by 11 routine analyses of a carefully synthesized mixture. Table VIII indicates the scope and accuracy of the analysis of this mixture.

TABLE VIII

Analysis of One of Four Overlapping Cuts from a 31-Component Mixture (110)

Component	Composition, liquid volume per cent	
	Synthesis	Analysis[a]
Cyclohexane......................	0.69	0.73 ± 0.05
3,3-Dimethylpentane...............	0.00	— —
1,1-Dimethylcyclopentane...........	1.93	2.05 ± 0.28
2,3-Dimethylpentane...............	4.10	4.71 ± 0.37
2-Methylhexane....................	9.16	9.06 ± 0.08
1,3-Dimethylcyclopentane...........	6.61	6.82 ± 0.37
3-Methylhexane...................	17.35	16.97 ± 0.55
1,2-Dimethylcyclopentane...........	5.04	4.69 ± 0.28
3-Ethylpentane....................	2.11	2.17 ± 0.24
n-Heptane.......................	36.82	36.29 ± 0.42
Methylcyclohexane.................	12.18	12.19 ± 0.07
Ethylcyclopentane.................	1.99	2.29 ± 0.02
1,1,3-Trimethylcyclopentane.........	2.02	2.03 ± 0.01
Total...........................	100.00	100.00

[a] Average of 11 runs. Individual analyses normally reported to nearest 0.1%.

C. TYPE ANALYSIS

Probably one of the most significant advances in the mass-spectrometric method of hydrocarbon analysis is the development of compound type analysis such as that described by Brown (18). In this method compound types (that is: paraffins; cycloparaffins and monoolefins; cycloolefins, diolefins, and acetylenes (the "coda" group); and aromatics) rather than specific compounds are determined quantitatively by applying the sums of mass peaks specific for each type. Numerous modifications of the method have been applied to determinations of the major compound types in the gasoline boiling range. For example, Lumpkin, Thomas, and Elliott

(67) describe a procedure designed to handle streams with low olefin content, and no "coda" group, but including condensed-ring naphthenes. In this method, olefins are first determined by bromide–bromate titration and then removed in a small-scale bromination–steam distillation apparatus before mass-spectrometric analysis. Paraffins, naphthenes, aromatics, and condensed-ring naphthenes are then determined by a single mass spectrometer analysis on a 70 to 200°C. boiling range sample involving the use of distinctive m/e ratios in the mass spectra of the hydrocarbon types. Table IX gives the results of single analyses of synthetic mixtures prepared by adding known amounts of naphthenes and olefins to stocks of known composition. The method is rapid and is accurate to ±10% of the type present.

TABLE IX

Type Analysis of Synthetic Mixtures (67)

Types	Synthesis	Analysis	Synthesis	Analysis
Paraffins.........	29.7	29.6	51.3	52.3
Naphthenes......	36.8	39.9	16.6	17.0
Aromatics.......	33.5	30.5	12.9	11.2
Olefins..........	0.0	0.0	19.2	19.5
Total...........	*100.0*	*100.0*	*100.0*	*100.0*

A rapid and accurate determination of total aromatics and aromatic molecular weight groups is frequently necessary in refineries producing motor fuel and aromatic solvents. The distillation, silica gel, acid absorption, and specific dispersion methods often become laborious. As mass spectra of aromatic compounds are sufficiently different from the other compound types in a hydrocarbon mixture to allow determination of aromatics only, Lumpkin and Thomas (66) have developed an analytical procedure with an elapsed time requirement of 45 to 60 minutes and an accuracy of about ±1% for the different aromatic molecular weight groups and for total aromatic content. Table X illustrates typical analyses of two synthetic mixtures containing C_6 to C_9 aromatics in aromatic-free base stock.

A particularly novel technique applied in conjunction with a type analysis has been described by Melpolder and co-workers (73). A thermal diffusion process was employed for the separation of a light lubricating oil into specific hydrocarbon types. Mass and ultraviolet spectrometry were used to identify 16 different hydrocarbon types in the thermal diffusion fractions.

TABLE X

Analysis of Aromatics in Synthetic Mixtures (66)

| | Volume per cent | | | |
Component	Synthesized-A	Analyzed-A[a]	Synthesized-B	Analyzed-B[b]
Benzene.................	3.9	3.75	1.05	0.87
Toluene.................	39.3	38.45	10.41	9.35
C$_8$ aromatics.............	15.9	16.80	36.46	37.35
C$_9$ aromatics.............	2.0	2.05	2.09	2.27
Total aromatics...........	61.1	61.05	50.01	49.84

[a] Average of 6 analyses over a 2-day period.
[b] Average of 6 analyses over a 2-month period.

Numerous other examples of type analyses have been published and the reader is directed to the various literature surveys previously listed for further details.

D. HIGH-TEMPERATURE ANALYSIS

In recent years the chemical constitution of petroleum fractions boiling above the gasoline range has become of considerable interest to the petroleum industry. In order to solve the numerous analytical problems associated with the high-boiling materials, O'Neal and Wier (88) greatly extended the range of application of the mass spectrometer to obtain spectra of compounds having molecular weights up to about 600. A heated sample introduction system was devised so that samples could be measured as a liquid volume and hydrocarbons up to C$_{40}$ completely vaporized into the reservoir.

The modification and extension of the principles of type analysis (18) to heavy hydrocarbon mixtures and the utilization of chromatographic concentrates have provided probably the most useful analytical method available to high molecular weight hydrocarbon chemistry. In a report on the application of mass spectrometry to oil constitution, O'Neal (87) describes analytical methods unique in the field of petroleum chemistry, permitting the direct determination of the isoalkane content of lubricating oils, and composition and molecular weight distribution in a low-melting paraffin wax, and the analysis of the aromatic portion of the 400°C. boiling range material from a catalytically cracked, clarified slurry oil.

Other work illustrative of the technique has been reported, including waxes and wax distillates (19,20) and high molecular weight saturated petroleum fractions (25).

E. POLLUTION STUDIES AND TRACE IMPURITIES

The mass-spectrometric determination of solvent vapors of the order of parts per million in air was reported by Happ, Stewart, and Brockmyre (46). In the examination of smog samples, Shepherd, Rock, Howard, and Stormes (106) have exceeded this limit by several orders of magnitude. The method by which this was accomplished consisted of three essential steps: (1) the trapping of gaseous and vaporous pollutants from the air on filters maintained at the temperature of liquid oxygen; (2) without prior evaporation (and possible reaction between components) separation of the condensate by isothermal distillation or sublimation at low temperatures and pressures; and (3) immediate analysis of the distillates introduced directly into the mass spectrometer.

The method employed by Shepherd et al. was capable of determining as little as 10^{-4} p. p. m. of some pollutants from a 100 liter sample of air and 10^{-6} p. p. m. of some substances from larger samples. The gaseous phase of some smog samples was found to be of the order of 0.5 p. p. m. of air. Approximately 60 compounds or types were positively or tentatively identified and the amounts of some of these determined. Table XI gives a brief indication of the types and amounts of compounds observed in the distillates of a typical smog concentrate, and of a truck exhaust. It is important to remember that the quantities tabulated refer to portions of the sample and not to the whole sample. Thus the amount of acetylene found in the first distillate of the truck exhaust reduced to 0.5 mole per cent when referred to the whole sample. The authors showed that the gaseous phase of smog was primarily a mixture of hydrocarbons and of hydrocarbon derivatives containing oxygen, nitrogen, and chlorine. The means of formation of some of these and their relation to eye and respiratory irritants were also investigated. An extension of this work and an important contribution toward the analysis of the extremely complex concentrates from Los Angeles air has been described recently by Weaver and Gunther (127a).

Other determinations of air contaminants, particularly near refineries, were described by Quiram, Metro, and Lewis (92). In this work gases were concentrated by adsorption on silica gel at $-73°C$. and later desorbed into an evacuated gas sampler. Relatively simple mixtures were examined containing methane, propane, and isopentane of the order of 3 to 8 p. p. m. Newton (81) describes techniques for the inverse case of noncondensable impurities in condensable gases. The method uses an inert internal standard and in the impurity range of 30 to 200 parts per 100,000

TABLE XI

Composition of Distillates of Typical Smog Concentrates and of Truck Exhaust in Mole per Cent (106)

Components	Distillates of sample X-C4-1						Truck exhaust S1
	S2	S3	S4	S5	S6	S7	
Acetylene............	58.8	22.2	—	—	—	—	70.5
Ethylene.............	5.9	—	—	—	—	—	27.6
Propylene............	—	7.8	—	—	—	—	4.2
Ethane..............	—	—	—	—	—	—	—
Propane.............	29.4	22.2	—	—	—	—	1.2
n- and/or Isobutane...	2.9	44.4	—	—	—	—	0.2
n- and/or Isopentane..	—	—	—	—	—	—	—
Benzene.............	—	—	2.1	1.5	3.7	2.2	—
Toluene.............	—	—	—	3.5	7.4	3.9	—
Xylenes.............	—	—	—	0.5	3.7	5.6	—
Trichloroethylene.....	—	—	—	1.7	2.2	0.6	—
Carbon tetrachloride..	—	—	1.5	0.5	1.1	1.1	—
Heavier hydrocarbons.	—	—	44.8	48.5	81.5	88.9	0.1
Nitrous oxide.........	—	—	53.4	34.9	—	—	—
Sulfur dioxide........	—	—	—	8.7	—	—	—
Distilling temp., °C....	−109	−87	−64	−35	−21	0	—

was generally accurate to about 5% based on the impurity added to the systems studied.

In the important field of water pollution abatement, Melpolder, Warfield, and Headington (74) have developed a method for qualitative and quantitative determination of traces of volatile contaminants which affect the taste and odor of water. These include such petroleum products as natural gas, gasoline, kerosine, and furnace oil. The method consists of stripping

TABLE XII

Analysis of Trace Amounts of Hydrocarbons in Water (74)

Concentration of each hydrocarbon (p. p. m.)	Analysis (p. p. m.)						
	n-Pentane	Benzene	n-Heptane	Toluene	m-Xylene	n-Butyl-cyclo-hexane	p-Diiso-propyl-benzene
0.0014	0.0010	0.0009	0.0010	0.0007	0.0005	0.0004	0.00
0.014	0.010	0.011	0.011	0.011	0.009	0.006	0.002
0.10[a]	0.068	0.072	0.067	0.068	0.059	0.037	0.033
0.10	0.13	0.11	0.10	0.10	0.08	0.07	0.04
0.14	0.14	0.15	0.14	0.14	0.13	0.13	0.08
1.0[a]	0.96	0.88	0.84	0.78	0.60	0.41	0.38
1.4	1.7	1.5	1.3	1.1	0.90	0.84	0.21

[a] Single sample trap used in analysis of these mixtures.

the volatile compounds from boiling water with hydrogen, condensing the vapor in a cold trap, and analyzing the condensate by mass spectrometer. Hydrocarbons boiling below 200°C. are determined at concentrations as low as 0.01 p. p. m. Table XII demonstrates the range of the method as applied to a synthetic mixture.

2. Nonhydrocarbon Mixtures

The erratic behavior of nitrogen dioxide in the mass spectrometer has long made difficult the analysis of mixtures containing this material. The results of a detailed study of this problem have been reported by Friedel et al. (41). For mixtures containing nitrogen dioxide, nitric oxide, nitrous oxide, carbon monoxide, carbon dioxide, nitrogen, oxygen, hydrogen, and water vapor, the analysis is routine for all components except NO_2. The latter requires prior conditioning of the mass spectrometer and particular attention to instrumental conditions if the partial pressure of the NO_2 is less than 15 microns. Other components required no preconditioning and the presence of these compounds had no effect on the spectral behavior of NO_2, and vice versa. The absence of chemical reaction between nitric oxide and oxygen was clearly demonstrated at total pressures less than 0.09 mm. Hg. Thus, in the analysis of synthetic blends, reaction between the various components was avoided by mixing at pressures of microns rather than millimeters. The results of the analysis of two synthetic blends prepared directly in the mass spectrometer reservoir are summarized in Table XIII.

TABLE XIII

Analysis of Synthetic Blends Containing Oxides of Nitrogen (41)

Blend		Components, mole per cent								
		NO_2	NO	N_2O	CO_2	CO	N_2	O_2	H_2O	H_2
1....	Anal.	5.3	3.9	—	13.1	13.1	16.2	4.3	44.1	—
	Synth.	5.1	4.0	—	13.2	13.3	16.3	4.3	43.8	—
2....	Anal.	9.4	10.1	12.1	12.4	12.0	25.2	6.7	—	12.1
	Synth.	10.2	9.6	12.0	12.0	12.1	25.4	6.8	—	11.9

The analysis of other simple gaseous mixtures was utilized by Bartels et al. (5) in the determination of respiratory dead space, by Miller et al. (76) to evaluate carbon dioxide accumulation in anesthetized patients, by Pratt et al. (90) in a study of respiratory metabolism, and by Brown et al. (17) in a study of metabolism of cells, tissues, and complete organisms.

The versatility of the mass spectrometer in analyzing organic substances other than hydrocarbons has been noted previously. Detailed mass spectra of acids, alcohols, aldehydes, esters, ketones, and compounds containing halogen, sulfur, nitrogen, boron, and phosphorus atoms have been published in the American Petroleum Institute's *Tables of Mass Spectral Data* (3). Successful analyses of mixtures containing compounds representative of all of these groups have been reported. Tables XIV and XV are brief examples suggesting the scope of the method. They illustrate the analysis of simple mixtures of oxygenated compounds reported by Taylor et al. (117). Taylor also gives details of the analysis of mixtures containing alkyl iodides, aliphatic chlorides, and silicanes.

TABLE XIV

Analysis of Ethylene Oxide Mixture (117)

Components	Composition, mole per cent		
	Known	Observed	Error
Ethylene oxide........	3.8	3.5	−0.3
Ethylene.............	6.3	6.1	0.2
Propane.............	1.2	1.2	0.0
Nitrogen.............	75.2	76.6	1.4
Oxygen.............	9.6	9.0	−0.6
Carbon dioxide........	3.9	3.6	−0.3

TABLE XV

Alcohol–Ether–Water Analyses (117)

Components	Composition, mole per cent		Average error
	Known	Observed	
Ethanol.....................	51.1	51.7 52.2	1.0
Diethyl ether................	1.8	1.6 1.1	0.2
Ethyl-*tert*-butyl ether..........	32.3	33.4 32.9	0.8
Water......................	14.8	13.3 13.8	1.3

Kelley (57) studied mixtures of various oxygenated organic compounds, most of which contained an hydroxyl group, to determine the importance of sorption effects. By suitable modification of apparatus and development of technique, remarkably complex mixtures of oxygenated compounds were analyzed with satisfactory precision. Table XVI shows the results of quadruplicate analysis of a known mixture of 8 aliphatic alcohols. Data were obtained four times during a two-week period.

TABLE XVI

Analysis of a Synthetic Mixture of C_1 to C_4 Alcohols (57)

Alcohol	1	2	3	4	Av.	Synthesis
Methyl..........	59.6	59.0	56.1	59.2	58.5	60.2
Ethyl............	18.8	19.0	21.1	19.7	19.7	18.9
Propyl..........	2.9	2.9	3.6	3.3	3.2	3.2
Isopropyl.......	1.7	1.4	1.7	1.9	1.7	1.7
Allyl............	3.7	3.5	4.2	3.8	3.8	3.6
Butyl............	9.2	10.1	9.0	8.3	9.2	8.2
Isobutyl........	2.6	2.5	2.8	2.6	2.6	2.6
sec-Butyl........	1.5	1.6	1.6	1.2	1.5	1.5

Kelley also gives details for the analysis of an aliphatic acid mixture and an alcohol–formate mixture.

The analysis of alcohols of high molecular weight is described by Brown, Young, and Nicolaides (22) in a study of the wax alcohols of human hair fat. For this study pure compounds in the C_{10}–C_{34} range were first run by means of the high-temperature techniques described in a preceding section. In the samples of hair fat investigated, aliphatic and monoolefinic straight-chain alcohols with 16 to 27 carbon atoms were detected. Table XVII indicates the distribution observed on various subjects identified by letters. The distribution is similar for all samples.

TABLE XVII

Mass-Spectrometric Analysis of Straight-Chain Alcohols (in Mole per Cent) from Human Hair Fat (22)

Type of alcohol	Men IW Aliph.	IW Olef.	Men AK Aliph.	AK Olef.	Women VFW Aliph.	VFW Olef.	Boys 6 to 12 IB Aliph.	IB Olef.
C_{16}	2	0	1	0	6	0	2	0
C_{17}	1	0	0	0	1	0	0	0
C_{18}	15	4	19	5	16	4	12	4
C_{19}	4	2	4	2	4	2	4	3
C_{20}	17	11	22	12	18	10	20	10
C_{21}	7	2	9	2	6	2	10	2
C_{22}	8	5	10	3	9	4	10	4
C_{23}	6	1	4	1	5	1	6	1
C_{24}	8	2	4	1	6	2	7	1
C_{25}	3	1	0.5	0.5	2	0.5	2	0.5
C_{26}	0.5	0.5	0	0	0.5	0.5	1	0.5
C_{27}	0	0	0	0	0.5	0	0	0
Total	71.5	28.5	73.5	26.5	74	26	74	26

TABLE XVIII. Analysis of Chlorine-Substituted Methanes and Ethanes (9)

	C₂Cl₅H		C₂Cl₄		C₂Cl₆		CCl₄		sym-C₂Cl₄H₂		CCl₃H		CCl₂H₂	
Mixtures	Known	Diff.	Known	Diff.	Known	Diff.	Known	Diff.	Known	Diff.	Known	Diff.	Known	Diff.
1...	3.42	0.00	3.22	0.00	3.15	-0.19	10.23	-0.12	3.29	-0.20	73.1	0.30	3.61	0.10
2...	1.40	±0.06	0.77	-0.03	0.55	0.14	7.10	0.23	1.09	0.10	85.4	0.10	3.70	0.23
3...	3.31	±0.09	4.08	-0.01	2.11	-0.16	6.76	-0.03	1.69	-0.14	73.8	0.60	8.22	-0.28
Av. % error....		±1.9		±0.8		±8.3		±1.6		±7.4		±0.4		±3.9

Composition, mole per cent

Bernstein, Semeluk, and Arends (9) have compared mass-spectrometric and infrared methods for determining some chlorine-substituted methanes and ethanes. Reference mass spectral patterns and relative ionization efficiencies were measured for the pure compounds: hexachloroethane, pentachloroethane, *sym*-tetrachloroethane, tetrachloroethylene, methylene chloride, carbon tetrachloride, and chloroform. A matrix suitable for analysis of mixtures of these compounds was devised and Table XVIII summarizes the results for three synthetic mixtures. For each component the first column gives the known composition and the second gives the difference between this and the observed composition.

Apparently the sensitivity of the method is good for pentachloroethane and carbon tetrachloride but because of extensive superposition it is difficult to detect small amounts of methylene chloride in these mixtures.

The increasing interest in fluorocarbon chemistry and technology has

TABLE XIX

Mass Spectra of Normal Perfluoro Paraffins (78a)

Ion	CF_4	C_2F_6	C_3F_8	C_4F_{10}	C_5F_{12}	C_6F_{14}	C_7F_{16}
C.....	7.8	1.49	2.4	0.19	0.05	0.25	0.03
F.....	6.7	1.22	0.98	0.14	0.08	0.23	0.05
CF....	4.9	18.3	28.8	12.2	9.2	11.3	6.06
CF_2...	11.8	10.1	9.3	4.16	3.12	2.50	1.86
CF_3...	100.0	100.0	100.0	100.0	100.0	100.0	100.0
CF_4...	0.0	—	—	—	—	—	—
C_2F_4...	—	0.55	6.55	8.40	7.2	13.2	7.34
C_2F_5...	—	41.3	9.0	18.3	29.5	27.8	27.0
C_2F_6...	—	0.15	—	—	—	—	—
C_3F_3...	—	—	0.55	1.20	2.06	4.24	2.38
C_3F_5...	—	—	0.23	8.37	6.54	13.9	13.3
C_3F_6...	—	—	0.05	2.55	1.10	1.96	0.88
C_3F_7...	—	—	24.6	2.14	9.73	18.9	20.5
C_3F_8...	—	—	0.0	—	—	—	—
C_4F_7...	—	—	—	0.03	3.25	2.36	2.53
C_4F_9...	—	—	—	2.57	0.27	3.96	8.48
C_4F_{10}..	—	—	—	0.0	—	—	—
C_5F_9...	—	—	—	—	0.0	2.67	0.80
C_5F_{11}..	—	—	—	—	0.77	0.08	1.20
C_5F_{12}..	—	—	—	—	0.03	—	—
C_6F_{11}..	—	—	—	—	—	—	1.08
C_6F_{13}..	—	—	—	—	—	1.11	0.02
C_6F_{14}..	—	—	—	—	—	0.05	—
C_7F_{15}..	—	—	—	—	—	—	0.09
C_7F_{16}..	—	—	—	—	—	—	0.0

made mass spectral studies of these compounds of primary importance. Although details of analyses of fluorocarbon mixtures have not been published, a summary of spectra for a variety of compounds is available (78a). Tables XIX and XX summarize the spectra of the normal perfluoro paraffins and perfluoro olefins, respectively.

TABLE XX

Mass Spectra of Perfluoro Olefins (78a)

Ion	C_2F_4	C_3F_6	1-C_4F_8	Iso-C_4F_8
C..........	12.6	12.6	4.6	6.0
F..........	2.77	4.0	1.78	2.63
CF........	100.0	100.0	72.9	58.9
CF_2........	29.5	12.1	7.76	8.55
CF_3........	2.83	77.1	36.2	100.0
C_2.........	3.03	4.06	1.02	1.39
C_2F........	1.44	4.13	2.00	2.83
C_2F_2......	0.99	5.04	3.09	2.45
C_2F_3......	63.1	14.2	3.20	3.57
C_2F_4......	33.8	36.1	4.62	6.68
C_3.........	—	0.77	0.86	0.92
C_3F........	—	1.96	2.30	3.05
C_3F_2......	—	2.59	4.33	4.19
C_3F_3......	—	5.87	13.0	30.0
C_3F_4......	—	1.21	4.75	11.2
C_3F_5......	—	72.0	100.0	15.0
C_3F_6......	—	28.6	0.35	6.40
C_4F_6......	—	—	0.49	0.24
C_4F_7......	—	—	12.1	73.3
C_4F_8......	—	—	8.78	18.7

Spectra are also published (78a) for isoparaffins, cyclics, and dicyclics. Although accumulated data are insufficient for generalizations concerning most types of compounds represented, the authors conclude that identification and analysis of mixtures of perfluoro paraffins is difficult because of the almost complete absence of molecule ions and of the generally low intensity of heavier ions in these spectra. Unsaturated molecules and cyclics have very distinctive spectra and possibilities of analysis of mixtures of these are favorable.

As there are numerous gaps of several mass units between peaks in fluorocarbon spectra, impurities other than fluorocarbons are usually conspicuous, e. g., compounds containing hydrogen atoms, or other halogen atoms.

3. Elemental Assay

The isotope dilution principle originally introduced by Hevesy and Paneth (47) for the radioactive isotopes of lead has been extended by Grosse, Hindin, and Kirshenbaum (43) to the determination of oxygen, carbon, and nitrogen in organic compounds.

The method in the case of oxygen, for example, is simply that of equilibrating a known weight of sample with a known weight of O^{18}. The equilibration is carried out by combustion in a platinum tube at 800°C. The carbon dioxide formed is analyzed by mass spectrometer and, from the O^{18} atom per cent excess in the equilibrated CO_2 and in that of the oxygen used, the weight per cent of oxygen in the sample can be determined using the equation:

$$\text{weight per cent O} = [b(m - n)/an] \times 100 \qquad (16)$$

where a is the sample weight, b is the known weight of oxygen added containing m atom per cent excess O^{18}, and n is the excess O^{18} concentration after equilibration. The method has been extended to the determination of sulfur using $S^{34}O_2$ as a tracer (60) and to the determination of oxygen in fluorocarbons (61).

V. NONVOLATILE ORGANIC MATERIALS

It has been known for some time (16,117) that certain classes of organic polymeric materials could be pyrolyzed in vacuum to give volatile decomposition products sufficiently characteristic so as to identify the original material. Mass-spectrometric analysis of degradation products has also been used in the more fundamental study of the structure of polymers (69,70,123).

1. Indirect Pyrolytic Methods

Zemany (130) describes a simple apparatus in which samples weighing a few tenths of a milligram are coated on or placed inside the coils of standard radio-receiving tube filaments and are then heated rapidly in vacuum to above 800° C. The pyrolysis vessel is attached to the inlet system of a mass spectrometer and cooled to liquid nitrogen temperatures, and the volatile gases are analyzed and pumped away. The vessel is then warmed to room temperature and another spectrum obtained. The nature and relative amounts of pyrolysis products were rather sensitive functions of the experimental conditions and reproducibility was not as high as that obtained for electron-impact dissociation patterns. For the simpler materials such as linear homopolymers, however, the reproducibility approached that of the mass spectra of molecules.

A variety of materials were studied and Table XXI shows the major products for some of the simplest.

TABLE XXI

Major Products from Pyrolysis of Several Homopolymers (130)

Polymer	Major product
Rubber	Isoprene
Neoprene	Chloroprene
Kel-F	$CF_2{=}CFCl$
Polystyrene	Styrene
Polythene	C_nH_{2n}
Teflon	C_nF_{2n}
Polyvinyl chloride	HCl + benzene

Patterns were also obtained for copolymers, alkyds, proteins, and numerous commercial materials. The distinctly different spectra obtained for most of these constituted an empirical method of recognizing the original material similar to that used for identifying compounds.

The apparatus and method used by Madorsky and co-workers in the pyrolysis and fractionation of pyrolysis products of polymers have been described in detail in a study of polystyrene (69). It consists essentially of heating a 25–50 mg. sample of a polymer, spread as a thin film on a platinum tray, to temperatures of 300 to 500° C. in a high vacuum. The separable fractions obtained are: (1) a solid residue, (2) a wax-like portion volatile only at the temperatures of the pyrolysis, (3) a liquid fraction, volatile at room temperature, and (4) a gaseous fraction volatile at liquid nitrogen temperatures. Fractions 3 and 4 are subjected to mass-spectrometric analysis. In the case of polystyrene, fraction 4 was principally carbon monoxide. The results of fraction 3 are summarized for a few experiments in Table XXII. Consideration of the data of Table XXII together with that provided by molecular weight and other analyses of the remaining fractions gives considerable information on the process by which degradation occurs in the polymer.

Pyrolytic fractionation has been extended to other hydrocarbon polymers (70) including polyisobutylene, polyisoprene, polybutadiene, polyethylene, and the copolymer GR-S, and to polytetrafluoroethylene, polyhydrofluoroethylene, and other polymers containing fluorine (68).

TABLE XXII

Analysis of Volatile Liquid Fraction from the Pyrolysis of Polystyrene (69)

Expt. No.	Temp., °C.	Monomer yield (wt. %)	Fraction 3 (mole %)			
			Styrene	Toluene	Ethyl-benzene	Methyl-styrene
2	250	0.96	91.8	8.0	0.1	0.1
15	361	8.56	92.2	7.8	0.0	0.0
17	364	29.63	96.1	3.9	0.0	0.04
4	379	22.67	95.5	4.4	0.06	0.03
10	400	38.58	95.0	5.0	0.0	0.0
Mean value.....................			94.3	5.6		

Mass-spectrometric analysis has also been applied to studies of the products of the degradation of polymers caused by heat and by ultra-violet radiation in vacuum (1) and under various atmospheric conditions (2). Wall (124) gives a detailed account of the theory and experimental results obtained from pyrolysis of a series of copolymers. The volatile products were analyzed by mass spectrometer and the variation in yield of individual monomers with composition of the copolymer was studied. In addition to theoretical aspects the results clearly indicate the value of pyrolysis products in identifying many types of polymers.

2. Direct Pyrolysis and Vaporization Techniques

Mass-spectrometric analyses of fractions from the indirect pyrolytic methods include only those stable products with appreciable vapor pressures at room temperature (exclusive of mass spectrometers utilizing high-temperature inlet systems). Thus information is precluded concerning larger fragments and molecules of possible importance in establishing the structure or degradation process of the polymeric substance.

Bradt, Dibeler, and Mohler (14) describe a technique in which vacuum pyrolysis of high molecular weight compounds is made to occur inside the mass spectrometer envelope with the degradation products evaporated directly into the ion source after comparatively few collisions. In a study of polystyrene, ions corresponding to monomer, dimer, trimer, tetramer, and pentamer were observed. Positive identification of the dimeric species was prevented only by the lack of comparison spectra of all possible isomers. The dimer spectrum was consistent with that expected for 2,4-diphenyl-1-butene and definitely ruled out the isomers 1,3-diphenyl-1 butene and 1-methyl-3-phenylindan.

In a further application of the technique, Bradt and Mohler (15) have studied the spectrum of polymeric substances obtained by heating p-$C_6F_4Br_2$ and p-$C_6F_4I_2$ in the presence of metallic copper. Samples of the products containing various lengths of the perfluorophenyl chains Br—$(C_6F_4)_x$—Br and I—$(C_6F_4)_y$—I were evaporated into the ion source at temperatures up to 260 and 431°C., respectively. As expected from the aromatic structure of the molecules, the molecular ions were relatively abundant. In the iodine compound, ions containing 6 or 7 phenyl rings were most abundant and ions containing up to 11 rings with molecule weights of 1755 were observed. As noted earlier in this chapter, unit resolution at this mass is not required for satisfactory identification of ions in this case.

VI. ADDITIONAL APPLICATIONS

There are a number of applications of the mass spectrometer to fundamental and applied organic chemistry the details of which are beyond the scope of this chapter, but which may be of sufficient interest for brief mention. These include: the use of isotopically substituted compounds to study the kinetics of chemical reactions (65); reaction mechanisms (95); studies of heterogeneous catalysis (7); the detection and identification of free radicals in flames (38), in thermal decomposition (56), and in various heterogeneous reactions (64); the measurement of low vapor pressures of hydrocarbons (121); and process monitoring and plant control (63,97). In related fields, isotope abundance measurements and tracer techniques permit studies of metabolic processes, biosynthesis, and photosynthesis. Apparently it is virtually impossible to overemphasize the importance and value of the mass-spectrometric method to the broadest aspects of organic analysis. Consequently this chapter should be considered as a partial guide to the performance of the method and the scope of its applications rather than an exhaustive survey of the field.

References

1. Achhammer, B. G., M. J. Reiney, L. A. Wall, and F. W. Reinhart, *Natl. Bur. Standards (U. S.), Circ. 525*, 253 (1953).
2. Achhammer, B. G., F. W. Reinhart, and G. M. Kline, *ibid.*, p. 205.
3. American Petroleum Institute, *Tables of Mass Spectral Data.* Carnegie Institute of Technology, Pittsburgh, Pa.
4. Aston, F. W., *Mass Spectra and Isotopes.* 2nd ed., Longmans, Green, New York, 1942.

5. Bartels, J., J. W. Severinghaus, R. E. Foster, W. A. Briscol, and D. V. Bates, *J. Clin. Investigation*, *33*, 41 (1954).
6. Barnard, G. P., *Modern Mass Spectrometry.* Institute of Physics, London, 1953.
7. Beeck, O., J. W. Otvos, D. P. Stevenson, and C. D. Wagner, Brookhaven Conference Report, BNL-C-8, December, 1948.
8. Bennett, W. H., *J. Appl. Phys.*, *21*, 143 (1950).
9. Bernstein, R. B., G. P. Semeluk, and C. B. Arends, *Anal. Chem.*, *25*, 139 (1953).
10. Berry, C. E., *J. Chem. Phys.*, *17*, 1164 (1949).
11. Berry, C. E., D. E. Wilcox, S. M. Rock, and H. W. Washburn, *J. Appl. Phys.*, *17*, 262 (1946).
12. Bleakney, W., *Phys. Rev.*, *34*, 157 (1929).
13. Bloom, E. G., F. L. Mohler, J. H. Lengel, and C. E. Wise, *J. Research Natl. Bur. Standards*, *41*, 129 (1948).
14. Bradt, P., V. H. Dibeler, and F. L. Mohler, *ibid.*, *50*, 201 (1953).
15. Bradt, P., and F. L. Mohler, *Anal. Chem. 27*, 875 (1955).
16. Brewer, A. K., *A. S. T. M. Bull.*, *140* (May, 1946).
17. Brown, A. H., A. O. C. Nier, and R. W. Van Norman, *Plant Physiol.*, *27*, 320 (1952).
18. Brown, R. A., *Anal. Chem.*, *23*, 430 (1951).
19. Brown, R. A., 2nd Annual Meeting A. S. T. M. E-14 Committee on Mass Spectrometry, New Orleans, 1954.
20. Brown, R. A., F. W. Melpolder, and W. S. Young, *Petroleum Processing*, *7*, 204 (1952).
21. Brown, R. A., R. C. Taylor, F. W. Melpolder, and W. S. Young, *Anal. Chem.*, *20*, 5 (1948).
22. Brown, R. A., W. S. Young, and N. Nicolaides, *ibid.*, *26*, 1653 (1954).
23. *CEC Recordings*, *4*, No. 3, September, 1950. Consolidated Electrodynamics Corp., Pasadena, California.
24. Charlet, E. M., Consolidated Electrodynamics Corp. Group Report No. 74, March, 1950.
25. Clerc, R. J., H. Hood, and M. J. O'Neal, 2nd Annual Meeting A. S. T. M. E-14 Committee on Mass Spectrometry, New Orleans, 1954.
26. Coggeshall, N. D., "Spectroscopic Functional Group Analysis in the Petroleum Industry," in *Organic Analysis.* Vol. I, Interscience, New York-London, 1953, p. 403.
27. Daigle, E. C., and H. A. Young, *Anal. Chem.*, *24*, 1190 (1952).
28. Dempster, A. J., *Phys. Rev.*, *11*, 316 (1918).
29. Dibeler, V. H., *Anal. Chem.*, *26*, 58 (1954).
30. Dibeler, V. H., and F. Cordero, *J. Research Natl. Bur. Standards*, *46*, 1 (1951).
31. Dibeler, V. H., and J. A. Hipple, *Anal. Chem.*, *24*, 27 (1952).
32. Dibeler, V. H., and F. L. Mohler, *J. Research Natl. Bur. Standards*, *39*, 149 (1947).
33. Dibeler, V. H., F. L. Mohler, L. Williamson, and R. M. Reese, *ibid.*, *43*, 97 (1949).
33a. Dudenbostel, B. F., Jr., and W. Priestley, Jr., *Anal. Chem.*, *26*, 1275 (1954).
34. Eden, M., B. E. Burr, and A. W. Pratt, *ibid.*, *23*, 1735 (1951).
35. Essig, S. F., *Rev. Sci. Instruments*, *3*, 762 (1932).
36. Ewald, H., and Hintenberger, H., *Methoden und Anwendungen der Massenspektroskopie.* Verlag Chemie, Wenheim, 1953.
37. Ezoe, H., *J. Sci. Research Inst. (Tokyo)*, *47*, 65 (1953).

38. Foner, S. N., and R. L. Hudson, *J. Chem. Phys.*, *21*, 1374 and 1608 (1953).

39. Fox, R. E., and J. A. Hipple, *ibid.*, *15*, 208 (1947).

40. Friedel, A. R., A. G. Sharkey, Jr., and C. R. Humbert, *Anal. Chem.*, *21*, 1572 (1949).

41. Friedel, A. R., A. G. Sharkey, Jr., J. L. Shultz, and C. R. Humbert, *ibid.*, *25*, 1314 (1953).

42. Gifford, A. P., S. M. Rock, and D. J. Comaford, *ibid.*, *21*, 1026 (1949).

43. Grosse, A. V., S. G. Hindin, and A. D. Kirshenbaum, *ibid.*, *21*, 386 (1949).

44. Grove, D., and J. A. Hipple, *Rev. Sci. Instruments*, *18*, 837 (1947).

45. Halstead, R. E., and A. O. C. Nier, *ibid.*, *21*, 1019 (1950).

46. Happ, G. P., D. W. Stewart, and H. F. Brockmyre, *Anal. Chem.*, *22*, 1224 (1950).

47. Hevesy, G., and F. Paneth, *Lehrbuch der Radioaktivität*. Leipzig, 1931, pp. 164–73.

48. Highhouse, F., and J. White, *Rev. Sci. Instruments*, *21*, 101 (1950).

49. Hipple, J. A., *J. Appl. Phys.*, *13*, 551 (1942).

50. Hipple, J. A., *Phys. Rev.*, *71*, 594 (1947).

51. Hipple, J. A., "Applications of the Mass Spectrometer," in R. E. Burk and O. Grummitt, eds., *Recent Advances in Analytical Chemistry*. Interscience, New York-London, 1949.

52. Honig, R. E., *J. Appl. Phys.*, *16*, 646 (1945).

53. Hoover, H. H., and H. W. Washburn, *Proc. Calif. Natural Gas Assoc.*, 16th Annual Fall meeting, 1941.

54. Inghram, M. G., "Modern Mass Spectroscopy," in L. Marton, ed., *Advances in Electronics*. Vol. I, Academic Press. New York, 1948.

55. Inghram, M. G., and R. J. Hayden, *A Handbook on Mass Spectroscopy*. Nuclear Science Series Report No. 14, Natl. Res. Council, Washington, 1954.

56. Ingold, K. U., and F. P. Lossing, *J. Chem. Phys.*, *21*, 368 (1953).

57. Kelley, H. M., *Anal. Chem.*, *23*, 1081 (1951).

58. King, W. H., Jr., and W. Priestley, Jr., *ibid.*, *23*, 1418 (1951).

59. Kinney, I. W., Jr., and G. L. Cook, *ibid.*, *24*, 1391 (1952).

60. Kirshenbaum, A. D., and A. V. Grosse, *ibid.*, *22*, 613 (1950).

61. Kirshenbaum, A. D., H. G. Streng, and A. V. Grosse, *ibid.*, *24*, 1361 (1952).

62. Langer, A., and R. E. Fox, *ibid.*, *21*, 103 (1949).

63. Lanneau, K. P., Conference on Applied Mass Spectrometry, Institute of Petroleum, London, 1953.

64. Leger, E. G., and C. Ouellet, *J. Chem. Phys.*, *21*, 1310 (1953).

65. Leifer, E., and H. C. Urey, *J. Am. Chem. Soc.*, *64*, 994 (1942).

66. Lumpkin, H. E., and B. W. Thomas, *Anal. Chem.*, *23*, 1738 (1951).

67. Lumpkin, H. E., B. W. Thomas, and A. Elliott, *ibid.*, *24*, 1389 (1952).

68. Madorsky, S. L., V. E. Hart, S. Straus, and V. A. Sedlak, *J. Research Natl. Bur. Standards*, *51*, 327 (1953).

69. Madorsky, S. L., and S. Straus, *ibid.*, *40*, 417 (1948).

70. Madorsky, S. L., S. Straus, D. I. Thompson, and L. Williamson, *ibid.*, *42*, 499 (1949).

71. Massey, H. S. W., and E. H. S. Burhop, *Electronic and Ionic Impact Phenomena*. Oxford Univ. Press, 1953.

72. Mattraw, H. C., R. E. Patterson, and C. F. Pachucki, *Appl. Spectroscopy*, *8*, 117 (1954).

73. Melpolder, F. W., R. A. Brown, T. A. Washall, W. Doherty, and W. S. Young, *Anal. Chem.*, *26*, 1904 (1954).
74. Melpolder, F. W., C. W. Warfield, and C. E. Headington, *ibid.*, *25*, 1453 (1953).
75. Meyerson, S., *ibid.*, *25*, 338 (1953).
76. Miller, F. A., A. Hemingway, E. B. Brown, A. O. C. Nier, R. Knight, and R. L. Varco, *Surg. Forum Proc. 36th Congr. Am. Coll. Surgeons*, *1950*, 602.
77. Mohler, F. L., *J. Wash. Acad. Sci.*, *38*, 193 (1948).
78. Mohler, F. L., E. G. Bloom, E. J. Wells, Jr., J. H. Lengel, and C. E. Wise, *J. Research Natl. Bur. Standards*, *42*, 369 (1949).
78a. Mohler, F. L., V. H. Dibeler, and R. M. Reese, *ibid.*, *49*, 343 (1952).
79. Mohler, F. L., L. Williamson, E. J. Wells, Jr., and H. M. Dean, *J. Chem. Phys.*, *17*, 1358 (1949).
80. Mohler, F. L., L. Williamson, C. E. Wise, E. J. Wells, Jr., H. M. Dean, and E. G. Bloom, *J. Research Natl. Bur. Standards*, *44*, 291 (1950).
81. Newton, A. S., *Anal. Chem.*, *25*, 1746 (1953).
82. Nier, A. O. C., *Phys. Rev.*, *50*, 1041 (1936).
83. Nier, A. O. C., E. P. Ney, and M. G. Inghram, *Rev. Sci. Instruments*, *18*, 294 (1947).
84. Nier, A. O. C., T. R. Roberts, and E. G. Franklin, *Phys. Rev.*, *75*, 349 (1949).
85. Norton, F. J., *Rev. Sci. Instruments*, *20*, 620 (1949).
86. O'Neal, M. J., Jr., *Anal. Chem.*, *22*, 991 (1950).
87. O'Neal, M. J., Jr., Gordon Research Conference on Petroleum, June, 1953.
88. O'Neal, M. J., Jr., and T. P. Wier, Jr., *Anal. Chem.*, *23*, 830 (1951).
89. Palevski, H., R. K. Swank, and R. Grenchik, *Rev. Sci. Instruments*, *18*, 298 (1947).
90. Pratt, A. W., B. E. Burr, M. Eden, and E. Lorenz, *ibid.*, *22*, 694 (1951).
91. Purdy, K. M., and R. J. Harris, *Anal. Chem.*, *22*, 1337 (1950).
92. Quiram, E. R., S. J. Metro, and J. B. Lewis, *ibid.*, *26*, 352 (1954).
93. Reese, R. M., V. H. Dibeler, and F. L. Mohler, *J. Research Natl. Bur. Standards*, *46*, 79 (1951).
94. Richards, P. I., E. E. Hays, and A. S. Goudsmit, *Phys. Rev.*, *84*, 824 (1951).
95. Roberts, I., and H. C. Urey, *J. Am. Chem. Soc.*, *60*, 2391 (1939).
96. Robinson, C. F., and L. G. Hall, 2nd Annual Meeting A. S. T. M. E-14 Committee on Mass Spectrometry, New Orleans, 1954.
97. Robinson, C. F., H. W. Washburn, C. E. Berry, and G. D. Perkins, *Instruments*, *24*, 221 (1951).
98. Rock, S. M., *Anal. Chem.*, *23*, 261 (1951).
99. Rosenstock, H. M., M. B. Wallenstein, A. L. Wahrhaftig, and H. Eyring, *Proc. Natl. Acad. Sci. (U. S.)*, *38*, 667 (1952).
100. Schuhmann, S., Symposium on Methods for Testing Liquefied Petroleum Gases, Liquefied Petroleum Gas Assoc., St. Louis, 1954.
101. Shepherd, M., *J. Research Natl. Bur. Standards*, *38*, 19 and 491 (1947); *Anal. Chem.*, *19*, 635 (1947).
102. Shepherd, M., *J. Research Natl. Bur. Standards*, *38*, 351 (1947).
103. Shepherd, M., *ibid.*, *36*, 313 (1946); *44*, 509 (1950).
104. Shepherd, M., *Light Hydrocarbon Analysis*. Reinhold, New York, 1951.
105. Shepherd, M., and J. A. Hipple, *Anal. Chem.*, *22*, 23 (1950).
106. Shepherd, M., S. M. Rock, R. Howard, and J. Stormes, *ibid.*, *23*, 1431 (1951).
107. Siri, W., *Rev. Sci. Instruments*, *18*, 54 (1947).

108. Smith, L. G., *Natl. Bur. Standards (U. S.), Circ. 522*, 117 (1953).
109. Smyth, H. D., *Rev. Mod. Phys., 3*, 347 (1931).
110. Sobcov, H., *Anal. Chem., 24*, 1386 (1952).
111. Sommer, H., H. A. Thomas, and J. A. Hipple, *Phys. Rev., 82*, 697 (1951).
112. Stevenson, D. P., *J. Chem. Phys., 15*, 409 (1947).
113. Stevenson, D. P., *ibid., 17*, 101 (1949).
114. Stewart, D. W., "Mass Spectrometry," in A. Weissberger, ed., *Physical Methods of Organic Chemistry (Technique of Organic Chemistry)*. Vol. II, Interscience, New York-London, 1949.
115. Tate, J. T., and P. T. Smith, *Phys. Rev., 46*, 773 (1934).
116. Taylor, R. C., Consolidated Electrodynamics Corporation Mass Spectrometer Group Meeting, Pasadena, 1950.
117. Taylor, R. C., R. A. Brown, W. S. Young, and C. E. Headington, *Anal. Chem., 20*, 396 (1948).
118. Taylor, R. C., and W. S. Young, *Ind. Eng. Chem., Anal. Ed., 17*, 811 (1945).
119. Thomas, B. W., and W. D. Seyfried, *Anal. Chem., 21*, 1022 (1949).
120. Thomson, J. J., *Rays of Positive Electricity and Their Application to Chemical Analyses*. Longmans, Green, New York, 1913; 2nd ed., 1921.
121. Tickner, A. W., and F. P. Lossing, *J. Phys. & Colloid Chem., 55*, 733 (1951).
122. Valentin, R., and G. Philbert, *J. phys. radium, 13*, 247 (1952).
123. Wall, L. A., *J. Research Natl. Bur. Standards, 41*, 315 (1948).
124. Wall, L. A., *Natl. Bur. Standards (U. S.), Circ. 525*, 239 (1953).
125. Wallenstein, M. B., A. L. Wahrhaftig, H. Rosenstock, and H. Eyring, *Proc. Symposium on Radiobiology*, Oberlin College, 1950, p. 20.
126. Washburn, H. W., "Mass Spectrometry," in W. G. Berl, ed., *Physical Methods in Chemical Analysis*. Vol. I, Academic Press, New York, 1950.
127. Washburn, H. W., C. E. Berry, and L. G. Hall, *Anal. Chem., 25*, 130 (1953).
127a. Weaver, E. R., and S. Gunther, *Proc. 3rd Natl. Air Pollution Symp.*, Pasadena, 1955, pp. 86–96.
128. Wiley, H. F., and C. E. Berry, "Mass Spectrometry," in D. F. Boltz, ed., *Modern Instrumental Analysis*. Vol. I, Edwards Brothers, Ann Arbor, 1949.
129. Young, W. S., *Natl. Petroleum News*, Tech. Section, March, 1946.
130. Zemany, P. D., *Anal. Chem., 24*, 1709 (1952).
131. Zemany, P. D., *J. Appl. Phys., 23*, 924 (1952).

SYNTHETIC ORGANIC COATING RESINS

Analytical Characterization and Determination of Some Commercially Important Classes

O. D. Shreve, *E. I. du Pont de Nemours & Co., Inc.*

CONTENTS (*continued*)

I. INTRODUCTION

Prior to World War I, primary film-forming materials for use in solution-type coating vehicles were largely confined to naturally occurring resins, such as rosin, shellac, the natural gums, and drying oils. Since then, and in particular, during the past two decades, developments in the field of synthetic polymers in this country have provided the paint and varnish industry with a large and increasing variety of synthetic organic film-forming materials for use in such products. This chapter is devoted to a discussion of analytical techniques and methods for the analysis of such materials and their determination in typical mixtures. The subject is discussed mainly under two major headings: (*a*) techniques and methods (both chemical and physical) for the detailed analytical characterization of some specific classes of solution type synthetic coating resins and (*b*) analysis of some typical resin mixtures as they occur along with associated ingredients as vehicle components of finished paint products. Since comprehensive treatment of the subject is much beyond the scope of a single chapter, presentation and evaluation of detailed procedures for resin characterization is confined to a few of the more important commercial classes. Types treated in detail include various modifications of the broad, diversified alkyd resin class (including styrenated alkyds), urea- and melamine-formaldehyde types, and phenol-formaldehyde resins. Some additional commercially important classes are briefly discussed with respect to kinds of determinations required for their characterization and literature sources of interest in this connection.

Organized information dealing with the analysis of coating-type resins specifically, and in the form of detailed up-to-date procedures, is still a relatively unfulfilled need in the field; however, the chapter devoted to the subject in the series edited by Mattiello (88), the work of Gardner (43), and other sources (93,94,123,141) will be found very useful. For an excellent guide to the literature in the general field of coatings analysis, the reader is referred to the series of annual reviews by Rochow and Stafford and Stafford and Shay (106–109,130).

II. GENERAL CONSIDERATIONS

1. Analytical Examination of Individual Resins as Manufactured and Supplied for Coatings Formulation

The vehicle components of "solution-type" coatings comprise non-aqueous solutions of synthetic organic polymers along with associated ingredients with or without a dispersed insoluble pigment phase, depending on end use. In contrast to their plastics resin analogs, resins designed for use in such coatings must be manufactured and supplied as solutions in organic solvents or as solids readily soluble in such solvents. While industrial production of polymers in the form of aqueous emulsions for water paint formulation is rapidly increasing, solution-type resins still account for the bulk of industrial coating resin production and the discussion in this chapter is confined to these.

A. QUALITATIVE CLASSIFICATION AND IDENTIFICATION OF COATING RESINS

Various schemes have been proposed for the classification and identification of polymeric materials of commercial importance by solubility behavior, chemical tests, behavior on ignition, simple physical tests, etc. (93,123). Such schemes are applicable with suitable modification to coating resins. Infrared spectroscopy, however, especially when supplemented by qualitative analysis for elements other than carbon, hydrogen, and oxygen and other simple supplementary tests, affords by far the most powerful and effective tool for such purposes. The use of the infrared method relies heavily on comparison of the infrared spectrum of the sample in the form of a film cast from solution on rock salt (or as a detached film) with spectra of films similarly prepared from solutions of known resins. When an extensive library of known reference spectra has been built up, classified, indexed, and adapted to appropriate systematic sorting procedures, resin identification becomes a rapid and relatively simple matter.

B. QUANTITATIVE ANALYTICAL CHARACTERIZATION OF INDIVIDUAL COATING
   RESINS

A pure monomeric organic compound is a well-defined single molecular species amenable to very exact analytical characterization. An "individual" organic polymer, on the other hand, even in the "purest" obtainable state, tends to be more or less ill defined; such an entity usually comprises a range of molecular weights and is often more or less heterogeneous with respect to type and distribution of basic monomers, molecular shape, and state of aggregation, etc.   In general, the detection and determination of various elements, functional groups, and atomic configurations in polymers can be handled by chemical and physical methods identical in principle with those employed for monomeric organic species.   In many cases, however, polymers present unique problems of sample handling and processing prior to the application of such techniques.   Most classes used in organic coatings require a variety of individual determinations and observations for reasonably complete characterization.   It is often desirable and, in some cases, essential that the polymer be resolved into its component parts insofar as possible by such procedures as acid or basic hydrolysis, pyrolysis, or other separation or degradation techniques as a preliminary step or as an integral part of the procedure in the application of such characterizing tests and determinations.

Most quantitative characterizing determinations are performed on samples in the form of resin solutions as commercially supplied or, in the case of those supplied as solids or viscous liquids, samples are dissolved in appropriate organic solvents for analytical purposes.   When the sample to be examined is submitted in solution form, quantitative data obtained on the solution are usually expressed on the "solids" basis after determination of the nonvolatile resin content by an appropriate drying procedure.

2. Analysis of Mixtures of Synthetic Resins

In addition to the analytical characterization of individual polymers in original manufactured form, the finishes analyst is frequently called upon to detect and/or estimate the total amount of one or more polymer species present in finished coatings formulations; detailed analytical characterization of one or more of the resins present may also be desired.

In the case of products of unknown or uncertain qualitative composition, a combination of infrared spectroscopy with suitable physical and chemical separation procedures affords the most effective means for establishing gross composition and quick semiquantitative information and suggesting lines along which detailed quantitative chemical analysis should proceed when this is required.

Quantitative analysis for the total amount of a given polymeric constituent in a mixture is often based on the determination of an element, functional group, or other characteristic entity in the polymer to be determined. As in the analysis of mixtures of monomeric compounds, consideration must, of course, always be given to interference from other constituents possessing the same or chemically similar functions. In some cases, very accurate and precise estimates of individual polymer components in mixtures can be made in this manner. In general, however, such estimates tend to be somewhat less accurate and precise than similar analyses on mixtures of monomeric compounds because of variability in the amount of element or functional group present in different samples or batches of the individual polymer being determined, inherent error in the estimation of the total resin solids content of the vehicle, etc.

In the absence of a function adapted to chemical determination, the polymer in question can sometimes be isolated by solvent precipitation or other nondestructive separation procedure in essentially uncontaminated form and estimated gravimetrically with reasonable accuracy by drying and weighing. Infrared spectrometry provides another useful and increasingly employed technique for obtaining quantitative polymer estimates in mixtures. While usually less precise and accurate than applicable chemical methods for this particular purpose, infrared methods are rapid and are sometimes possible when chemical procedures are inapplicable or very difficult to develop.

Complete quantitative characterization of an individual coating resin in admixture with other resins in paint vehicles can seldom be performed satisfactorily without isolation or partial separation of the resin from the mixture. In the absence of suitable separation procedures, however, much can be done; the completeness and degree of reliability depends, of course, on the nature of the particular system containing the resin and the number and type of determinations required for characterization.

III. METHODS FOR DETAILED ANALYTICAL CHARACTERIZATION OF SOME COMMERCIALLY IMPORTANT RESIN CLASSES

In a survey conducted for the A. S. T. M. in 1947, Bradley (28) summed up the general status of existing methods for the testing and analytical characterization of the more common classes of synthetic resins used in the commerical manufacture of coatings. His survey covered alkyds, urea- and melamine-formaldehyde types, rosin esters, phenol-aldehyde resins, and vinyl resins. Developments since this survey have resulted in fulfillment of some of the needs pointed out by Bradley and progress with respect to others; this has been notably true of the oil-modified alkyd class on which much has been published in recent years and which has been the subject of extensive study by Subcommittee XI of A. S. T. M. Committee D-1.

The broad alkyd class in its many and diverse modifications represents by far the most important and widely used type of synthetic film-forming material now available for large-scale manufacture of industrial finishes (automotive, household appliances, etc.) and many other coating products. For this reason and because quantitative methods for their detailed characterization are more advanced and better standardized than for any other class, much of this section is devoted to the various alkyd modifications and the urea- and melamine-formaldehyde types with which they are commonly associated in the formulation of industrial baking enamels.

This discussion will serve: (a) to bring together for the convenience of practicing analysts an organized set of detailed procedures for the analysis of individual resins belonging to the classes treated and (b) to illustrate the general approach and methodology involved in the problem of detailed coating resin characterization.

1. Oil-Modified Alkyd Resins

Oil-modified alkyds are polyesters comprising the esterification products of one or more polyhydric alcohols with one or more dibasic acids and drying oil fatty acids. The most common type is based on *glycerol* (glycerin) as the polyhydric alcohol, *o-phthalic* acid as the dibasic acid, and the mixed fatty acids from one or more drying, semidrying, or nondrying vegetable oils as the oil modifier. The type of structure involved is indicated in formula I. In recent years, a variety of other dibasic acids (e. g., succinic, adipic, sebacic, and other saturated dibasic acids; isomers of phthalic acid; fumaric and other monounsaturated types) and many polyols other than glycerine (e. g., various glycols, pentaerythritol, sorbitol, etc.) have come into use as alkyd raw materials. The most commonly used oil modifiers are linseed, soya, chinawood, castor, coconut, cottonseed, and dehydrated castor.

$$\left[\begin{array}{c} \underset{\displaystyle \bigcirc}{\overset{O\quad O}{-C\;\;\overset{\|}{C}-O-}} \quad \overset{H}{\underset{H}{\overset{|}{C}}}-\overset{H}{\underset{O}{\overset{|}{C}}}-\overset{H}{\underset{H}{\overset{|}{C}}}-O- \\ O{=}\overset{|}{C}{-}C_{17}H_{31} \end{array} \right]_n$$

(I)

Alkyd resins designed for use in formulating surface coatings are usually supplied in the form of resin solutions in commercial hydrocarbon solvents. Various physical tests used for specification and control of alkyd manufacture include color, viscosity, specific gravity, etc. Procedures for such tests are given in the work by Gardner (43). The complete analytical characterization of the resin solids of an alkyd solution requires at least seven separate determinations as follows: solids content of resin solution; excess hydroxyl content; acid value; dibasic acid component; polyhydric alcohol component; total fatty acids present as modifiers; component fatty acid analysis of oil modifier fraction. Determinations of hydroxyl, acid value, dibasic acid, polyol, and total fatty acids are carried out via appropriate procedures applied to samples of the resin solution; results are normally expressed, however, on the basis of total resin solids as obtained in an oven-drying procedure of the type given below.

Analysis of the solvent in which the alkyd is dissolved is sometimes required, but is usually of secondary interest in connection with the problem of characterizing the resin itself for research, control, or specification purposes.

A. RESINS BASED ON STRAIGHT OIL-MODIFIED GLYCERYL PHTHALATE

(1) Methods for Direct Examination of Resin Solution. (a) *Solids* (nonvolatile content) of alkyd resin solutions is determined by oven drying under specified conditions. The following procedure has proved satisfactory in long use in the author's laboratory.

Apparatus. Isotemp forced draft oven. Aluminum foil dishes, 2.25 × 0.75 in., weight approximately 1.3 g., having "no measurable weight change" when subjected to the heat schedule prescribed. Small vials, RPC viscosity tubes, 10.60 mm., or hypodermic syringe without needle.

Procedure. Place a portion of a representative sample in a small vial or viscosity tube and stopper, or use a hypodermic syringe without a needle. Weigh a clean, dry aluminum dish. Weigh the sample and container and quickly transfer to the weighed aluminum dish sufficient sample to yield a residue of 0.5 ± 0.05 g. Reweigh rapidly and calculate the weight of the sample by difference. Proper sample size is indicated by the following table:

Expected solids, %	Amount of sample solution to be used, g.
80	0.62 ± 0.06
70	0.71 ± 0.07
60	0.83 ± 0.08
50	1.00 ± 0.10
40	1.25 ± 0.12

A dropper inserted in the stopper of the vial or tube may be used to transfer very thin and dilute solutions, but the more viscous solutions may be poured directly.

Carefully tilt the dish and rotate to spread the sample evenly over the bottom and add 2 ml. of xylene (free of suspended matter). Transfer the dish to a 105 ± 2°C. forced draft oven, placing in a level position. Dry for 1 hour and transfer to a desiccator to cool. Reweigh the dish.

Calculate the residue by difference:

$$\% \text{ solids} = \frac{\text{weight of residue} \times 100}{\text{weight of sample}}$$

Precision, calculated as "95% confidence limits" for duplicate averages from data obtained at 50% solids level by a single operator, is ±0.3% solids.

(*b*) *Acid Number.* This value is determined as follows:

Dilute an appropriate size sample of the resin solution with a neutral solvent comprising equal volumes of toluene and ethyl alcohol (190 proof 2-B) and titrate with standard alcoholic alkali to a phenolphthalein end point. The result is expressed as milligrams of KOH required to neutralize one gram of resin solids.

(*c*) *Excess hydroxyl* is usually expressed as per cent unesterified hydroxyl (on resin solids basis) over and above that equivalent to the unesterified carboxyl present in the resin. This determination can be satisfactorily performed by acetylation of an appropriate size sample with acetic anhydride in pyridine using reagents as specified and prepared in the method of Wilson and Hughes (144), which is described and critically discussed in Volume I of this series (89). If *total free hydroxyl* is desired, the results must be corrected for the acid value of the resin.

(2) Determinations Involving Breakdown of Resin by Saponification. The next step in the complete analysis of an alkyd involves resolution of the polyester into its three basic monomeric components (i. e., a dibasic acid fraction, a polyhydric alcohol fraction, and a fatty acid modifier fraction) and the determination of each. This is accomplished by saponification of the resin with absolute ethanolic potassium hydroxide in one of the various modifications of the well-known Kappelmeier procedure (68–70). In the case of a straight oil-modified glyceryl phthalate-type resin, this treatment results in quantitative precipitation of dipotassium phthalate monoalcoholate, which is filtered off and determined gravimetricallly to yield an estimate of the total phthalate (usually expressed as total phthalic anhydride equivalent). After evaporation of ethyl alcohol and resin solvents from the filtrate, followed by dilution with water and acidification, the liberated mixed fatty acids from the oil present as modifier are extracted with ether; this fraction is dried in an inert gas atmosphere (to prevent oxidation) and weighed to yield an estimate of total fatty acid modifiers. The type and amount of the various long-chain fatty acids comprising this fraction can be determined by ultraviolet spectrophotometry supplemented by a measure of total unsaturation, as determined by halogenation or semimicro catalytic hydrogenation. The residual water phase from the fatty acid extraction contains the glycerine, which is determined by oxidation with sodium periodate or periodic acid utilizing the well-known Malaprade reaction (82). Glycerin is oxidized by this reagent to formaldehyde and formic acid, one mole of the acid being formed for each mole of glycerin present. Titration of the formic acid with standard alkali affords an estimate of the glycerol present in this fraction of the saponificate.

The following procedures can be followed systematically to perform all of these determinations on the same sample of an alkyd resin solution. The method for total phthalate (as phthalic anhydride) is A. S. T. M. designation D-563–52 (5), as adopted after extensive cooperative study of the original Kappelmeier method by A. S. T. M. Committee D-1; the procedures for total fatty acid content and glycerin are based on procedures now under study by A. S. T. M. Committee D-1 and are similar to those long in use in the author's laboratory.

(a) Total Phthalate (as Phthalic Anhydride):

Apparatus and Reagents. 500 ml. erlenmeyer flask (24/40 taper joint) fitted with 30 in. air-cooled glass reflux condenser. 30 ml. fritted-glass filter crucible, fine porosity. Guard tube filled with soda-lime. Crucible holder. Benzene. Alcoholic potassium hydroxide solution (dissolve 66 g. of reagent-grade KOH in 1 liter of absolute ethyl alcohol; allow the solution to stand overnight protected against CO_2 absorption; filter just before use). Ether, anhydrous analytical-reagent grade. Alcohol–benzene wash solution (1 volume absolute ethyl alcohol with 3 volumes benzene). 1 N hydrochloric acid.

Procedure. Weigh by difference from a closed container into the 500 ml. erlenmeyer flask a sample of resin or resin solution sufficient to yield from 0.8 to 1.2 g. of potassium phthalate monoalcoholate. Add 150 ml. of benzene, warming slightly on the steam bath, if necessary, to effect solution. Add 60 ml. of alcoholic KOH solution, and attach the condenser. Place the flask in a water bath to a depth approximately equal to that of its contents; warm the bath, maintaining a temperature of 40°C. for 1 hour, then gradually raise the temperature until the alcoholic solution boils gently. Reflux for 1.5 hours.

Remove the flask from the bath, and wash down the inside of the condenser with a few milliliters of alcohol–benzene wash solution. Remove the condenser, cap the flask with a soda-lime guard tube, and cool by means of running water or an ice bath.

When cool, filter immediately and as rapidly as possible through a fritted glass crucible that previously has been tared, using the alcohol–benzene wash solution for transferring the precipitate and washing the reaction flask. Wash the precipitate with successive portions of alcohol–benzene wash solution until a few milliliters of washings collected in a second suction flask are no longer alkaline to phenolphthalein. (Normally about 75 ml. of wash solution is sufficient.) Do not allow air to be drawn through the crystals, as they are hygroscopic. Finally, pour 25 ml. of ether into the crucible and draw through the precipitate with the aid of suction. Reserve the combined filtrate and washings for the glycerin and fatty acid determinations below.

Wipe the outer surface of the crucible with a clean cloth and place in a gravity convection oven at 60°C. for 1 hour (see note below). Cool to room temperature in a desiccator containing concentrated H_2SO_4 and weigh.

Note: The precipitate is the alcoholate $C_6H_4(COOK)_2 \cdot C_2H_5OH$ and the alcohol of crystallization will be slowly driven off on prolonged heating (34,48). It is safe, however, to dry the alcoholate at temperatures up to 60°C. for as long as 1 hour.

Correction for Carbonates. Coprecipitation of K_2CO_3 with the potassium phthalate monoalcoholate may be a source of error. If a correction for K_2CO_3 is desired, proceed as follows: dissolve the weighed precipitate in about 50 ml. of distilled water that has been neutralized to phenolphthalein. Add 3 to 4 drops of phenolphthalein indicator and, if the solution is alkaline, titrate with 0.1 N HCl.

Calculate the phthalic anhydride equivalent of the sample as follows:

$$\% \text{ P. A.} = 51.36 \ (P - 0.1382 \ VN)/WS$$

where V is milliliters of HCl, N the normality of the HCl used in the carbonate correction (if determined), P the weight in grams of the phthalate precipitate, W the sample weight in grams, and S the fractional solids content of resin solution.

Table I gives some data obtained in an interlaboratory study of this method in which several laboratories analyzed a carefully prepared standard alkyd of known phthalate content.

TABLE I

Determination of Total Phthalic Anhydride in Oil-Modified Alkyd Resin
by Gravimetric Method—A.S.T.M.-D-563-52

Laboratory	Per cent phthalic anhydride		
	Present	Found	
		(1)	(2)
A.................	19.90	19.91	19.92
B.................		19.94	19.95
C.................		20.25	20.07
D.................		20.00	20.20

(b) Total Fatty Acids:

Transfer the combined filtrate and washings from the phthalate determination in (a) above to a 400 ml. beaker with the aid of 25 ml. of water from a wash bottle. Concentrate on the steam bath to a volume of approximately 25 ml. under a blanket of nitrogen to prevent oxidation.   Transfer to a 500 ml. separatory funnel with the aid of water from a wash bottle, dilute with water to approximately 300 ml., and add 10 ml. of ethyl alcohol.   Extract the unsaponifiable and volatile thinners with successive 50 ml. portions of ether (not less than three or until a colorless ether extract is obtained), combining the ether extracts in the separatory funnel and using the other two funnels for the successive extractions.   Finally, wash the combined ether extracts with three 15 ml. portions of water, adding the water washes to the main aqueous phase.   Discard the combined ether extracts.   If there is any difficulty with ether–water emulsion, add alcohol dropwise with swirling to break the emulsion.

Acidify the aqueous phase to a pH of approximately 2 by slowly adding concentrated hydrochloric acid and cooling under running tap water.   When the mixture has cooled to room temperature, extract the fatty acids with successive 25 ml. portions (not less than three) of ether until a colorless ether extract is obtained, combining the ether extracts in the first separatory funnel and using the other two funnels for the successive extractions.   Wash the combined ether extracts with successive 10 ml. portions of water until free of mineral acid when tested with indicator paper or methyl orange solution.   Discard the aqueous phase.   Dry the combined ether extracts in the separatory funnel by the addition of successive small quantities of anhydrous sodium sulfate.

Note: The free water will have been removed when, by the addition of a small quantity of sodium sulfate and gentle swirling, the excess sodium sulfate will be seen to disperse as a freely moving powder.

Filter the dried ether extract through Whatman #40 paper portionwise into a 150 ml. beaker (containing a small boiling stone) which has been previously weighed to the nearest milligram. Decant the ether extract from the top opening of the separatory funnel. Evaporate the ether portionwise by placing the beaker and its contents on the steam bath. While evaporating, cover the filter funnel with a watch glass. During the evaporations apply a blanket of nitrogen or carbon dioxide gas over the beaker. Remove the last portions of fatty acids from the sodium sulfate by washing with successive small portions of ether until a colorless extract is obtained, removing the final traces of fatty acids from the filter paper by several successive small portions of ether. Then evaporate the fatty acid ether solution on the steam bath while maintaining an inert atmosphere over the acids. Remove the final traces of ether by heating 30 minutes in a vacuum oven at 60°C., and take the fatty acids to constant weight in the oven. Cool the beaker and its contents to room temperature in a desiccator, and weigh to the nearest milligram.

Calculation.

$$\% \text{ total fatty acids} = \frac{(A - B) \times 100}{WS}$$

where A = weight of beaker plus residue, B = weight of beaker, W = weight of sample, and S = fractional solids content of resin solution.

Precision, calculated as 95% "confidence limits" for duplicate averages from data obtained by a single analyst on an alkyd containing 35% fatty acids is ±0.2%.

(c) *Glycerin:*

Add 50 ml. ethanol to the combined aqueous phase from (b) above, and evaporate the solution in a 250 ml. beaker on a steam bath to a volume of about 75 ml. Then neutralize the solution to pH 7 using pH indicator paper. If the solution is perfectly clear, transfer with rinsing to a 100 ml. volumetric flask, dilute to the mark with distilled water, and mix. If, however, a slight cloudiness is evident, filter through #40 Whatman filter paper, transfer with rinsing to a 100 ml. glass stoppered volumetric flask, dilute to the mark, and mix.

Transfer an aliquot of the 100 ml. solution, expected to contain not more than 110 mg. of glycerin or its equivalent, to a 250 ml. ground-glass stoppered erlenmeyer flask. Add 1 drop of methyl red and sufficient dilute HCl to make the solution neutral to methyl red. Add by pipet 25.0 ml. of 0.1 M sodium periodate (13.2 g./200 ml. H_2O), stopper, and mix by swirling. Let the flask stand 1 hour at room temperature, and then titrate with standardized 0.1 N KOH. Run a reagent blank in the same way, substituting an aliquot of distilled water.

Calculate the glycerin content of the solids portion of the original resin solution as follows:

$$\% \text{ glycerin} = \frac{(B - A) \times \text{normality of KOH} \times 9.2 \times \text{aliquot factor}}{\text{sample wt.} \times \text{fractional solids content}}$$

where B = milliliters of KOH for blank and A = milliliters of KOH for sample.

(d)   *Component Analysis of Fatty Acid Fraction:* Table II taken from
Mattiello (88) gives the fatty acid composition of various oils in which these
acids occur as glycerides.

TABLE II

Fatty Acid Composition of Various Oils

Oil	Average fatty acid composition	Per cent
Coconut.................	Capric, caproic, and caprylic	16–21
	Lauric	45–50
	Myristic	16–20
	Palmitic	5–9
	Stearic	1–5
	Oleic	5–8
	9,12-Linoleic	3–4
Cottonseed..............	Palmitic	20–26
	Stearic	2–3
	Oleic	35–45
	9,12-Linoleic	30–40
Castor..................	Saturated acids	3–5
	Oleic	7–10
	9,12-Linoleic	3–4
	Ricinoleic	80–87
Soybean.................	Palmitic	6.5–10
	Stearic	4.2–6.3
	Oleic	22–29
	9,12-Linoleic	50–55
	Linolenic	7–10
Dehydrated castor..........	Saturated Acids	3–4
	Oleic	6–9
	9,12-Linoleic	55–68
	9,11-Linoleic	17–30
Linseed.................	Palmitic	2–4
	Stearic	5–8
	Oleic	6–12
	9,12-Linoleic	35–47
	Linolenic	37–42

Ultraviolet spectrophotometry is now widely used in oil analysis as the
result of work by Mitchell, Kraybill and Zscheile (90), Brice and co-workers
(29,30), and others.   A good general discussion of this subject will be found
in Volume V of the series edited by Matiello (88).   The methods used are
based on the fact that (a) the doubly and triply conjugated polyunsaturated
acids occurring in certain drying oils absorb strongly at 234 and 268 mμ,
respectively, and (b) the nonconjugated, nonabsorbing polyunsaturated

acids can be converted to a reproducible extent to the corresponding conjugated absorbing forms by heating with KOH in ethylene glycol or glycerin in an alkali-isomerization method (29,90; see also p. 62). Figure 1 shows the ultraviolet absorption spectra (116) of a sample of soybean oil before (curve 1) and after (curve 2) such alkali isomerization treatment (30 minutes in glycerolic KOH at 180°C.). Because the original oil (curve 1) contains little

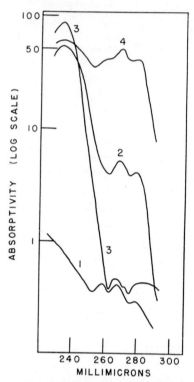

Fig. 1. Ultraviolet absorption spectra of soybean oil and related fatty acids.

or no conjugation, the absorption is low. On alkali isomerization, however, two strong maxima develop at 234 and 268 mμ as a result of isomerization of nonabsorbing, nonconjugated double bonds and triple bonds, respectively, to the conjugated absorbing forms. Curves 3 and 4 show spectra (after isomerization) of pure 9,12-linoleic and 9,12,15-linolenic acids, which together comprise the polyunsaturated portion of soybean oil acids. Using the known absorptivity values at 234 and 268 mμ for pure alkali-isomerized acids, the complete acid composition of such an oil in terms of linoleic, linolenic, oleic, and saturated acids can be calculated readily from the observed absorptivities of the alkali-isomerized sample at the two analytical wave lengths, together with the iodine value or other measure of unsaturation on the original oil. If an oil contains conjugated components before isomerization (e. g., dehydrated castor and chinawood) these can also be determined from the two measured absorptivities of the original oil when suitable calibration data on pure conjugated acids are available.

A detailed procedure for carrying out the above type of analysis by ultraviolet spectrophotometry was published in 1949 by the Spectroscopy Committee of the American Oil Chemists' Society (127). Since that time, the procedure has been subject to a great deal of further study. Numerous improvements have been proposed and more adequate spectroscopic standards have been developed (9,15,23,30,31,57,61,87,98,138,140). Reference to the detailed A. O. C. S. method mentioned above and to the later 1952–53 report of the same committee (128) will supply sufficient information for those wishing to set up the necessary apparatus and carry out analyses of this type. For the determination of total unsaturation, which together with the spectroscopic data is needed for complete characterization of the fatty acids, halogenation methods may be used but are often unreliable. Semimicro catalytic hydrogenation, using an apparatus and procedure similar to that described by Ogg and Cooper (99), is recommended for this purpose (see chapter on Determination of Olefinic Unsaturation in this volume).

B. ALKYDS CONTAINING OTHER DIBASIC ACIDS AND/OR OTHER POLYHYDRIC ALCOHOLS

(1) Methods for _o_-Phthalic Acid in the Presence of Other Dibasic Acids. The gravimetric Kappelmeier method for total _o_-phthalic acid (Section III.1A(2)(a) above) cannot be applied in the presence of other dibasic acids that yield potassium salts insoluble or only partially soluble in anhydrous ethanolic alkali under the conditions of the procedure. These include such acids as maleic, fumaric, citraconic, itaconic, and other monounsaturated cibasic acids and all saturated dibasic acids, such as succinic, adipic, sebacic, many of which are encountered in the analysis of present-day alkyds.

In some cases, interference from other dibasic acids in the _o_-phthalate determination can be obviated by a procedure first proposed by Kappelmeier and co-workers (78), in which advantage is taken of the fact that the acids likely to be encountered do not precipitate as the alcoholates, but rather as straight dipotassium salts from alcoholic alkali solutions. Since o-phthalic acid always precipitates as the dipotassium salt with one molecule of alcohol of crystallization, the precipitate of mixed salts can be dried first at 60° in vacuum as directed above and then at 150°C. for several hours to remove quantitatively this alcohol of crystallization. The phthalate content of the mixed salts (and hence of the resin) is then given by dividing the observed percentage weight loss by the corresponding theoretical value for pure potassium phthalate monoalcoholate. This procedure is useful, but is subject to the assumption that prolonged drying at 150°C. causes no significant gain or loss of weight by the nonphthalate constituents; this assumption has been found valid, however, for salts of maleic, fumaric, succinic, and adipic acids within reasonable limits of error (78,114).

A more rapid, accurate, and precise method for determination of the combined o-phthalate content of alkyds in the presence of such dibasic acids as well as many other materials which interfere in the Kappelmeier procedure is based on spectrophotometric measurements in the ultraviolet region of the spectrum (117). Since publication, this method has undergone some improvements and revision as a result of a cooperative study conducted by A. S. T. M. Committee D-1. The revised recommended procedure (now A. S. T. M. Method D-1307–54T) is as follows:

Apparatus and Reagents. Same as for phthalic procedure given in Section III.1A(2)(a) above. In addition, Beckman DU spectrophotometer with matched silica or quartz 1 cm. cells. Pure potassium acid phthalate for calibration (N. B. S. standard sample 84D).

Calibration of Spectrophotometer. Weigh accurately to 4 decimal places about 0.3 g. of the pure potassium acid phthalate calibration standard into a calibrated 1 liter volumetric flask, dissolve in distilled water, pipet in exactly 10 ml. concentrated HCl (sp. gr. 1.19) and dilute to the mark with distilled H_2O. Pipet a 50 ml. aliquot of this solution into a 250 ml. volumetric flask and dilute to the mark with HCl stock solution (approximately 0.1 N). Measure the absorbance (optical density) at 276 mμ against 0.1 N HCl stock solution as blank using matched 1 cm. silica or quartz absorption cells. Repeat the measurement with the blank in the cell formerly used for the standard and vice versa. Average the measurements to obtain the absorbance, A; record the slit width setting used.

Calculate the absorptivity of phthalic acid, a_p, from the formula: $a_p = A/C_p$, where C_p is the concentration, expressed as grams per liter of phthalic acid (not salt), present in the final diluted solution measured.

Analytical Procedure. Proceed as in the method for phthalate in Section III.1A(2)(a) above up to and including the point at which the potassium phthalate monoalcoholate has been isolated, dried at 60°C., and cooled in the desiccator.

Extract this precipitate by passing about 200 ml. of distilled water through the crucible with suction. To the aqueous extract in the suction flask add 20 ml. concentrated HCl (sp. gr. 1.19). If sebacic or other slightly soluble acidic material is present, a precipitate or cloudiness may appear. If the acidified solution is perfectly clear, transfer with rinsing to a *2 liter* volumetric flask and dilute to the mark with distilled water. If, however, even a slight cloudiness is evident, filter the entire solution (before dilution) with suction through #42 Whatman filter paper on a büchner funnel, wash the residue with 100 ml. of distilled H$_2$O, transfer the combined filtrate and washings to a *2 liter* volumetric flask, and dilute to the mark with distilled H$_2$O. After thorough mixing, pipet a 50 ml. aliquot of the diluted extract into a 250 ml. volumetric flask and dilute to the mark with HCl stock solution (approximately 0.1 N). Using a spectrophotometer slit width identical with that used in the calibration procedure above, measure the absorbance at 276 mμ against a blank of HCl stock solution (approximately 0.1 N), following the cell switching practice used in calibrating.

For maximum accuracy, the measured absorbance of the final diluted solution should fall between 0.3 and 0.6 absorbance unit for a Beckman DU instrument using the cells specified above. If the observed absorbance is too low, appropriately decrease the dilution factor in the final dilution. If the absorbance is too high, saponify a new pair of samples of appropriately adjusted size, since an increase in the final dilution factor is undesirable.

Calculate the phthalic acid concentration (in grams per liter), C_p, of the final diluted solution from the formula: $C_p = A/a_p$, where A is the measured absorbance and a_p is the absorptivity value for pure phthalic acid, as determined in the calibration procedure. Convert C_p to per cent phthalic anhydride using the formula given below.

Special Procedure for Phthalic in the Presence of Maleic or Fumaric Acid. If maleic or fumaric acid is present, it is necessary to determine the absorptivity of a pure sample of the interfering acid as follows:

Measure the absorbance, A_i, of a pure sample of the interfering acid at a suitable concentration, C_i (g./l.), in HCl stock solution (approximately 0.1 N) at 276 mμ.

Calculate the absorptivity, a_i, of the acid from the formula $a_i = A/C_i$.

Then carry out the analysis exactly as described above, but record the weight of the dried precipitate as B.

Finally *calculate* the phthalic acid concentration, C_p, of the final diluted solution from the following pair of simultaneous equations:

$$a_p C_p + a_i C_i = A$$
$$F_p C_p + F_i C_i = B/2f$$

where A is the measured absorbance of the final diluted solution as before, a_p, C_p, a_i, C_i, and B have been defined above, f is the aliquot factor used in the final dilution, and F_p and F_i are the factors that convert phthalic acid and interfering acid, respectively, to their potassium salt equivalents as they occur in the precipitate. (For phthalic acid use $F_i = 1.735$. For maleic or fumaric acid use $F_i = 1.654$.)

Final Calculation of Phthalic Anhydride Content. The phthalic anhydride content of the resin is calculated from the C_p value, as obtained in either procedure above as follows:

$$\% \text{ phthalic anhydride} = \frac{89.16 \times C_p \times 2f}{\text{sample wt.} \times \text{fractional solids}}$$

where f is the aliquot factor defined above.

The above method is applicable in the presence of almost any nonaromatic dibasic acid likely to be encountered along with *o*-phthalic acid in

TABLE III

Analysis of Synthetic Ester Mixtures

Sample		P. A. present, %[a]	P. A. found, % (spectrophotometric)			Error, %
			1	2	Av.	
Oil-modified alkyd + adipate polyester	1	34.20	34.01	34.19	34.10	−0.10
	2	25.14	25.12	24.82	24.97	−0.17
	3	18.61	18.55	18.29	18.42	−0.19
	4	8.57	8.10	8.31	8.21	−0.36
	5	2.07	2.40	2.18	2.29	+0.22
Oil-modified alkyd + sebacate polyester	1	33.71	33.71	33.51	33.61	−0.10
	2	23.82	23.51	23.68	23.60	−0.22
	3	17.94	18.29	17.95	18.12	+0.18
	4	7.76	7.99	7.85	7.92	+0.16
	5	3.16	3.27	3.57	3.42	+0.26
Dimethyl phthalate + dimethyl succinate	1	68.21	68.72	68.51	68.62	+0.41
	2	52.42	52.42	52.20	52.31	−0.11
	3	39.86	39.76	39.86	39.81	−0.05
	4	21.32	21.30	21.04	21.17	−0.15
	5	5.27	5.51	5.31	5.41	+0.14
Dimethyl phthalate + dimethyl sebacate	1	68.26	67.91	68.11	68.01	−0.25
	2	51.51	51.66	51.42	51.54	+0.03
	3	35.92	35.86	35.72	35.79	−0.13
	4	21.98	21.60	21.94	21.77	−0.21
	5	6.04	5.76	5.99	5.88	−0.16
Dimethyl phthalate + dibutyl maleate	1	71.74	71.79	71.60	71.69	−0.05
	2	65.41	65.33	65.07	65.20	−0.21
	3	60.82	60.94	61.24	61.09	+0.27
Dimethyl phthalate + dimethyl adipate	1	67.15	67.15	67.33	67.24	+0.09
	2	54.12	54.40	54.24	54.32	+0.22
	3	36.54	36.42	36.24	36.33	−0.21
	4	20.82	20.91	21.08	21.00	+0.18
	5	4.93	5.19	5.32	5.26	+0.33

[a] Calculated from phthalic anhydride content of phthalate ester present as determined by Kappelmeier method.

modern alkyd resins (terephthalic and isophthalic acids interfere). Table III shows results obtained for the phthalic content of an oil-modified alkyd in the presence of various other dibasic acid esters.

While its chief advantage is realized when applied to mixtures that cannot be analyzed by the gravimetric Kappelmeier procedure, the method also offers some advantages over this procedure, even in the case of a straight o-phthalate-type alkyd or other straight o-phthalate ester. (As indicated by the data of Table IV, results on this type of sample agree very well with those obtained by the gravimetric procedure.) The somewhat controversial question regarding the best weighing form of the precipitated phthalate salt is obviated and the possibility of high results due to insoluble unsaponifiable matter, etc., which may appear in this precipitate is minimized. Also, the method is free from the so-called carbonate error characteristic of the Kappelmeier procedure.

TABLE IV

Comparison of gravimetric and Spectrophotometric Methods

	Phthalic anhydride, % (Kappelmeier)			Phthalic anhydride, % (spectrophotometric)			Error, %
Sample	1	2	Av.	1	2	Av.	
1....Oil-modified alkyd resin	35.85	35.95	35.90	35.98	36.06	36.04	+0.14
2....Dimethyl phthalate	75.48	75.62	75.55	75.60	75.60	75.60	+0.05
3....Dibutyl phthalate	53.24	53.18	53.21	53.17	53.21	53.19	−0.02
4....Dioctyl phthalate	38.40	38.42	38.41	38.57	38.81	38.69	+0.28

Another great advantage of the spectrophotometric method lies in the fact that it can be applied (with results adequate for most purposes) in the presence of a number of typical resins, pigments, etc. used along with alkyd resins in finished coatings formulations. Such materials will not interfere unless they possess the combined properties of insolubility in alcoholic KOH, solubility in water, and significant ultraviolet absorption at the analytical wave length used. This advantage is illustrated by the data of Table V, showing results for phthalate content of a dibutyl phthalate plasticized vinyl resin system. Saponification of such a resin in absolute ethanolic KOH yields a potassium phthalate precipitate highly contaminated with KCl and vinyl resin degradation products. The gravimetric Kappelmeier procedure is obviously inapplicable and the alcoholate loss method mentioned above gives poor results, due to instability of the vinyl resin degradation products when heated.

Swann has described gravimetric methods for determining phthalic acid and several other dibasic acids in alkyd resins (134). His procedure for phthalic in the presence of other acids (which is also under study by A. S. T. M. Committee D-1) involves isolating the dibasic acids as potassium salts in a saponification procedure similar to that given above, dissolving the precipitated salts in water, acidifying with HNO_3 to pH 2.5, and evaporating an aliquot to dryness to liberate the solid dibasic acids. Phthalic acid is then precipitated as the lead salt from glacial acetic acid; other acids do not precipitate under the conditions of the method. This method is useful when spectrophotometric equipment is not available; however, it is time consuming and suffers from the disadvantages inherent in most procedures based on precipitation and determination of heavy metal salts.

TABLE V

Analysis of Vinyl Resin-Phthalate Ester Blends

Sample	P. A. present, %	P. A. found, % (spectrophotometric)			Error, %
		1	2	Av.	
Polyvinyl chloride acetate + dibutyl phthalate.............	13.44[a]	13.85	13.57	13.71	+0.27
Polyvinyl chloride acetate + dioctyl phthalate.............	9.54[a]	9.15	9.33	9.24	−0.30

[a] Calculated from phthalic anhydride content of phthalate ester present as determined by Kappelmeier method.

(2) Methods for Other Dibasic Acids. As previously noted, esters of dibasic acids other than o-phthalic form insoluble potassium salts when saponified with absolute ethanolic KOH in the procedure of Section III.1A (2)(a). Evaluation of this procedure on some pure diethyl esters of dibasic acids (132) suggests that the method may be extended to the determination of maleic, fumaric, adipic, and sebacic acids when one of these comprises the sole acid component of a polyester. Such methods, however, have not been completely worked out and standardized for polyester analysis and, of course, would not be applicable to alkyds in the presence of the ubiquitous o-phthalic acid.

Perhaps the most useful available methods for determination of dibasic acids other than o-phthalic in alkyds are those proposed by Swann (134), whose methods are applicable to alkyds containing maleic, fumaric, succinic, adipic, or sebacic acid in addition to the usual o-phthalic acid. After saponification of the resin by a modified Kappelmeier technique, the precipitated potassium salts are dissolved, acidified, and converted to the solid dibasic acids. *o*-Phthalic is determined (as already noted above) by precipitation as the lead salt from glacial acetic acid. Sebacic acid is determined by precipitation as zinc sebacate; maleic, in the absence of fumaric, is determined by bromination; if fumaric is present, it is determined as mercurous fumarate (when succinic and sebacic are absent) or as cadmium fumarate, precipitated from glacial acetic acid. Succinic or adipic cannot be determined in mixtures, but, if either is present alone, it is determined by precipitation as the silver salt.

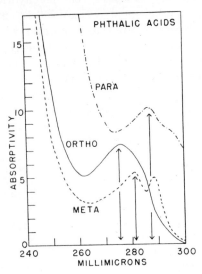

Fig. 2. Ultraviolet absorption spectra of *o*-, *m*-, and *p*-phthalic acids.

As noted above in the case of phthalic acid, these methods, while useful, are very tedious and time consuming and suffer from the inherent deficiencies of methods based on gravimetric heavy metal precipitation procedures.

Recently, Swann, Adams, and Weil developed an extension of the Shreve-Heether spectrophotometric method described above (117) to include the determination of isophthalic and terephthalic acids in alkyd resins (135). Figure 2, taken from Swann's work, shows ultraviolet spectra of these three acids in acidic 1:1 water–methanol medium. The method involves isolation of the dibasic acids from the alkyd as potassium salts by a modified Kappelmeier saponification procedure, followed by spectrophotometric measurements on an acidified water–methanol solution of the salts at 275, 281, and 287 mμ where the ortho, meta, and para phthalic acid isomers, respectively, exhibit absorption maxima.

Among various possibilities that may ultimately provide a basis for additional improved methods in this phase of alkyd analysis are the work of Stafford et al. on dibasic acid derivatives (129,131), Marvel's work on application of partition chromatography to analysis of polybasic acid mixtures (85), and similar work by Higuchi et al. (56).

(3) Methods for Polyhydric Alcohols Other Than Glycerin. (a) *Glycerin in the Presence of Other Polyols.* The polyhydric alcohol fraction as isolated in the procedures given above may consist entirely of one or more polyols other than glycerin. More often, however, when polyols other than glycerin are involved, this fraction will comprise glycerin along with one or two additional polyols. Table VI lists the products formed by some of the more important polyols used in alkyds when these are subjected to

TABLE VI

Products of Periodic Acid (or Periodate) Oxidation of Some Polyhydric Alcohols Used in Alkyd Manufacture

Polyhydric alcohol	Oxidation products (moles per mole polyol)
Glycerin	$2HCHO$; $1HCOOH$
Sorbitol	$2HCHO$; $4HCOOH$
Ethylene glycol	$2HCHO$
1,2-Propylene glycol	$1HCHO$; $1CH_3CHO$
Diethylene glycol	No reaction
Trimethylene glycol	No reaction
Pentaerythritol	No reaction

periodic acid oxidation. As the table indicates, with the exception of sorbitol most polyols likely to be encountered will not interfere in the formic acid titration procedure for glycerin given above. Thus this procedure is rather generally applicable.

(b) *Methods for Other Polyols.* Alkyds containing glycerin along with ethylene glycol or 1,2-propylene glycol can be analyzed for both polyol components by periodic acid (or sodium periodate) oxidation of an aliquot of the isolated polyol fraction, as outlined in the procedure of Section III.1A(2)(c) above followed by a combined acidimetric and iodometric titration procedure (4). This combined titration procedure is also applicable in the presence of a third polyol, such as trimethylene glycol (102), diethylene glycol (4), or pentaerythritol, which is not oxidized by periodic acid or periodate. These latter nonoxidized types (i.e., polyols that do not contain vicinal hydroxyls) may be determined in admixture with oxidizable types by difference after determination of total polyol content by acid dichromate oxidation (4) or acetylation (102). One of these (pentaerythritol) can be directly estimated in such mixtures by the following gravimetric procedure based on reaction of this polyol with benzaldehyde in methanol to produce the dibenzal derivative (this method is presently being evaluated by A. S. T. M. Committee D-1):

Procedure for Pentaerythritol. From the final diluted aqueous solution in Section III.1A(2)(c) for the glycerin determination, transfer an aliquot expected to contain 0.15 to 0.35 g. pentaerythritol to a 100 ml. beaker. Evaporate on a steam bath until crystals appear, indicating a supersaturated solution. To the hot solution (incipient boiling) add 15 ml. benzaldehyde–methanol reagent (20 ml. Merck N. F. grade benzaldehyde in 100 ml. anhydrous methanol) and 12 ml. concentrated HCl. Swirl and allow to stand at room temperature 15 minutes, swirling occasionally during this time to prevent the precipitate from adhering to the bottom of the beaker. Place the beaker in an ice bath, maintaining the temperature at 0–2° C. for 1 hour or more.

At the end of this time, remove the reaction mixture from the ice bath and immediately filter with suction through a weighed fritted-glass crucible of medium porosity. Rinse the beaker with 25 ml. of cold (0–2°C.) methanol–water wash solution (1:1 anhydrous methanol–water mixture) and add to the crucible. Continue to transfer and wash the precipitate with 100 ml. of 1:1 methanol–water solution at 20–25° in the following manner: disconnect the vacuum line; pour a 10 ml. portion of the wash solution from the beaker to the crucible and stir the precipitate to form a homogeneous slurry, using a short flat-ended glass rod. Connect the vacuum line and draw the wash solution through the crucible. Repeat this washing operation six times. With the last 30 ml. of 1:1 methanol–water solution, rinse the interior walls of the crucible and rinse and remove the short stirring rod. Aspirate thoroughly and dry the precipitate at 105°C. for 2 hours; cool in a desiccator and weigh.

Calculation.

$$\% \text{ pentaerythritol} = \frac{(\text{ppt. wt.} + 0.0269) \times 43.6}{\text{sample wt.} \times \text{aliquot factor} \times \text{fractional solids content}}$$

Note: The value 0.0269 is an empirical correction factor used to compensate for the solubility of the benzaldehyde derivative under the conditions of the method.

The above method determines only pentaerythritol monomer. Commercial pentaerythritol used in alkyds, however, usually comprises only about 85% monomer, the remainder being dipentaerythritol and higher polymers. Results for monopentaerythritol are usually converted to the approximate commercial equivalent, assuming 85% purity.

Jaffe and Pinchas (64) have published an interesting paper describing an infrared spectrometric procedure for the estimation of dipentaerythritol in the presence of pentaerythritol monomer. This method, with suitable adaptations, should provide a basis for obtaining additional information on the polyol fraction of alkyds containing this polyol. Further present and potential applications of infrared spectroscopy in alkyd characterization are discussed in part 5 of this section.

Another technique very useful for qualitative purposes and, under proper conditions, adapted to quantitative estimation of polyols as isolated from alkyds is paper chromatography. Hough (62) has published paper chromatographic procedures for various polyhydroxy compounds and these can be easily adapted to examination of the aqueous polyol fraction obtained in the alkyd saponification breakdown.

C. STYRENATED ALKYD RESINS

Reaction of drying oils and drying oil modified alkyds with styrene produces synthetic materials which have found wide acceptance in the manufacture of surface coatings. Though representing a relatively new development, these materials are now used in a variety of coatings applications. In recent years, increasing interest has centered on styrenated alkyds as distinguished from styrenated oils. While there are various methods for the synthesis of styrenated alkyd resins, a manufacturing procedure coming into increasing use involves the direct styrenation of a previously formed oil-modified alkyd resin with monomeric styrene to produce a resin in which some of the styrene is presumably reacted with the unsaturated linkages of the alkyd oil modifier. Due to the complexity of such resins and the lack of suitable analytical procedures for their reliable characterization, a great deal of confusion has existed in the literature with regard to the reaction mechanism, the exact nature of the styrenated reaction product, etc. As pointed out by Armitage and Kut (8), much of this confusion has arisen from failure of investigators to recognize that, in addition to any "copolymer" formed between styrene and the double bonds in the drying oil or alkyd drying oil modifier, these resins contain substantial quantities of polystyrene as such (i. e., uncombined styrene). Since this fact was finally recognized, the problem of isolating and estimating the uncombined polystyrene present in styrenated oils and styrenated alkyds and further characterizing such resins has occupied the attention of several investigators (11,25–27,71–75,101,136).

All approaches to the analysis of such resins involve, as the first step, breakdown by saponification using procedures similar to that described above for a straight glyceryl phthalate-type alkyd resin. Work in the author's laboratory and cooperative studies by A. S. T. M. Committee D-1 have established the fact that the phthalic anhydride content of styrenated alkyd resins can be accurately and reliably determined by the method described in Section III.1A(2)(a) above for phthalic anhydride in regular alkyds. The use of a substantial quantity of benzene in the saponification and washing procedure was incorporated, in fact, to obviate interference from uncombined styrene which might otherwise precipitate with the phthalate salt. The methods of Section III.1A(1) above for solids, excess hydroxyl, and acid number are directly applicable to styrenated alkyds without modification. The remaining determinations necessary for reasonably complete characterization of such a resin are: determination of total polymerized styrene, "uncombined" polystyrene; combined (copolymerized) styrene; polyhydric alcohols; and total fatty acids. The following general approach has been found useful in the author's laboratory:

After saponification of a styrenated alkyd, and precipitation and removal of potassium phthalate by the procedure given in III.1(2)(a) above, evaporation of the filtrate and dilution with water will produce a flocculent precipitate that can be filtered off, washed to remove adhering fatty acid soaps, dried, and weighed to yield a fairly good but not too precise estimate of "uncombined styrene."

Acidification of the filtrate from this precipitation followed by extraction with ether and evaporation of the ether yields a fraction containing the fatty acid modifiers along with the remainder of the styrene, present presumably in the form of styrene-fatty acid copolymer. The weight of this fraction plus its acid value, as determined by titration with standard base, affords a basis for an approximate estimate of total fatty acids and per cent "combined styrene" in the resin solids. An aliquot of the aqueous layer remaining after the ether extraction can be employed for the glycerin or other polyol determination using procedures already discussed.

Swann (136) has published a gravimetric procedure somewhat similar to the above for estimating total polymerized styrene.

In this method the filtrate from the phthalic determination is transferred to a 400 ml. beaker, being washed with small portions of benzene. The solvents are evaporated under a hood, using an 80°C. glycol bath and a current of air. When the solvent volume has been reduced to approximately 5 ml., 5 ml. of absolute methanol is added, the sample is agitated, and the evaporation is continued to apparent dryness. If the sample contains appreciable quantities of styrene monomer, repeated evaporations with methanol are necessary. 15 ml. of water is thoroughly mixed with 100 ml. of absolute methanol (or 115 ml. of 87% methanol) and added to the sample. A glass stirring rod is inserted and the beaker is covered and warmed in a bath at 65°C. The sample is stirred every 10 minutes and all portions of the solid matter are loosened from the sides and bottom of the beaker. All lumps or large particles are broken up with the rod.

After 30 minutes, the sample is removed from the bath, cooled to room temperature, then filtered through a dried, weighed, fritted-glass crucible of coarse porosity, previously prepared with a mat of asbestos. When all of the methanol solution has drained through the crucible, transfer of the sample is continued with water only. When all of the sample has been transferred to the crucible, washing with water is continued until the washings show no alkalinity when tested with indicator paper. The residue is then dried at 110°C., cooled, and weighed. Calculation is made directly on the nonvolatile vehicle:

$$\% \text{ polystyrene} = \frac{\text{weight of residue} \times 100}{\text{weight of vehicle} \times \text{vehicle solids}}$$

Swann reports that, in the case of the samples examined in the development of the above method, all of the styrene present was precipitated, none being found in the fatty acids isolated after separation of the styrene. Several resins examined in the author's laboratory, however, show substantial amounts of styrene remaining in the fatty acids after precipitation of polystyrene from the aqueous saponificate, as described above. This residual styrene appears to be copolymerized with the fatty acid modifiers, since efforts to remove it by ion exchange or other separation techniques were unsuccessful.

Another method for determination of total polymerized styrene in styrenated fatty acids and styrenated alkyds has recently been proposed by Hirt and co-workers (58). This method is based on spectrophotometric measurements in the ultraviolet region of the spectrum. In the case of a styrenated alkyd, the filtrate from the phthalic determination is neutralized with HCl, the precipitated KCl is filtered off, and the filtrate is concentrated and extracted with ether. After evaporation of the ether, the residue containing polystyrene, fatty acids, and copolymer is dissolved in cyclohexane and the absorbance measured at selected wave lengths. Calibration involves the use of absorptivity values for pure polystyrene and for monomeric styrene and conjugated triene fatty acids, since these interfere if present. The published method gives no data on the analysis of styrenated alkyds, but results on styrenated fatty acids show good agreement with those calculated from saponification number.

Present and potential applications of absorption spectroscopy in the characterization of styrenated alkyds are discussed in part 5 of this section.

2. Urea-Formaldehyde and Melamine-Formaldehyde Resins

Urea-formaldehyde and melamine-formaldehyde resins (commonly called "nitrogen resins") are extensively used in combination with oil modified alkyds as vehicles for a large volume and variety of industrial baking enamels as well as for many other applications. For use in coatings such resins comprise condensation products of formaldehyde with urea or melamine modified with an alcohol, usually butanol; i. e., butoxy groups are incorporated in the resin to produce a soluble polymer suitable for solution coatings use.

Structurally such resins may be represented by formulas II (for urea-formaldehyde) and III (for melamine-formaldehyde). Both types are manufactured and sold in the form of solutions of the butylated condensate in butanol or butanol–hydrocarbon mixture as solvent.

II   III

Analytical characterization of such resins usually involves determination of the total "solids" and free formaldehyde contents of the resin solution and the composition of the dissolved resin itself in terms of per cent total urea or melamine, per cent combined formaldehyde, and per cent combined butanol.

A. METHODS FOR DIRECT EXAMINATION OF RESIN SOLUTION

(1) Total Solids. Nitrogen resins are very unstable to heat, being designed to split out butanol, water, and formaldehyde and thus undergo further intermolecular condensation when enamels containing them are applied in the form of thin films and baked; thus the true solids (non-volatile) content of a solution of such a resin (if indeed such a value exists) cannot be obtained by methods involving oven drying; for this reason, the solids content is normally specified as the per cent nonvolatile obtained when the resin solution is oven dried under empirically established, arbitrarily specified conditions that must be carefully controlled if reproducible results are to be obtained. The following procedure, which involves dilution with xylol, will yield good precision if all conditions are carefully controlled:

Apparatus. Aluminum dishes, $3^1/_2''$ diameter and $^1/_4''$ deep; bottom of dish must be perfectly flat, variation not exceeding 0.001 inch in 4 inches. Forced draft Isotemp oven regulated to 105 ± 2°C. Weighing pipet (or weighing bottle fitted with hypodermic syringe through stopper). Desiccator containing P_2O_5 or drierite ($CaCl_2$ must not be used).

Procedure. Accurately weigh 40 g. of the resin solution and 80 g. of xylol (b. p. 135–146°C.) into a pint jar, using a torsion balance accurate to 0.1 g. Mix thoroughly by shaking. Transfer a portion of this diluted sample to a clean, dry weighing pipet or weighing bottle. Weigh to 4 decimal places a clean aluminum dish that has been previously heated for 15 minutes at 105°C. and cooled in a desiccator. Weigh the pipet and sample. Quickly transfer from weighed pipet to aluminum dish sufficient sample to yield a residue of 0.5 ± 0.05 g. Reweigh pipet. *Calculate* weight of sample by difference.

To obtain sufficient sample to yield 0.5 ± 0.05 g. of resin film, the following weights of diluted resin solution must be used:

Expected solids, %	Wt. of diluted sample to be used, g.
70	1.93 to 2.36
60	2.25 to 2.75
50	2.70 to 3.30
40	3.38 to 4.13

Carefully spread the sample evenly over the bottom of the dish by a gentle swirling motion. If the sample does not spread easily, 2 or 3 ml. of butanol or xylol may be added to facilitate spreading. Transfer the dish to the forced draft Isotemp oven regulated to 105 ± 2°C. placing the dish perfectly level so that uniform thickness of residual film is deposited. Dry exactly one hour as timed with a stopwatch; then transfer to desiccator to cool. Reweigh.
Calculate weight of residue by difference.

$$\% \text{ solids} = \frac{\text{weight of residue} \times 300}{\text{weight of sample}}$$

Precision, calculated as 95% confidence limits from data obtained at the 50% solids level by a single operator, is ±0.2%.

Sub-Committee XI of A. S. T. M. Committee D-1 has for some time been conducting a cooperative study of methods for determining nonvolatile content of heat-unstable resins. While this study is not complete, as of this date, promising results have been obtained with a method in which the resin solution is spread by pressure between two sheets of aluminum or tin foil and the sheets separated and oven dried under appropriate conditions.

(2) Free (Uncombined) Formaldehyde. Determination of free formaldehyde in nitrogen resin solutions is complicated by the fact that the usual reagents used for the determination of formaldehyde tend to promote hydrolysis of the resin to release combined formaldehyde, thus yielding high results. Hydrolysis can usually be prevented (or minimized), however, by rapid titration procedures at reduced temperature. Dilution and mixing of an appropriate size sample with water followed by a rapid sodium sulfite titration of the aqueous phase at 0–5°C. usually gives reasonably good precision. Details of sulfite methods and other procedures for formaldehyde have been discussed elsewhere in this series (91).

B. ANALYSIS OF DISSOLVED RESIN

If the butanol combined in the resin condensate is to be determined, the analysis cannot be performed on samples of the resin solution because of the presence of a large excess of free butanol as solvent. For this reason and others—having to do with the difficulty of obtaining a true solids value for the resin solution and considerations of accuracy and precision in the other two determinations required—the complete analytical characterization of the dissolved nitrogen resin condensate is best performed on samples of powdered film prepared by "doctor blading" thin films on aluminum foil or thin glass plates, drying to constant weight at room temperature in a vacuum desiccator containing concentrated H_2SO_4, and removal in powdered form by scraping with a razor blade.

(1) **Total Urea or Melamine.** The urea or melamine content of coating-type nitrogen resins is normally calculated from total nitrogen, as determined by any reliable version of the Kjeldahl method. Kappelmeier, however, has described a method (76,77) for the quantitative determination of urea, as such, by reaction with benzylamine to produce the benzyl urea derivative, which is isolated, dried, and weighed. The reaction is indicated by the following:

$$\text{urea-formaldehyde} + C_6H_5 \cdot CH_2NH_2 \xrightarrow{\text{aminolysis}} H_2N\text{—}C(\text{=O})\text{—}NH_2$$

$$H_2N\text{—}C(\text{=O})\text{—}NH_2 + 2(C_6H_5 \cdot CH_2NH_2) \longrightarrow$$
$$C_6H_5 \cdot CH_2NH\text{—}C(\text{=O})\text{—}NHCH_2 \cdot C_6H_5 + 2NH_3$$

Grad and Dunn (49) have studied the reaction further and proposed an improved procedure for this determination. They did not evaluate their procedure on alcohol-modified coating-type urea-formaldehyde resins, but it is presumably applicable to these in the form of powdered film samples prepared as indicated above. These authors are of the opinion that the reaction involves the coordination of the free electrons of the nitrogen of benzylamine with the electropositive carbon atoms of the carbonyl groups of the condensate. This is followed by rearrangements and the splitting of ammonia and formaldehyde from the molecule. The dibenzylurea is highly insoluble in acidic medium and separates readily from the reaction mixture with the addition of excess acid.

Reagents. Benzylamine (Eastman Kodak). HCl solution (1 volume concentrated acid to 3 volumes water). Congo red paper.

Procedure. Weigh into a 125 ml. iodine flask 0.5 g. of the powdered film and add 15 ml. of benzylamine. Provide an interjoint side arm adapter with a thermometer for measuring the temperature of the distillate. Assemble the apparatus, place the flask in a sand bath, and connect the side arm to a suitable manifold for the disposal of fumes and distillate. Apply heat until a water–benzylamine mixture is observed to distil. The temperature will rise to some point below 100°C. The mixture should distil at or below this temperature as long as moisture is present in the sample. Should the temperature of the distillate rise above 100°C., reduce the amount of heat applied to the sand bath. The water-free benzylamine (b. p. 182°C.) should reflux from the sides of the flask, but should not distil over. Reflux liquid and spray dried resins for 8 hours and cured resins for 16 hours. Allow the reaction mixture to cool to 40°C. and, while stirring mechanically, add the hydrochloric acid solution dropwise until the mixture is acid to congo red indicator paper. Place the flask in an ice bath and continue stirring until any oil that may have formed becomes crystalline. Collect the crystals in a previously dried (150°C.) and weighed sintered-glass crucible of medium porosity. Wash the crystals with cold water until free from acid. Dry the crucible and contents to constant weight at 105°C. The melting point of the crystals should be 165–167°C. If the resin contains a nitrogen-free filler (wood and shell flours), determine the nitrogen content of the residual dibenzylurea-filler mixture. Since dibenzylurea is the only nitrogen-containing compound present, per cent nitrogen can be converted to dibenzylurea and the weight present in the residue calculated.

$$\% \text{ urea} = \frac{\text{dibenzylurea wt.} \times 25.01}{\text{sample wt.}}$$

Table VII, taken from the paper by Grad and Dunn (49), compares results obtained by this method with those calculated from total nitrogen in the analysis of various urea-formaldehyde condensates.

Estimation of urea from total nitrogen assumes, of course, that no other nitrogen compound is present in significant amount. Where the validity of this assumption is suspected, the direct method for urea should find useful application.

As far as the author is aware, no direct method for the estimation of melamine in melamine-formaldehyde resins is presently available; such estimates are based exclusively on total nitrogen.

(2) Combined Formaldehyde. Determination of combined formaldehyde in either urea-formaldehyde or melamine-formaldehyde resins involves acid hydrolysis of the resin followed by distillation, collection, and

TABLE VII

Determination of Urea in Various Types of Urea-Formaldehyde Resins

Type of resin	Urea recovered, %	
	From total nitrogen	From dibenzylurea wt.
Spray dried, I......................	57.4	57.3
	57.4	57.4
Spray dried, II......................	60.8	60.7
	60.8	60.7
Heat cured, I......................	60.3	57.7
	60.3	57.5
Heat cured, II......................	49.3	49.1
	49.3	49.1

determination of the liberated formaldehyde. Grad and Dunn (49) have recently presented a critical study of several hydrolyzing reagents that have been proposed and concluded that 1:1 phosphoric acid is the most efficient and convenient. They point out that a reliable procedure for this determination must employ, in addition to an efficient hydrolyzing agent, provision for collecting the liberated formaldehyde in a medium which chemically binds it (to prevent losses). Their proposed procedure, with slight modification, has been found applicable to this type of determination on both urea-formaldehyde and melamine resins of the alcohol-modified coating variety. The method involves hydrolysis with 1:1 phosphoric acid followed by distillation and collection of liberated formaldehyde in alkaline potassium cyanide in which it is chemically bound as formaldehyde cyanohydrin. Formaldehyde can then be estimated by volumetric or gravimetric determination of excess cyanide, as determined by runs on a blank and the distillate from the sample. The procedure given utilizes a gravimetric determination for which the authors' claims of improved accuracy and precision seem to be justified.

Procedure. Pipet into a 500 ml. volumetric flask 50 ml. of cyanide solution (24.8 g. of KCN and 10 g. of KOH dissolved in 1 liter H_2O). Introduce about 0.5 g. of powdered film (prepared by doctor blading and vacuum drying at room temperature) into a claisen-type distillation flask equipped through ground-glass joints with a dropping funnel, thermometer, and a condenser with a suitable adapter that fits into the 500 ml. volumetric flask as receiver. Introduce into the dropping funnel 50 ml. of phosphoric acid solution (1:1 dilution). Allow the solution to run into the flask in a dropwise manner. Adjust the temperature and water flow from the dropping funnel so that the temperature is maintained at about 110°C.

and the system delivers 65–70 drops per minute. The distillation should take at least two hours. Disconnect the apparatus and wash down the condenser and delivery tube with distilled water. Dilute the distillate to the 500 ml. mark. Introduce into a 250 ml. beaker 25 ml. of silver nitrate solution (10.2 g. of AgNO$_3$ dissolved in 300 ml. water). Acidify with 2 ml. of 1:1 nitric acid solution. While stirring, pipet into this solution 100 ml. of the distillate. Allow the precipitate to digest until the supernatant liquid is clear. Collect the silver cyanide precipitate in a previously dried (105°C.) and weighed gooch crucible. Wash the precipitate until the washings are free from silver nitrate (chloride test). Dry the crucible to constant weight at 105°C. Prepare a blank by pipetting 50 ml. of the cyanide solution into a 500 ml. volumetric flask and diluting to the mark. Treat the blank in the same manner as the sample.

$$\% \text{ formaldehyde} = \frac{(W_b - W_s) \times 112.1}{S}$$

where W_b = weight of silver cyanide in the blank, W_s = weight of silver cyanide in the sample, and S = weight of the sample.

TABLE VIII

Formaldehyde Recovery from Urea-Formaldehyde Resin of Known Composition

Determination No.	HCHO added, g.	HCHO recovered, g.	HCHO recovered, %
1	0.2625	0.2620	99.81
2	0.1575	0.1574	99.94
3	0.2100	0.2097	99.86

TABLE IX

Determination of Formaldehyde in a Liquid and a Solid Resin

Analyst	Formaldehyde recovered, %	
	Liquid resin	Solid resin
A	39.18	51.04
	39.24	51.02
	39.20	51.08
	39.20	51.08
	39.22	51.06
	39.17	51.10
B	39.23	51.10
	39.16	51.04
	39.19	51.05
	39.20	51.07
	39.23	51.09
	39.17	51.06

The accuracy and precision of the method are indicated by the data of Tables VIII and IX, taken from the publication by Grad and Dunn (49).

(3) Combined Butanol. The following procedure, which has proved satisfactory in the author's laboratory, is based on quantitative conversion of the combined butanol in a urea-formaldehyde or melamine resin to butyl acetate by refluxing with acetic anhydride–acetic acid reagent in the presence of sodium acetate as catalyst. The butyl acetate produced is separated by distillation and determined by measurement of saponification value on the distillate.

Procedure. Place a weighed sample of the powdered vacuum dried film (about 0.5 g.) in a 50 ml. flask provided with a glass jointed claisen-type distilling head with thermometer and condenser. Reflux for one hour with a mixture of glacial acetic acid (10 ml.), acetic anhydride (25 ml.), and sodium acetate (2 g.). After the acetylation period, cool the mixture in an ice bath, add water slowly to decompose the acetic anhydride, and then partially neutralize (to pH 6) with concentrated ammonium hydroxide while cooling. Raise the temperature and distil the butyl acetate into a 250 ml. erlenmeyer flask containing a few milliliters of water, the flask being immersed in an ice bath. Collect about 50 ml. of distillate. Analyze the distillate as follows: Neutralize the small amount of free acid with standardized 0.2 N aqueous caustic, add an excess, and reflux for one hour to saponify the esters. Cool and back-titrate with 0.2 N H_2SO_4 (phenolphthalein end point). Repeat the above procedure with the omission of the resin sample as a blank determination.

Calculation.

$$\% \text{ butanol} = 7.412N(V_b - V_b)_s/S$$

where V_b = milliliters of acid for blank, V_s = milliliters of acid for sample, N = normality of standard acid, and S = sample weight.

3. Phenol-Formaldehyde Resins

These are condensation products of phenol or substituted phenols with formaldehyde. A variety of such resins based on different phenols and manufactured to yield various properties is available for use in coatings. Most are sold in solid form rather than as resin solutions. Aldehydes other than formaldehyde are used, but those based on formaldehyde are by far the most important commercially and the present discussion is confined to this type. Phenolics are structurally quite complex, but the general type of structure involved can be represented by formula **IV**.

$$\underset{\text{IV}}{\underset{\text{R}}{\bigcirc}} \overset{\text{OH}}{\underset{\text{H}}{\overset{\text{H}}{\underset{}{-\text{C}-}}}}$$

By analogy with the type of analytical breakdown described in preceding sections for alkyds, styrenated alkyds, and nitrogen resins, it would be desirable to be able to degrade phenolic resins in such a way as to make possible the quantitative estimation of parent phenol, combined formaldehyde, and perhaps other characteristic structural entities; at present, however, the author knows of no well-standardized procedures adapted to this purpose. Smooth quantitative conversion to parent phenol, or a reproducibly obtainable derivative thereof, and quantitative liberation of formaldehyde cannot be achieved by acid or basic hydrolysis. Pyrolysis of such resins usually yields complex products, including phenols other than those originally incorporated. Controlled pyrolysis followed by infrared or mass-spectrometric examination of the products has been used for identification of various polymers (22,51,80,148), and further study of such techniques as applied to phenolics may in the future provide a basis for more complete characterization than is now possible.

A. DETERMINATION OF ALCOHOLIC AND PHENOLIC HYDROXYL

In view of the above, standardized or reasonably well-established methods for the analytical characterization of phenolics are, of necessity, largely confined at present to those directly applicable to the original resin without degradative breakdown. One such type of determination is the estimation of total hydroxyl content and breakdown of this in terms of phenolic hydroxyl and alcoholic hydroxyl (or uncondensed methylol groups), respectively. This can be done by first determining total hydroxyl on an appropriate sized sample by acetylation with acetic anhydride in pyridine using the procedure recommended in III.1A(1)(c) above for excess hydroxyl in alkyds; alcoholic hydroxyl is then determined by phthalation with phthalic anhydride in pyridine, a reagent that does not attack phenolic hydroxyls under the conditions employed (35). Phenolic hydroxyl is calculated by difference.

Special Reagents. Phthalic anhydride–pyridine reagent (36 g. of reagent grade phthalic anhydride diluted to 250 ml. with pyridine that has been dried over solid KOH for at least 72 hours). Standard normal aqueous sodium hydroxide.

Procedure. Weigh accurately a sample containing approximately 0.006 mole alcoholic hydroxyl into a 250 ml. iodine flask and add 25 ml. of the phthalic anhydride–pyridine reagent, accurately measured from a pipet. Stopper the flasks loosely, pour a small amount of anhydrous pyridine into the lip of the flask so as to moisten the stopper, and warm on a steam bath for two and one-half to three hours.

At the end of this time, cool the flask slightly, add 50 ml. of distilled water, and replace on the steam bath for a few moments to hydrolyze excess reagent. Cool the flask to room temperature, add 1 ml. of a 1% phenolphthalein solution, and titrate with standard normal alkali until a permanent pink color is obtained on shaking. Run a pair of blanks using the same conditions as employed with the sample.

Calculation.

$$\% \text{ alcoholic hydroxyl} = 1.7N(A - B)/W$$

where N = normality of NaOH, A = milliliters of NaOH for blank, B = milliliters of NaOH for sample, and W = sample weight.

In a different approach Martin (84) has described a very useful method in which the alcoholic hydroxyl bearing groups (i. e., methylol groups— CH_2OH) are determined by reaction with excess phenol followed by azeotropic distillation and estimation of the water split out:

$$RCH_2OH + C_6H_5OH \longrightarrow RCH_2C_6H_4OH + H_2O$$

The accuracy of the method was established on pure compounds containing methylol groups and applied to various condensates of known phenol-formaldehyde ratio. The details involved are as follows:

A solution containing 500 g. of phenol (commercial redistilled), 250 ml. of benzene, and 15 g. of *p*-toluenesulfonic acid monohydrate was placed in a 1 liter flask equipped with a Bidwell and Sterling take-off trap provided with a stopcock and reflux condenser. The take-off trap was of 5 ml. capacity, graduated in units of 0.1 ml. The phenol solution was dried by refluxing vigorously, any water being removed by distilling into the take-off trap where it was withdrawn. The trap was calibrated by adding known quantities of water from a pipet to the phenol solution and distilling until no more water collected in the trap. In calibrating the trap it was necessary to add the water to the phenol solution and distil it into the trap rather than add the water directly to the trap, as a small quantity of phenol codistils with the water. The correction was mainly due to the large contact angle between the water and the glass and changed from about 0.12 ml. for 1 ml. to 0.15 ml. for 4 ml. By treating the inside of the trap and condenser with G. E. Dri-Film water repellent (applied in the form of a toluene solution and cured by baking one hour at 150°C.), the tendency for water droplets to adhere to the glass and not sink to the bottom of the trap was essentially eliminated.

After the trap was calibrated, a sample of known weight and sufficient size to yield 2 to 4 ml. of water was introduced into the phenol solution. The solution was refluxed until no more water separated. The volume of aqueous phase collected in the trap was measured and corrected, by use of the calibration data, to give the quantity of water formed by reaction of the sample with the phenol. From this figure, the methylol content can be calculated. For routine tests on resins, it was found practical to run a number of samples without changing the phenol solution; care was taken to see that reaction was complete for one sample before a second sample was added. When it seems advisable to use fresh phenol for each test, 100 to 150 ml. of phenol solution is adequate.

The phenolic hydroxyl content of phenolic resins cannot be determined directly by conventional acid-base titration methods; however, it should be possible to determine such groups by titration in a nonaqueous medium, such as ethylenediamine, using procedures similar to those given by Moss, Elliott and Hall (95) for resinous materials containing such groups (see chapter on Determination of Organic Acids in this volume).

B. DETERMINATION OF FREE PHENOL

While the final composition of phenolic resins depends on the catalyst and other conditions employed in their manufacture, most resins contain significant amounts of the unreacted monomeric "parent" phenol used. In the case of resins based on unsubstituted phenol, the unreacted phenol is determined by separating it from the resins by distillation or solvent extraction and measuring the amount by chemical methods, usually bromination (105,124). Such methods, however, are not too reliable. Distillation may cause further condensation of the resin, thus yielding low results and solvents, usually extract low molecular weight resin, which also brominates and causes high results.

Smith and co-workers (126) have proposed a direct infrared spectrophotometric method for free unsubstituted phenol in both heat-reactive and heat-stable phenolics. This method, which requires no separation of monomeric phenol from resin, is based on direct absorption measurements on the resin in acetone solution at 14.4 microns, where unsubstituted phenol exhibits strong infrared absorption with little or no interference from the more highly substituted aromatic structures in the resin. The method is, of course, not applicable to the direct determination of free phenols containing substituents on the aromatic ring.

Other applications of infrared spectrometry to phenolic resin characterization are discussed in part 5 of this section.

4. Other Commercially Important Resins

Many classes of resins other than those selected for detailed treatment in this chapter have achieved positions of importance in large-scale commerical coatings manufacture.

A few of these are enumerated and briefly commented on in this section with respect to their analytical characterization as individual resins.

Many useful literature references to techniques and methods specifically designed for the characterization of such classes, or adaptable thereto with suitable modification, as well as methods for their examination in mixtures, will be found in the series of reviews in *Analytical Chemistry* on the general subject of coatings analysis. (106–109,130).

A. CELLULOSE DERIVATIVES

Nitrocellulose and cellulose esters of organic acids (particularly cellulose acetate) represent the most important cellulose types used in coatings, although cellulose ethers such as methyl and ethyl cellulose have specialized uses in the field.

Cellulose derivatives are usually characterized analytically by determination of the substituted groups. Genung and associates (40,46,47,86) have presented and critically discussed methods for the analytical characterization of cellulose ethers, cellulose acetate, and other cellulose esters. Methods adapted to the estimation of acyl content by saponification and free hydroxyl by acetylation in such materials are critically discussed and a nomographic scheme for conversion of this type of information to number of groups present per anhydroglucose unit in the cellulose is presented (47).

Methods for the determination of nitrate nitrogen, including detailed procedures applicable to nitrocellulose, will be found in Volume II of this series (16).

B. ROSIN DERIVATIVES

Rosin and synthetic resins based on rosin are used in a variety of coatings applications. The more important synthetic derivatives comprise esterification products of rosin with glycerin, glycols, or pentaerythritol and similar esters of maleic anhydride or phenolic resin "adducts" of rosin.

Saponification procedures suitable for the characterization of rosin esters are discussed in the preceding volume of this series (50). Such procedures with suitable modifications can be used for isolation and determination of the polyol and rosin acids fractions for analytical determination and examination. Ultraviolet spectrophotometry has been found very useful for the component analysis of rosin acids (52) and application of this and other spectroscopic techniques to such studies are discussed in a recent review article by Ahlers and O'Neill (3).

C. VINYL CHLORIDE AND VINYL CHLORIDE-ACETATE COPOLYMERS

While numerous vinyl types have achieved positions of importance in coatings applications, polyvinyl chloride and vinyl chloride-vinyl acetate copolymers are perhaps the most widely used at present in the manufacture of solution type coatings.

Polyvinyl chloride is characterized mainly by determination of total chlorine by Parr bomb fusion with sodium peroxide followed by any suitable gravimetric or volumetric method for determination of the liberated halide ions. Solvent fractionation of such resins, followed by determination of chlorine and infrared examination of each fraction, provides more detailed characterization (53).

Vinyl chloride-acetate types may be characterized by total chlorine determination, as above, and determination of acetate content. Determination of acetate may be carried out by hydrolysis with phosphoric acid. After precipitation of liberated chloride with silver phosphate or sulfate, the acetic acid formed in the hydrolysis is distilled into standard alkali and determined by back titration. Infrared spectra are also useful in the characterization of such resins as well as other vinyl chloride copolymers.

D. SILICONE RESINS

Methods applicable to quantitative elemental analysis of silicone resins of the type available for coatings use are given by Rochow (110). Methods for the determination of hydroxyl and other functional groups in such resins do not appear to be well standardized as yet, but suitable modifications of procedures selected from those given in previous volumes of this series should be adaptable to this purpose. Infrared spectral background on silicone-type compounds is steadily being built up (32,42,104,113,122, 145,146) and infrared methods will undoubtedly prove increasingly useful in the characterization of silicone-type polymers.

E. SYNTHETIC RUBBER TYPES

For coatings use, these include butadiene-styrene and butadiene-acrylonitrile copolymers, chlorinated rubber, and others.

Various published techniques and methods for the analysis of synthetic rubbers for noncoating applications are applicable to the characterization of rubber-like resins used in coatings with suitable modifications. Published methods in this field have been reviewed annually for the past several years by Bekkedahl and Bekkedahl and Stiehler (17–21), and these reviews afford a wealth of reference material for those concerned with analysis of rubber-type polymers.

F. EPOXY RESINS

Condensates of epichlorohydrin with diphenylolpropane, sold under the trade name Epon, have recently come into wide use in applicance finishes and other types of coatings. Methods specifically applicable to the determination of epoxide content of such resins are given in Volume I of this series (66). This, plus determination of hydroxyl content by a procedure that takes into account the presence of epoxide groups, serves to characterize such resins fairly well from the coatings point of view.

Esters of Epon resins with drying oil fatty acids (e. g., dehydrated castor oil acids) represent a modification also used in coatings. The fatty acids from this type can usually be isolated in fairly pure form by saponification, removal of the liberated Epon by dilution with water and filtration, and final extraction of the fatty acid fraction with ether. Such procedures are not yet well standardized, however, and modifications to suit the individual case are necessary.

Epoxidized vegetable oils represent another epoxy type of resin that has found use in coatings. Determination of epoxide content by appropriate procedures of the kind discussed in a previous volume of this series (66) and infrared and ultraviolet spectroscopic examination may be used for characterization.

G. POLYAMIDES

Claspar and Haslam (33) have reviewed existing methods for the analysis of nylon and related polymers and presented procedures for their analytical breakdown by acid hydrolysis (20% HCl) and determination of the dibasic acid and amine components in the hydrolysate. Zahn and Wolf (147) have described procedures for this type of polymer, including the application of paper chromatography to the examination of the amine and dibasic acid components obtained on acid hydrolysis.

H. POLYVINYL ACETAL TYPES

These are condensation products of polyvinyl alcohol with aldehydes, e. g., formaldehyde, acetaldehyde, or butyraldehyde. The use of polyvinyl formal (Formvar) as an ingredient of wire enamels is an example of an important solution coatings application. Some specific methods adaptable to the characterization of resins of this class dealing with determination of acetal groups have been discussed in Volume I of this series (92).

I. POLYACRYLATES AND METHACRYLATES

Polyacrylates can be characterized by saponification value, but polymethacrylates are very difficult to saponify. Since both types depolymerize readily when dry distilled to give good yields of the parent monomer, pyrolysis followed by saponification value and other determinations on the pyrolysis products affords useful characterizing information.

Haslam and Soppet (54) have published an interesting paper on the analytical characterization of polymethyl methacrylate and various copolymers by procedures based on vacuum pyrolysis under conditions designed to yield the purest obtainable monomer. Infrared spectroscopy and other physical methods, as well as chemical methods, were used in examining the products obtained.

Dal Nogare, Perkins, and Hale (97) have described a method for the determination of residual monomer in polymethyl methacrylate by its distillation from an aqueous acetic acid solution of the polymer followed by titration with permanganate under appropriate conditions. Methods based on mercaptan addition are more rapid and satisfactory for this purpose, but interference is encountered if a hydroquinone inhibitor is present.

5. Infrared Spectroscopy in the Characterization of Individual Synthetic Resins

Of the various modern instrumental techniques now available, absorption spectroscopy, particularly infrared, offers great present and potential utility in analytical studies of coating resins and related materials. Some quantitative applications of ultraviolet and infrared spectroscopy have already been discussed in preceding sections. Applications of this latter type (i. e., well-standardized quantitative methods suitable for inclusion in schemes for the more or less routine breakdown of resins for characterization purposes) are still relatively few in number. In recent years, however, a large and steadily increasing body of information involving qualitative, semiquantitative, and structural studies of resinous materials by spectroscopic means has appeared in the literature. This information is scattered and widely varied in nature and no attempt will be made to review it completely here; it includes, however, several quantitative methods applicable to coating-type resins and much that is not directly applicable provides background information for the development of such methods. The following discussion of applications to some of the resin classes discussed in the preceding sections will point up the present and potential utility of infrared in this field. Applications of this technique to the characterization and determination of synthetic resin components in finished paint products are discussed in Section IV of this review.

A. PRESENT AND POTENTIAL APPLICATIONS IN ALKYD RESIN ANALYSIS

Infrared spectroscopy is particularly useful in problems involving the characterization of alkyd resins in the presence of associated resins and other components in finished paint product analysis. Infrared studies on individual oil-modified alkyds as such, however, have also resulted in useful applications and have pointed the way to many potential uses.

The infrared spectrum shown in Figure 3 for an alkyd film of the oil-modified glyceryl phthalate type is taken from a publication from the author's laboratory (116). The three strong bands in the 8–10 micron region are characteristic of phthalate esters with some contribution from the ester linkages of the oil modifier. The two bands at 13.5 and 14.2 microns arise from vibrations of the ortho disubstituted aromatic ring in the phthalic structure and the doublet near 6.2 microns probably arises from overtones of these vibrations. The band at 2.9 microns is due to unesterified glycerolic hydroxyl and that at 5.8 microns is due to carbonyl groups in both the phthalate and oil-modifier structures. These assignments, plus the bands attributable to various carbon-hydrogen vibrations at 3.3, 3.9, and 7.3 microns, account for all but a few very weak bands of uncertain origin. Such a spectrum will distinguish phthalate-type alkyds from those based on other dibasic acids and afford semiquantitative information with respect to the relative amount of unesterified hydroxyl present. Using base line absorbance ratio techniques, a rough estimate of the ratio of total phthalate to oil content can sometimes be made. It is also possible to detect and follow semiquantitatively changes occurring in alkyds on exposure to baking or air drying conditions, etc., by means of selected absorption bands.

If the alkyd has been modified by styrenation, its spectrum will be altered as indicated in the second curve of Figure 3, where the sharp bands in the 6–7 micron region and the shoulder at 13.2 microns on the strong phthalate ring absorption give evidence of the presence of styrene. Some of these differences may afford a possible basis for quantitative estimates of

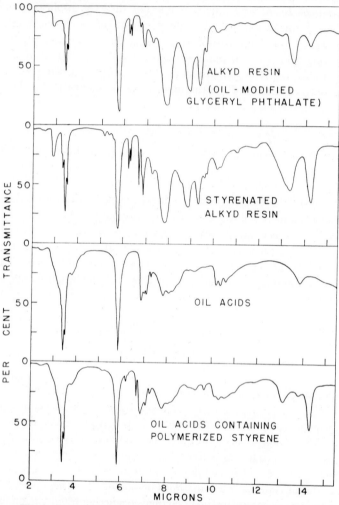

Fig. 3. Infrared spectra of alkyd resins and oil acid fractions.

styrene in such resins. Replacement of some of the ortho phthalic with saturated or mono-unsaturated dibasic acids in alkyds will also, of course, produce alterations in the spectrum, but introduction of such acids in the amounts generally used does not as a rule produce new bands of sufficient definition and intensity to provide a basis for useful quantitative estimates. Replacement of o-phthalic with terephthalic or isophthalic or other aromatic acids, however, produces marked changes of potential quantitative analytical usefulness.

In the saponification of an alkyd and resolution into its dibasic acid, fatty acid, and polyhydric alcohol components by the procedures outlined in Section III.1 above, infrared methods can be used to follow the various steps and check each fraction for purity, and can be applied to each fraction to yield a great deal of additional information.

(1) **Dibasic Acid Fraction.** Stafford and co-workers have reported on the infrared spectra as well as other properties of the N-benzylamides, diethyl esters, and potassium salts of various dibasic acids of importance in modern alkyd resin manufacture (129,131,132). While qualitative identification has received primary emphasis in these studies, they provide background material for possible development of quantitative methods. The potassium salts obtained in the "Kappelmeier precipitate" from saponification of alkyds can be examined in the infrared as Nujol mulls or pressed KBr pellets; comparison with appropriate reference spectra serves to check purity, detect salts of acids other than phthalic, etc. Current attention being given to the development and refinement of the KBr pelleting technique (6,7,63,65,112,133) will undoubtedly increase the potentialities of infrared as applied to the quantitative analysis of mixed salts when they appear in this fraction.

(2) **Fatty Acid Fraction.** Determination of various types of unsaturated fatty acids in the oil modifier fraction from an alkyd resin is best performed by the ultraviolet spectrophotometric procedure outlined in part 1 of this section. In practice, however, application of this technique is often complicated by the presence of *cis-trans* isomers, modification of the fatty acid fraction with styrene, maleic anhydride or other coreacting species, chemical alteration of the oil as a result of partial oxidation, polymerization, etc. For these reasons, infrared spectroscopy affords a very valuable supplement to the ultraviolet spectrophotometric method in the examination of this fraction.

With respect to *cis-trans* isomerism, it has been found that unsaturated fatty acids having the *trans* configuration at the double bond show strong infrared absorption at 10.36 microns, where the *cis* isomers show little or no absorption (103,118). A method utilizing this band for estimation of *trans* components in long-chain fatty acid mixtures and similar systems was developed in the author's laboratory (119) and modifications of this procedure have been applied to the identification and estimation of *trans* isomers in various unsaturated materials (24,37,139). The limitations on quantitative applications of ultraviolet spectrophotometry when *trans* isomers are present has been discussed in a recent review by Ahlers (3).

The utility of the infrared technique when coreactants or other materials are present in the fatty acid fraction has been discussed by the author in a previous publication (116). For example, Figure 3 shows a comparison of the infrared spectrum of the oil acid fraction from a styrenated alkyd with that of the corresponding fraction from the same alkyd prior to styrenation. The presence of styrene is reflected by the aromatic bands at 13.2 and 14.2 microns and other spectral differences; under suitable conditions, an estimate of styrene in the fatty acid fraction isolated from a styrenated alkyd can be obtained from infrared absorption measurements. Other coreacted materials can be detected in this fraction and, in some cases, determined by infrared methods. With respect to oxidation, polymerization, etc. as a result of the past history of the resin or in the study of alkyds in various environments, comparison of the spectrum of the isolated fatty acid fraction with suitable reference spectra provides qualitative and semiquantitative information as to types of oxygenated functional groups present. Infrared has been widely applied in studies of oxidation of various unsaturated materials, including the study of the mechanism of oxidation of drying oils. While reference infrared spectra on pure oxygenated derivatives of long-chain fatty acids, esters, and alcohols for use in such studies were practically nonexistent a few years ago, recent work has provided increasing background in this area (13,38,39,100,120,121). Further discussion of this subject will be found in the review by Ahlers and O'Neill (3).

(3) **Polyhydric Alcohol Fraction.** Quantitative analysis of the polyhydric alcohol fraction as isolated in alkyd analysis is presently handled largely by chemical methods. Recent developments, however, indicate that infrared spectroscopy may have possibilities in the analysis of this fraction. For example, Stafford and co-workers (115) have published procedures for the infrared identification of single polyhydric alcohols and some binary mixtures thereof; the polyols are isolated from alkyds by a modified Kappelmeier method and identified by comparison of their spectra with those of reference compounds. The infrared method of Jaffe and Pinchas (64) for the determination of dipentaerythritol in the presence of pentaerythritol was mentioned in a previous section. It should be noted, however, that, because of the strongly polar nature of polyols, resulting in broad, poorly defined absorption bands and insolubility in solvents adapted to infrared work, it seems doubtful that quantitative infrared

methods for these materials will ever approach the accuracy and precision
of chemical methods.

B. PRESENT AND POTENTIAL APPLICATIONS IN PHENOLIC RESIN CHARACTERIZATION

Reference has already been made in Section III.3 to the infrared spectrometric determination of free phenol in phenolic resins (126).   As pointed

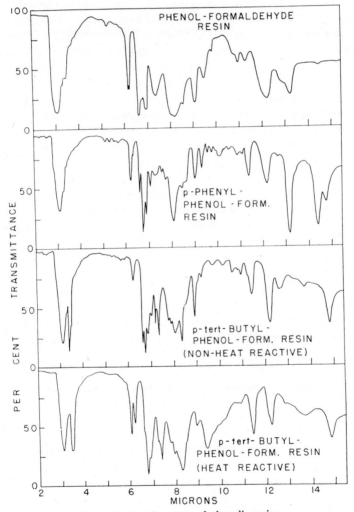

Fig. 4. Infrared spectra of phenolic resins.

out in a previous publication (116), infrared spectroscopy affords a valuable tool for the identification of phenolic resins and the study of their structure. Phenolic resin spectra vary significantly, depending on the parent phenol involved, type of catalyst used in manufacture, etc.   Figure 4 shows comparative spectra of films of such resins based on unsubstituted phenol, *p*-phenylphenol and *p-tert*-butylphenol, respectively.   The spectral pattern observed in the 10 to 15 micron region in the top curve is characteristic of resins based on unsubstituted phenol and that seen in the next curve is characteristic of *p*-phenylphenol-formaldehyde types.   The absorption in this same region in the other two spectra of Figure 4 will be observed with minor variations in all resins based on *p-tert*-butylphenol.   The strong absorption near 9.5 microns in the bottom curve of Figure 4 arises from uncondensed methylol (CH_2OH) groups in this heat-reactive resin; the absence of strong absorption at this wave length in the other *p-tert*-butylphenolic resin reflects the absence of appreciable uncondensed methylol, in this nonheat-reactive resin based on the same parent phenol.   Absorption measurements at this wave length afford a basis for approximate relative estimation of methylol linkages in phenolic resins.   On baking a heat-reactive resin, this band diminishes in intensity, due to further condensation. Detailed study of the hydroxyl absorption region at 3 microns and other regions of phenolic resin spectra, particularly when supplemented by physical fractionating techniques (solvent precipitation, chromatography, etc.) as has been done in at least one recent study (41), should increasingly extend presently available information on phenolic resin structure.   Pyrolysis of phenolic resins followed by infrared examination of the pyrolyzate has been used for identification of unknown phenolic resins (51) and for estimation of phenolics in intractable blends with other resins (22).   Detailed study of such pyrolysis products by infrared and associated separation techniques and chemical methods also offers a possible means for further detailed characterization.

6. Other Specialized Techniques in Coating Resin Analysis

A. POLAROGRAPHY

Developments in the field of organic polarography during the past several years have provided solvent systems and supporting electrolytes that should lead to a number of applications in the field of coating resin analysis.   The method offers particular promise in applications involving the determination of minor ingredients such as driers, inhibitors, catalysts, trace metal components, etc. Although published methods are still not numerous, several applications of interest in the coatings field have appeared in recent years. Garn and Halline (44) have described a polarographic procedure for the determination of total phthalate in alkyd resins. This method offers an alternative to the previously described spectrophotometric method and has the advantage of being applicable in the presence of nitrocellulose, whose interference can be nullified by electrolytic reduction of the nitrocellulose at controlled potential. Hobart (60) has developed a polarographic method for the determination of maleate and fumarate unsaturation in polyesters. Analyses can be performed directly on the sample as received without the necessity of preliminary saponification. Whitnack and Gantz (142) have reported diffusion current constants and half-wave potentials for dibutyl phthalate and other phthalate esters of the type used as plasticizers and have described a polarographic method for determination of such plasticizers in cellulose acetate and other plastic materials. Lewis and Quackenbush (81), Willits and co-workers (143), and Kalbag and co-workers (67) have obtained a great deal of information on the application of polarography to the identification and determination of various types of peroxides of interest in the oxidation of fatty materials. These studies should provide useful background for similar applications in the field of drying oils and unsaturated coating resins. Skoog and Focht (125) have described a polarographic method for the direct determination of lead content of lead naphthenate and other lead salts of organic acids of the type used as paint driers. Many additional applications of polarography and related electrical methods, such as amperometric titrimetry in the field of coatings analysis, will undoubtedly appear as a result of the rising tempo of research and development in this general field.

B. ULTRAVIOLET SPECTROSCOPY

Several applications of this technique to coating resin analysis have been described above. As in the case of polarography, the great sensitivity of the ultraviolet method will undoubtedly result in additional applications in the area of minor additives, trace components, etc. However, since many coating resins are manufactured in the form of solutions containing ultraviolet-absorbing solvents and since many of the polymers themselves exhibit ultraviolet absorption, preliminary separation procedures will probably be necessary in many such applications.

In addition to those already described, the following applications are of interest in the coating field: Banes and Eby (12) have described ultraviolet spectrophotometric methods for the determination of inhibitors in polymers.

Newell (96) describes a method for determination of 0.1 to 0.2% styrene monomer in polystyrene by absorption measurements at 250 to 260 millimicrons. Ball and Vardell (10) describe the analysis of the rosin acid components of tall oil by absorption in the range 240 to 250 millimicrons characteristic of abietic acid types. Using a modification of the ultraviolet method for phthalate in alkyd resins described above, Agarwal and Spagnolo (2) have analyzed mixtures of phthalic acid and phthalic anhydride, and the phthalyl content of phthalic acid esters of cellulose and polyvinyl alcohol has been determined by Malm, Genung and Kuchmy (83). Achhammer (1) has discussed applications of ultraviolet spectrophotometry to the study of polymer degradation products, and Scheibe and Fauss (111) have written a review on absorption of ultraviolet by high polymers. Haslam and co-workers (55) have combined ultraviolet spectroscopy with chemical methods to detect and determine low concentrations of ultraviolet absorbers and other additives in polymethyl methacrylate and acrylate-methacrylate copolymers.

C. NONAQUEOUS TITRIMETRY

Acid-base titrimetry in nonaqueous solvents, while a long-established technique in principle, has only recently received the attention merited by its great potential utility. This technique is well suited to the titration of many polymeric materials containing acidic or basic functional groups and to the analysis of many raw materials and intermediates of importance in finishes technology. Mention of some published applications of interest in the coating resin field will indicate the possibilities. Garrett and Guile (45) describe combined aqueous and nonaqueous titration methods for the analysis of maleic anhydride-styrene copolymers. Basu (14) has determined the molecular weight of nylon dissolved in phenol by titration of end groups with perchloric acid in ethylene glycol and isopropanol. Moss, Elliott, and Hall (95) have determined weakly acidic carboxyl and phenolic groups in Vinsol resin by titration in ethylenediamine using sodium aminoethoxide as titrant. Many other published applications should be applicable with suitable modification to coatings analysis problems. For example, the broadly useful technique of titrating salts of weak organic acids in glacial acetic acid using perchloric acid as titrant is readily applicable to the titration of salts of many polymeric acids. Many new applications of nonaqueous titrimetry in the field of coatings analysis can be confidently anticipated. Further details on nonaqueous titrimetry are given in the chapter on Determination of Amines and Amides in this volume.

IV. ANALYSIS OF SYNTHETIC RESIN COMPONENTS OF FINISHED PAINT PRODUCTS

A typical "clear" finished coatings formulation will contain one or more synthetic and/or natural coating resins, with associated minor ingredients, such as driers, etc., dissolved in an appropriate organic solvent system. A pigmented product will contain, in addition, one or more insoluble inorganic and/or organic pigments dispersed in finely ground form in this liquid "vehicle."

The first step in the analysis of such a product involves separation of the suspended pigment from the vehicle. For vehicle analysis purposes this is best accomplished by high-speed centrifugation in an air-driven "super-centrifuge" using a bowl of 1 pt. capacity. For very finely divided pigments such as carbon black, centrifugation should be preceded by dilution with a suitable polar solvent. A discussion of various procedures for pigment/vehicle separation, including difficultly separable types, is given in the work of Gardner (43).

The separated vehicle solution is analyzed for its nonvolatile resinous components by an appropriate combination of physical and chemical methods and separation procedures depending on the nature of the product. The various chemical determinations involved are usually performed on the solution, rather than on films (unless solvent components interfere), results being calculated to the solids basis after determination of total vehicle solids by a suitable oven-drying procedure. If the solvent portion of the vehicle is to be analyzed, a separate sample is vacuum distilled and the distillate analyzed by methods that usually involve fractional distillation and/or other separations and examination of fractions by infrared and ultraviolet absorption and chemical methods. The pigment phase is washed, dried, and subjected to infrared examination as a Nujol mull or potassium bromide pressed pellet (112) for qualitative and semiquantitative purposes and to chemical analysis for more exact quantitative purposes. Conventional methods for the examination of the pigment and solvent portions of paints are detailed by Gardner (43).

1. Preliminary Qualitative and Semiquantitative Examination of Paint Vehicles by Infrared Spectroscopy and Associated Tests

In the examination of paint vehicles of unknown or uncertain qualitative composition or for high spot semiquantitative work on known samples, a technique of rapid preliminary survey analysis built around infrared spectroscopy is extensively employed in the author's laboratory. Such a survey includes all information obtainable in a short time from the following: (1) infrared spectrum from 2 to 15 microns on a thin film prepared by spreading a small sample of the vehicle solution on rock salt and removing solvent by drying in a vacuum oven at 60°C. for 30 minutes; (2) infrared spectra on films similarly prepared from fractions obtained in quick fractionations by solvent precipitation, chromatography, etc., when these seem to be needed to concentrate minor ingredients to bring out their spectra; (3) qualitative and/or quantitative analysis for elements other than carbon, hydrogen, and oxygen; (4) any additional preliminary physical and chemical tests (on the resin solution or a dried film) that may seem desirable in the light of information revealed by 1, 2, and 3 above.

Since such an approach leans heavily on infrared spectroscopy, a large and ever-increasing library of reference spectra is a *sine qua non*—as is a suitable system for the indexing, classification, and sorting of spectra comprising such a library. For this purpose, the system proposed by Kuentzel (79) and now under study by A. S. T. M. Committee E-13 on Absorption Spectroscopy is recommended. In addition to qualitative information, the infrared spectra of films of the vehicle and any fractions separated will usually afford a basis for rough quantitative estimates of major resinous components via measurement of absorbance ratios at selected wave lengths using "base line" methods.

The information obtained in a quick survey of this type will often suffice for solution of the problem involved; if not, in nearly all cases, it will suggest an efficient plan of attack for further breakdown when a more complete analysis is required.

As indicated above, the infrared part of such a survey is also used in the case of many samples of known qualitative composition for making approximate estimates of components via absorbance ratios when such estimates are adequate or for confirmation of gross qualitative and/or semiquantitative composition.

2. Detailed Characterization and Determination of Individual Resins in Paint Vehicle Mixtures

While many paint vehicle analysis problems can be satisfactorily resolved for the purpose at hand by the rapid survey analysis approach, more complete and detailed information is often required.

Problems calling for the quantitative determination of a given resin, as such, in a mixture are usually best handled when possible via the determination of an element or other function which (a) is unique to the resin in question in that particular mixture, (b) can be determined in the mixture by a procedure involving no interference from other components, and (c) is known (or can reasonably be assumed) to be present in given fixed amount in resins of the type being determined. A simple example is the determination of urea- or melamine-formaldehyde resin in the analysis of alkyd-nitrogen resin blends by determination of total nitrogen content. Where this type of procedure is not possible or when more rapid or nondestructive methods are desired, methods based on infrared absorption measurements may be used. Such methods are usually possible in all cases in which the component being determined exhibits a sufficiently strong absorption band free or relatively free from interfering absorption by other components and when sample handling or similar considerations are not unfavorable. Since the chances of finding suitable absorption bands for quantitative work are greatly diminished in spectra run on "wet" samples (because of the multiplicity of bands present in the solvents normally used), quantitative infrared measurements on resin solutions and resinous paint vehicles are usually best made on vacuum-dried thin films (using absorbance ratio techniques to obviate difficulties in film thickness measurements) or, where feasible, on vacuum-dried films redissolved in carbon disulfide or other suitable infrared transparent solvent.

When interfering constituents preclude direct estimation of a resin by a chemical method, infrared measurements or other direct means, physical separations—such as molecular distillation, chromatography, solvent precipitation—and/or chemical separations based on saponification or other chemical treatment may be employed to remove interferences or isolate the resin as such for gravimetric estimation.

Often the problem will require complete characterization of one or more of the resin components of the vehicle mixture as distinguished from the usually simpler problem of merely estimating the total percentage of that resin species present. In some cases, a reasonably good—though usually incomplete and relatively inaccurate—characterization can be achieved via appropriate characterizing determinations of the type discussed in preceding sections when these are applied directly to the vehicle mixture. Usually, however, other components will interfere with one or more of the required procedures and isolation or concentration of the resin to be characterized is necessary or desirable.

The general approach and techniques and methods involved in the characterization and determination of synthetic resins in mixtures are illustrated in the following discussions dealing with analysis of the resinous vehicle film-forming fraction of some typical finished paint products.

A. ALKYD-NITROGEN RESIN BLENDS

Combinations comprising oil-modified alkyds with urea-formaldehyde and/or melamine-formaldehyde resins are widely used in industrial baking enamels. Complete analysis of the resinous film-forming components of this type of vehicle includes estimation of the total amount of each type of resin present and, to the extent possible, characterization of each by procedures of the type given in Sections III.1 and 2.

The total phthalic anhydride content of the alkyd resin in this type of blend can usually be determined without serious sacrifice in accuracy and precision by direct application of the combined saponification–ultraviolet absorption method described in Section III.1B(1). Alternatively, an approximate estimate may be calculated from the alcoholate weight loss on drying this precipitate at elevated temperature (Section III.1B(1)). If the phthalic content of the alkyd present is known (or can reasonably be assumed) the total oil-modified alkyd content of the blend can be calculated from the phthalic thus determined on the mixture.

In a two-component blend (alkyd–urea-formaldehyde or alkyd–melamine) total nitrogen resin content is usually estimated from the nitrogen content of the blend, as determined by the Kjeldahl method, provided the nitrogen content of the nitrogen resin present is known or can reasonably be assumed.

Three-component systems (alkyd–urea-formaldehyde–melamine) pose the special problem of estimating the urea-formaldehyde–melamine ratio. Even in cases where total urea-formaldehyde plus melamine is known or can be determined accurately by difference (from alkyd estimate via phthalic), total nitrogen does not afford a basis for such an estimate because the individual nitrogen resins do not differ sufficiently in nitrogen content. Evaluation of the direct dibenzylurea method for urea-formaldehyde (discussed above) indicates it cannot be applied to the independent determination of urea-formaldehyde in such a blend (nor is it applicable to the estimation of urea-formaldehyde in the two-component urea-formaldehyde–alkyd blend). Hirt and co-workers (59) have published a procedure for the determination of melamine resin in wet-strength paper utilizing hydrolysis of the paper sample with HCl to extract the resin and convert it to melaminium ion and determination of this by ultraviolet absorption at 235 millimicrons. While it has not been evaluated on urea-formaldehyde–melamine–alkyd blends, a suitable modification of this method might possibly afford a basis for estimation of the melamine content.

A recently published procedure (89a) used in the author's laboratory for estimation of alkyd as well as urea-formaldehyde and melamine in this type of vehicle is based on infrared spectrometric measurements. Since conventional solvent systems used in alkyd–nitrogen resin-type vehicles interfere

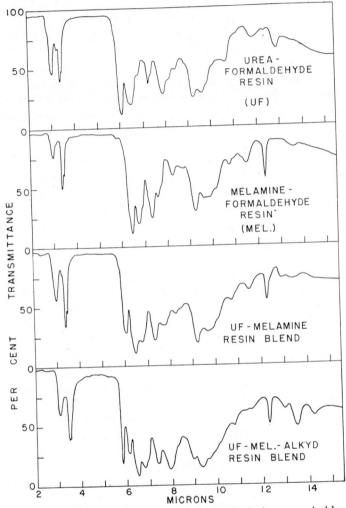

Fig. 5. Infrared spectra of nitrogen resins and alkyd-nitrogen resin blend.

and removal of solvent and resolution in an infrared transparent solvent is not feasible in this case, the infrared measurements are made on films of appropriate thickness prepared by spreading on rock salt and drying at 60°C.

in a vacuum oven for one hour. Figure 5 shows comparative infrared spectra run on films of butanol-modified urea-formaldehyde resin, butanol-modified melamine-formaldehyde resin, a blend of the two, and a blend of both with an oil-modified alkyd. Unique absorption bands suitable for the necessary measurements occur at 12.25 microns for melamine (heterocyclic ring vibration), 6 microns for urea-formaldehyde (amide carbonyl absorption) and 5.8 microns for alkyd (ester carbonyl absorption).

The method is calibrated on films from known blends by scanning through the 5.8, 6.0, and 12.25 micron regions and measuring absorbance by a base line technique. Plots of absorbance ratios against concentration ratios are obtained for each combination of two constituents. Appropriate use of the absorption laws then makes possible the estimation of each component in a three-component blend.

Considering next the problem of complete characterization of the alkyd resin in this type of blend, the total phthalic content can be determined, as noted above, with moderate accuracy and precision by direct saponification of the vehicle solution with absolute alcoholic alkali, followed by water extraction of the precipitate containing the potassium phthalate plus any precipitated nitrogenous material and ultraviolet measurement at 276 millimicrons. The total phthalate value so obtained is calculated to phthalic glyceride equivalent unless other polyols are present.

Satisfactory results in the remaining determinations necessary for alkyd characterization are difficult to obtain by direct application of the procedures of Section III.1 without separation. If separation by solvent precipitation (or otherwise) can be achieved, such determinations can then be performed on the isolated alkyd without interference from the nitrogen resins. Kappelmeier (76) has proposed a procedure for this type of separation based on steam distillation to remove solvent and harden the nitrogen resin component, followed by ether extraction of the alkyd, which can then be analyzed by the usual methods. This procedure is useful, but has not proved generally applicable in the author's experience.

If alkyd characterization is attempted directly on the blend, suitable means must be used to eliminate or minimize interference from nitrogen resin degradation products that appear in the polyol and fatty acid fractions as isolated by the procedures of Section III.1. The fatty acid modifiers can usually be purified by extraction of this fraction with petroleum ether rather than ethyl ether, and refluxing with acetic acid further to decompose the nitrogenous products, followed by a second extraction with petroleum ether. While water-soluble nitrogen resin degradation products also accumulate in the aqueous polyol fraction, these do not usually cause serious interference with the analysis of this fraction by the methods of Section III.1. In general, however, alkyd characterization determinations run directly on such blends must be interpreted cautiously due to their relative unreliability as compared with similar analyses on unblended or successfully separated alkyds.

With the exception of total nitrogen, none of the nitrogen resin characterization procedures given in Section III.2 has been evaluated as directly applied to alkyd–nitrogen resin blends; they are, in general, probably not applicable and the author knows of no presently available means for isolating nitrogen resins from such blends in unaltered form suitable for characterization by these methods.

B. NITROCELLULOSE LACQUERS

Lacquer formulations based on nitrocellulose in combination with various plasticizing materials are widely used in automotive and other industrial finishing applications. A commonly encountered type of automotive finish comprises as plasticizing ingredients a nondrying oil-modified alkyd resin (e. g., cocoanut and/or castor oil as modifier) along with a monomeric phthalate plasticizer (e. g., dioctyl phthalate); these with the nitrocellulose are dissolved in a mixture of esters, ketones, alcohols, etc. as solvent system.

In the case of pigmented lacquers, pigment–vehicle separation can usually be achieved by supercentrifugation. Various procedures for separating difficultly separable pigments and chemical methods for analysis of the solvent and pigment fractions of such lacquers are given by Gardner (43).

The nitrocellulose content of the separated lacquer vehicle can usually be estimated by direct determination of nitrate nitrogen and calculation to the solids basis (assuming 12% as the nitrogen content of the nitrocellulose present if this value is not known). In the previous volume of this series, Becker and Shaefer review the status of methods for nitrate nitrogen and include a detailed procedure directly applicable to the estimation of nitrocellulose in lacquer mixtures (16).

The nitrocellulose content of lacquer vehicles can also be estimated directly by evaporation of the solution to a small volume, and dilution with a large volume of benzene to precipitate this ingredient, which is then removed by filtration, dissolved and reprecipitated, dried, and weighed.

While this type of procedure will afford an estimate sufficing for many purposes, it is not generally applicable in the presence of alkyd resins, since higher molecular weight fractions of some alkyds precipitate and cannot be completely removed.

Federal Specification TT-P-141b (36) is the source of the following procedure for the separation and estimation of nitrocellulose.

Procedure. Place a portion of the sample in a stoppered bottle or weighing pipet. Weigh container and sample. Transfer 10 to 15 g. of the sample to a 200 ml. beaker. Weigh the container again.

By difference *calculate* the exact weight of the sample taken.

Place the beaker and contents on a steam bath and evaporate the contents to about 5 ml. Remove from steam bath and dilute the contents of the beaker with 100 to 150 ml. of benzene. Stir to mix thoroughly and set aside until a gelatinous precipitate forms.

This precipitate consists essentially of nitrocellulose and will usually settle out rather rapidly to the bottom of the beaker. Filter the solution through a filter paper. Dissolve the precipitate from the filter paper using 25 to 30 ml. of ethyl acetate and evaporate the acetate solution on a steam bath to approximately 5 ml. volume. Dilute with 100 to 150 ml. of benzene to precipitate the nitrocellulose and again filter.

Repeat the solution, evaporation, and dilution procedures, and filter through a weighed soxhlet extraction thimble placed in a filter funnel, using suction if necessary. The transfer of the precipitate to the thimble may be facilitated by use of a policeman and a stream of benzene from a wash bottle. Place the thimble in a soxhlet tube and extract with hot benzene. A continuous extraction for one hour should be sufficient. The extraction should be continued until the hot benzene in the extraction tube is colorless. Remove the thimble from the extraction apparatus and dry in a hot water oven to constant weight.

From the weight of the precipitate in the thimble and the weight of the nonvolatile matter in the sample taken, *calculate* the percentage of nitrocellulose in the nonvolatile portion.

The next problem to be considered is the analysis of the plasticizer fraction of the lacquer. When, as in a typical case, this fraction includes an oil-modified alkyd and a monomeric phthalate ester, only limited analytical information can be obtained by direct analysis without separation of nitrocellulose. Infrared absorption will supply some qualitative information, but, due to the strong broad absorption bands characteristic of nitrocellulose, this technique affords a basis for only limited information as applied to the whole lacquer vehicle film. The benzene precipitation procedure detailed above will effect satisfactory separation of nitrocellulose from plasticizing ingredients in some cases but, as noted above, such separations may not be quantitative when alkyds are present. In cases in which a satisfactory separation can be achieved, however, the total plasticizer fraction can be estimated by evaporation of the filtrate from the nitrocellulose precipitation, followed by drying and weighing; the solid isolated plasticizer fraction can then be analyzed by the procedures given for alkyd characterization in Section III.1 above. Total phthalic anhydride, total glycerin, total fatty acids, and excess alkyd hydroxyl are run by these procedures. The glycerin equivalent to the total fatty acids found is added to that equivalent to any excess (unesterified) hydroxyl found and this value subtracted from the total glycerin content. The phthalic anhydride equivalent to this residual glycerin value is then calculated to glyceryl phthalate. The remainder of the total phthalic found is due to the monomeric phthalate ester and gives an estimate of this component after multiplication by an appropriate factor.

The sum of the glyceryl phthalate, fatty acid glyceride, and excess hydroxyl affords an estimate of total alkyd resin and these values, plus the data obtained in a component analysis of the isolated fatty acid fraction by the ultraviolet spectrophotometric procedure of Section III.1, will serve to characterize this component.

Although benzene precipitation often fails to give a clean separation of plasticizer fraction from nitrocellulose, the soluble plasticizer fraction will seldom contain sufficient unprecipitated nitrocellulose to interfere significantly with the analysis of this fraction in the manner outlined above. In most cases, however, as much as 5 to 10% of the alkyd resin present will remain behind with the precipitated nitrocellulose. The total alkyd precipitated can be estimated by difference after determination of the total weight of this fraction and its nitrocellulose content by the nitrate-nitrogen method. This value can then be added to the total alkyd found in the soluble plasticizer fraction to yield an estimate of total alkyd content of the lacquer. Since the alkyd characterization data in such a case must be obtained by analysis of that portion of the alkyd found in the soluble fraction only, these data must be cautiously interpreted.

In connection with their work on determination of nitrate nitrogen in nitrocellulose, Shaefer and Becker (114) have developed an interesting and novel method for the quantitative separation of alkyds from nitrocellulose lacquers. This method is based on reduction of nitrocellulose to water-soluble form by reaction with ferrous chloride in glacial acetic acid, under which conditions the alkyd is not affected and can be extracted from the reaction mixture with a suitable solvent. Shaefer and Becker did not report complete analytical characterizing data on alkyds thus isolated from lacquers, but made a careful study of the determination of combined phthalate in such resins. With one exception, they found the usual method for phthalate unsatisfactory as applied to alkyds isolated from lacquers by the reduction–extraction procedure. Erratic and high results were traced to the formation of an insoluble potassium salt of an acid of lower equivalent weight than potassium phthalate when such resins were subjected to saponification with alcoholic KOH. To circumvent this, these authors employ a modified procedure of the type discussed in Section III.1 above based on loss of alcohol of crystallization on heating potassium phthalate monoalcoholate. Their detailed procedure for the ferrous chloride reduction and extraction of alkyds and determination of combined phthalate on resins thus isolated is given below:

Reagents. Solution for the removal of water by azeotropic distillation, consisting of benzene–anhydrous ethyl alcohol, 4:1. Absolute alcoholic potassium hydroxide solution, approximately 0.6 N; allow the solution to stand overnight protected from carbon dioxide; filter just before using; prepare fresh reagent once each week.

Procedure. Weigh, from a suitable closed dispenser, an amount of the lacquer containing phthalate equivalent to approximately 0.25 g. of phthalic anhydride. Add 50 ml. of hot glacial acetic acid and a few particles of 10-mesh carborundum. Swirl the solution in order to dissolve the sample without overheating it. Place the flask on a hot plate and heat the solution until the acetic acid vapor ascends halfway to the top of the flask. Add about 5 g. of powdered ferrous chloride tetrahydrate; immediately fit a condenser into the neck of the flask, and boil the mixture for 3 to 5 minutes. Cool the flask.

Decant the liquid portion of the reaction mixture into a 250 ml. centrifuge bottle and rinse the flask with several portions of methylene chloride, using a total of 50 ml. Add about 100 ml. of water to the centrifuge bottle, insert a rubber stopper, shake the bottle cautiously, vent the methylene chloride vapor, reinsert the stopper, and shake the bottle vigorously. Centrifuge and then draw off the upper aqueous layer by means of a 25 ml. pipet connected to a water aspirator. Repeat the extraction with two more 100 ml. portions of water, as just described, to reduce the concentration of acetic acid, iron salts, and other water-soluble substances to such a low point that they will not interfere.

In order to extract the alkyd resin quantitatively from the methylene chloride solution and the emulsion interface that accompanies it, a special separation procedure is required. It consists of separating the methylene chloride solution from the interface and then extracting the latter with alcohol and benzene.

Transfer the contents of the centrifuge bottle to a separatory funnel and filter the lower methylene chloride layer into a 500 ml. erlenmeyer flask, using a coarse porosity fritted-glass funnel and a bell jar filtering device. Rinse the bottle with methylene chloride, transfer the methylene chloride to the separatory funnel, and filter the lower layer. Repeat this operation, this time swirling the methylene chloride gently over the walls of the separatory funnel before filtering. By this technique the formation of an emulsion is avoided.

Replace the erlenmeyer flask with a small beaker. Rinse the centrifuge bottle with 10 to 15 ml. of anhydrous ethyl alcohol, transfer the contents to the separatory funnel containing the interface left from centrifuging, and shake the separatory funnel. Filter the whole mixture through the same funnel used before, and then repeat the operation of washing with alcohol. Rinse the centrifuge bottle with 10 to 15 ml. of benzene, transfer the benzene to the separatory funnel, and shake the latter. Then filter the benzene, collecting it in the beaker along with the alcohol. Discard the interface residue. Evaporate the filtrate rapidly on a steam bath in a current of air. If the residue appears to contain droplets of water, add to it 10 to 15 ml. of 4:1 benzene–anhydrous ethyl alcohol solution, and evaporate to dryness again to remove water completely from the residue. Dissolve the residue in methylene chloride and combine it with the methylene chloride filtrate in the 500 ml. erlenmeyer flask.

Evaporate the methylene chloride solution to a small volume on the steam bath and remove; then, by using a current of air, evaporate it to dryness. Excessive heating of the resins makes them insoluble in benzene. Dissolve the residue in 50 ml. of benzene.

To the benzene solution of the resin, add 150 ml. of freshly filtered 0.6 N anhydrous alcoholic potassium hydroxide solution. Stopper the flask loosely with a cork stopper and heat in an oven at 60 to 70°C. for 3 hours.

Cool the flask, rinse down the walls with 50 ml. of ether, and filter, within an hour, through a weighed, fritted-glass crucible of medium porosity. Use 1:1 ethyl alcohol–ether wash solution for transferring the precipitate and washing the reaction flask. Do not allow air to be drawn through the crystals unnecessarily, as they are hygroscopic. Finally, pour 25 ml. of ether into the crucible and draw it through the precipitate. Wipe the outer surface of the crucible and heat it at 60°C. for 1 hour. Allow it to cool in a desiccator containing concentrated sulfuric acid for 30 minutes or longer and weigh it.

Heat the crucible at 150°C. for 3 hours, cool it, and weigh it again. The decrease in weight that occurs on heating represents alcohol of crystallization in potassium phthalate alcoholate.

Calculation

$$\frac{\text{decrease in weight} \times 3.215 \times 1.052 \times 100}{\text{grams of sample}} = \% \text{ phthalic anhydride}$$

where 3.215 is the theoretical factor and 1.052 is a correction factor that needs to be applied under the prescribed conditions.

While evaluation indicates need for further development and refinement for more general application, the above procedure should prove useful in many cases for the isolation of alkyds from lacquers in a form suitable for all or most of the determinations necessary for alkyd characterization. When monomeric phthalate plasticizers are present, these would presumably be isolated along with the alkyd by the above procedure.

In a recent paper (137), Swann and co-workers proposed a complete set of procedures for the analysis of lacquers containing nitrocellulose, alkyd resins, and monomeric phthalate plasticizers. Their procedures include one for the direct estimation of total phthalate in such a formulation via a modification of the Shreve-Heether (117) spectrophotometric method wherein correction is made for the ultraviolet absorption caused by nitrocellulose decomposition products that accumulate in the "Kappelmeier precipitate" on saponification.

For the complete analysis of this type of formulation, these authors describe a procedure which they state gives a clean separation of nitrocellulose from the plasticizer fraction and a reliable estimate of nitrocellulose content. After addition of acetone, the lacquer sample is poured into a large volume of boiling water and the precipitated lacquer solids are filtered off and then refluxed in benzene and benzene–ethanol. Finally, the nitrocellulose precipitated from the benzene–alcohol refluxing is filtered off, washed, dried, and weighed. Total phthalate (in the alkyd plus monomeric phthalate plasticizer) is determined on the filtrate in the usual way.

To separate the monomeric phthalate from the alkyd in the plasticizer fraction, a sample of the original lacquer is dissolved in acetone, ethyl alcohol is added slowly, and the acetone is then removed by distillation. The residue is cooled and filtered cold to remove nitrocellulose and the filtrate is percolated through a charcoal–asbestos adsorption column. The alkyd resin remains on the column, the monomeric phthalate plasticizer being eluted by washing with ethanol. The total phthalate determined on the eluate is subtracted from the total phthalate found in the lacquer to give the phthalate content of the alkyd alone.

C. ANALYSIS OF RESIN COMPONENTS OF DRIED COATING FILMS

Many problems encountered in coatings research and development require the analytical examination of applied coating products in the form of dried cured films. These may be detached clear or pigmented films, samples in powdered form scraped from the substrate, or a sample submitted in the form of film attached to substrate.

In the case of lacquers or similar types, application and drying usually involve only volatilization of solvent with little or no conversion of the resinous vehicle ingredients to the "set up" insoluble form. Dried lacquer films can therefore be cut up and extracted in a soxhlet with suitable lacquer solvents to produce a solution that can be analyzed by procedures of the type already discussed for "wet samples."

Dried films of baking enamels and other coatings that undergo conversion to insoluble form in the application and drying process present a much more difficult type of problem. When these are unpigmented and a small portion of continuous film can be obtained in detached form, it can be mounted on a piece of cardboard with a small opening and subjected to infrared spectroscopic examination. Microinfrared spectroscopic techniques now available make it possible to obtain spectra when necessary on as little as a square millimeter of film or less. Also, when the clear film to be analyzed is attached to a metal panel, or a metal substrate from which a small panel can be cut, an infrared spectrum can sometimes be obtained without detachment of film from substrate. This is done by means of a suitable reflectance attachment for the infrared spectrometer in which radiation is passed through the clear film, reflected at the metal–film interface for a second pass, then directed into the spectrometer for dispersion, detection, and recording of the spectrum in the usual way. Commercial equipment is now available for modifying spectrometers to permit recording of reflectance spectra in the infrared.

When pigmented, insoluble, intractable films are to be examined, difficulties mount but much can nevertheless be accomplished. In some cases, e.g., very finely divided pigments such as carbon black or iron blue, an infrared spectrum on a small portion of continuous film (when obtainable) will supply considerable information with reference to both vehicle and pigment composition. More often, however, infrared spectra on pigmented films yield little useful information due to scattering of the incident radiation by the pigment particles.

For more detailed chemical and physical examination of insoluble intractable films, pigmented or unpigmented, it is usually necessary to resort to degradation of the resin components by chemical reagents, dry distillation, etc., and examination of the products so obtained. For example, cured films comprising drying oil-modified alkyds as the primary film former can be subjected to prolonged saponification with absolute alcoholic KOH to degrade the film. Filtration of the resulting saponificate produces a residue containing the potassium phthalate along with pigment and other insoluble material. Water extraction followed by application of the ultraviolet-spectrophotometric method of Section III.1 will usually afford an acceptable estimate of the phthalate content. Further processing of the filtrate by suitable modifications of procedures already given for alkyd analysis together with infrared and other examination of fractions obtained will usually provide considerable additional information.

When other types of resins are involved, saponification, acid hydrolysis, or other chemical attack may be employed when applicable for degradation; the reagent used and procedures employed for examination of degradation products must, of course, be adapted to the particular problem at hand. For cured films comprising resins not amenable to acid or basic hydrolysis or other chemical attack suitable for analytical purposes, dry distillation (pyrolysis) under controlled conditions followed by examination of the pyrolysis products has been found very useful. Pyrolysis of various polymers followed by infrared or mass spectrometric examination of products has been the subject of several recent publications (22,51,80,148). While these have been primarily concerned with qualitative applications, they have shown that unique reproducible spectra can be obtained and the background being built up by such studies will undoubtedly lead to various quantitative applications and provide a basis for extension of knowledge of polymer structure. One interesting example of a quantitative application has already appeared in a recent paper by Bentley and Rappaport (22) on the semiquantitative analysis of intractable phenolic resin–Buna N rubber blends via the infrared spectra of their pyrolyzates. Calibration of the method involves pyrolysis of known blends at reduced pressure (2 mm. of mercury) for 15 minutes at 550°C. in a specially constructed combustion assembly. The pyrolysis products are removed by washing with an acetone–chloroform mixture and the tarry residue from evaporation of this solution is placed between rock salt plates for infrared measurements. A plot is made of per cent phenolic resin versus the ratio of base line absorbances measured at 2.95 and 4.48 microns. The per cent phenolic in similar blends of unknown composition can then be estimated from absorbance ratio measurements on their pyrolysis products with an apparent accuracy of about ±2% in the range 0 to 33% phenolic resin.

References

1. Achhammer, B. G., *Anal. Chem.*, *24*, 1925 (1952).
2. Agarwal, M. M., and Spagnolo, F., *ibid.*, *25*, 1412 (1953).
3. Ahlers, N. H. E., and O'Neill, J., *J. Oil & Colour Chemists' Assoc.*, *37*, 533 (1954).
4. Allen, N., Charbonnier, H. Y., and Coleman, R. M., *Anal. Chem.*, *12*, 384 (1940).
5. American Society for Testing Materials, Philadelphia, *A. S. T. M. Standards on Paint, Varnish, Lacquer and Related Products*, Method D-563-52, 1952, pp. 332–3.
6. Anderson, D. H., and Miller, O. E., *J. Opt. Soc. Amer.*, *43*, 777 (1953).
7. Anderson, D. H., and Woodall, N. B., *Anal. Chem.*, *25*, 1906 (1953).
8. Armitage, F., and Kut, S., *J. Oil & Colour Chemists' Assoc.*, *35*, 195 (1952).
9. Baldwin, A. R., and Longenecker, H. E., *Oil & Soap*, *22*, 151 (1945).
10. Ball, F. J., and Vardell, W. J., *J. Am. Chem. Soc.*, *28*, 137 (1951).
11. Baltes, J., *Fette u. Seifen*, *53*, 160 (1951).
12. Banes, F. W., and Eby, L. T., *Ind. Eng. Chem., Anal. Ed.*, *18*, 535 (1946).

13. Barnes, R. B., Gore, R. C., Liddel, V., and Williams, V. Z., *Infrared Spectroscopy, Industrial Applications and Bibliography*, Reinhold, New York, 1944.
14. Basu, S., *J. Polymer Sci.*, *5*, 735 (1950).
15. Beadle, B. W., and Kraybill, H. R., *J. Am. Chem. Soc.*, *66*, 1232 (1944).
16. Becker, W. W., and Shaefer, W. E., in *Organic Analysis*. Vol. II, Interscience, New York-London, 1954, p. 103.
17. Bekkedahl, N., and Stiehler, R. D., *Anal. Chem.*, *21*, 266 (1949).
18. Bekkedahl, N., *ibid.*, *22*, 253 (1950).
19. Bekkedahl, N., *ibid.*, *23*, 243 (1951).
20. Bekkedahl, N., *ibid.*, *24*, 270 (1952).
21. Bekkedahl, N., *ibid.*, *25*, 54 (1953).
22. Bentley, F. F., and Rappaport, G., *ibid.*, *26*, 1980 (1954).
23. Berk, L. C., Kretchmer, N. J., Holman, R. T., and Burr, G. O., *ibid.*, *22*, 718 (1950).
24. Bickford, W. G., DuPre, E. F., Mack, C. H., and O'Conner, R. T., *J. Am. Oil Chemists' Soc.*, *30*, 376 (1953).
25. Bokhout, B., *Chem. Weekblad*, *46*, 836 (1950).
26. Bokhout, B., *ibid.*, *47*, 159 (1951).
27. Bokhout, B., *Paint Technol.*, *15*, 344 (1950).
28. Bradley, J. J., Jr., Official Digest Federation Paint and Varnish Production Clubs, No. 266, 162 (1947).
29. Brice, B. A., and Swain, M. L., *J. Opt. Soc. Amer.*, *35*, 532 (1945).
30. Brice, B. A., Swain, M. L., Herb, S. F., Nichlos, P. L., and Riemenschneider, R. W., *J. Am. Oil Chemists' Soc.*, *29*, 279 (1952).
31. Brice, B. A., Swain, M. L., Schaeffer, B. B., and Ault, W. C., *Oil & Soap*, *22*, 219 (1945).
32. Clark, H. A., Gorden, A. F., Young, C. W., and Hunter, M. J., *J. Am. Chem. Soc.*, *73*, 3798 (1951).
33. Claspar, M., and Haslam, J., *Analyst*, *74*, 224 (1949).
34. Doyle, C. D., *Ind. Eng. Chem.*, *Anal. Ed.*, *16*, 200 (1944).
35. Elving, P. J., and Warshowsky, B., *Anal. Chem.*, *19*, 1006 (1947).
36. "Federal Specification: Paint, Varnish, Lacquers and Related Materials; Methods of Inspection, Sampling and Testing," TTP-141 (b), Method 520.1.
37. Feuge, R. O., Pepper, M. B., O'Conner, R. T., and Field, E. T., *J. Am. Oil Chemists' Soc.*, *28*, 420 (1951).
38. Field, E. J., Cole, J. O., and Woodford, D. E., *J. Chem. Phys.*, *18*, 1298 (1950).
39. Field, E. J., Cole, J. O., and Woodford, D. E., *ibid.*, *18*, 1298 (1950).
40. Fordyce, C. R., Genung, L. B., and Pile, M. A., *Ind. Eng. Chem.*, *Anal. Ed.*, *18*, 547 (1946).
41. Freeman, J. H., *Anal. Chem.*, *23*, 1413 (1951).
42. Frisch, K. C., Goodwin, P. A., and Scott, R. E., *J. Am. Chem. Soc.*, *74*, 4589 (1952).
43. Gardner, H. A., and Sward, G. G., *Physical and Chemical Examination of Paints, Varnishes, Lacquers and Colors*. 11th ed., Henry A. Gardner Laboratory, Inc., Bethesda, Md., 1950.
44. Garn, P. D., and Halline, E. W., *Anal. Chem.*, *27*, 1563 (1955).
45. Garrett, E. R., and Guile, R. W., *J. Am. Chem. Soc.*, *73*, 4533 (1951).
46. Genung, L. B., and Mallatt, R. C., *Ind. Eng. Chem.*, *Anal. Ed.*, *13*, 369 (1941).
47. Genung, L. B., *Anal. Chem.*, *22*, 401 (1950).
48. Goldberg, A. I., *Ind. Eng. Chem.*, *Anal. Ed.*, *16*, 198 (1944).

49. Grad, P. P., and Dunn, R. J., *Anal. Chem.*, *25*, 1211 (1953).
50. Hall, R. T., and Shaefer, W. E., in *Organic Analysis.* Vol. II, Interscience, New York-London, 1954, pp. 29, 33, 36, 62.
51. Harms, D. L., *Anal. Chem.*, *25*, 1140 (1953).
52. Harris, G. C., and Sanderson, T. E., *J. Am. Chem. Soc.*, *70*, 334, 339, 2079, 2081, 3671 (1948).
53. Haslam, J., and Newlands, G., *J. Soc. Chem. Ind. (London)*, *69*, 103 (1950).
54. Haslam, J., and Soppet, W., *Analyst*, *75*, 63 (1950).
55. Haslam, J., Grossman, S., Squirrell, D. C. M., and Loveday, S. F., *ibid.*, *78*, 92 (1953).
56. Higuchi, T., Hill, N. C., and Corcoran, G. B., *Anal. Chem.*, *24*, 491 (1952).
57. Hilditch, T. P., Morton, R. A., and Riley, J. P., *Analyst*, *70*, 68 (1945).
58. Hirt, R. C., Stafford, R. W., King, F. T., and Schmitt, R. G., *Anal. Chem.*, *27*, 226 (1955).
59. Hirt, R. C., King, F. T., and Schmitt, A. G., *ibid.*, *26*, 1273 (1954).
60. Hobart, E. W., *ibid.*, *26*, 1291 (1954).
61. Holman, R. T., and Burr, G. O., *Arch. Biochem.*, *19*, 474 (1948).
62. Hough, L., *Nature*, *165*, 400 (1950).
63. Ingebrigtson, D. N., and Smith, A. L., *Anal. Chem.*, *26*, 1765 (1954).
64. Jaffe, J. H., and Pinchas, S., *ibid.*, *23*, 1164 (1951).
65. Jones, N., *J. Am. Chem. Soc.*, *74*, 2681 (1952).
66. Jungnickel, J. L., Peters, E. D., Polgar, A., and Weiss, F. T., in *Organic Analysis.* Vol. I, Interscience, New York-London, 1953, pp. 137, 140, 141, 152.
67. Kalbag, S. S., Narayan, K. A., Chang, S. S., and Kummerow, F. A., *J. Am. Oil Chemists' Soc.*, *32*, 271 (1955).
68. Kappelmeier, C. P. A., *Farben-Ztg.*, *40*, 1141 (1935).
69. Kappelmeier, C. P. A., *ibid.*, *41*, 161 (1936).
70. Kappelmeier, C. P. A., *Paint Oil Chem. Rev.*, *99*, Nos. 12, 20, 22, 24 (1937).
71. Kappelmeier, C. P. A., van Goor, W. R., van der Neut, J. H., and Kist, G. H., *Chim. peintures*, *14*, 92 (1951).
72. Kappelmeier, C. P. A., van Goor, W. R., van der Neut, J. H., and Kist, G. H., *Paint Oil Chem. Rev.*, *114*, Nos. 3, 16, 18, 32, 34 (1951).
73. Kappelmeier, C. P. A., van Goor, W. R., van der Neut, J. H., and Kist, G. H., *Verfkroniek*, *23*, 263 (1950).
74. Kappelmeier, C. P. A., and van der Neut, J. H., *Chem. Weekblad*, *47*, 157 (1951).
75. Kappelmeier, C. P. A., van Goor, W. R., van der Neut, J. H., and Kist, G. H., *Deut. Farben-Z.*, *5*, 233 (1951).
76. Kappelmeier, C. P. A., *Paint Oil Chem. Rev.*, *3*, No. 4, 8 (1948).
77. Kappelmeier, C. P. A., *ibid.*, *115*, No. 2, 14 (1952).
78. Kappelmeier, C. P. A., and van Goor, W. R., *Verfkroniek*, *16*, 8–10, 17–20 (1943).
79. Kuentzel, L. E., *Anal. Chem.*, *23*, 1413 (1951).
80. Kruse, P. R., and Wallace, W. B., *ibid.*, *25*, 1156 (1953).
81. Lewis, W. R., and Quackenbush, F. W., *J. Am. Oil Chemists' Soc.*, *26*, 53 (1949).
82. Malaprade, L., *Bull. soc. chim. France*, (4e), *43*, 683 (1928); (5e), *1*, 833 (1934).
83. Malm, C. J., Genung, L. B., and Kuchmy, W., *Anal. Chem.*, *25*, 245 (1953).
84. Martin, R. W., *ibid.*, *23*, 883 (1951).
85. Marvel, C. J., and Rands, R. D., *J. Am. Chem. Soc.*, *72*, 2742 (1950).
86. Maten, C. J., and Tanghi, L. J., *Ind. Eng. Chem., Anal. Ed.*, *14*, 940 (1942).

87. Matthews, N. L., Brode, W. R., and Brown, J. B., *J. Am. Chem. Soc.*, *63*, 1064 (1941).
88. Mattiello, J. J., ed., *Protective and Decorative Coatings*. Vol. V, Wiley, New York, 1946.
89. Mehlenbacher, V. C., "Determination of Hydroxyl Groups," in *Organic Analysis*. Vol. I, Interscience, New York-London, 1953, pp. 23–25.
89a. Miller, C. D., Shreve, O. D., *Anal. Chem.*, *28*, 200 (1956).
90. Mitchell, J. H., Kraybill, H. R., and Zscheile, F. P., *Ind. Eng. Chem., Anal. Ed.*, *15*, 1 (1943).
91. Mitchell, J., Jr., Determination of Carbonyl Compounds," in *Organic Analysis*. Vol. I, Interscience, New York-London, 1953, p. 243 *et seq.*
92. Mitchell, J., Jr., in *Organic Analysis*, Vol. I, p. 318.
93. *Modern Plastics Encyclopedia*. Plastics Catalog Corp., New York, 1947.
94. *Modern Plastics Encyclopedia Charts*. Plastics Catalog Corp., New York, 1948.
95. Moss, M. L., Elliott, J. H., and Hall, R. T., *Anal. Chem.*, *20*, 784 (1948).
96. Newell, J. E., *ibid.*, *23*, 445 (1951).
97. Nogare, S. Dal, Perkins, L. R., and Hale, A. H., *ibid.*, *24*, 512 (1952).
98. O'Conner, R. T., Heinzelman, D. C., and Dollear, F. G., *Oil & Soap*, *22*, 257 (1945).
99. Ogg, C. L., and Cooper, F. J., *Anal. Chem.*, *21*, 1400 (1949).
100. Patterson, W. A., *ibid.*, *26*, 823 (1954).
101. Petit, J., and Fournier, P., *Peintures, pigments, vernis*, *26*, 357 (1950).
102. Pohle, W. D., and Mehlenbacher, V. C., *J. Am. Oil Chemists' Soc.*, *24*, 155 (1947).
103. Rao, P. C., and Daubert, B. F., *J. Am. Chem. Soc.*, *70*, 1102 (1948).
104. Richards, R. E., and Thompson, H. W., *J. Chem Soc.*, *71*, 124 (1949).
105. Robitschek, P., and Lewin, A., *Phenolic Resins*. Iliffe, London, 1950, p. 209.
106. Rochow, T. G., and Stafford, R. W., *Anal. Chem.*, *21*, 196 (1949).
107. Rochow, T. G., and Stafford, R. W., *ibid.*, *22*, 206 (1950).
108. Rochow, T. G., and Stafford, R. W., *ibid.*, *23*, 212 (1951).
109. Rochow, T. G., and Stafford, R. W., *ibid.*, *24*, 232 (1952).
110. Rochow, E. G., *Introduction to Chemistry of the Silicones*. Wiley, New York, 1946.
111. Scheibe, G., and Fauss, R., *Kolloid-Z.*, *125*, 139 (1952).
112. Scheidt, V., and Reinwein, H., *Z. Naturforsch.*, *7b*, 270 (1952).
113. Scott, R. E., and Frisch, K. C., *J. Am. Chem. Soc.*, *73*, 2599 (1951).
114. Shaefer, W. E., and Becker, W. W., *Anal. Chem.*, *25*, 1226 (1953).
115. Shay, J. F., Skilling, S., and Stafford, R. W., *ibid.*, *26*, 652 (1954).
116. Shreve, O. D., *ibid.*, *24*, 1692 (1952).
117. Shreve, O. D., and Heether, M. R., *ibid.*, *23*, 441 (1951).
118. Shreve, O. D., Heether, M. R., Knight, H. B., and Swern, D., *ibid.*, *22*, 1498 (1950).
119. Shreve, O. D., Heether, M. R., Knight, H. B., and Swern, D., *ibid.*, *22*, 1261 (1950).
120. Shreve, O. D., Heether, M. R., Knight, H. B., and Swern, D., *ibid.*, *23*, 277 (1951).
121. Shreve, O. D., Heether, M. R., Knight, H. B., and Swern, D., *ibid.*, *23*, 282 (1951).
122. Simon, I., and McMahon, H. O., *J. Chem. Phys.*, *20*, 905 (1952).
123. Simonds, H. R., Weith, A. J., and Bigelow, M. H., *Handbook of Plastics*. 2nd ed., Van Nostrand, New York, 1949.
124. Simonds, H. R., Weith, A. J., and Bigelow, M. H., *Handbook of Plastics*. 2nd ed., Van Nostrand, New York, 1949, p. 1097.
125. Skoog, D. A., and Focht, R. L., *Anal. Chem.*, *25*, 1922 (1953).
126. Smith, J. J., Rugg, F. M., and Bowman, H. M., *ibid.*, *24*, 497 (1952).

127. Spectroscopy Committee Report, *J. Am. Oil Chemists' Soc.*, *26*, 399 (1949).
128. Spectroscopy Committee Report, *ibid.*, *30*, 352 (1953).
129. Stafford, R. W., Francel, R. J., and Shay, J. F., *Anal. Chem.*, *21*, 1454 (1949).
130. Stafford, R. W., and Shay, J. R., *ibid.*, *25*, 8 (1953).
131. Stafford, R. W., Shay, J. F., and Francel, R. J., *ibid.*, *26*, 656 (1954).
132. Stafford, R. W., Shay, J. F., and Francel, R. J., *ibid.*, *26*, 660 (1954).
133. Stimson, M. M., and O'Donnell, M. J., *J. Am. Chem. Soc.*, *74*, 1805 (1952).
134. Swann, M. H., *Anal. Chem.*, *21*, 1448 (1949).
135. Swann, M. H., Adams, M. L., and Weil, D. J., *ibid.*, *27*, 1604 (1955).
136. Swann, M. H., *ibid.*, *25*, 1735 (1953).
137. Swann, M. H., Adams, M. L., and Esposito, G. G., *ibid.*, *27*, 1426 (1955).
138. Swain, M. L., and Brice, B. A., *J. Am. Oil Chemists' Soc.*, *26*, 272 (1949).
139. Swern, D., Knight, H. B., Shreve, O. D., and Heether, M. R., *ibid.*, *27*, 17 (1950).
140. Vandenheuvel, F. A., and Richardson, G. H., *ibid.*, *30*, 104 (1953).
141. Von Fisher, W., *Paint and Varnish Technology*. Reinhold, New York, 1948.
142. Whitnack, G. C., and Gantz, E. St. Clair, *Anal. Chem.*, *25*, 553 (1953).
143. Willits, C. O., Riccuti, C., Knight, H. B., and Swern, D., *ibid.*, *24*, 785 (1952).
144. Wilson, H. N., and Hughes, W. C., *J. Soc. Chem. Ind.*, *58*, 74 (1939).
145. Wright, N., and Hunter, M. J., *J. Am. Chem. Soc.*, *69*, 803 (1947).
146. Young, C. W., Servais, P. C., Currie, C. C., and Hunter, M. J., *ibid.*, *70*, 3758 (1948).
147. Zahn, H., and Wolf, H., *Melliand Textilber.*, *32*, 317 (1951).
148. Zemany, P. D., *Anal. Chem.*, *24*, 1709 (1952).

SUBJECT INDEX

Volume III plus Major Subjects in Volumes I and II

Roman numbers refer to the volume. The present volume is Volume III. *Italic* numbers refer to pages giving procedures.

Abbreviations used

active H, active hydrogen
addn., addition
av., average
CCD, countercurrent distribution
CO, carbonyl group. *Example:* "Acetaldehyde, CO detn.," represents "carbonyl determination of acetaldehyde." Note that functional group determinations are listed as separate subentries under the name of the compound being tested
compd., compound
compn., composition
concn., concentration
COOH, carboxyl group. See note to CO above

defin., definition
deriv., derivative
detn., determination
i. r., infrared
LiAlH, lithium aluminum hydride
max., maximum
mol. wt., molecular weight
N, nitrogen
OH, hydroxyl group. See note to CO at left
ppt., precipitation
prepn., preparation
soln., solution
tert, tertiary
unsat., unsaturate, unsaturation
u.v., ultraviolet

A

Abietic acid, reaction with bromine, III, 235, 236
Acetals, detn., I, 309–328
Acetamide, detn., III, 188, 192
  detn. by reaction rate, II, 245
  detn. with lithium aluminum pyrrolidide, II, 162
  N detn., III, 140
Acetanilide, detn., II, 44, 133, 142, 162; III, 186, 188, 190
Acetates, ester detn., II, 42, 51
  interference in acid detn., III, 13
Acetic acid, azeotrope with benzene, III, 88
  COOH detn., III, 11, 12, 20, 22, *24*, 29, 31, 38

COOH microdetn., II, 4, 6
chromatographic separation, III, 73, 80, 86
coulometric detn., III, 59
detn. by mass spectrometry, III, 70
  by microscopy and x-ray diffractometry, III, 70
detn. in anhydride, III, 12, *24*
  in presence of hydrochloric acid and phenol, III, 20, 29, 31, 38
i.r. absorption, III, 67
ionization constant, III, 2, 4, 5
solvent for detn. of strong acids, amino-acids, metal salts, III, 25, 27
  for amine detn., III, 145, 196, 197, 490
  for unsat. detn., III, 232, 260